The Design and Performance of Road Pavements
Second Edition

THE DESIGN AND PERFORMANCE OF ROAD PAVEMENTS

The Design and Performance of Road Pavements is a new title in the **McGraw-Hill International Series in Civil Engineering**

The Design and Performance of Road Pavements

SECOND EDITION

David Croney, OBE, FICE, FIHT

and

Paul Croney, MICE

David Croney Associates
Geotechnical and Highway Engineering Consultants

McGRAW-HILL BOOK COMPANY

London · New York · St Louis · San Francisco · Auckland
Bogotá · Caracas · Hamburg · Lisbon · Madrid · Mexico
Milan · Montreal · New Delhi · Panama · Paris · San Juan
São Paulo · Singapore · Sydney · Tokyo · Toronto

Published by
McGRAW-HILL Book Company Europe
Shoppenhangers Road, Maidenhead, Berkshire, SL6 2QL, England
Tel 0628 23432; Fax 0628 770224

British Library Cataloguing in Publication Data
Croney, David
  The design and performance of road pavements.
  1. Roads. Pavements. Design
  I. Title II. Croney, Paul
  625.8
  ISBN 0-07-707408-4

Library of Congress Cataloging-in-Publication Data
Croney, David
The design and performance of road pavements / David Croney and Paul Croney.—
2nd ed.
    p. cm.
  Includes bibliographical references and index
  ISBN 0-07-707408-4
  1. Pavements—Great Britain—Design and construction. 2. Pavements—Great
Britain—Maintenance and repair. 3. Pavements—Great Britain—Testing. I.
Croney, Paul. II. Title.
  TE251.C76 1991
  625.8—dc20   90-21537 CIP

Based on *The Design and Performance of Road Pavements* published on behalf of the Transport and Road Research Laboratory, 1977. Some material has been adapted and reproduced from the First Edition with the permission of the Controller of Her Majesty's Stationery Office.

2345 CL 9432

Typeset by Interprint Limited, Malta
and printed and bound in Great Britain by Clays Ltd, St Ives plc

Contents

Part Three Pavement Materials—Specification and Properties

Foreword

There are two complementary approaches to pavement design. One uses structural analysis with idealized concepts of the components of a pavement in order to establish a design theory comparable to those used in designing other engineering structures. The other uses observation and experiment to produce a method based on the performance of real pavements under traffic. The authors of this book, while being strongly oriented towards the second of these approaches in situations where it can be used, have devoted considerable effort to examining the compatibility of the two approaches.

Dr David Croney has spent most of his professional life in research into pavement design and performance. Among his contributions to knowledge in this field two merit special mention. One is his early work on soil thermodynamics to establish how different topographic and climatic environments influence moisture conditions in the soil beneath pavements, an essential step in determining the support which the subgrade will provide for the pavement and the traffic that it will carry. The other concerns the acquisition of knowledge on how pavements perform as composite structures.

In the fifties and sixties a series of full-scale road experiments was put in train in Great Britain. These experiments were designed to explore the effects of variations in materials and their thickness on the performance of both concrete and flexible pavements on heavily-trafficked roads. Dr David Croney as head of the Pavement Design Division of the Transport and Road Research Laboratory was the main initiator of these and of the detailed observations that were maintained of their performance. These observations have been continued until quite recently and it is his analysis of these records together with published experience gathered from other parts of the world that provide much of the information contained in this second edition of the book. In preparing it he has been joined by his son, Dr Paul Croney, a consultant specializing in geotechnical and pavement engineering.

The declared purpose of the book is to provide a comprehensive guide to practising engineers concerned with the design of pavements throughout the world. It has value, too, as a textbook for students because of the comprehension it will give them of the nature of roadmaking materials and of the forces which act upon them in pavements. This comprehension will make them better able to make the judgements that are so necessary in planning the construction and maintenance of particular roads.

R.S. Millard
Formerly Deputy Director of the Transport and Road Research Laboratory
Advisor to The World Bank on Overseas Road Projects

Acknowledgements

The authors of this book wish to thank the British Standards Institution for permitting extracts from BS 5930 (*Code of Practice for Site Investigations*) to be included in Chapter 10 and to the American Association of State Highway and Transportation Officials (AASHTO) for allowing material from the AASHTO *Guide for the Design of Pavement Structures*, 1986 to be reproduced in Chapter 20.

Thanks are also extended to the many authors whose papers are listed in the references at the end of each chapter. These include many publications issued by the Transport and Road Research Laboratory (TRRL) the use of which is acknowledged with gratitude extended both to the Laboratory and to the individual authors concerned.

PART ONE Introduction

1. Scope of the book

1.1   The first edition of this book was published more than 12 years ago. When it went out of print in the autumn of 1986, a decision had to be taken on whether there should be a reprint or a revised second edition. Since 1977 many of the British and American standards relating to road materials and pavement testing have been revised or rewritten and there have been several important conferences including the 4th, 5th, and 6th International Conferences on the Structural Design of Asphalt Pavements, and two meetings of the International Society of Soil Mechanics and Foundation Engineering. These meetings have influenced markedly current ideas, particularly in respect of the design and maintenance of road pavements.

1.2   In the United Kingdom several large pavement design experiments constructed on major in-service highways in the sixties have reached the end of their design lives. Much of the early motorway system also constructed in Britain in that decade is now more than 20 years old and it seems an ideal time to review the past performance and future maintenance problems.

1.3   The above are some of the factors which pointed to the need for a second edition, and a major rewrite has therefore been undertaken.

1.4   As with the previous edition, the book is concerned primarily with the design, performance, and maintenance of pavements. Construction is considered in detail only when it impinges on design and performance, as is particularly the case with concrete pavements. It is based largely on British and American experience, but where the conclusions are likely to be influenced by climatic conditions the likely effects of rainfall and temperature are considered in detail and the reader should have no difficulty in using the book in tropical and semitropical conditions.

1.5   The text is divided into eight parts. Part One is largely introductory. It introduces the question of design life and performance criteria, and discusses the state of competition which has existed for many years between flexible and concrete construction, and the effect this has had on both types of construction.

1.6   Part Two deals with the basic information which engineers need before they can start the design process. This information relates to the climate of the site, which affects the construction season, the type of plant which can operate, and the likely design strength of the subgrade. It relates also to the broad geology of the site as well as the more detailed information obtained from the site investigation made in connection with the project. Finally, this section deals with what is probably the most important aspect of design—the traffic to be carried and its constitution in terms of axle loading.

1.7   Part Three is concerned with the construction materials which form part of the pavement including the soil foundation and the preparation of the subgrade. A separate chapter is devoted to each of the materials currently in common use in pavements. Because of the growing importance of structual design procedures, the structural properties of each material are discussed within the chapter dealing with that material.

1.8   Part Four discusses current British and American design procedures based wholly or partly on experience gained from full-scale pavement design experiments using either test tracks or sections of in-service highways.

1.9   Part Five reviews analytical design procedures available for both flexible and concrete pavements and discusses detailed correlation with full-scale evidence from in-service road sections carrying heavy traffic.

1.10   Part Six deals with three specialized topics. The first is the design of heavy-duty port and industrial pavements operated by specialized lifting plant such as front- and side-lift trucks, rubber-tyred gantry cranes, and straddle carriers. The second is the design of haul roads to carry construction plant, and the last is specialized surfacings for roads over concrete and steel bridges.

1.11   Part Seven discusses the riding quality and skid resistance of pavements and the design of antisplash surfacings or friction courses.

1.12   Part Eight is devoted to the structural maintenance of flexible and concrete pavements and the design of overlays.

Notes

1.13   In January 1972 the name of the Road Research Laboratory (RRL) was changed to the Transport and Road Research Laboratory (TRRL). All publications prior to that date carry the original name and in referring to them and the associated research work we have used the former name or initials.

Later in the seventies the American Association of State Highway Officials (AASHO) changed its name to the American Association of State Highway and Transportation Officials AASHTO). In referring to work carried out and published prior to the change we have used the original initials. As a consequence, the very important 1958–61 road trials are referred to as the AASHO Road Test. All Specifications are referred to as AASHTO irrespective of the date of origin, as these are revised annually.

1.14   In the last 25 years there has been a gradual adoption in the UK of the metric system to replace the imperial units formerly used. Some confusion still exists, however, in relation to the metric units adopted. For example, to define stress and pressure, research workers generally use the Pascal while civil engineering specifications adopt N/mm^2 or MN/m^2. In addition, for specifying operational and maximum pressures, tyre manufacturers prefer to use bars.

1.15   This book refers to a wide variety of publications, and in general the units quoted are those adopted by the authors of those publications, and no attempt to convert to a common system has been made.

2. Historical introduction to road construction

2.1   Although it would be naive to compare the roads constructed by the Romans more than 1800 years ago with modern highways, the sheer scale of their operations throughout the whole of Europe seems incredible even by today's standards. In Britain alone, in the space of 150 years they drove some 3000 miles of principal roadways across the country, extending deep into Wales, and north as far as Hadrian's Wall. As they advanced through the wet clay lands of western Europe thicknesses were modified to take into account the strength of the foundation. The layout seldom varied; two trenches were dug 5 m apart to act as drains and the soil between was excavated down to a firm foundation on which a multilayer granular base was laid using the materials locally available. Where feasible the pavements were surfaced with flat quarried stone to give the appearance familiar to all visitors to Pompeii. The engineers responsible for setting out the roads and supervising them would have known the elements of soil mechanics and were probably trained at what would now be called a school of military engineering.

2.2   The Roman roads in Europe were purely military and had no economic function in the lives of the indigenous population. Life in Europe during the first millennium AD was lived on a very parochial basis, consisting of self-supporting enclaves between which there was little peaceful intercourse.

2.3   Improved agricultural methods slowly changed this situation. The need to barter surplus crops led to the establishment by the tenth century of small market towns surrounded by satellite village communities. As wheeled transport replaced pack animals, roads began to replace tracks. Within the towns these were financed by levies on householders, but road users were reluctant to maintain the rural roads, which for centuries remained close to impassible in winter.

2.4   A road system of this type presented an almost impossible barrier to long-distance coach travel, which the growing wealth of the seventeenth and eighteenth centuries encouraged, particularly between the European capitals. Various expedients to finance improvements, such as the levying of tolls and the setting up of Turnpike Trusts, were adopted with mixed success. Telford and Macadam were worthy products of the turnpike era in Britain, but in general the appointed engineers had little experience and training and the payment of tolls by no means guaranteed ease of travel.

2.5   In the middle eighteen-fifties perfection of the railways virtually stopped further developments in the construction of rural roads. However, railway termini indirectly led to a massive increase in road traffic in the larger towns, particularly in relation to heavily laden railway waggons. As a consequence, after 1840 there were developments in road construction and road materials which originated in the great cities, notably Paris, London, and New York. These developments are summarized below.

2.6   *Stone sett and brick pavements*   Throughout Europe from medieval times stone setts were the most widely used form of pavement construction. The setts were of various sizes but in London 3 in × 8 in × 9 in deep was favoured. The upper surface was crowned to give a better foothold for horses. Originally laid on a granular foundation, differential settlement became a problem under heavy railway waggons and a lime concrete foundation 12 in thick was used. A great deal of research was carried out in different countries to locate sources of stone which gave a satisfactory balance between wear under the passage of steel tyres and polishing beneath the hoofs of horses.

2.7   Ceramic brick or block pavements were widely used in New York and other American cities between 1870 and 1890. The blocks were of brick size, but only 2–3 in thick. Fracture, probably due to inadequate quality control, appears to have been the main problem with these. In western Holland brick pavements were widely and very successfully used up to the nineteen-fifties. The bricks resembled building bricks but were much harder. They were laid on the natural sand, suitably compacted, and were relevelled to correct traffic deformation at intervals of often less than 5 years. Although this form of pavement was economical in terms of first cost and maintenance costs, the build-up of traffic after the Second World War resulted in increased deformation and unacceptable traffic delays during relevelling.

2.8   *Wood block pavements*   Wood block pavements were introduced into many European cities after 1850 as a less noisy alternative to stone setts. They were also extensively used later in New South Wales and Victoria in Australia. The blocks were similar in size to stone setts, and again a great deal of research was carried out to establish the most suitable timber and pretreatment. Wear was greater than with stone setts, but the relatively low cost meant that this form of paving was economical. The blocks were generally laid on a concrete or lime mortar bed. The use of wood blocks in London continued until the nineteen-fifties. In later years their life was extended by tar spraying and chipping. This also ensured an adequate resistance to skidding.

2.9   *Asphalt pavements*   Asphalt was first used as a paving material in Paris in 1854. The material used was natural rock asphalt, i.e., limestone rock impregnated with asphalt. This was crushed to a fine grading, heated to a temperature of 250 °C and spread with rakes at that temperature. It was then compacted with heavy iron rammers maintained at a high temperature by frequent heating in a roadside brazier. The material provided a quiet, easily cleaned surfacing but the skid resistance was very low in wet weather. By 1870, this type of surfacing was being widely used also in Britain, Germany, Switzerland, and in the United States, and it continued to be used until the nineteen-thirties in the City of London. The availability of refined bitumen in North America encouraged experiments with graded-stone–bitumen mixtures, as an alternative to rock asphalt. This led to the first asphaltic concrete specifications in the eighteen-nineties. At much the same time coal tar–aggregate mixtures were being developed in Europe for use in road surfacings.

2.10   *Concrete roads*   Concrete, generally to a low strength specification, was widely used over a century ago as a base for stone setts, wood blocks, and asphalt, but it was not used as a running surface. Early experiments were carried out in Scotland in 1865. Two lengths of concrete paving were laid on heavily trafficked roads in Edinburgh. The water/cement ratio must have been low as the material was compacted by a heavy road roller. After several years of satisfactory service the roads failed by deep surface scaling. This followed a very severe winter and the damage was almost certainly frost scaling. However, at the time it was concluded that concrete became too brittle with age to serve as a running surface. The serious use of concrete roads almost certainly started in the USA in the first decade of the twentieth century, and spread to Europe in the twenties.

2.11   *Effect of motor transport on rural road construction*   By 1910 it was clear that motor transport had come to stay and that water-bound macadam rural roads, in their normal poorly maintained condition, would need to be upgraded as a matter of urgency. This was too costly an operation to be financed by the local authorities responsible for rural road maintenance and in general it was paid for by central government grants. In Britain, Parliament set up the Road Board in 1909 to advise local authorities on the best way to pave their existing rural roads and to make the necessary grants. It was also required to carry out any research necessary to fulfil its advisory role. In the decade 1909–1919, despite the First World War, some 150 000 miles of rural roads were surfaced at a total cost of little more than £1 million per year. The treatment generally consisted of scarifying the existing waterbound macadam, adding stone where necessary, and then spraying with hot coal tar to form a type of penetration macadam. On the whole this was effective and it provided an excellent basecourse for future strengthening.

2.12   The problem in the United States over the same period was very different from that in Europe. Although the existing road network was less dense the distances involved were much larger and a massive road-building programme was undertaken. This called for mechanization on a large scale and for this reason developments in earth-moving and compaction plant, in bituminous pavers and concrete plant have generally originated in the United States. Europe has tended to concentrate on the smaller types of plant suited both to construction and maintenance.

2.13   Research into road design and construction has been world-wide. Most countries and states have permanent research organizations specializing in the subject, and work is also sponsored by bitumen and cement producers. Since 1909 the Permanent Association of Road Congresses has held regular meetings, generally in Paris, to encourage road engineers to present papers and interchange their ideas. The International Society of Soil Mechanics and Foundation Engineering meets in different countries every 5 years and devotes one session to road foundations and subgrades. More recently the five-yearly International Conferences on the Structural Design of Asphalt Pavements, organized by the University of Michigan, have provided a valuable forum for the discussion of developments in flexible road design.

3. Modern pavements and the principles of pavement design

The pavement

3.1 The pavement is the structure which separates the tyres of vehicles from the underlying foundation material. The latter is generally the soil but it may be structural concrete or a steel bridge deck. Pavements over soil are normally of multilayer construction with relatively weak materials below and progressively stronger ones above. Such an arrangement leads to the economic use of available materials.

3.2 In Europe pavements have traditionally been classified as flexible or rigid; the former consist of unbound compacted stone under a bituminous surfacing, and the latter of a concrete slab laid on a shallow granular bed. In the United States the more descriptive terms asphaltic concrete and Portland cement concrete pavements are often used. In this book pavements in which a normal-strength concrete slab provides the major component of the strength will be referred to as concrete (even when they have a bituminous surfacing) and all other pavements will be termed bituminous or flexible.

3.3 The implied difference of flexibility between the two forms of pavement is misleading, in the sense that the same theoretical or structural method of design can be applied to both types, although some factors involved in such analyses may be more important in one type than in the other.

Pavement layers

3.4 Flexible pavements consist of three main layers, the bituminous surfacing, the base (or roadbase), and the sub-base. The surfacing is generally divided into the wearing course and the basecourse (or binder course), laid separately. The base and sub-base may also be laid in composite form using different materials designated the upper and lower base or sub-base. Where the soil is considered to be very weak a capping layer may also be introduced between the sub-base and the soil foundation. This may be of an inferior type of sub-base material or it may be the upper part of the soil improved by some form of stabilization (e.g., with lime or cement). The soil immediately below the sub-base (or capping layer) is generally referred to as the subgrade and the surface of the subgrade is termed the formation level.

3.5   Concrete pavements normally consist of two layers only, the concrete slab and the sub-base. The slab may be laid in composite form using different aggregates in the upper and lower layers. Upper and lower sub-base layers and a capping layer may also be used but this is unusual with concrete pavements.

3.6   Concrete pavements may be reinforced with steel mesh or they may be unreinforced (often referred to as plain). Unreinforced concrete pavements have frequent transverse joints (approximately 5 m apart) to prevent thermal cracking. Reinforced concrete pavements have less-frequent joints (15–35 m apart). The function of the reinforcement is to keep any cracks which form from opening. Continuously reinforced concrete pavements have much heavier reinforcement and joints are used only when necessary for construction purposes. The heavy reinforcement is intended to distribute cracks uniformly along the length of the pavement, the intention being to prevent isolated wide cracks. The length of concrete between joints is generally referred to as a slab or a bay.

3.7   The elements of flexible and concrete pavements as defined above are shown in Fig. 3.1.

The principles of pavement design

3.8   The tensile and compressive stresses induced in a pavement by heavy wheel loads decrease with increasing depth. This permits the use, particularly in flexible pavements, of a gradation of materials, relatively strong and expensive materials being used for the surfacing and less strong and cheaper ones for base and sub-base. The pavement as a whole must limit the stresses in the subgrade to an acceptable level, and the upper layers must in a similar manner protect the layers below. In a concrete pavement the slab is sufficiently strong to protect the soil foundation and the sub-base can be regarded as a protection for the subgrade during the construction of the concrete slabs and as a drainage layer. It must be remembered that each layer of any pavement must be able adequately to support the machinery placing the materials above. The sub-base also has a role in protecting the subgrade from the action of frost.

3.9   Pavement design is the process of developing the most economical combination of pavement layers (in relation to both thickness and type of materials) to suit the soil foundation and the traffic to be carried during the design life.

3.10   This broad definition of pavement design implies that both flexible and concrete pavements should be considered on the same basis and a choice between them made on economic grounds. This will normally be the case unless special factors are operative. As examples of such special factors, public-utility services close to the surface may dictate the shallow construction depth associated with concrete pavements, while unusual settlement problems may favour a form flexible construction. The economic decision between alternative forms of pavement will normally be made on first cost, although some account of maintenance costs may be taken when

FLEXIBLE PAVEMENT LAYERS

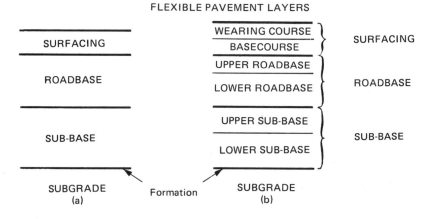

Notes:

1. Where the roadbase is laid in two different materials as in (b) the pavement is often referred to as COMPOSITE

2. Where bituminous or unbound stone or gravel materials are used exclusively in the pavement it is often referred to as FULLY FLEXIBLE

CONCRETE PAVEMENT LAYERS

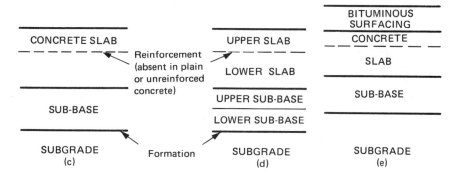

Notes :

1. Where no reinforcement is used joints are provided at intervals of about 5m

2. Where reinforcement is used joints can be placed at much greater intervals depending on the weight of reinforcement

3. Where heavy reinforcement is laid without breaks and no slab joints are used the construction is referred to as continuously reinforced concrete

4. Where two aggregates are used in the slab as in (d) above, two-layer construction is essential and the break is made at the reinforcement level if present

Figure 3.1 Components of flexible and concrete pavements

these can be estimated with sufficient accuracy. The choice between the two forms of construction is discussed in more detail in Chapter 5.

The two approaches to pavement design

3.11   Throughout the world many different empirical methods of pavement design have been developed during the last 60 years. Most are based on observations of the performance of existing roads under a variety of traffic conditions. In Britain since the forties many hundreds of experimental pavement sections have been injected into heavily trafficked routes and the performance has been regularly monitored for periods sometimes in excess of 40 years. In a number of such roads recording weighbridges have been installed so that the axle load distribution of the traffic is known. This work has enabled designs suitable for different traffic intensities to be developed. This type of research is time-consuming and quicker alternatives are constantly being sought.

3.12   In the United States large test tracks using a variety of pavement structures have been trafficked with specific vehicle types operating with known axle loads. This has given a valuable understanding of the relative damaging effect of different axle loads on a variety of pavements constructed to different thicknesses. These experiments have provided the basis for the design procedures used in the United States and many other parts of the world. In many countries circular 'road machines' have been constructed to give a rapid evaluation of specific pavement structures.

3.13   Concurrently with the development of empirical design methods work has been in progress relating to a more fundamental design procedure based on structural theory and the behaviour of road materials under repeated stress. Useful progress has been made in the last decade, and, provided the appropriate inputs are used, the structural approach agrees well with full-scale experimental evidence. The influence of both temperature and age on the elastic properties of bituminous materials is particularly important. At present, the theoretical approach is proving most useful in interpreting and extending the conclusions reached from experimental pavement research.

3.14   Both of these approaches are dealt with in detail in later chapters.

Responsibilities of the design engineer

3.15   Road construction is, and should be regarded as, a partnership between the engineer, the client, and the contractor. In major international contracts it is not at all unusual for the engineer to come from one country, for the client to be in another country, and for the contractor to be a consortium from two other countries. This is not an easy situation and it demands firmness, tact, and above all knowledge and expertise on the part of the engineer. On the engineer falls the responsibility to formulate the design, to prepare the drawings, and to provide a detailed specification of all the materials to be used. The engineer must also at every stage of the design have a clear understanding of exactly how to carry out the work involved. No specification should be written, for example, which entails operations which it may be impossible to carry out at the site because of the soil or environmental conditions; recent litigation and arbitration proceedings indicate that it is no longer possible for the engineer to take the attitude that it is the contractor's responsibility to carry out an operation required by the contract which the contractor has signed, even if events show it to be impossible. The engineer would be well advised to draw attention, in a preamble to the contract documents, to any difficulties which may arise, particularly in relation to soil conditions and climate, and to give any advice felt to be relevant to the type of plant likely to be inoperable on the site.

3.16   The engineer should, without fail, place on file all the detailed reasoning relating to each stage of the design procedure. In the event of litigation this may be required as evidence, perhaps several years after the work has been completed.

Basic information necessary to the design of pavements

3.17   The basic pieces of information which the engineer must have before starting to design a road or industrial pavement are as follows:

1. climatic environment (rainfall and temperature) at the site;
2. a detailed knowledge of the soil conditions;
3. constitution and volume of the traffic to be carried.

The first of these requirements is dealt with in Chapter 6, the second in Chapters 7 and 9, and the third in Chapter 8.

4. Design life—performance and failure criteria

Design life

4.1   Roads seldom become redundant. Even when a route is duplicated by a bypass, freeway, or motorway, the old road continues to carry traffic, although the volume may be temporarily reduced. The concept of design life has to be introduced to ensure that a new road will carry the volume of traffic associated with that life without deteriorating to the point where reconstruction or major structural repair is necessary.

4.2   In the fifties and sixties economists were advocating the use of short initial design lives for roads on the assumption that the interest on the money saved on the first cost would finance subsequent maintenance costs. For flexible pavements lives as short as 15 years were proposed. The calculations on which such conclusions were based included the traffic delay costs involved in repair work, and these, when discounted, were shown to be negligibly small. Such arguments are now known to be invalid. The cost of constructing either a flexible or a concrete road is little affected by increasing the design life by a factor of two. This is because the increase in thickness of the pavement is comparatively small, and because the cost of a major highway includes many factors such as earthworks, bridges, and drainage which are independent of the thickness of the pavement.

4.3   In recent years, public protest has made it clear that road users are no longer prepared to accept the frequent lane closures on major highways which inevitably occur when short design lives are adopted. Furthermore, the lane-switching and contraflow conditions which result from lane closures on motorways are increasingly becoming a cause of multivehicle accidents.

4.4   For roads in Britain the currently recommended design lives are 20 years for flexible pavements and 40 years for concrete. Many engineers feel that for trunk roads and motorways the design life for both forms of construction should be 40 years. It is true that under heavy traffic an adequate skid resistance is difficult to maintain for more than 15 years on flexible pavements and about 20 years on concrete surfaces. This necessitates surface dressing, or the provision of a thin overlay. This work can, and frequently is, undertaken at night, with little interruption to daytime traffic. Renting individual lanes or carriageways to the contractor for this type of work has been found to be an effective way of reducing closure times, although close supervision by the client's engineer is essential.

Performance and failure criteria

4.5   Both flexible and concrete roads should be designed and constructed to provide, during the design life, a riding quality acceptable for both private cars and commercial vehicles. There should be no significant ponding of water, and the skid resistance should be maintained at a level appropriate to the type of road. Acceptable levels of riding quality and skid resistance are defined in Chapters 26 and 27.

4.6   The assumption is often made that road pavements begin to deteriorate as soon as they are opened to traffic. This is true for underdesigned pavements, but where the design life is of the order of 20 years or more, there should be no visible deterioration for the first 5 years. If there is, then serious problems must be expected in the later life. This is in part due to the increase in strength which both bituminous materials and concrete experience during their early life. If the traffic stresses are excessive due to faulty design, the pavement cannot take advantage of this increase in strength.

Failure criteria for flexible pavements

4.7   Deterioration of flexible pavements arises from deformation under traffic loading, generally associated, in the later stages, by cracking. Such deformation is associated with heavy commercial vehicles; the contribution of private cars and light commercial vehicles is negligible. Figure 4.1(a) shows the characteristic behaviour of flexible pavements. The surface deformation is shown for one carriageway of a dual two-lane highway. The pavement consisted of 100 mm of asphalt laid on a 150-mm wet-mix base. The measurements which were made after various intervals of time show the deformation measured from the original surface level. The road carried about 2000 heavy commercial vehicles per day, and the design life was expected to be about 10 years. The deformation is largely restricted to the nearside wheel track of the slow lane, which carried more than 90 per cent of the heavy commercial vehicles. This is mainly because the wheel loads are more concentrated in this area. Contributory factors may arise from the crossfall and the ingress of moisture from the verge.

4.8   Figure 4.1(b) shows the development of maximum deformation in the nearside wheel tracks of a similar road carrying heavier traffic. In this case the performances of two adjacent pavements with different road bases are compared. The age of the road is expressed both in years and in millions of standard axles (msa) carried (see Chapter 8). The pavement with a 200-mm wet-mix stone base had a life of about 18 years, while an adjacent pavement with a 150-mm base of bitumen macadam should have an estimated life in excess of 30 years.

4.9   Experience shows that once the permanent deformation exceeds 15 mm there is an increasing probability of cracking in the wheel tracks. Water entering the cracks is then likely to accelerate failure. In Britain, for flexible pavements, a maximum deformation of 25 mm in the wheel tracks has been defined as the failure condition, and a maximum deformation of 15–20 mm is regarded as the optimum condition for

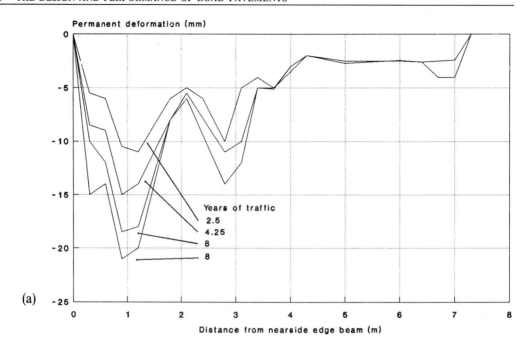

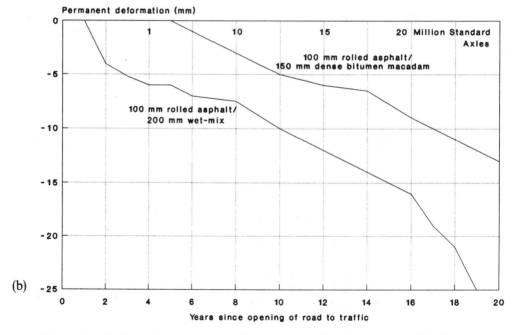

Figure 4.1 Surface deformation related to pavement life. (a) variation with distance from nearside edge, (b) development of maximum deformation

remedial work, such as the provision of an overlay, or replacement of the surfacing. These figures relate to measurements made from the original level of the surface. In practice, measurements of rutting are more likely to be made with a 2-m straight-edge. For such measurements, the failure condition will be represented by a 20-mm gap under the straight-edge, and the optimum condition for remedial work, by a 12–18-mm gap.

4.10 The measurement of deformation from the original level of the pavement involves transverse levelling against a deep benchmark prior and subsequent to trafficking. In experimental work, metal studs are set into the wearing course of the surfacing at transverse intervals of about 300 mm. Routine levelling involves the closure of at least one traffic lane. Even where a straight-edge is used to assess rut depth, measurements are hazardous unless the traffic is diverted. For this reason, the measurement of rut depth by a vehicle moving at normal road speed has long been an objective. One of the functions of the Transport and Road Research Laboratory (TRRL) Road Monitor, described in Chapters 26 and 27, is to measure and record rut depth using the reflection of laser light from the road surface. More recently a transverse profilometer has been developed at the Laboratory, which uses 21 sensor wheels spaced 100 mm apart each independently mounted with its own transducer to record vertical movement.[1] It is interesting to note that what was probably the first transverse profilometer of this type was made at the National Physical Laboratory (NPL) in the UK in 1913. At that time the NPL was responsible for all road research in Britain, under the aegis of the technical committee of the Road Board (see Para. 2.11). This machine, photographs of which still exist,[2] had eight sensor wheels which operated pushrods linked to pen recorders. Continuous records of the vertical movement of each sensor wheel were made over a distance of about 10 m. The rut depth was deduced by a process of differencing at intervals of about 1 m along the length examined. It appears that the machine was found to be useful since the secretary of the Technical Committee of the Road Board, H. P. Boulnois, writing at the time of the dissolution of the Board in 1919, said: 'It is hoped that the experiments with the machine will be renewed under the new Ministry of Ways and Communications which has been established'.[2]

The Ministry of Ways and Communications was the title originally selected by the then government for what subsequently became the Ministry of Transport. It appears that 70 years later modern technology has allowed Mr Boulnois's hopes to be fulfilled.

4.11 Figure 4.2(a) shows an example of a flexible road which has 20 mm of deformation in the nearside wheel track. This pavement is in a critical condition close to failure. In Fig. 4.2(b) the pavement has already failed with a deformation of approximately 30 mm under the straight-edge.

4.12 Flexible pavements which are called upon to carry much heavier traffic loads than their design would permit often crack as a result of the large elastic deflections which occur. This condition can cause breakup of the surface and give rise to potholing, before appreciable permanent deformation has occurred.

4.13 As part of the American Association of State Highway Officials (AASHO)

Figure 4.2 (a) Critical condition in a flexible pavement with a 100-mm asphalt surfacing and a 75-mm dense bitumen macadam base. (b) Failure condition in a flexible pavement with a 100-mm asphalt surfacing and a 75-mm dense tarmacadam base

road test carried out in the USA early in the sixties a rating system, known as the present serviceability index (PSI), was developed to classify the condition of pavements. This is discussed in detail in Chapter 17. However, the failure condition for flexible roads, defined above, corresponds to a PSI value of between 2 and 2.5.

Failure criteria for concrete pavements

4.14   Performance criteria for concrete pavements in relation to riding quality and skid resistance are the same as those for flexible pavements as indicated in para. 4.5. However, much greater care is generally needed in the construction of concrete roads to ensure that these requirements are met. If the strength of the concrete and the thickness of the slabs are sufficiently great it is relatively easy to lay a concrete road which will last virtually for ever. However, it is unlikely to meet with the client's approval if it has a poor riding quality and a low skid resistance. Failure criteria for reinforced and unreinforced concrete pavements are different and they are dealt with separately below.

4.15   *Failure criterion for reinforced concrete pavements*   Reinforced concrete pavements are expected to show some cracking during their design life, which should not be less than 40 years. The function of the reinforcement is to keep the cracks closed so that wheel loads are transferred across the cracks without overstressing the reinforcement. If the thickness or strength of the concrete is underdesigned for the traffic to be carried then abrasion at the cracks and subsequent failure of the reinforcement due to rusting or 'necking' will permit wide cracks to develop, leading eventually to failure. If the dowel bars across expansion and contraction joints are badly placed then relative movement between adjacent slabs will not occur and this will contribute to cracking and failure.

4.16   For experimental concrete pavements in Britain a failure condition corresponding to a total length of cracking of 250 m per 100 m of lane width has been adopted. This includes all the following types of cracking:

- hair cracks, which often become apparent only when the concrete is drying and which are normal features of reinforced concrete;
- fine cracks, which are less than 0.5 mm wide at the surface of the concrete;
- narrow cracks, which are between 0.5 and 1.2 mm wide at the surface;
- wide cracks, of width exceeding 1.2 mm at the surface.

Figure 4.3 shows results from a concrete road carrying heavy commercial traffic, which included lengths of concrete pavements of thicknesses 175 mm and 200 mm. For each of these thicknesses two weights of reinforcement were used, as indicated on the figure. The 175 mm slabs with the lighter reinforcement failed, using the above definition of failure, after 16 years. The same thickness with the heavier weight of reinforcement is likely to give a 20-year life. The 200 mm slabs with the lighter reinforcement will have a life approaching 40 years. In this example the performance is also expressed in terms of standard axles, as in Fig. 4.1(b).

4.17   Figures 4.4 and 4.5 show examples of areas of reinforced concrete pavement

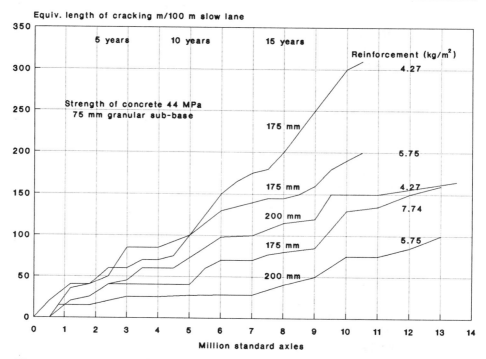

Figure 4.3   Development of cracking in reinforced concrete pavements

having average cracking of 500 m and 200 m of total cracking per 100 m of lane width. Most of the cracking is in the wide category.

4.18 *Failure criterion for unreinforced concrete roads*   A failure criterion for unreinforced pavements is more difficult to quantify. The slabs are made short between contraction joints (5 m or less) to reduce the probability of thermal cracking. They are then designed to be thick enough to resist traffic cracking. If a crack occurs, it tends to widen rapidly and granular interlock is lost. Detritus entering the crack tends to cause spalling and water entering the crack results in loss of strength in the sub-base and sometimes pumping of fines. The commonest cause of such cracking is low-strength concrete. It is inevitable that in a large contract a few cracks will occur during the early life, owing perhaps to sticking dowel bars. This can be overcome by taking out the affected bays and reconstructing them. If, however, the cracking in the early life affects more than one in four of the bays, consideration must be given either to reconstruction or to the provision of a thick overlay of bituminous material. Figure 4.6 shows the type of cracking typical of unreinforced concrete pavements. Initial transverse cracks are rapidly joined by longitudinal cracks, accompanied by progressive spalling.

4.19 *Failure criterion for continuously reinforced concrete roads*   Continuously reinforced concrete pavements rely on heavy reinforcement, without gaps for joints,

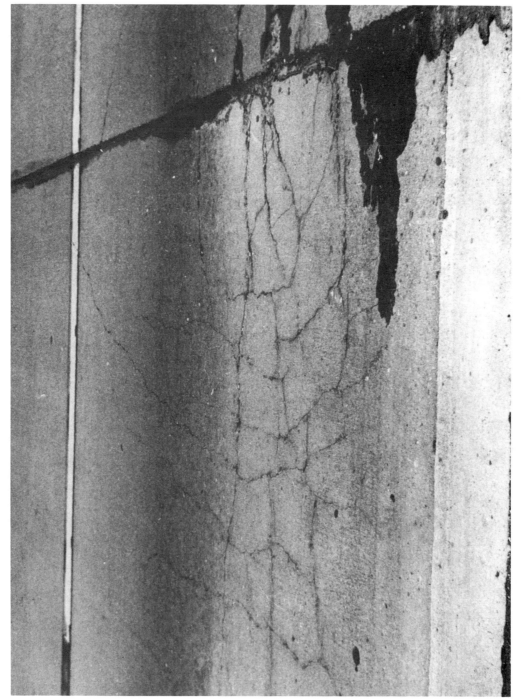

Figure 4.4 Appearance of local area of 125-mm-thick reinforced concrete slab with average cracking of 500 m per 100 m of the left-hand lane

21

Figure 4.5 Appearance of local area of 150-mm-thick reinforced concrete slabs with average cracking of 200 m per 100 m of the left-hand lane

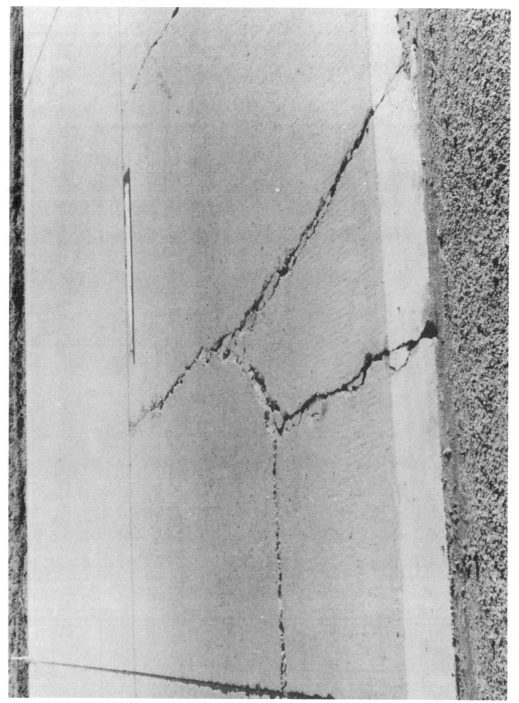

Figure 4.6 Cracks in 200-mm-thick unreinforced concrete slab

23

Figure 4.7   Typical cracking in continuously reinforced concrete pavement

to distribute uniformly a large number of fine cracks, which the reinforcement holds closed. This requires much heavier reinforcement than is normally used in jointed reinforced concrete pavements. In terms of the transverse cross-sectional area of the slab the area of the reinforcement is generally between 0.6 and 1 per cent. For a 200-mm slab this corresponds to 9.6–16 kg/m^2 reinforcement. Figure 4.7 shows the type of cracking expected on a well-designed and constructed pavement using continuous reinforcement. Even a single wide crack in a pavement of this type represents failure and requires urgent attention. The normal cause is fracture of the welds in the reinforcement or the use of a low-strength batch of concrete. The whole area around the crack must be broken out and the broken bars rewelded prior to the relaying of the concrete.

References

1. Potter, J. F. and M. G. D. O'Connor: *The TRRL Transverse Profilometer for measuring wheeltrack rutting*, Transport and Road Research Laboratory Research Report 195, TRRL, Crowthorne, 1989.
2. Boulnois, H. P.: *Modern Roads*, Edward Arnold, London, 1919.

5. Concrete versus flexible construction

Introduction

5.1   Perhaps the most difficult decision the road engineer has to make is whether to specify flexible or concrete construction. On minor works such as housing estates there is generally little difference in costs, since the concrete will normally be hand-laid to forms. Generally speaking, if the roads are to be put in first and are to be used by construction traffic then concrete will provide the best solution. On the other hand, if temporary haul roads of granular construction are used then a final topping of bituminous material may be the cheaper solution. For industrial estates, where the likely axle loading is unknown at the design stage, and where oil and hydraulic fluid spillage is likely, concrete pavements and hardstanding are best specified.

5.2   Major roads and motorways pose a more difficult problem and the following notes have been prepared for the guidance of engineers.

Costs

5.3   The cost of building a major concrete road to the very high standard necessary for present-day motorway or trunk road traffic is generally rather greater than the corresponding cost of an equivalent flexible road. However, the availability of materials more suited to one or other of the two forms of construction will influence this situation.

Life expectancy

5.4   A well-designed and properly constructed concrete road has the potential for a very long structural life with low maintenance costs. Experience shows that such a road designed for a 40-year life is in fact likely to have a much longer structural life, although a renewable bituminuous overlay may be necessary to maintain adequate skid resistance. Although it is possible to design flexible pavements with a life expectancy of 40 years, some structural maintenance must be expected during that period. As with concrete pavements, surface treatment will be necessary to retain skid resistance.

It can be argued that the higher cost of a concrete pavement is offset by the longer maintenance-free life. To some extent this is true, provided the concrete pavement is built to the required standard. However, in Britain at the present time this is not always the case and the engineer responsible for the construction of a major machine-laid concrete road must be prepared to put in a great deal of effort at every stage of the construction phase.

Riding quality

5.5 Before the introduction of bituminous pavers in the thirties the riding quality of concrete roads, laid either by hand or by rail-guided paving trains, was superior to that being obtained on hand-laid bituminous pavements. With bituminous pavers now being used to lay bases and sub-bases as well as surfacings, there are at least four passes of the machine, each contributing to an improved riding quality. During the same period, slip form pavers have largely replaced concreting trains, often with some deterioration of riding quality. The result is that today it is easier to guarantee a good riding quality with flexible construction than is the case with concrete, particularly if adequate care is not taken in forming the joints.

Construction expertise

5.6 Any large contracting organization will be experienced in flexible road construction, and provided the work is supervised by an energetic and knowledgeable resident engineer, a satisfactory end-product should result. Outside the United States the number of contractors experienced in the construction of modern concrete roads is more limited. For a major concrete road project it would be unwise to employ a contractor without experience of modern concreting machinery. For this reason, the contractor should be drawn from a nominated list of contractors with this expertise. It should also be the design engineer's responsibility to ensure that the resident engineer and his or her senior staff are thoroughly conversant with the paver to be used, well before concreting commences. The contract should also require the construction of trial bays well in advance of the commencement of paving. It should be the duty of the resident engineer to ensure that this requirement is strictly enforced.

Competition between concrete and flexible road construction

5.7 A spirit of competition between concrete and flexible road construction originated in the United States at least 50 years ago. It spread to Europe in the forties. The main protagonists have been the trade organizations concerned with the production and marketing of bitumen and cement. To an extent this competition has been healthy in so far as it has encouraged research into both forms of pavement construction. However, the marginal advantage which flexible pavements have over concrete in relation to first cost has led to a demand from the concrete side for relaxation of the rather tight specification advocated for concrete roads. This has led to the almost exclusive use of unreinforced concrete and to reductions in both slab and base thickness. These in turn have contributed to the construction of some unsatisfactory concrete roads and have affected the image of that form of construction with road users.

5.8   In the USA, and currently in some developing countries, there is sufficient road construction work to encourage contractors to develop the expertise which is undoubtedly necessary to ensure a high standard of concrete construction on every contract. In Britain, and in Europe generally, this is much less the case and a measure of government intervention is often necessary if major concrete roads are to be built. Without this intervention the future of concrete construction in relation to major roads, and particularly to high-speed ones, appears unsure.

PART TWO Basic Design Data

6. Climatic data

Introduction

6.1   Before commencing the design of any form of pavement it is the responsibility of the engineer to become familiar with all aspects of the climatic conditions under which the pavement will operate. This is particularly important if the construction is to be in an unfamiliar part of the world. It is inadvisable for this purpose to rely on the climatic data given in the average world atlas. To give an example, on the island of Mauritius in the Indian Ocean, which is less than 45 km from east to west, the average rainfall is only 800 mm on the west coast but is 4000 mm in the central highlands. As a consequence an earthworks specification suitable for the west coast would be found to be inoperable in the highlands, to the east.

6.2   The influence of rainfall, evaporation, and temperature on pavement specifications is discussed below.

Rainfall and evaporation

6.3   Rainfall is of importance in the design process for roads in three main respects. These are:

1. construction of earthworks;
2. determination of subgrade strength;
3. surface water drainage.

6.4   *Construction of earthworks*   The earthworks specification for a contract will normally define, either directly or in terms of a standard compaction test, the moisture content range between which the earthworks are to be compacted. It is the responsibility of the design engineer to ensure that it will be possible for the contractor to meet the requirements of the specification during at least part of the contract period. This means that if the excavated soil is required to be dried prior to being incorporated in the earthworks, the rate of evaporation must be significantly greater than the rainfall during the period of earthworks construction. This is discussed in detail in Chapter 10. Failure to appreciate this fact is a frequent cause of litigation between client and contractor, in which the engineer will become involved.

6.5   *Subgrade strength*   The natural moisture content of the soil will determine the subgrade strength to be used in the design of the pavement. At the design stage, after receiving the site investigation report, it is the responsibility of the engineer to estimate the moisture content and corresponding strength of the subgrade, and also to ensure that this moisture content will not be exceeded at the time the subgrade is finally prepared and covered by sub-base. To ensure that these various requirements are met the engineer may need to specify the periods of the year when earthworks and pavement construction may be carried out. In general, the engineer should overestimate rather than underestimate the equilibrium moisture content and strength of the subgrade. (These matters are discussed more fully in Chapters 10 and 11.)

6.6   *Surface water drainage*   The maximum intensity of rainfall is required for the design of the surface water drainage system of a road. The latter will normally be designed for a 5-, 10-, or 20-year storm. The period chosen should be approved by the client and a record placed on file. Special attention should be given to surface water drainage in low rainfall areas. In parts of the Middle East, for example, the annual rainfall may be less than 100 mm, but 50 per cent of this may fall in a single afternoon. In such circumstances, if the client decides not to have a surface water drainage system, the danger of washouts affecting verges and embankment slopes should be clearly stated by the engineer.

6.7   *Availability of data*   It is surprising how much data are now available on rainfall and evaporation, even in relatively undeveloped parts of the world. This is mainly because of the importance of these factors in agriculture. With modern methods of retrieval there is seldom difficulty in obtaining the required information. The Meteorological Office in Britain provides an excellent and most efficient world-wide service. If they are unable to offer information about a particular area, they will generally recommend a source within the country concerned to which the engineer can apply.

Temperature

6.8   Temperature is important in the design of flexible pavements because of its influence on the stiffness of bituminous materials. In concrete roads it influences thermal stresses, and in this way affects the thickness requirements for the slabs and the spacing of joints (see Chapters 9 and 22).

6.9   *Influence on the stiffness of bituminous material*   All bituminous road surfacings and bases decrease in stiffness as the temperature is increased over the working range of below 0 °C to above 40 °C. The stiffness is also influenced by the constitution of the mix and the hardness of the binder used. At low temperatures, to minimize thermal contraction cracking, a relatively soft binder and a high binder content would be used, whereas for hot conditions the hardness of the binder would be increased and the binder content reduced to minimize plastic flow in the materials. In cases where there is a large seasonal fluctuation of temperature, as in the northern states of the USA, the design would be a compromise biased towards the hotter end of the temperature range.

6.10   *Influence of temperature on the design of concrete roads*   The warping stresses in concrete pavements are generated by the diurnal temperature changes, and the longitudinal foundation restraint stresses are determined principally by the annual temperature swing. The effect of these stresses is reduced by shortening the slab length. Since these stresses are at some periods of the day and of the year additive to the traffic stresses, they also influence the slab thickness requirements (this is discussed in detail in Chapter 22).

Minimum climatic data required at the design stage

6.11   The minimum climatic data required in the design of pavements is as follows:

- Rainfall and evaporation
  - Mean monthly rainfall
  - Mean monthly evaporation
  - Maximum daily rainfall

The above should be based on the longest period in years for which measurements are available.

- Temperature
  - Mean monthly maximum temperature
  - Mean monthly minimum temperature

These temperatures should be based on the longest period in years for which measurements are available.

7. Geological data—site investigation

Introduction

7.1 Once the need for a road between two points has been established, the exact line which it will follow must be decided. In developed urban situations minimum interference with existing buildings and services will be the main consideration, while in developed rural areas environmental considerations will be a major factor. In developing countries the starting point may well be an aerial survey followed by a ground contour survey. The line will then be selected to avoid natural barriers as far as possible. The levels chosen for such rural roads will depend on the acceptable gradients, and the amount of cut and fill which these gradients will dictate. The final levels chosen will also depend to some extent on the nature of the soils found in the subsequent site investigation.

Preparation of the site investigation report

7.2 The engineer is responsible for writing, or approving, the site investigation report which will form part of the contract documents on which the contractors will base their tenders.

7.3 If the site is in a country or a location with which the engineer is not familiar the starting point of the site investigation should be the geological drift maps of the area. A surprising amount of geological information world-wide is now available on data bank. The Geological Survey and Museum in Britain can generally give information on what is available for particular sites and where it can be obtained or consulted.

7.4 The temperate soils of North America and Europe have been extensively studied and their properties are well documented. Less is known about tropical volcanic and laterite soils. For such areas it is advisable to have a literature survey made. In Britain the TRRL will generally make such literature surveys for a modest fee. The key words required will be the country followed by 'geology', 'soil properties', etc. This will give references to papers relating to the soils and to their properties.

Scope of the site investigation report

7.5 Having established the soil conditions of the area it is the engineer's responsibility to obtain reliable information concerning the soil types which will be found

34

1. at foundation level in cut areas;
2. beneath the embankments in fill areas; and
3. in cut areas to evaluate the suitability of the excavated soil for use in embankments.

7.6   The boring and sampling work will normally be carried out by a specialist organization appointed and supervised by the engineer. The borings must be sufficiently closely spaced to locate any significant quantities of unsuitable or contractually difficult materials present along the route. Deep borings are expensive and the temptation is to reduce the frequency to keep costs down. Engineers generally attempt to safeguard their position by stating in the preamble to the site investigation document that it is provided only for the guidance of the contractor and that it is the latter's responsibility to verify the information given by further borings if considered desirable. In the event of the contractor entering into litigation on the grounds of inadequate or incorrect information in the site investigation report, this escape clause now has little influence on judges and arbitrators. They recognize that a contractor with perhaps only 3–4 weeks to complete a tender cannot possibly arrange for an independant soil survey, particularly if the contract relates to a distant country.

7.7   Borings should be made at a maximum spacing of 5 per kilometre and these should be supplemented by intermediate bores if obvious changes of soil strata are found between the initial boreholes. Borings should be continued to a depth of at least 3 m below the proposed formation level in areas of cut and to a depth in excess of 3 m below existing ground level in areas of fill. Separate boreholes may be required to evaluate the soil conditions beneath bridge and other structural foundations.

7.8   Samples weighing at least 2 kg should be taken at depth intervals of 500 mm in fine-grained soils, for classification tests. In granular soils this weight should be increased to 10 kg. These samples should be placed in airtight containers immediately after excavation, and at the same time a representative sample of not less than 0.5 kg should be taken at the same depths for moisture content determination. These samples should be placed in preweighed sample containers and the wet weight determined without any loss of moisture by evaporation. The oven-dry weight can be determined at a convenient later time.

7.9   All the boreholes should be temporarily capped and checked for ground water level at intervals until the equilibrium condition is reached.

Tests to be carried out on samples

7.10   Tests will normally be carried out by the site Investigation organization, as directed by the engineers. Too often, insufficient attention is given by engineers when deciding exactly what tests should be carried out. Moisture content determinations should be made on all the samples taken, as indicated in Para. 7.8 above. The appropriate classification tests should also be made on all the samples. Very frequently, moisture content and classification tests are made on different samples, so that the contractor has no indication of how the natural moisture content related to the classification tests. The classification tests for cohesive soils are the liquid and plastic limits and for granular soils the wet-sieve particle size determination is carried out (see Chapter 10).

7.11   To establish the degree of compaction to be specified in earthworks and in the subgrade, laboratory compaction tests relating density and moisture content should be carried out on at least half of the samples taken. Both standard and heavy compaction should be specified (see Chapter 10).

7.12   In the design of flexible pavements the engineer will need to know the California bearing ratio (CBR) of the subgrade after the earthworks have been completed. For this he will need to know the relationship between moisture content, dry density, and CBR value. This involves preparing CBR test samples at a range of moisture contents and dry densities. The work involved is considerable and the testing programme will normally be confined to the main soil types found at the site. A limited number of triaxial tests will be needed to check the stability of the embankment and cutting slopes, and consolidation tests may also be necessary if highly compressible soils are present.

7.13   Detailed laboratory testing is best planned after the engineer has considered the moisture content and classification test results. In the past this has been difficult if the design is being prepared at a great distance from the project site. However, the advent of the facsimile transmission system means that the results of moisture content and classification tests can be transmitted and considered before the decision on further testing is made. This could lead to much-improved site investigation reports.

7.14   The amount of money allocated to site investigation will obviously be related to the size of the contract. Experience shows that a large proportion of the disputes which arise between engineers and contractors originate in what the contractor regards, often with good reason, as an inadequate site investigation. Such disputes, if they end in litigation, can be very costly to the client, in relation to the cost of well-planned and well-executed site investigations.

8. Road traffic and axle loading

Introduction

8.1   Road traffic embraces a mixture of vehicles ranging from bicycles to truck-and-trailer combinations with seven or more axles.

8.2   A road must be wide enough to permit all the vehicles to operate at an acceptable speed and it must be strong enough to cater for the heaviest commercial axle loads. The first of these requirements is the concern of the traffic engineer and the second is the responsibility of the pavement engineer. Both require to know the constitution of the traffic. For planning and administrative purposes governments need to know the volume and constitution of traffic on different classes of road. In Europe the conducting of regular traffic censuses is the responsibility of central governments, but in the USA the work is carried out by the different states, which are responsible for road construction and maintenance.

Role of the traffic engineer

8.3   The job of the traffic engineer is to keep traffic flowing with the least inconvenience to all road users, and with an appropriate degree of safety. The primary concern is with the number, size, and speed of vehicles and the interaction of these factors on the road width and layout requirements. To quantify traffic requires a system which as far as possible takes into account the interference to other traffic which a particular type of vehicle engenders. For this purpose the passenger car is usually adopted as the 'standard' vehicle in relation to road occupancy and other vehicles in the traffic spectrum are assessed in terms of 'passenger car units' (pcu), as indicated in Table 8.1.

8.4   The differences in the pcu ratings in rural and urban situations arise because of the higher speeds normal in rural areas which render certain vehicles more obtrusive. The total traffic flow per day in pcu gives a misleading indication of road width requirements and it is usual to make this decision on the peak hourly traffic flow. In Britain the maximum capacity for a four-lane highway with grade separation (two-lane dual carriageway) is considered to be 3000 pcu/h and for a six-lane (three-lane dual carriageway) 4500 pcu/h. For an all-purpose road with intersections these figures would be reduced to 1100 and 1900 pcu/h respectively.

Table 8.1 Classification of traffic in passenger car units

Type of vehicle	Equivalent pcu	
	Rural	Urban
Private cars, motor cycle combinations, taxis, and light goods vehicles up to 1.5 t unladen	1	1
Motorcycles (solo), scooters, and mopeds	1	0.75
Goods vehicles over 1.5 t unladen weight	3	2

Role of the pavement engineer

8.5   The pavement engineer is concerned almost entirely with providing an adequate thickness and composition of pavement to carry the expected traffic, without the development of unacceptable deterioration (deformation and cracking) during the design life of the road. There is evidence that the damage caused to pavements increases very steeply with the axle loading, and that the axle loads of private cars and light vans contribute very little to structural deterioration. For the purpose of designing pavement thickness commercial traffic only is considered. The private car content of the total traffic is important only in determining the distribution of commercial traffic between the traffic lanes.

8.6   Information concerning the total number of vehicles in use can be obtained from vehicle licensing records. In Britain and western Europe the growth rate of private cars registered was about 8 per cent per annum, between 1945 and 1960. The growth rate of commercial vehicles registered was also about 8 per cent per annum, but since 1960 this has dropped to about 3 per cent. This is largely due to the increase in the size of modern commercial vehicles and the corresponding increase in payload.

8.7   The pavement engineer is concerned not so much with the total traffic as with the distribution of traffic over the road network, and between the traffic lanes. The constitution of the traffic in terms of vehicle types can be obtained from traffic censuses. In most developed countries such censuses are carried out at regular intervals on different classes of road and these give some guidance on the constitution of traffic in terms of private cars and of light commercial and heavy commercial vehicles. An engineer designing a new road would be unwise to rely heavily on this type of information. Where a new road is improving access between two points, some time should be spent studying the volume and constitution of the traffic on the roads likely to shed traffic onto the new route. The problem becomes increasingly difficult when the new road is comparatively long and provides access to and from a large town, e.g., a motorway providing an alternative to part of the trunk road system. In such a case, a detailed traffic survey will need to be made on the whole of the surrounding network and an assessment made of the percentage of the vehicles of different type likely to transfer to the new route. This could well involve several months of work. Experience has shown that it is wise to over- rather than underestimate the traffic. However small or large the project, the pavement engineer should record carefully how conclusions regarding the volume and constitution of the traffic, have been reached.

Classification of commercial vehicles

8.8   A comprehensive system of classifying commercial traffic in terms of vehicle type and axle configuration is shown in Fig. 8.1. For most purposes, whether or not axles are fitted with single or twin tyres is not very important and the classification can be simplified by defining only the number of axles and whether the vehicle has a rigid chassis or it is articulated. Two-axle commercial vehicles range from light delivery vans to trucks capable of being loaded to a gross weight of about 16 t. Only those vehicles of unladen weight exceeding 1.5 t are classified as commercial vehicles. This excludes panel trucks and similar light delivery vehicles. Most public-service vehicles (buses and coaches) are classed as commercial vehicles. In addition to the vehicles shown in Fig 8.1, there are other specialized types used for the conveyance of heavy indivisible loads.

8.9   In conducting a traffic census it is difficult to operate the complete classification scheme of Fig. 8.1 on fast-moving vehicles but there is no difficulty in noting the chassis type (rigid or articulated) and the number of axles. With traffic intensities

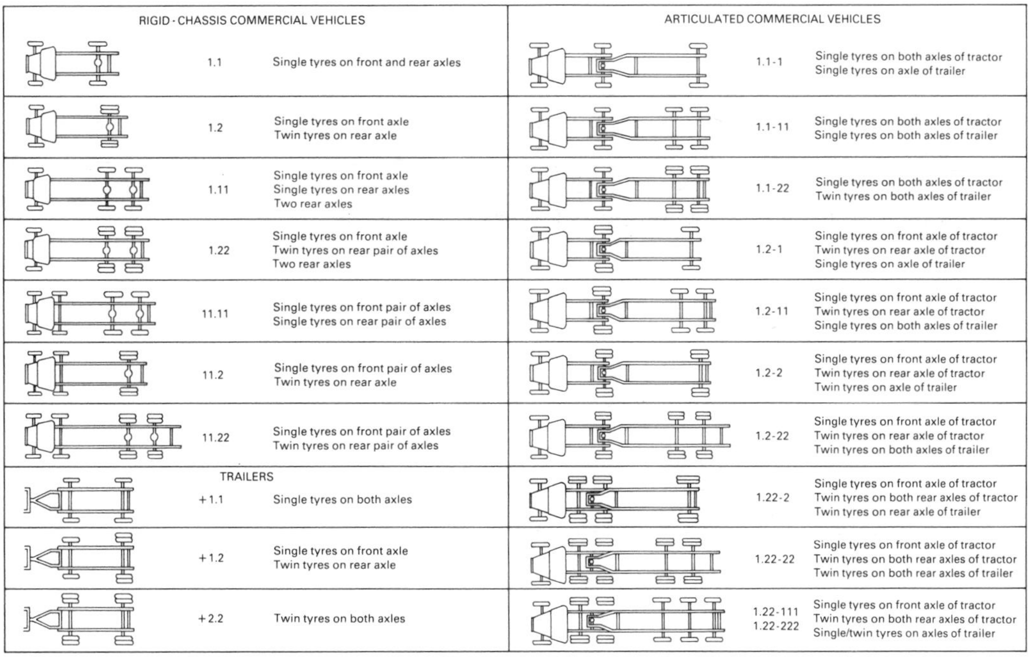

RIGID - CHASSIS COMMERCIAL VEHICLES			ARTICULATED COMMERCIAL VEHICLES		
	1.1	Single tyres on front and rear axles		1.1-1	Single tyres on both axles of tractor Single tyres on axle of trailer
	1.2	Single tyres on front axle Twin tyres on rear axle		1.1-11	Single tyres on both axles of tractor Single tyres on both axles of trailer
	1.11	Single tyres on front axle Single tyres on rear axles Two rear axles		1.1-22	Single tyres on both axles of tractor Twin tyres on both axles of trailer
	1.22	Single tyres on front axle Twin tyres on rear pair of axles Two rear axles		1.2-1	Single tyres on front axle of tractor Twin tyres on rear axle of tractor Single tyres on axle of trailer
	11.11	Single tyres on front pair of axles Single tyres on rear pair of axles		1.2-11	Single tyres on front axle of tractor Twin tyres on rear axle of tractor Single tyres on both axles of trailer
	11.2	Single tyres on front pair of axles Twin tyres on rear axle		1.2-2	Single tyres on front axle of tractor Twin tyres on rear axle of tractor Twin tyres on axle of trailer
	11.22	Single tyres on front pair of axles Twin tyres on rear pair of axles		1.2-22	Single tyres on front axle of tractor Twin tyres on rear axle of tractor Twin tyres on both axles of trailer
TRAILERS	+1.1	Single tyres on both axles		1.22-2	Single tyres on front axle of tractor Twin tyres on both rear axles of tractor Twin tyres on rear axle of trailer
	+1.2	Single tyres on front axle Twin tyres on rear axle		1.22-22	Single tyres on front axle of tractor Twin tyres on both rear axles of tractor Twin tyres on both axles of trailer
	+2.2	Twin tyres on both axles		1.22-111 1.22-222	Single tyres on front axle of tractor Twin tyres on both rear axles of tractor Single/twin tyres on axles of trailer

Figure 8.1   Method of classifying axle types

greater than 250 vehicles per hour per carriageway it is necessary to have one observer for each traffic lane.

Size and weight of commercial vehicles in Europe

8.10   The majority of countries specify the maximum total weight, the maximum axle load, and the maximum dimensions of commercial vehicles permitted to operate on their roads. Most manufacturers of goods vehicles hope to sell their products to other countries and most operators expect their vehicles to be able to cross country borders without serious difficulty. Because of these factors, commercial vehicles throughout the world are built to sizes which will be acceptable in most countries. However, the maximum permitted gross weight and the maximum axle load do vary significantly from country to country. The regulations governing the use of commercial vehicles in Great Britain are summarized in Table 8.2.[1] The maximum permitted axle load is applicable only to axles which are more than 1.85 m from neighbouring axles. For two closely spaced axles the maximum permitted load for each of two equally loaded axles falls from 10.17 t at an axle spacing of 1.85 m to 8.13 t at 1.02 m. For three closely spaced axles the maximum load on each axle falls from 7.5 t at a spacing of 1.3 m to 6 t at a spacing of 0.7 m.

8.11   Different regulations apply to the movement of heavy indivisible loads in the UK.[2] Such loads are permitted to move over certain routes after permission has been granted by the appropriate road authorities. In this case the maximum axle load carried by not less than four wheels in line, spaced along the axle, is 45.7 t and the maximum overall weight is 152 t. The number of such movements is small and seldom exceeds one or two per week even on major trunk routes.

8.12   During the last 10 years efforts have been made to unify the maximum axle loading and gross vehicle weights permitted in the various countries of the European Community. The current regulations for France, Germany, Italy, The Netherlands, and Britain are summarized in Table 8.3. For these countries Table 8.4[3] shows present loading restrictions for six types of articulated truck and the proposals for

Table 8.2   Maximum permitted dimensions and weights of commercial vehicles in the UK

Vehicle	Length, m	Width, m	Gross weight, t
two-axle rigid	11	2.5	16.3
three-axle articulated	15.5	2.5	24.4
three-axle rigid	11	2.5	24.4
four-axle articulated	15.5	2.5	32.5
four-axle rigid	11	2.5	30.5
five- and six-axle articulated	15.5	2.5	38.0
Vehicle–trailer combination	18	2.5	32.5
Tractor–trailer combination	26	2.5	32.5

Maximum axle load: 10.2 t for wheels at end of axles, 11.2 t for wheels spaced along axles

Table 8.3   Maximum axle loads and gross vehicle weights for some European countries

Country	Maximum load on single axle, t	Gross vehicle weight, t
France	12	38
Germany	10	36
Italy	12	40
Netherlands	9	50
UK	10.2	38

Table 8.4   Summary of typical heavy goods vehicle configurations

Country	Configuration (axle weights in t)		Trailer combined	Gross vehicle weight, t	Payload, t	Payload/ GVW, %
	Tractor					
	Two-axle tractors			**Four axles total**		
	Steer	Drive				
France	6	12	20	38.0	26.4	70
Germany	6	10	20 (>2 m)	36.0	24.8	69
Italy	6	12	22 (>2 m)	40.0	28.0	70
UK	6	10.2	16.3	32.5	22.0	68
UK	5	7.1	20.4 (>2 m)	32.5	22.0	68
Proposed for EC	6	11	18	35.0	24.0	69
				Five axles, three-axle trailer		
France	6	12	20	38.0	26.4	70
Germany and UK	6	10	22	38.0	26.4	70
Italy	6	12	26	44.0	31.2	71
Proposed for EC	6	11	23	40.0	28.0	70
	Three-axle tractors					
	Steer	Drive				
		A B				
Proposed for EC	6			**Five axles, two-axle trailer**		
Single drive	6	11 7	18	42.0	29.6	71
Double-drive	6	18 (comb.)	18	42.0	29.6	71
				Six axles total		
Netherlands	6	18 (comb.)	26	50.0	36.0	72
Proposed for EC						
Single drive	6	11 7	20	44.0	31.2	71
Double drive	6	18 (comb.)	20	44.0	31.2	71

unification which are currently under consideration. These proposals involve increasing the gross weight to 35–44 t depending on the number of axles and whether the traction unit has single- or double-axle drive. The maximum load proposed for single axles is 11 t. For double- and triple-axle bogies the maximum axle load is reduced to take into account the assumed interaction of the pavement stresses from individual axles as detailed in Table 8.4. The overall saving on transport costs, with respect to vehicles conforming with the present UK regulations, has been estimated as 5–10 per cent depending on the type of vehicle.[3] Because additional axles are introduced to accompany the increased gross weight the damaging effect on the pavement should not be increased.

Size and weight of commercial vehicles in the USA

8.13   The regulations which govern the axle loading and size of commercial vehicles in the USA vary markedly from state to state. Table 8.5 summarizes the following information by state:

- maximum load permitted on any axle;
- maximum load permitted on a tandem axle;

Table 8.5   Regulations relating to the maximum axle loading applicable in the USA

Max. loading		
lb	t	States
Single axles		
18 000	8.2	Arkansas, Georgia, Illinois, Indiana, Mississippi, Missouri, Montana, Nebraska, Tennessee
19 000	8.6	North Carolina
20 000	9.1	Alabama, Alaska, Arizona, California, Colorado, Delaware, Florida, Idaho, Iowa, Kansas, Kentucky, Louisiana, Michigan, Minnesota, Nebraska, Nevada, North Dakota, Ohio, Oklahoma, Oregon, South Carolina, South Dakota, Texas, Utah, Virginia, Washington, West Virginia, Wisconsin, Wyoming
21 600	9.8	New Mexico
22 000	10.0	Maine, District of Columbia
22 400	10.2	Connecticut, Hawaii, Maryland, Massachusetts, New Hampshire, New Jersey, New York, Pennsylvania, Rhode Island, Vermont
Tandem axles		
32 000	14.5	Arkansas, Illinois, Indiana, Mississippi, Missouri, Montana, Tennessee
34 000	15.4	Alaska, Arizona, California, Hawaii, Idaho, Iowa, Kansas, Kentucky, Louisiana, Maine, Michigan, Minnesota, Nebraska, Nevada, New Jersey, New Mexico, North Dakota, Ohio, Oklahoma, Oregon, Pennsylvania, South Dakota, Texas, Utah, Virginia, Washington, West Virginia, Wisconsin
36 000	16.3	Colorado, Connecticut, Georgia, Massachusetts, New Hampshire, New York, North Carolina, Rhode Island, South Carolina, Vermont, Wyoming
37 000	16.8	District of Columbia
40 000	18.1	Alabama, Delaware, Florida, Maryland

- maximum gross weight of the fully loaded vehicle;
- maximum overall length of tractor/semi-trailer combinations.

8.14   The maximum load on a single axle permitted in all of the states is considerably less than that permitted in European countries, although certain states permit the 10.2 t axle load currently allowed in the UK. The maximum tandem load is generally less than twice the maximum load permitted on a single axle, presumably on the assumption that there is a degree of interaction between two axles in close proximity. Alabama, Delaware and Florida, on the other hand, permit a tandem-axle load very close to double the permitted single-axle load. Structural analysis (see Chapter 21) indicates that this is more reasonable.

8.15   The maximum gross weights of fully loaded trucks are given in Table 8.6. For 29 of the states it is below the 38 t currently permitted in Europe, but if the maximum permitted for EC countries is eventually increased to 44 t, as appears likely, only 12 states will permit higher gross weights.

8.16   The major difference between United States and European trucks is the maximum permitted length. In the USA this varies between 16.8 and 25.9 m (55 and 85 ft), although in some states the longer vehicles are allowed only on designated routes. In Europe the maximum length is 15.5 m (50.8 ft). The narrower and generally winding road systems of Europe cannot cater for very long vehicles.

Factors relating to commercial traffic important in pavement design

8.17   Structural damage to road pavements is caused almost entirely by commercial traffic. The nearside traffic lanes carry the bulk of the commercial vehicles and for this reason the life of the pavement is generally defined by the peformance of the left-hand lanes. In dual-carriageway roads the near-side lanes will deteriorate first and if all the lanes are constructed to the same thickness then the overtaking lanes will have a considerably greater structural life. This may be taken into account by graduating the thickness of the lanes across the carriageway, although this is not usually done.

8.18   If pavements are designed empirically using experience gained by the long-term observation of full-scale trial pavements, or from the observed performance of in-service roads, it is generally sufficient to assess traffic in terms of the number of heavy commercial vehicles using the left-hand lane, and the extent to which these vehicles load the pavement. Seasonal effects such as the proportion of loads imposed during hot and cold periods of the day or of the year, or immediately following freezing conditions are included in the nature of the long-term evidence used in the design procedure and need not be specifically considered by the pavement engineer. As discussed in Chapters 21 and 22, there are situations which are not adequately covered by the empirical methods and then structural theory must be used. In this case it is necessary to relate traffic more closely to climatic factors and to seasonal changes in the support provided by the subgrade. This is

Table 8.6   Regulations relating to the maximum gross vehicle weight and maximum overall length applicable in the USA

Max. gross weight		
lb	t	States
73 280	33.2	Arkansas, District of Columbia, Illinois, Indiana, Mississippi, Missouri, Tennessee
76 000	34.5	Virginia
79 800	36.2	North Carolina
80 000	36.3	Arizona, California, Connecticut, Delaware, Florida, Georgia, Iowa, Maine, Maryland, Minnesota, New Hampshire, New Jersey, New York, Ohio, Pennsylvania, Texas, Vermont, Wisconsin
80 600	36.6	South Carolina
82 000	37.2	Kentucky
85 500	38.8	Kansas
86 400	39.2	New Mexico
88 000	39.9	Louisiana
88 880	40.3	Hawaii
90 000	40.8	West Virginia, Oklahoma
92 400	41.9	Alabama
95 000	43.1	Nebraska, South Dakota
99 000	44.9	Rhode Island
101 000	45.8	Wyoming
104 000	47.2	Massachusetts
105 500	47.9	Idaho, Montana, North Dakota, Oregan, Washington
109 000	49.4	Alaska
122 000	55.3	Utah
129 000	58.5	Nevada
164 000	74.4	Michigan

Maximum overall length (tractor and semi-trailer combinations)		
ft	m	States
55	16.8	Connecticut, District of Columbia, Florida, Indiana, Kentucky, Maryland, Missouri, New Jersey, North Carolina, Rhode Island, Tennessee, Virginia, Washington, West Virginia
58	17.7	Hawaii
60	18.3	Alabama, Arkansas, California, Delaware, Georgia, Iowa, Maine, Massachusetts, Michigan, Minnesota, Mississippi, Montana, New Hampshire, New York, Ohio, Oregon, Pennsylvania, South Carolina, Vermont
65	19.8	Alaska, Arizona, Idaho, Kansas, Louisiana, Nebraska, New Mexico, North Dakota, Oklahoma, Texas, Utah
70	21.4	Colorado, Nevada, South Dakota
85	25.9	Wyoming

because the strength and fatigue properties of some road materials are related to their temperature or moisture content.

8.19   Ideally the design engineer will want to know:

- how much commercial traffic is likely to be carried by the left-hand lanes and how this will be affected by the total traffic intensity;
- how the intensity of the commercial traffic on the lanes varies with the time of day and time of year;
- how damaging the commercial traffic is likely to be in terms of axle loading.

The remainder of this chapter is devoted largely to these aspects of traffic.

8.20   The traffic census form used in the UK for detailed traffic counts is shown in Fig. 8.2. To obtain the daily average traffic flow for any carriageway or carriageway lane, 4 day, 24-hour counts are made from Friday to Monday. In relation to other days of the week Friday traffic is rather heavy and Saturday and Sunday traffic light. It has been found from seven-day counts that a close approximation to the average daily traffic is obtained by adding four times the Monday traffic to the combined Friday, Saturday, and Sunday traffic and dividing by seven, as indicated by the right-hand columns of Fig. 8.2.

Distribution of traffic between carriageway lanes

8.21   In the discussion which follows, light commercial vehicles will be compounded with private cars and the term commercial traffic will include only heavy commercial vehicles of unladen weight exceeding 1.5 t and public-service vehicles.

8.22   Twenty-four hour observations have been made to study the hourly distribution of commercial and private vehicles between the carriageway lanes on the various types of road, as indicated in Table 8.7. The information obtained at the seven sites listed is summarized in Tables 8.8–8.15.

8.23   Using the Tables 8.8–8.15, the percentage of the total traffic using each of the lanes can be related to the total number of vehicles per hour carried by the road. The percentages of the commercial vehicles in the lanes available for their use can also be related to the intensity of the commercial traffic expressed in the number of such vehicles per hour. Figures 8.3 and 8.4 show examples, for the M4 motorway at Harlington, in April 1972 (Table 8.9) of these two types of analysis.

8.24   Figure 8.3 shows that once the total traffic intensity reaches about 2500 vehicles per hour, then all the three lanes were carrying equal numbers of vehicles. This condition would have prevailed, because of the considerable commuter traffic, from about 2 p.m. to 8 p.m. It would also have prevailed on the eastbound carriageway during the morning migration of commuters to London. The fact that the percentage of traffic on the right-hand lane is hardly increasing after the traffic flow exceeds 2500 vehicles per hour suggests that bunching is occurring on that lane, reducing headroom. Figure 8.4 shows that the left-hand lane and the centre or overtaking lane for commercial vehicles will be carrying the same number of such vehicles when the commercial vehicle flow reaches about 700 per hour.

LOCATION _____ DATES _____ HOURS OF COUNT _____

VEHICLE TYPE	Column 1 = FRIDAY				Column 2 = SATURDAY				Column 3 = SUNDAY				Column 4 = MONDAY				Col 5 =4×col 4+(Cols 1+2+3)/7			
	L/H	Centre	R/H	Total	L/H	Centre	R/H	Total	L/H	Centre	R/H	Total	L/H	Centre	R/H	Total	L/H	Centre	R/H	Total
CARS																				
Light commercial																				
PSV 2A×I																				
3A×I																				
4A×I																				
1 1																				
1 11																				
1 2																				
1 12																				
1 22																				
11 1																				
11 2																				
11 12																				
11 22																				
122 22																				
111 11																				
112 11																				
11 1																				
12 1																				
11 11																				
11 22																				
12 11																				
12 21																				
12 22																				
12 111																				
12 112																				
12 222																				
111 11																				
111 22																				
112 11																				
112 22																				
112 111																				
122 2																				
122 22																				
122 44																				
122 4444																				
+1																				
+2																				
+11																				
+12																				
+22																				
+111																				
+4444																				
+4444 4444																				
Total vehicles																				
Total com. vehicles																				
Total axles																				
Total com. axles																				
Axles per vehicle																				
Axles per com. veh.																				

Row group labels (vertical): RIGID CHASSIS VEHICLES, ARTICULATED VEHICLES, TRAILERS

Figure 8.2 Form for daily and period mean traffic

Table 8.7 Roads used for 24-hour traffic distribution studies

Road description	Layout	Direction of traffic flow	Date
1. M4 motorway at Harlington near London Airport	Dual three-lane carriageway	Westbound	May 1969
2. M4 motorway at Harlington near London Airport	Dual three-lane carriageway	Westbound	April 1972
3. M4 motorway at Datchet (Windsor)	Dual three-lane carriageway	Westbound	April 1972
4. M1 motorway at Friars Wash	Dual three-lane carriageway	Southbound	June 1973
5. M6 motorway at Perry Barr	Dual three-lane carriageway	Eastbound	July 1972
6. M6 motorway at Perry Barr	Dual three-lane carriageway	Westbound	July 1972
7. M4 motorway* at Datchet	Dual two-lane carriageway	Westbound	April 1969
8. A1 trunk road at Alconbury Hill	Dual two-lane carriageway	Northbound	February 1969

*Prior to widening to three-lane dual carriageway layout.
Note: The information obtained at the sites listed above is summarized in Tables 8.8–8.15.

8.25   A similar analysis for the M1 motorway at Friars Wash (Table 8.11) is shown in Figs 8.5 and 8.6. This road carries a significantly larger number of commercial vehicles and a much smaller number of private vehicles than does the M4 motorway at Harlington. In 1973, when the measurements were made, all the lanes carried approximately the same number of vehicles when the total flow reached 1600 vehicles per hour. However, at that stage the percentage and number of vehicles on the right-hand lane was still increasing, indicating at that time there was still some capacity for further private cars. The percentage of the commercial vehicles on the two available lanes (see Fig. 8.6), indicated that parity would occur at a flow of about 900 commercial vehicles per hour. After that, bunching of the commercial vehicles would be expected. Between 1972 and 1988 the daily flow of commercial vehicles on the M1 motorway at Friars Wash increased by a total of 15 per cent and private car traffic by about 2 per cent per annum, giving an overall increase of about 1.5 times. The present position at Friars Wash is therefore likely to be similar to that on the M4 at Harlington in 1972.

8.26   It is to be regretted that comprehensive 24-hour surveys of this type have not been carried out since 1972. This type of information is essential to the proper

Table 8.8 Distribution of vehicles between carriageway lanes on the M4 motorway at Harlington in May 1969—westbound lanes

Time period	Commercial vehicles only					All vehicles						
	Number of vehicles			Percentage of vehicles		Number of vehicles				Percentage of vehicles		
	LL*	CL*	Total	LL	CL	LL	CL	RL	Total	LL	CL	RL
0–1	41	6	47	87	13	387	274	179	840	46	33	21
1–2	37	4	41	90	10	291	167	80	538	54	31	15
2–3	36	4	40	90	10	126	97	33	256	49	38	13
3–4	36	3	39	92	8	94	65	14	173	54	38	8
4–5	32	3	35	91	9	87	50	7	144	60	35	5
5–6	50	4	54	93	7	109	86	17	212	51	41	8
6–7	111	15	126	88	12	260	246	18	524	50	47	3
7–8	201	102	303	66	34	493	589	150	1 232	40	48	12
8–9	255	127	382	67	33	749	797	361	1 907	39	42	19
9–10	259	171	430	60	40	763	853	537	2 153	35	40	25
10–11	283	146	429	66	34	746	879	687	2 312	32	38	30
11–12	295	129	424	70	30	749	794	617	2 158	25	37	28
12–13	295	141	436	68	32	737	771	464	1 972	37	40	23
13–14	258	118	376	69	31	693	736	421	1 850	37	40	23
14–15	226	102	328	69	31	676	720	384	1 780	38	40	22
15–16	237	96	333	71	29	667	729	380	1 776	38	41	21
16–17	204	79	283	72	28	706	749	397	1 852	38	40	22
17–18	196	84	270	73	27	821	836	439	2 096	39	40	21
18–19	139	59	198	70	30	860	1 050	581	2 491	35	42	23
19–20	109	48	157	69	31	733	818	891	2 447	30	36	34
20–21	95	35	130	73	27	640	710	1 147	2 497	26	28	46
21–22	66	14	80	83	17	486	580	974	2 040	24	28	48
22–23	56	10	66	85	15	426	461	399	1 286	33	36	31
23–24	49	6	55	89	11	373	414	186	973	38	43	19
Total in 24 h	3 566	1 506	5 062	77 mean	23	12 672	13 471	9 363	35 515	40	38 mean	22

*LL = left-hand lane, CL = centre lane, RL = right-hand lane (in the case of three-lane carriageways no heavy commercial vehicles are permitted to use the right-hand lane).

48

Table 8.9 Distribution of vehicles between carriageway lanes on the M4 motorway at Harlington in April 1972—westbound lanes

Time period	Commercial vehicles only — Number of vehicles			Commercial vehicles only — Percentage of vehicles		All vehicles — Number of vehicles				All vehicles — Percentage of vehicles		
	LL*	CL*	Total	LL	CL	LL	CL	RL	Total	LL	CL	RL
0–1	44	21	65	67	33	363	429	201	993	37	43	20
1–2	52	14	66	79	21	206	300	99	605	34	50	16
2–3	48	9	57	84	16	109	140	49	298	37	47	16
3–4	46	5	51	90	10	81	61	26	168	48	36	16
4–5	47	5	52	90	10	84	46	23	153	55	30	15
5–6	74	8	82	90	10	381	50	24	455	84	11	5
6–7	141	31	172	82	18	707	114	181	1 002	71	11	18
7–8	201	120	321	68	37	831	404	499	1 734	48	23	29
8–9	202	164	356	57	43	720	929	611	2 260	32	41	27
9–10	268	132	400	67	33	850	1 047	496	2 393	36	44	20
10–11	266	126	392	68	32	867	854	610	2 331	37	37	26
11–12	276	154	430	64	36	850	927	609	2 386	36	39	25
12–13	296	103	399	74	26	887	920	700	2 507	35	37	28
13–14	279	64	343	81	19	839	837	487	2 163	39	39	22
14–15	251	114	365	69	31	969	887	531	2 387	41	37	22
15–16	238	98	336	71	29	1 164	864	640	2 668	44	32	24
16–17	224	97	321	70	30	1 289	911	893	3 093	42	29	29
17–18	159	89	248	64	36	1 121	1 107	1 293	3 521	32	31	37
18–19	121	77	198	61	39	780	1 401	1 564	3 745	21	37	42
19–20	109	94	203	54	46	723	1 247	1 130	3 100	23	40	37
20–21	100	41	141	71	29	667	910	680	2 257	30	40	30
21–22	84	33	117	72	28	647	624	411	1 682	38	37	25
22–23	62	27	89	70	30	593	576	266	1 435	41	40	19
23–24	58	24	82	71	29	457	526	163	1 146	40	46	14
Total in 24 h	1 646	1 640	5 286	72 mean	28	16 185	16 114	12 186	44 485	41	36	23 mean

*LL = left-hand lane, CL = centre lane, **RL** = right-hand lane (in the case of three-lane carriageways no heavy commercial vehicles are permitted to use the right-hand lane).

Table 8.10 Distribution of vehicles between carriageway lanes on the M4 motorway at Datchet in April 1972 (three-lane dual carriageway)

Time period	Commercial vehicles only					All vehicles						
	Number of vehicles			Percentage of vehicles		Number of vehicles				Percentage of vehicles		
	LL*	CL*	Total	LL	CL	LL	CL	RL	Total	LL	CL	RL
0–1	29	6	35	83	17	284	514	149	947	30	54	16
1–2	34	4	38	89	11	200	350	74	624	32	56	12
2–3	32	2	34	94	6	117	179	20	316	37	57	6
3–4	28	5	33	85	15	79	74	8	161	49	46	5
4–5	41	4	45	91	9	80	64	6	150	53	43	4
5–6	70	19	89	79	21	114	107	7	228	50	47	3
6–7	113	64	177	64	36	223	201	76	500	45	40	15
7–8	159	56	215	74	26	351	320	154	825	43	39	18
8–9	221	54	275	80	20	476	569	280	1 325	36	43	21
9–10	217	61	278	78	22	484	659	479	1 622	30	41	29
10–11	206	66	272	76	24	560	669	479	1 708	33	39	28
11–12	216	60	276	78	22	544	696	400	1 640	33	42	25
12–13	209	67	276	76	24	551	696	421	1 668	33	42	25
13–14	205	59	264	78	22	547	673	427	1 647	33	41	26
14–15	203	54	257	79	21	569	686	436	1 691	34	41	25
15–16	186	61	247	75	25	571	727	467	1 765	32	41	27
16–17	159	66	225	71	29	520	867	670	2 057	25	42	33
17–18	130	48	178	73	27	630	1 141	750	2 522	25	45	30
18–19	111	22	133	83	17	729	1 376	900	3 005	24	46	30
19–20	62	11	73	85	15	729	1 017	1 186	2 932	25	35	40
20–21	59	14	73	81	19	558	794	1 236	2 588	22	31	47
21–22	48	14	62	77	23	453	583	839	1 875	24	31	45
22–23	42	11	53	79	21	373	497	201	1 071	35	46	19
23–24	42	8	50	84	16	350	411	140	901	39	46	15

*LL = left-hand lane, CL = centre lane, RL = right-hand lane (in the case of three-lane carriageways no heavy commercial vehicles are permitted to use the right-hand lane).

50

Table 8.11 Distribution of vehicles between carriageway lanes on the M1 motorway at Friars Wash, June 1973—southbound lanes

Time period	Commercial vehicles only					All vehicles						
	Number of vehicles			Percentage of vehicles		Number of vehicles				Percentage of vehicles		
	LL*	CL*	Total	LL	CL	LL	CL	RL	Total	LL	CL	RL
0–1	50	10	60	83	17	284	313	108	705	40	44	15
1–2	45	6	51	88	12	213	170	69	452	47	38	15
2–3	51	1	52	98	2	150	100	19	269	56	37	7
3–4	71	2	73	97	3	146	54	9	209	70	26	4
4–5	100	7	107	93	7	180	58	8	246	73	24	3
5–6	162	11	173	94	6	246	80	11	337	73	24	3
6–7	316	35	351	90	10	427	229	47	703	61	33	7
7–8	329	10	339	97	3	536	751	166	1 453	37	52	11
8–9	373	148	521	72	28	631	896	90	1 617	39	55	6
9–10	394	271	668	59	41	636	829	1 143	2 603	24	32	44
10–11	373	252	625	60	40	621	741	1 010	2 372	26	31	43
11–12	341	235	576	59	41	620	446	819	1 885	33	24	24
12–13	297	194	491	60	40	579	647	637	1 853	35	35	34
13–14	283	120	403	70	30	564	616	487	1 667	34	37	29
14–15	264	124	388	68	32	567	634	480	1 681	34	38	29
15–16	247	117	364	68	32	550	689	477	1 716	32	40	28
16–17	277	122	399	69	31	554	769	530	1 853	32	38	31
17–18	240	119	359	67	33	700	830	679	2 209	32	38	31
18–19	169	102	271	62	38	611	540	806	1 957	31	27	41
19–20	148	96	244	61	39	501	613	571	1 685	30	36	34
20–21	120	53	173	69	31	473	517	429	1 419	33	36	30
21–22	116	39	155	75	25	430	396	361	1 187	36	33	30
22–23	88	16	104	85	15	396	313	291	1 000	40	31	29
23–24	84	11	95	88	12	387	160	67	614	63	26	11

*LL = left-hand lane, CL = centre lane, RL = right-hand lane (in the case of three-lane carriageways no heavy commercial vehicles are permitted to use the right-hand lane).

Table 8.12 Distribution of vehicles between carriageway lanes on the M6 motorway at Perry Barr in July 1972—eastbound lanes

Time period	Commercial vehicles only					All vehicles						
	Number of vehicles			Percentage of vehicles		Number of vehicles				Percentage of vehicles		
	LL*	CL*	Total	LL	CL	LL	CL	RL	Total	LL	CL	RL
0–1	46	4	50	92	8	210	103	11	324	65	32	3
1–2	55	1	56	98	2	149	61	8	218	68	28	4
2–3	54	1	55	98	2	103	43	4	150	69	29	2
3–4	53	1	54	98	2	94	39	5	138	68	28	4
4–5	69	4	73	95	5	114	40	5	159	72	25	3
5–6	142	24	166	86	14	194	49	20	263	74	19	7
6–7	239	94	333	72	28	397	89	56	551	72	16	12
7–8	332	191	523	63	37	579	309	185	773	75	40	5
8–9	346	195	541	64	36	713	541	554	1808	39	30	31
9–10	351	159	510	69	31	660	686	657	2003	33	34	33
10–11	361	114	475	76	24	650	813	464	1937	34	42	24
11–12	357	102	459	78	22	643	761	347	1751	37	43	20
12–13	315	82	397	79	21	621	719	294	1634	38	44	18
13–14	292	96	388	75	25	590	617	216	1423	41	43	16
14–15	279	82	361	77	23	607	583	267	1457	42	40	18
15–16	294	67	361	51	49	627	653	297	1577	40	41	19
16–17	261	46	307	85	15	614	677	326	1617	38	42	20
17–18	202	26	228	89	11	589	703	329	1621	36	43	21
18–19	149	21	170	88	12	540	787	344	1671	32	47	21
19–20	118	15	133	89	11	501	729	269	1499	33	49	18
20–21	88	10	98	90	10	411	614	178	1203	34	51	15
21–22	83	14	97	86	14	346	406	107	859	40	47	13
22–23	82	3	85	96	4	277	253	67	597	46	42	12
23–24	70	1	71	99	1	241	154	29	424	57	46	9

*LL = left-hand lane, CL = centre lane, RL = right-hand lane (in the case of three-lane carriageways no heavy commercial vehicles are permitted to use the right-hand lane).

Table 8.13 Distribution of vehicles between carriageway lanes on the M6 motorway at Perry Barr in July 1972—westbound lanes

Time period	Commercial vehicles only					All vehicles						
	Number of vehicles			Percentage of vehicles		Number of vehicles				Percentage of vehicles		
	LL*	CL*	Total	LL	CL	LL	CL	RL	Total	LL	CL	RL
0–1	45	4	49	92	8	316	143	19	478	66	30	4
1–2	44	4	48	92	8	169	59	10	238	71	25	4
2–3	42	4	46	91	9	116	31	11	158	73	20	7
3–4	44	0	44	100	0	110	22	11	143	77	15	8
4–5	45	1	46	98	2	104	16	6	128	81	13	6
5–6	73	9	82	89	11	121	24	7	152	80	16	4
6–7	152	27	179	85	15	206	94	17	317	65	30	5
7–8	270	45	315	86	14	383	306	89	778	49	39	12
8–9	310	135	445	70	30	549	569	210	1 328	41	43	16
9–10	295	114	409	72	28	573	661	357	1 591	36	42	22
10–11	326	125	451	72	28	596	716	366	1 678	36	43	21
11–12	324	109	433	75	25	614	736	323	1 673	37	44	19
12–13	322	97	419	77	23	584	699	293	1 576	37	44	19
13–14	302	89	391	77	23	576	631	221	1 428	40	44	16
14–15	284	195	479	59	41	561	654	274	1 489	38	44	18
15–16	289	172	461	63	37	664	707	353	1 724	39	41	20
16–17	281	125	406	69	31	676	816	546	2 038	33	40	27
17–18	229	91	320	72	28	704	1 017	750	2 471	29	41	30
18–19	178	64	242	74	26	707	1 097	869	2 673	26	41	33
19–20	126	64	190	66	34	587	736	264	1 587	37	46	17
20–21	99	24	123	80	20	474	536	176	1 186	40	45	15
21–22	41	19	60	68	32	429	406	124	959	45	42	13
22–23	81	19	100	81	19	361	327	66	754	48	43	9
23–24	76	1	77	99	1	307	234	34	575	53	41	6

*LL = left-hand lane, CL = centre lane, RL = right-hand lane (in the case of three-lane carriageways no heavy commercial vehicles are permitted to use the right-hand lane).

Table 8.14 Distribution of vehicles between carriageway lanes on the M4 motorway at Datchet in May 1969—westbound lanes (motorway a two-lane dual carriageway at this date)

Time period	Commercial vehicles only					All vehicles						
	Number of vehicles			Percentage of vehicles		Number of vehicles				Percentage of vehicles		
	LL*	RL*	Total	LL	RL	LL	CL	RL	Total	LL	CL	RL
0–1	40	2	42	95	5	339		189	529	64		36
1–2	29	2	31	94	6	286		149	435	66		34
2–3	39	2	41	95	5	159		56	215	74		26
3–4	17	4	21	81	19	101		21	122	83		17
4–5	42	4	46	91	9	96		15	111	86		14
5–6	82	10	92	89	11	170		31	201	85		15
6–7	156	15	171	91	9	333		116	449	74		26
7–8	201	40	241	83	17	600		346	946	63		37
8–9	212	57	269	79	21	693		827	1 520	46		54
9–10	226	47	273	83	17	691		811	1 502	46		54
10–11	243	59	302	80	20	677		776	1 453	47		53
11–12	226	57	283	80	20	726		797	1 523	48		52
12–13	207	93	300	69	31	549		689	1 238	44		56
13–14	214	32	246	87	13	561		724	1 285	44		56
14–15	181	40	221	82	18	714		769	1 483	48		52
15–16	156	33	189	83	17	733		1 443	2 176	34		66
16–17	122	34	156	78	22	1 070		1 987	3 057	35		65
17–18	124	32	156	79	21	979		1 343	2 322	42		58
18–19	80	29	109	73	27	769		977	1 746	44		56
19–20	56	26	82	68	32	551		680	1 231	45		55
20–21	49	16	65	75	25	486		354	840	58		42
21–22	39	4	43	91	9	473		291	764	62		38
22–23	33	4	37	89	11	419		270	689	61		39
23–24	34	4	38	89	11	349		220	569	61		39

*LL = left-hand lane, CL = centre lane, RL = right-hand lane (in the case of three-lane carriageways no heavy commercial vehicles are permitted to use the right-hand lane).

Table 8.15 Distribution of vehicles between carriageway lanes on the A1 trunk road in February 1969—northbound traffic lanes (two-lane dual carriageway)

Time period	Commercial vehicles only					All vehicles						
	Number of vehicles			Percentage of vehicles		Number of vehicles				Percentage of vehicles		
	LL*	RL*	Total	LL	RL	LL	CL	RL	Total	LL	CL	RL
0–1	33	3	36	92	8	136		10	146	93		7
1–2	26	3	29	90	10	97		7	104	93		7
2–3	21	3	24	87	13	60		7	67	90		10
3–4	20	3	23	87	13	41		6	47	87		13
4–5	21	3	24	87	13	38		5	43	88		12
5–6	30	3	33	91	9	41		5	46	89		11
6–7	48	3	51	94	6	74		9	83	89		11
7–8	65	8	73	89	11	114		23	137	83		17
8–9	83	6	89	93	7	181		66	247	73		27
9–10	101	6	107	94	6	259		81	340	76		24
10–11	112	7	119	94	6	301		77	378	80		20
11–12	126	11	137	92	8	316		61	377	84		16
12–13	133	11	144	92	8	326		101	427	76		24
13–14	130	10	140	93	7	309		129	438	71		29
14–15	116	8	124	94	6	305		119	424	72		28
15–16	127	15	142	89	11	313		113	426	73		27
16–17	129	13	142	91	9	316		120	436	72		28
17–18	119	9	128	92	8	351		121	472	74		26
18–19	99	10	109	91	9	323		133	456	71		29
19–20	83	8	91	91	9	315		121	436	72		28
20–21	66	8	74	89	11	270		93	363	74		26
21–22	51	5	56	91	9	207		50	257	81		19
22–23	73	5	78	94	6	179		31	210	85		15
23–24	61	3	64	95	5	154		19	173	89		11

*LL = left-hand lane, CL = centre lane, RL = right-hand lane (in the case of three-lane carriageways no heavy commercial vehicles are permitted to use the right-hand lane).

55

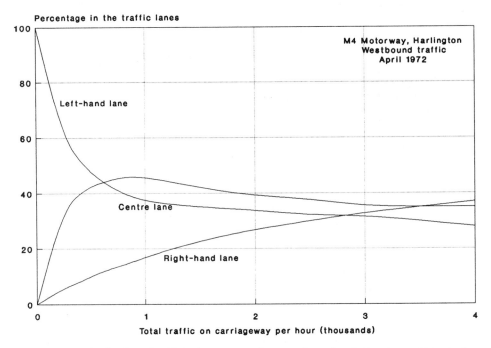

Figure 8.3 Distribution of vehicles between carriageway lanes in relation to total hourly flow (M4 at Harlington)

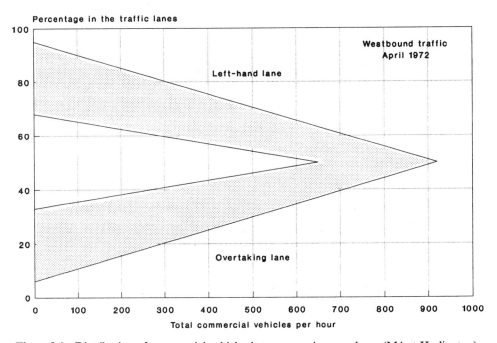

Figure 8.4 Distribution of commercial vehicles between carriageway lanes (M4 at Harlington)

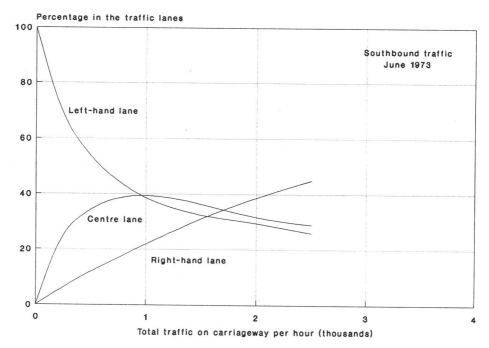

Figure 8.5 Distribution of total traffic between carriageway lanes in relation to total hourly flow (M1 at Friars Wash)

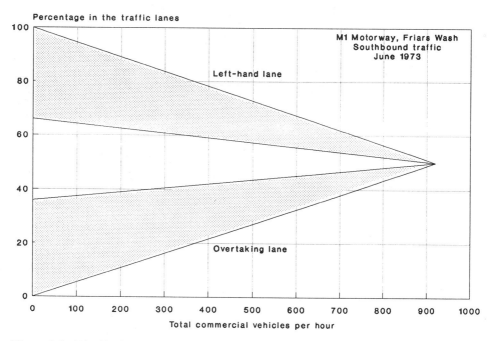

Figure 8.6 Distribution of commercial vehicles between carriageway lanes (M1 at Friars Wash)

57

design of major highways. Had up-to-date information been available for the roads covered by all the 1969–72 surveys then the need to design the M25 orbital motorway to at least dual four-lane layout would have been apparent.

8.27   As an example of the corresponding traffic distribution on two-lane dual carriageways, Figs 8.7 and 8.8 refer to a section of the M4 motorway at Datchet some 8 miles west of Harlington (after the turnoff to London Airport). At the time the observations were made, the road had the original two-lane layout. It was widened to three-lane two years later (Table 8.10). Figure 8.7 shows that the condition of equal numbers of vehicles on the two lanes was reached at a total traffic flow of 1200 vehicles per hour, compared with a flow of 2600 vehicles per hour on the left-hand and right-hand lanes of the three-lane layout. This is a measure of the increased capacity of the road. For the two-lane situation, Fig. 8.8 shows much less scatter in the points giving the distribution of the commercial vehicles between the two lanes when compared with three-lane carriageways. This suggests that, on the latter, commercial drivers tend to use the overtaking lane much more freely than is the case with two-lane carriageways.

8.28   The information given in Tables 8.8–8.15 can also be used to obtain the relationship between the percentages of commercial vehicles in the left-hand and overtaking lanes and the number of commercial vehicles carried by the carriageway each day. This relationship is shown in Fig. 8.9.

Constitution of commercial vehicles in terms of numbers of axles

8.29   In recent years studies have been made of the constitution of commercial traffic, in terms of number of axles and type of body, on motorways and other roads. In some cases the information has been obtained for individual traffic lanes as well as for the carriageway as a whole. Some counts have been repeated at intervals to investigate possible trends in the way goods are transported by road. Table 8.16 shows the composition of the commercial traffic on the UK M1–M6 link between London and Carlisle, over the period 1966–1983. This is the major motorway route between London and the north, and the composition of the traffic would be expected to be similar along its length. The observations are plotted in Fig. 8.10,[4,5] which shows very significant trends in usage of different types of commercial vehicles during the 20-year period. There has been a steady decline in the use of two-, three- and four-axle rigid bodied trucks. The data show that by the end of 1984 the number of four-axle articulated vehicles carried by this section of the motorway system exceeded the number of two-axle heavy goods vehicles. The use of five- and six-axle articulated trucks is also increasing rapidly. A survey on trunk road A2 made in 1984[6] showed that 24 per cent of the commercial traffic consisted of five- and six-axle trucks. This evidence suggests that increasing the gross weight of such vehicles from 32 to 38 t has much increased their use and that the trends indicated by extrapolation of the curves in Fig. 8.10 may be misleading.

8.30   Table 8.17 shows, for the same two motorways considered above, the percentages of the different types of commercial vehicle on the left-hand and the

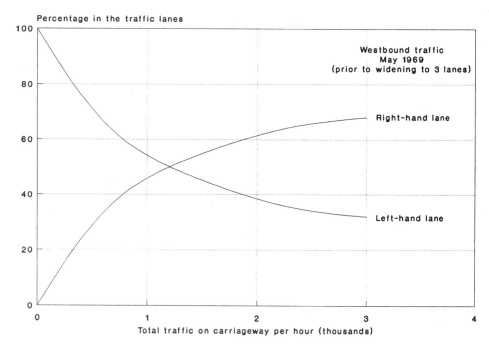

Figure 8.7 Distribution of vehicles between carriageway lanes in relation to total hourly flow (M4 at Datchet)

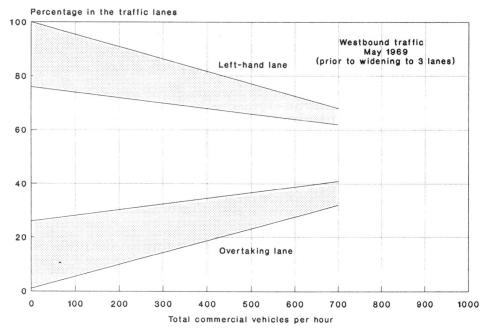

Figure 8.8 Distribution of commercial vehicles between carriageway lanes (M4 at Datchet)

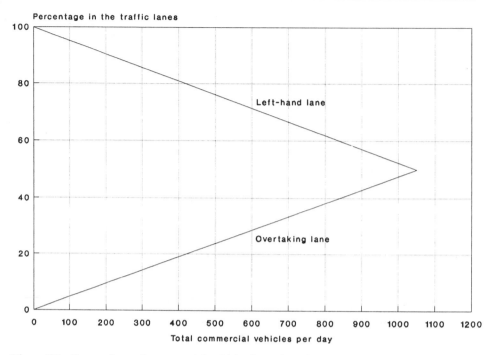

Figure 8.9   Proportions of commercial vehicles in each traffic lane

overtaking lanes. As would be expected, commercial traffic in the overtaking lanes has a rather greater percentage of two-axle vehicles, but otherwise the constitution of the commercial traffic on both lanes is very similar. Also included in Table 8.17 are measurements made on the UK M4 motorway at two locations close to the London end. East of London Airport, towards London, the traffic contains a much larger proportion of two-axle heavy commercial vehicles than is the case with the M1 and M6 motorways. However, at Datchet, a few miles west of the airport, traffic from the M1 has joined the M4 via the M25 and the composition of the commercial traffic becomes very similar to that on the M1 and M6.

8.31   Table 8.18 gives similar information for the UK major industrial road A1 and two rural A-class roads. The composition of the commercial traffic on the A1 in 1969 is very similar to that on the motorways for the same year. The other two roads have a much larger proportion of two-axle heavy commercial vehicles and the composition of the commercial traffic on these roads is probably typical of rural trunk roads not carrying heavy industrial traffic.

8.32   The increasing use of four-, five- and six-axle articulated commercial vehicles means that the average number of axles per commercial vehicle has increased in recent years on almost all roads, but particularly on motorways and industrial trunk roads. Figure 8.11 shows this trend for various classes of road. The average number of axles per motor vehicle, including all cars, light delivery vans,

Table 8.16 Commercial traffic in percentages of vehicle types and number of axles on the M1 and M6 motorways in 1966–83

| | M1 motorway | | | | M6 motorway | |
| | Friars Wash (southbound) | | | Newport Pagnell (southbound) | Midlands Link (eastbound) | Doxey (southbound) |
	Dec. 1966	June 1972	June 1973	Jan. 1967	July 1972	Sept. 1983
Two-axle rigid	60	51	52	55	50	43
Three-axle rigid	10	6	6	10	7	3
Four-axle rigid	7	5	3	8	3	3
Three-axle articulated	15	15	13	19	16	4
Four-axle articulated	7	20	24	8	23	42
Five-axle articulated	—	2	1	—	1	5
Six-axle articulated	—	—	—	—	—	0.5

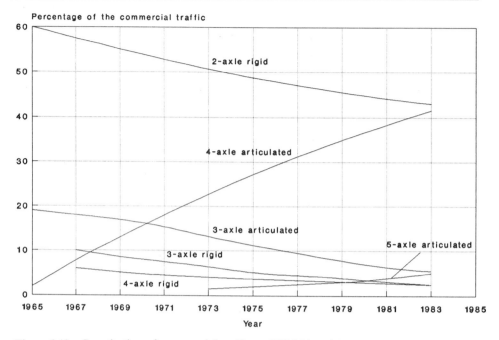

Figure 8.10   Constitution of commercial traffic on UK M1 and M6 motorways, 1966–87

public services vehicles and heavy commercial vehicles has not increased significantly in recent years, but has remained between 2.2 and 2.3. This is because the number of cars and delivery vans has increased at a greater rate than has the number of heavy commercial vehicles. Where for pavement design purposes the only traffic information available is the average number of axles per day (e.g., from a road counter), this number should be divided by 2.25 to give the average number of vehicles per day. The appropriate number of heavy commercial vehicles per day can be calculated from the percentage given in Table 8.19.

Axle loading of commercial vehicles

8.33   The axle loads of private cars and light delivery vans do virtually no structural damage to road pavements and they can be neglected in any thickness design calculations. The damage which a heavy commercial vehicle does is a function of the degree to which the various axles are loaded. The maximum load permitted on any axle is determined by the country or state laws as discussed in Paras 8.10–8.16. In practice, one or two axles may be overloaded at a particular time, but generally the average loading for a particular type of vehicle is likely to be below the maximum because some journeys will be made with the vehicle only partially loaded or completely unloaded. Where both the maximum gross vehicle weight and the maximum axle load are specified by law, the former restricts the number of axles which may be loaded to the maximum.

Table 8.17   Constitution (per cent) of commercial traffic on nearside and centre lanes of UK three-lane motorways

	M1 Friars Wash								M1 Newport Pagnell			
	Southbound						Northbound		Southbound		Northbound	
	Dec. 1966		July 1970		June 1973		Dec. 1966		Jan. 1967		Jan. 1967	
	LH lane	Centre lane	LH lane	Centre lane	LH lane	Centre lane	LH lane	Centre lane	LH lane	Centre lane	LH lane	Centre lane
Two-axle rigid	59.7	59.4	59.7	63.9	50.5	54.3	58.4	67.7	54.7	61.8	54.4	65.3
Three-axle articulated	15.6	17.2	12.5	10.1	12.8	9.7	18.4	13.2	18.9	17.2	19.6	14.3
Three-axle rigid	10.1	9.6	7.1	7.0	7.0	4.5	7.8	8.8	11.0	9.2	10.5	3.0
Four-axle articulated	7.1	7.9	15.3	15.9	26.2	28.8	6.6	7.4	7.8	9.0	7.7	8.5
Four-axle rigid	8.4	5.9	4.3	1.8	3.3	1.9	7.8	3.0	7.4	2.6	7.6	2.9
Five-axle articulated	—	—	1.1	1.5	1.3	0.65	—	—	—	—	—	—

Table 8.17   *Continued*

| | M4 Harlington | | | | M4 Datchet | | M6 Perry Barr | | | | Mean all sites | |
| | Westbound May 1969 | | Westbound April 1972 | | Westbound May 1972 | | Eastbound July 1972 | | Westbound July 1972 | | | |
	LH lane	Centre lane	LH lane	Centre lane	LH lane	Centre lane	LH lane	Centre lane	LH lane	Centre lane	LH lane	Centre lane
Two-axle rigid	65.1	73.0	58.3	60.2	53.7	60.0	50.7	55.4	47.9	54.9	55.0	61.4
Three-axle articulated	12.2	10.1	11.0	9.6	15.4	12.0	15.0	10.8	14.0	14.2	15.0	12.6
Three-axle rigid	6.9	4.9	10.0	7.5	6.6	6.5	6.1	5.6	7.9	5.0	8.3	7.1
Four-axle articulated	9.8	9.2	14.4	18.3	18.9	18.5	23.3	25.7	24.0	23.4	14.7	15.7
Four-axle rigid	5.7	2.2	4.5	3.2	4.1	1.7	3.6	1.8	4.1	1.7	5.6	2.6
Five-axle articulated	0.4	0.6	1.9	1.2	1.6	1.2	0.7	1.2	1.2	0.7	0.8	0.6

Table 8.18 Constitution (per cent) of commercial traffic on left- and right-hand lanes of UK dual-carriageway roads

	A1 Alconbury Hill, southbound, Jan. 1969		A1 Alconbury Hill, northbound, Jan. 1969		A24 Pollards Hill, northbound, Aug. 1971		A4091 Wishaw–Tamworth, southbound, Oct. 1971		Mean of three sites	
	LH lane	RH lane	LH lane	RH lane	LH lane	RH lane	LH lane	RH lane	LH lane	RH lane
Two-axle rigid	48.0	51.3	49.1	53.7	73.8	85.2	63.1	71.3	59.1	66.0
Three-axle articulated	22.4	19.1	19.6	15.8	8.6	0	6.2	0	14.9	9.7
Three-axle rigid	8.8	7.0	8.2	10.5	8.2	8.8	15.4	7.1	8.8	7.6
Four-axle articulated	14.9	17.3	17.3	15.8	5.6	3.0	7.0	11.9	11.3	11.6
Four-axle rigid	5.5	5.2	5.2	3.2	3.2	3.0	7.2	2.4	5.2	3.1
Five-axle articulated	0.5	0	0.6	0	0	0	0.7	4.7	0.5	1.1

Table 8.19 Average percentages of various classes of vehicle

	Urban						Rural				
	Motorway	Trunk	Class 1	Class 2	Class 3	Unclassified	Trunk	Class 1	Class 2	Class 3	Unclassified
Cars plus taxis	70.4	72.6	73.0	76.4	76.1	75.3	69.7	74.4	74.1	71.0	69.9
Light commercial	5.4	9.7	9.7	10.0	11.4	12.3	8.4	9.8	11.6	14.2	16.8
Heavy commercial plus PSV	23.7	13.4	13.4	9.5	7.4	7.1	20.2	13.9	11.0	10.5	9.2

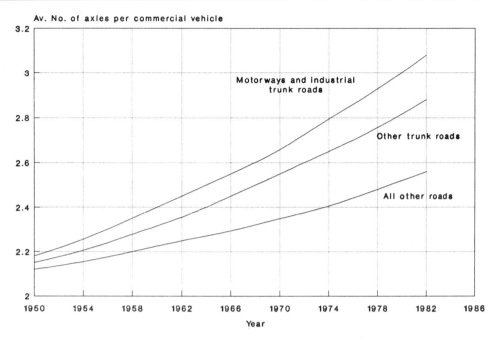

Figure 8.11 Increase in average number of axles per heavy goods vehicle, 1950–82

8.34 To design pavements by the structural method it is necessary to know the distribution of axle loads in the traffic to which the pavement will be subjected during its design life. This distribution can be referred to as the axle load spectrum. In the case of a new road this information is unlikely to be available. The policy adopted in Britain has been to study the axle load distribution on a variety of roads, so that an appropriate axle load spectrum can be established for each class of road and then used in the design procedure for new roads or in the maintenance stratagem for existing roads.

8.35 There are three methods available for the measurement of axle loading. The first consists of stopping a representative sample of commercial vehicles and measuring the load on each axle using some form of portable loadometer. The second method is to direct the representative sample to a nearby public weighbridge where the axle weights can be measured individually. Alternatively, a recording weighbridge can be set into the surface of the road so that all axle loads can be weighed and recorded as the vehicles move at normal speed. All these methods are in use world-wide, but the last is favoured as giving the most complete information. There is considerable difficulty with the other methods in determining what is a representative sample and the relatively small number of overloads are likely to be missed. In comparing the three methods it is necessary to consider the effects of camber and of dynamic loading in the case of the permanent weighbridge. Such weighbridges are set at the normal camber of the road which is about 1 : 40. This will increase the nearside wheel loads by about three to four per cent and decrease the offside wheel loads by the same amount. If only the nearside wheel-load is measured, the axle load derived by doubling will be an overestimate by this percentage. Such an overestimate can be safely neglected. With portable loadometers the camber effect can be much greater if a suitable 'dummy' is not put under the wheel at the other end of the axle.

8.36   The axle load measured statically with the vehicle at rest may be different from the value measured as the vehicle passes at normal speed over a recording weighbridge installed in the pavement surface. For a very smooth pavement the 'dynamic effect' would be expected to be small. In practice, pavements constructed to normal standards may have several undulations of amplitude 4–6 mm in each 100 m length. Such undulations cause fluctuations of applied axle loading both above and below the static value. Work carried out by the UK TRRL using seven recording weighbridges set in the surface of different motorways and trunk roads showed that the dynamic factor depended on the axle load and the speed of the vehicle. For heavy axle loads in the range 7–10 t the maximum dynamic factor measured was 1.15 and it occurred at about 15 km/h. At 50 km/h the value ranged from 0.94 to 1.10, with a mean close to 1.0. Values as high as 1.50 have been reported from various parts of the world generally where vehicles have been driven over shallow obstructions placed on the road surface. Dynamic effects can safely be ignored in the design of normal pavements.

8.37   With vehicles of high centre of gravity, such as the straddle carriers used to transport and stack container boxes, there is a transfer of load between wheels on the two sides of the vehicle on turning, and between wheels at the front and rear of the vehicle on accelerating or braking. This can result in a form of dynamic loading which can increase the static load on individual wheels by a factor of up to 1.5. This should be taken into account in the design of relevant industrial pavements (see Chapter 23).

8.38   A recording weighbridge requires a shallow pit in the traffic lane in which measurements are to be made. The pit accommodates an appropriate number of platform modules each 0.6 m square, to cover the recording width required. Generally rather more than half the lane width is covered to record half-axle weights, but the full width can be covered if necessary. Each platform module is supported on four load cells, and the output connected to a preamplifier and then to a digitizer and classifier with an hourly printout. The equipment is normally calibrated to record half axles in increments of 910 kg (2000 lb). Alternatively the individual axles of particular vehicles can be weighed and grouped in association with a photograph of the vehicle concerned. A three-module weighbridge is shown in position in Fig. 8.12.

8.39   Weighbridges of this type have been installed at various sites in the UK, mainly on motorways and principal roads, but some information has been obtained for less heavily trafficked roads. Normally measurements are made in the left-hand lane only, but at some sites the traffic on the overtaking lane has also been weighed.

Figure 8.12   Weighbridge platform modules in position

8.40   Figure 8.13 shows the axle load spectrum determined in 1965 from a weighbridge installed at Alconbury Hill, the site of a full-scale pavement design experiment constructed on the northbound carriageway of the A1 trunk road in 1957.[7] The spectrum refers to the left-hand lane, which carried at that time about 90 per cent of the commercial traffic. About 3 per cent of the axle loads exceeded the limit of 10.2 t. Such an axle load spectrum combined with a knowledge of the total number of commercial axles passing over the weighbridge per day would enable the calculation of the cumulative number of axles in each weight category which would be carried during the design life. This is the information required when pavements are designed using structural theory (see Chapter 21). When pavements are designed on the basis of past experience gained either from in-service roads or from experimental roads designed to compare the performance of different forms of construction, it is difficult to compare the damaging effect of the traffic on the basis of the axle-load spectrum and the volume of commercial traffic. It is to meet this problem that the concept of the damaging effect of traffic in terms of standard axles has been introduced.

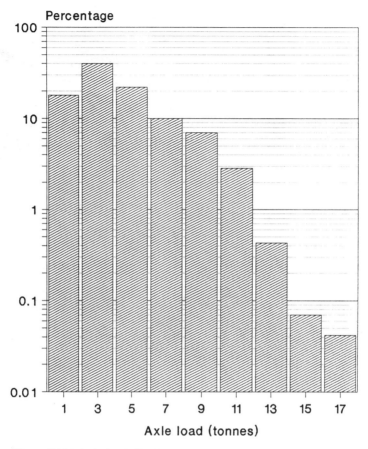

Figure 8.13 Axle load distribution on the A1 trunk road, northbound, at Alconbury Hill, 1965 (commercial axles only)

The concept of standard axles and the damaging effect of traffic

8.41 A major objective of the AASHO road test[8] carried out between 1957 and 1961 was to study, using normal forms of road construction and normal road vehicles, the damaging effect of commercial vehicles relative to their axle loading. This test is described in Chapter 17 but a brief reference to it must be made here.

8.42 A number of test loops were constructed at the site of a new freeway in Illinois. Each was made up of trial sections of flexible and concrete construction and each loop was trafficked 24 hours per day by one of six vehicle types. These ranged from two-axle trucks of maximum axle load 0.9 to 2.7 tons and maximum gross weight 3.6 tons, to five-axle trucks to maximum axle load 10.7 tons and maximum gross weight 48 tons. The thickness of construction on each loop varied between what the design engineer considered less than adequate and more than adequate for the vehicles allotted to that particular loop. The thickest section on one loop was reproduced as the thinnest section of the next more heavily trafficked loop. In this way, the relative performance of the sections could be assessed and conclusions drawn regarding the actual thickness of construction necessary. The flexible sections included bases of crushed stone, unbound and bound with bitumen and cement. The concrete sections were both reinforced and unreinforced. Statistical analysis of the data collected showed that the relative damaging effect of an axle was approximately proportional to the fourth power of the load which it carried, irrespective of the type or thickness of the pavement.

8.43   An axle carrying a load of 18 000 lb (8160 kg or 8.160 t) was arbitrarily defined in the AASHO road test as a standard axle, with a damaging effect of unity. The damaging effects of lighter and heavier axles were expressed as equivalence factors as shown in Table 8.20. The equivalence factor of 0.0002 for the 910-kg axle load means that 5000 passes of such an axle would do the same damage as one pass of a standard axle, and the equivalence factor of 22.8 for the 18 140-kg axle means that one pass of this axle load would do as much damage as 23 passes of a standard axle.

The relationship given in Table 8.20 is shown graphically in Fig 8.14.

8.44   In using Table 8.20 it must be remembered that the AASHO road test was not fully factorial in the sense that all axle loads were not applied to all pavements, the axle loads and the pavement thicknesses being to some extent matched. Furthermore, the maximum axle load used was 10.7 t. Table 8.20 extends the application of the fourth-power law up to more than 18 t. There is some evidence to indicate that as the axle load is increased the index of the power law may increase to 5 or 6. Further extrapolation beyond the axle loads in Table 8.20 would not be advisable.

8.45   From Fig. 8.13 the number of axles in each weight range per 100 axles can be determined. Each of these numbers can be expressed as an equivalent number of standard axles using Table 8.20. This is shown in Fig. 8.15. This histogram can be

Table 8.20   Damaging effect of different axle loads (AASHO road test)

Axle load		Equivalence factor	Axle load		Equivalence factor
kg	lb		kg	lb	
910	2 000	0.0002	9 980	22 000	2.3
1 810	4 000	0.0025	10 890	24 000	3.2
2 720	6 000	0.01	11 790	26 000	4.4
3 630	8 000	0.03	12 700	28 000	5.8
4 540	10 000	0.09	13 610	30 000	7.6
5 440	12 000	0.19	14 520	32 000	9.7
6 350	14 000	0.35	15 420	34 000	12.1
7 260	16 000	0.61	16 320	36 000	15.0
8 160	18 000	1*	17 230	38 000	18.6
9 070	20 000	1.5	18 140	40 000	22.8

*Standard axle.

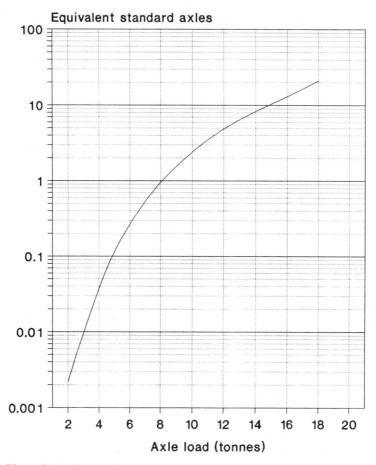

Figure 8.14   Conversion of axle load to equivalent standard axles

summed to give the total number of standard axles per 100 commercial axles, conforming to this particular axle load spectrum. In this case the equivalent number of standard axles is 31, and it will be noted that more than 12 of these arise from the three per cent of axles exceeding the legal limit of 10.2 t.

8.46   There is evidence that the damaging effect of heavy commercial vehicles has increased markedly in recent years on the more heavily trafficked motorways and trunk roads of Britain. Figure 18.16 shows for the Alconbury Hill experimental site on the northbound carriageway of trunk road A1, already referred to in Figs 8.13 and 8.15, the damaging effect of the traffic expressed as the number of standard axles per 100 commercial axles. The data cover the period 1958 to 1985. Until 1972 the value remained between 25 and 31, but since then it has risen to above 40. This indicates either an increase in loading or a more intensive use of the commercial vehicles to reduce the number of unloaded trips. Figure 18.16 also shows the

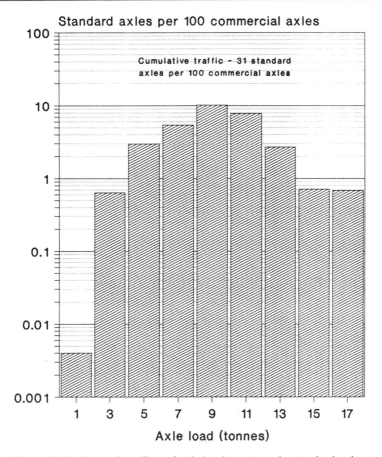

Figure 8.15 Damaging effect of axle load spectrum in standard axles on the A1 trunk road at Alconbury Hill, northbound left lane

damaging effect of the traffic on the southbound carriageway taking traffic towards London. In this direction the vehicles are clearly more heavily loaded, although the trends in damaging effect are similar on both carriageways.

8.47   Figure 8.17 gives similar information for the three motorways, M1, M6 and M4, over the period 1972–85.[9] The growth in damaging effect is apparent on all three roads between 1972 and 1980, although it has subsequently increased only on the M1. Figure 8.18 compares the growth in damaging effect on the A1 trunk road referred to in Fig. 8.15 with similar information from three other trunk roads. In this figure, the damaging effect is expressed in terms of standard axles per commercial vehicle, i.e., the damaging effect per commercial axle multiplied by the average number of axles per commercial vehicle given in Fig 8.11. Both the A1 and the A38, which are primarily heavy commercial routes, show the increase in damaging effect already indicated for the A1 in Fig. 8.16. The observations on the A30 and A40 trunk

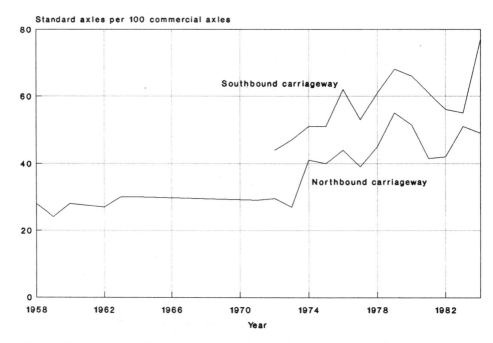

Figure 8.16 Damaging effect of commercial traffic on the A1 trunk road at Alconbury Hill, 1958–84

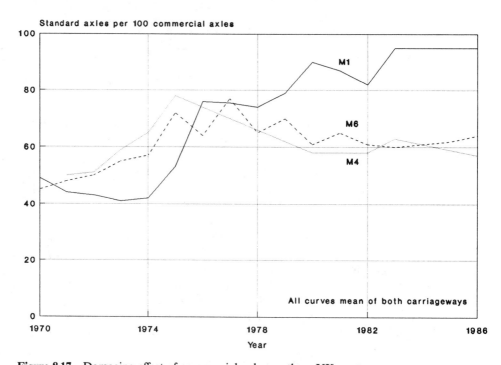

Figure 8.17 Damaging effect of commercial axles on three UK motorways

72

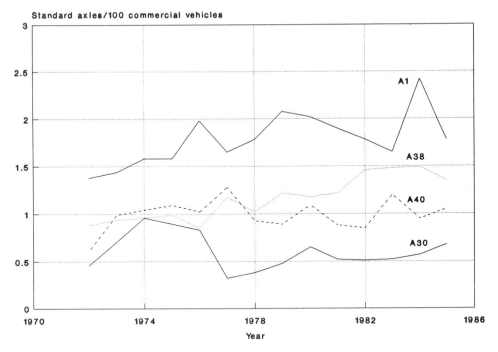

Figure 8.18 Damaging effect of commercial vehicles on four UK A-class roads

roads, which do not carry a great deal of commercial traffic, indicate that the damaging effect of the commercial vehicles has remained fairly constant. In connection with these and other studies an analysis has been made of the damaging effect of commercial traffic in relation to the total amount of commercial traffic carried.

8.48 The vehicle damaging factors formerly and currently in use in the UK for converting commercial vehicle flows to cumulative standard axles are shown in Table 8.21. The current recommendations are also included on Fig. 8.19 for

Table 8.21   Vehicle damaging factors for design of UK roads

Category of road (commercial vehicles per day in each direction)	Standard axles per commercial vehicle	
	Road Note 29[10] (1970)	Present (1985)
> 2000	1.08	2.9
1000–2000	1.08	2.25
250–1000	0.72	1.25
< 250	0.45	0.75

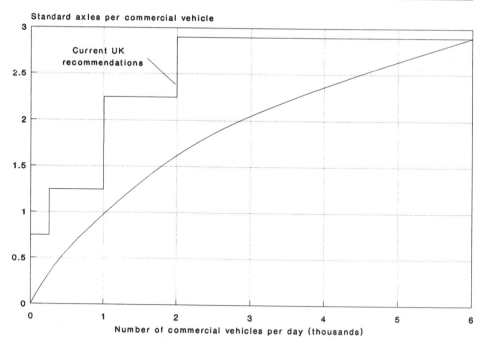

Figure 8.19 Relationship between volume of commercial traffic and damaging effect in standard axles per commercial vehicle

comparison with the observed data. It is clear that the 1983 recommendations are still relevant and are likely to remain so for a considerable time.

8.49   The investigation at Doxey near Stafford on the M6 motorway, referred to in Para. 8.29 and Table 8.16, suggests that since the change in the UK Construction and Use Regulations in April 1983 permitting the use of five- and six-axle commercial vehicles with a gross weight of 38 t there has been a rapid increase in the proportion of such vehicles in the commercial traffic. The introduction of one or two additional load axles should have significantly reduced the damaging effect of vehicles and this would be expected to have reduced or halted the increase in the damaging effect of commercial axles shown in Figs 8.16 and 8.17. The axle load spectrum from the Doxey survey corresponded, in the autumn of 1983, to a damaging effect of 47 standard axles per 100 commercial axles. Considered in relation to Fig. 8.17, this suggests a considerable reduction in the damaging effect. The Doxey measurements were made statically on a selected sample of the commercial traffic and the small percentage of heavy axles (which contribute much to the damaging effect of the traffic) may have been missed. There may also have been a dynamic component associated with the recording weighbridges used in the measurements shown in Fig. 8.17 and 8.18.

8.50   The inference from the research on axle loading in the UK is that after 1970 the large increase in the cost of oil resulted in a more cost-effective use of commercial vehicles. This was achieved by increased loading and the reduction in the number of unloaded journeys. As a consequence the average equivalent number of standard axles per commercial axle increased on major industrial routes from about 0.4 to 0.7. Since 1983 the increasing use of five-, six-, and seven-axle vehicles appears to have stabilized the figure at about 0.7 on heavily trafficked roads. For more lightly trafficked roads the figure is currently between 0.2 and 0.4.

Traffic studies on housing estate roads

8.51   Observations relating to the constitution of commercial traffic have been made on a number of housing estate roads. Such roads form a significant proportion of all new road construction. The majority of the commercial and public service vehicles have only two axles, but three-, four-, and five-axle vehicles servicing shops will use the main entry and exit roads.

8.52   Table 8.22 summarizes the site observations made on three estates and the table also gives information which can be used in the design of such roads, in the absence of more specialized information. Clearly, the inclusion of a hypermarket or a sports arena in a proposed development would necessitate further consideration of the traffic likely to be generated.

Traffic in developing countries

8.53   The design of roads in developing countries is complicated by the difficulty in assessing the probable axle loading of the heavy commercial vehicles. In those territories previously under colonial government the policy was generally to maintain 'low-cost' roads in a passable condition, particularly during those periods

Table 8.22   The design of housing estate roads

Site observations			Design recommendations	
	Vehicles per day in each direction		Commercial vehicles per day in each direction (including PSVs)	Damaging effect of traffic (standard axles per commercial vehicle)
Type of road	Commercial	PSVs		
Main entrance/ exit road to estate	200	65	400	1.25
Main link roads 1	135	35	250	1.0
2	70	40		
Minor link roads	25	10	100	0.75
Estate roads 1	15	0		
2	10	0	50	0.75
3	2	0		
Culs-de-sac 1	4	0		
2	3	0	10	0.75
3	1	0		

Table 8.23   Results of axle load surveys in different countries

Year	Country	Legal axle load limit, t	ESA per 100 axles*	Average ESA per payload, t	Range of axle load distribution
1976	Ethiopia	8.0	491 (Aseb to Addis Adaba)	0.66	45% > 8 t 34% > 10 t 24% > 12 t 15% > 14 t
1976	Ethiopia	8.0	233 (mean of 5 trunk routes)	0.45	28% > 8 t 19% > 10 t 12% > 12 t 7% > 14 t
1975	Nigeria	10.0	389	0.62	30% > 10 t 10% > 13 t 4% > 16 t
1975	Turkey	8.2	57	0.21	28% > 8.2 t 17% > 10 t 7% > 12 t 4% > 14 t
1974	Kenya	8.0	281 (336) Mombasa to Nairobi road	0.75	67% > 8 t 52% > 10 t 30% > 12 t 4% > 14 t
1974	Jordan	12.0	2 axle = 1100 3 axle = 1600 4 axle = 675	1.48 1.79 0.93	77% > 8 t 58% > 10 t 45% > 12 t 28% > 14 t 14% > 16 t
1971	Abu Dhabi	No limit	127	0.49	23% > 8 t 8% > 10 t 4% > 12 t 1% > 14 t
1970–71	Qatar	No limit	109	0.50	21% > 8 t 13% > 10 t 6% > 12 t 2% > 14 t 1% > 16 t
1970–71	Qatar selected route	No limit	452	1.08	43% > 8 t 36% > 10 t 27% > 12 t 14% > 14 t 13% > 16 t 10% > 18 t
1967	Malaysia	7.0	19	0.15	12% > 8 t 4% > 10 t 2% > 12 t
1963	Jamaica	7.0	36	0.33	13% > 8 t 6% > 10 t 2% > 12 t

Table 8.23 (*contd.*)

Year	Country	Legal axle load limit, t	ESA per 100 axles*	Average ESA per payload, t	Range of axle load distribution
1984	Philippines N. Luzon (Isabela to Manila)	8.0	383	—	51% > 8 t 35% > 10 t 26% > 12 t 18% > 14 t 8% > 16 t
	(Alicia to Echaque)		516	—	75% > 8 t 49% > 10 t 34% > 12 t 22% > 14 t 10% > 16 t
	Mindanao (Davao to Ampayon)		293	—	41% > 8 t 30% > 10 t 23% > 12 t 13% > 14 t 5% > 16 t

*ESA = Equivalent Standard Axles.

when local products were being transferred to ports for export. Major administrative towns were of course provided with a local road network generally to European standards. In the post-war period when many African and Asian countries became independent, they were encouraged to continue with the development of low-cost road systems. More recently the emphasis has changed towards the construction of all-weather spinal roads, integrated with feeder roads maintained on the low-cost principle. The major problem which engineers face in these circumstances is that new paved roads quickly generate additional traffic with respect both to numbers of commercial vehicles and to the severity of the axle loading.

8.54   Although most developing countries have well-defined upper legal limits for axle loading, normally in the range 8–10 t , little attempt is generally made to enforce the law in this respect. Furthermore, dispensations are often easily obtained in the interest of transporting products quickly. Vehicle operators often show remarkable ingenuity in 'stretching' vehicles by chassis and body modifications. Table 8.23 shows the results of axle load surveys made during the last 20 years in 11 developing countries by the Overseas Unit of the TRRL.[11] Also included are more recent measurements made in the Philippines.[12] In relation to the maximum axle load all the measurements indicate severe overloading. This is understandable in situations where commercial vehicles are scarce. For the foreseeable future pavements in developing countries will need to be designed to cater for the present axle loading conditions. The average number of axles per commercial vehicle will be close to 2.6, which means that the average damaging effect per commercial vehicle may be as high as 13 standard axles. This is approximately double that for the maximum loading condition of the EC vehicles considered in Table 8.4.

8.55   Any engineer required to design pavements in developing countries would be well advised to disregard axle loading regulations and to make the assumption that there will be a significant proportion of axles carrying more than 15 t, particularly where the road connects with large towns or ports. The nature of the goods being carried provides some indication of the degree of overloading likely to be encountered. Some investigation of the traffic on site is essential, supplemented if possible by an axle load study using portable weighbridges. In the absence of any other information it is recommended that a damaging effect of 15 standard axles per commercial vehicle be used.

The influence of axle configuration and loading regulations on the damaging effect of commercial vehicles

8.56   Table 8.4, already discussed in relation to European axle loads and gross weight proposals, considers typical commercial vehicles currently in use, or proposed in relation to future regulations. In Table 8.24 are shown the damaging factors

Table 8.24 Damaging effect of various four-, five-, and six-axle vehicles to European and proposed EC standards

Country	Configuration (axle weights in tonnes)			Gross vehicle weight, t	Max. equiv. std axles	Std axles per tonne payload
	Tractor		Trailer combined			
	Two-axle tractors			**Four axles**		
	Steer	Drive				
France	6	12	20	38.0	9.7	0.37
Germany	6	10	20 (>2 m)	36.0	7.2	0.29
Italy	6	12	22 (>2 m)	40.0	11.9	0.43
UK	6	10.2	16.3	32.5	4.8	0.22
UK	5	7.1	20.4 (>2 m)	32.5	5.7	0.26
Proposed for EC	6	11	18	35.0	6.4	0.28
				Five axles, three-axle trailer		
France	6	12	20	38.0	6.4	0.24
Germany and UK	6	10	22	38.0	4.6	0.17
Italy	6	12	26	44.0	9.1	0.29
Proposed for EC	6	11	23	40.0	6.1	0.22
	Three-axle tractors					
	Steer	Drive				
		A B		**Five axles, two-axle trailer**		
Proposed for EC						
(single drive)	6	11 7	18	42.0	7.3	0.25
(double drive)	6	18	18	42.0	6.5	0.22
				Six axles		
Netherlands	6	18	26	50.0	7.3	0.20
Proposed for EC						
(single drive)	6	11 7	20	44.0	5.5	0.18
(double drive)	6	18	20	44.0	4.7	0.15

expressed in standard axles per fully loaded vehicle and standard axles per tonne of payload for all the four-, five-, and six-axle configurations considered in Table 8.4. Because of the lower permitted axle loading and gross weight conditions, the damaging effect of British four-axle articulated vehicles when fully loaded is much lower than those of France, Germany, and Italy. The EC proposals for such vehicles represent an intermediate position between British and European practice.

8.57 For five-axle vehicles, current British regulations correspond closely to those of Germany, but French and Italian regulations permit the use of much more damaging vehicles. Again, the EC proposals represent a compromise close to the French position. Currently, six-axle vehicles in the UK are restricted to a maximum gross weight of 38 t with a maximum axle load of 10.2 t. The European proposal is to increase the gross weight to 44 t. Table 8.24 shows that were this agreed then the damaging factor for the fully loaded vehicles would be less than for the five-axle configurations. The damaging effect per tonne of payload is less than for four- and five-axle articulated vehicles. The current typical four-axle vehicle, fully loaded, has a damaging effect per tonne of payload of about 0.24 standard axle, compared with 0.15 for a fully loaded 6-axle vehicle to the proposed EC standard, with a payload of 31.2 t . The latter vehicle offers a 10 per cent reduction in operating costs per tonne/mile compared with a 4-axle vehicle,[3] and at the same time a 30 per cent reduction in pavement damage.

8.58 Table 8.25 compares the EC proposals for five- and six-axle trucks with similar trucks loaded in accordance with the regulations applying to Arkansas, California, and Massachusetts. These three states were selected as representing low, medium, and high axle loading and gross weight within the various state regulations summarized in Table 8.5. The equivalent standard axles bracket the values for the proposed new EC regulations. The general conclusion is that although US trucks

Table 8.25 Comparison of damaging effects of two types of truck operating to proposed EC maximum limits with equivalent USA trucks fully loaded

Country	Configuration (axle weights in tonnes)				
	Three-axle tractor				
	Steer	Drive combined	Trailer combined	Maximum laden weight, t	Maximum equivalent standard axles
Five axles					
EC proposal	6	18	18	42	6.5
USA, Arkansas	5.2	14	14	33.2	2.2
California	5.5	15.4	15.4	36.3	4.2
Six axles					
EC proposal	6	18	20	44	4.7
USA, Massachusetts	6.5	16.3	24.45	47.2	5.4

are, in general, longer than those in use in Europe the damaging effect in relation to pavements is less severe.

Contact area between the tyre and the road

8.59   The shape of the contact area between a tyre and the road is approximately circular when the load applied is small relative to the recommended maximum for the tyre, but it becomes increasingly elongated as the wheel load is increased at constant inflation pressure this is shown in Fig. 8.20, where the highest load considered is 50 per cent above the tyre manufacturer's rating. In calculating pavement stresses resulting from the passage of traffic it is usual to assume that the load carried by the wheel is uniformly distributed over a circular area. The radius of loading is calculated from the wheel load and the tyre pressure.

8.60   The relationship between contact area and wheel load obtained in this way for the tyre and loading conditions of Fig. 8.20 is shown in Fig. 8.21, in which the figures in brackets close to the points give the calculated radii of loading in millimetres. Also included in Fig. 8.21 are the similar relationships based on the measured contact area of the tyre print envelope and the actual area of contact indicated by the black areas of the prints in Fig. 8.20. The curves for the actual contact area and the computed area are similar for the lowest two wheel loads used when the contact envelope is approximately circular, but they diverge considerably for the higher wheel loads. This is because at the high wheel loads a significant proportion of the applied load is taken by the tyre walls and the area of contact is accordingly reduced.

8.61   Measurements of the actual pressure acting between the tyre and the road (Fig. 8.22)[13] show that where the load ratio (actual wheel load : recommended

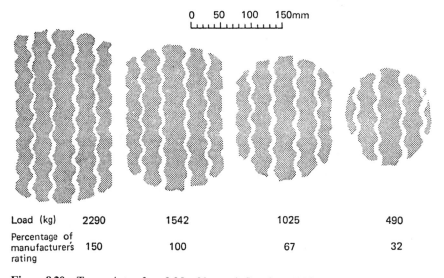

| 0 | 50 | 100 | 150mm |

| Load (kg) | 2290 | 1542 | 1025 | 490 |
| Percentage of manufacturer's rating | 150 | 100 | 67 | 32 |

Figure 8.20   Tyre prints of an 8.25 × 20 tyre inflated to 480 kPa

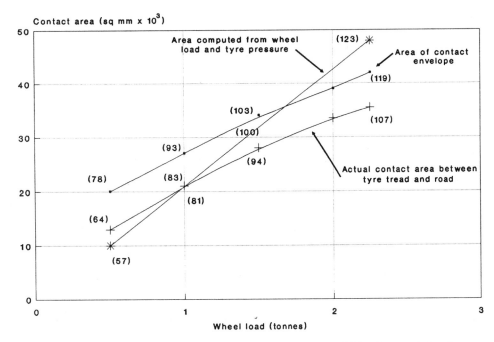

Figure 8.21 Calculated and measured contact areas for an 8.25×20 tyre inflated to a pressure of 480 kPa

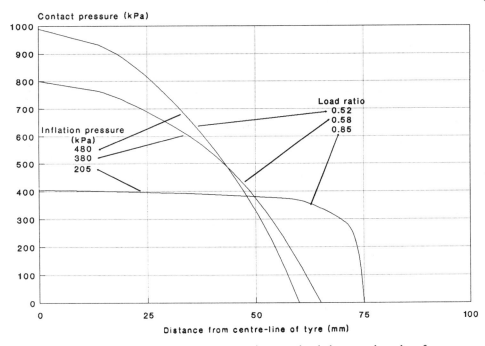

Figure 8.22 Measured lateral contact pressure between loaded tyre and road surface

Table 8.26   Typical radial truck tyres in UK highway service—axle loads and tyre pressures

Nominal size	Min. dual wheel spacing, mm	Inflation pressure, bar								
		3.0	3.25	3.50	3.75	4.0	4.25	4.5	4.75	5.0
		Axle load, kg								
6.50-20	Single	1 500	1 500	1 600	1 700	1 800	1 900	2 000	2 120	2 210
	Dual 208	2 820	2 820	3 010	3 200	3 400	3 600	3 800	4 000	4 220
7.00-20	Single	1 800	1 800	1 900	2 000	2 100	2 200	2 300	2 400	2 500
	Dual 222	3 400	3 400	3 600	3 800	4 020	4 240	4 360	4 540	4 720
7.50-20 A20	Single	1 910	1 910	2 050	2 200	2 350	2 500	2 650	2 800	2 900
	Dual 239	3 480	3 480	3 750	4 020	4 290	4 560	4 830	5 280	5 520
8.25-17 B17	Single	2 100	2 100	2 250	2 400	2 540	2 680	2 820	2 960	3 100
	Dual 263	3 800	3 800	4 090	4 350	4 600	4 850	5 100	5 350	5 600
8.25-20 B20	Single	2 220	2 220	2 370	2 520	2 670	2 820	2 970	3 120	3 260
9-22.5 (B22.5)	Dual 263	4 000	4 000	4 300	4 600	4 900	5 200	5 500	5 800	6 100
9.00-20 C20	Single	2 640	2 640	2 810	2 980	3 150	3 300	3 450	3 600	3 780
10-22.5 C22.5	Dual 311	4 610	4 610	4 920	5 230	5 540	5 850	6 160	6 470	6 780
10.00-20 D20	Single	3 000	3 000	3 160	3 320	3 480	3 640	3 800	3 960	4 120
11-22.5 D22.5	Dual 329	5 400	5 400	5 690	6 000	6 310	6 620	6 930	7 240	7 550
11.00-20 E20	Single	3 160	3 160	3 330	3 500	3 680	3 860	4 040	4 220	4 400
12-22.5 E22.5	Dual 354	5 720	5 720	6 030	6 340	6 650	6 960	7 270	7 580	7 890
11.00-22 E22	Single	3 240	3 240	3 420	3 600	3 780	3 960	4 140	4 320	4 500
	Dual 329	5 830	5 830	6 160	6 480	6 800	7 130	7 510	7 840	8 170

maximum wheel load) for the tyre is small, the distribution of pressure across the tyre area is parabolic, but as the load ratio is increased the pressure becomes more uniform. These tests were carried out at three tyre pressures, which accounts for the difference in mean contact pressures indicated by the curves. Further tests have shown that as the load increases above the recommended limit for the tyre, a peak stress develops around the perimeter of the contact envelope. The conclusion is that for a tyre loaded to its maximum rating the contact pressure will be reasonably uniform and the error involved in calculating the radius of loading from the wheel load and the tyre pressure will be small. This has been verified analytically.

8.62   Most heavily loaded wheels are fitted with dual tyres, so spaced that at the correct tyre pressure the deformed parts of the tyres in contact with the road do not touch each other. In analysing the pavement stresses generated by such wheels it is usual to assume that each tyre carries one-half of the wheel load.

8.63   In the UK more than 95 per cent of commercial vehicles use radial tyres. Table 8.26 gives for some of the more common sizes of radial tyre the axle load–tyre pressure relationship both for single and dual wheels. Also shown in the table is the minimum spacing between centres of dual wheels.

8.64   During the past five years certain types of five- and six-axle articulated

Table 8.26 (*contd.*)

5.25	5.5	5.75	6.0	6.25	6.5	6.75	7.0	7.25	7.5	7.75	8.0
2 320	2 430										
4 410	4 600										
2 600	2 700	2 800									
4 900	5 090	5 280									
3 000	3 100	3 200	3 300	3 400	3 500	3 600					
5 760	6 000	6 200	6 400	6 600	6 800	7 000					
3 200	3 260	3 400	3 480	3 590	3 700	3 800					
5 800	6 000	6 200	6 450	6 700	6 950	7 200					
3 400	3 520	3 660	3 800	3 900	4 010	4 120					
6 400	6 660	6 930	7 200	7 400	7 600	7 800					
3 950	4 120	4 240	4 360	4 480	4 610	4 740	4 870	5 000			
7 090	7 400	7 680	7 960	8 240	8 480	8 720	8 960	9 200			
4 280	4 440	4 600	4 770	4 940	5 120	5 300	5 440	5 580	5 720	5 860	6 000
7 860	8 170	8 480	8 740	9 010	9 280	9 720	9 820	10 090	10 360	10 630	10 900
4 580	4 760	4 940	5 120	5 300	5 400	5 600	5 800	6 000	6 200	6 350	6 500
8 200	8 510	8 820	9 130	9 440	9 760	10 140	10 520	10 900	11 140	11 370	11 600
4 680	4 860	5 040	5 220	5 400	5 600	5 800	6 000	6 150	6 330	6 510	6 700
8 500	8 830	9 160	9 480	9 800	10 140	10 470	10 800	11 200	11 460	11 730	12 000

vehicles have been fitted with single wheels on the trailer rear tandem or triple axles. This is in place of the more usual dual-wheel assemblies. When such single tyres are fitted, the maximum permitted load on each axle is reduced from 10 to 9 t in the UK. This applies to both dual and triple axles. The tyre size used is 385/65/R255 or equivalent. The width of the tyre print at the recommended pressure is about 0.9 times the combined width for an equivalent dual wheel assembly.

References

1. Department of the Environment: *The Motor Vehicle (Construction and Use) Regulations*, Statutory Instrument 1078, HMSO, London, 1986.
2. Department of the Environment: *The Motor Vehicle (Authorisation of Special Types) General Order*, Statutory Instrument 1101, HMSO, London, 1973.
3. Corcoran, P. J., M. H. Glover, and B. A. Shane: *Higher Gross Weight Goods Vehicles— Operating Costs and Road Damage Factors*. Transport and Road Research Laboratory Supplementary Report 590, TRRL, Crowthorne, 1980.
4. Currer, E. W. H.: *Commercial Traffic Studies*, Transport and Road Research Laboratory Report LR 628, TRRL, Crowthorne, 1974.
5. JMP Consultants Ltd.: *Results from the Doxey Axle Weight Survey (1983)*, Transport and Road Research Laboratory Contractors Report 33, TRRL, Crowthorne, 1986.

6. JMP Consultants Ltd.: *Results from the A2 (Broughton) Axle Weight Survey (1983)*, Transport and Road Research Laboratory Contractors Report 34, TRRL, Crowthorne, 1986.

7. Croney, D. and J. A. Loe: Full-scale pavement design experiment on A.1 at Alconbury Hill, Cambridgeshire, *Proc. Instn Civ. Engrs*, **30** (Feb), 225–70, 1965.

8. Highway Research Board: *The AASHO Road Test, Report 5*, Special Report 61E, Publication 954, National Academy of Science, National Research Council, Washington, D.C., 1962.

9. Robinson, R. G.: *Trends in Axle Loading and Their effect on the Design of Road Pavements*, Transport and Road Research Laboratory Research Report 138, TRRL, Crowthorne, 1988.

10. Department of the Environment Road Research Laboratory: *A Guide to the Structural Design of Pavements for New Roads*, Road Note 29, 3rd Ed, HMSO, London, 1970.

11. Jones, T. E.: *Axle Loads on Paved Roads in Kenya*, Transport and Road Research Report LR 763, TRRL, Crowthorne, 1977.

12. Ministry of Public Works and Highways, Republic of the Philippines. *Pavement and Axle Load Study Report*, vol. 2, October 1985.

13. Lister, N. W. and R. Jones: The behaviour of flexible pavements under moving wheel loads, *Proc. 2nd Int. Conf. on the Structural Design of Asphalt Pavements, Ann Arbor, Michigan, 1967*, University of Michigan, Ann Arbor, Michigan, 1968.

9. Pavement temperatures

Introduction

9.1   Temperature influences the design and performance of road pavements in a variety of ways. Freezing in the soil foundation can give rise to heaving, followed by a considerable reduction in the strength of the soil during the subsequent thaw. This in turn increases the traffic stresses in all the pavement materials (see Chapters 10 and 12).

9.2   The elasticity, deformation and fatigue of bituminous materials are all temperature-dependent. The elastic modulus decreases with increasing temperature and as a result the stresses imposed by traffic on the materials below a bituminous surfacing, or a bituminous roadbase, will increase as the temperature rises. Under the influence of large surface stresses bituminous materials tend to flow viscously, and this tendency also increases with temperature. As a result of these two effects, permanent deformation of flexible pavements is more likely to occur in summer than in winter, and the effect of summers which include abnormally hot periods is further to increase deformation.

9.3   At lower temperatures bituminous materials become increasingly brittle and more liable to fatigue failures under repeated stress. At very low temperatures thermal cracking due to tensile failure is not unusual.[1]

9.4   Thermal gradients in concrete pavements create internal stresses which give rise to curling or warping of the slabs. Curling is resisted by the weight of the concrete and tensile and compressive stresses are generated which are compounded with the traffic stresses. Similarly, a change in average slab temperature, combined with the frictional force between the slab and its support, creates longitudinal stresses which are additional to the traffic stresses when the slab is cooling.

9.5   Where design experience for flexible or concrete pavements is derived from the observation of the performance of in-service roads, the influence of temperature is automatically taken into account, provided the period of observation is long enough to include the full temperature variations likely to be encountered during the design life. However, where structural theory is applied to pavements the influence of temperature must be considered in detail.

9.6   In the following chapters dealing with pavement materials the influence of temperature on the structural properties is fully discussed, so that the influence of climate can be taken into account, wherever the road is located. The main objective of this chapter is to illustrate the type of information required in the structural design of pavements in the United Kingdom.

Air temperatures in Britain

9.7 In connection with its long-range forecasts the UK Meteorological Office publishes monthly a document which includes long-term mean daily temperatures for some 35 stations distributed over England, Wales, Scotland, and Northern Ireland.[2]

9.8 Because of Britain's small size and maritime climate, geographical location is not a major factor in determining temperature. However, there is a tendency for the mean daily temperature to decrease towards the north at all seasons of the year, but particularly during the summer months. Height above sea level and proximity to coasts are also factors which introduce local variations of temperature. In the present

Figure 9.1 Climatic zones considered for the UK

stage of the development of structural theory applied to road design it is considered sufficient to divide Britain into three temperature zones. These are a southern zone south of a line between Aberporth and Ipswich, a central zone between this line and another joining Whitby and Blackpool, and a northern zone including the remainder of England, mainland Scotland, and Northern Ireland. These zones are shown in Fig. 9.1. Temperature conditions in the mountainous areas of Scotland are more severe than in the lowlands and coastal areas and special consideration would need to be given to the design of any major road project in the Highlands.

9.9   Table 9.1 gives daily mean temperatures for the three zones based on monthly returns for the major meteorological stations within the three zones. Some indication of the range of air temperatures likely to be encountered in practice is given in Table 9.2. This uses the Meteorological Office five-point scale for assessing temperature variations, applied to the weather stations in the southern, central, and northern zones.

9.10   Most of the available measurements of pavement temperatures have been made in connection with experimental roads constructed in the central zone.

9.11   Because the temperature data required for flexible and concrete pavements are rather different the two forms of construction are considered separately below.

Temperatures of flexible pavements

9.12   All roads carry a much higher intensity of traffic during daylight hours than during the night. It is further shown in Chapter 8 that the hourly flow of commercial traffic during the day depends on the nature of the traffic and often on the direction of flow. A road connecting a centre of manufacture to a centre of distribution will often carry heavily loaded vehicles in one direction in the early morning when temperatures are relatively low and predominantly empty vehicles in the other

Table 9.1   Average daily temperatures in three zones

Month	Temperature, °C		
	Southern zone	Central zone	Northern zone
January	4.2	3.3	3.0
February	4.7	3.7	2.9
March	6.2	5.7	5.1
April	8.7	8.5	7.3
May	11.4	11.3	9.7
June	14.5	14.4	12.7
July	16.0	16.0	14.1
August	15.9	15.6	14.0
September	14.3	14.0	12.4
October	12.5	10.2	9.4
November	7.5	6.6	5.9
December	5.2	4.5	3.9

Table 9.2   Fluctuations of air temperature about the mean (based on the Meteorological Office five-point scale)

| Month | Zone | Temperature ranges (difference from average), °C | | | | |
		Much below average	Below average	Average	Above average	Much above average
January	Southern	< −1.3	−1.3 to −0.3		0.7 to 1.6	> 1.6
	Central	< −1.4	−1.4 to −0.2		0.7 to 1.4	> 1.4
	Northern	< −1.1	−1.1 to −0.4		0.5 to 1.3	> 1.3
February	Southern	< −1.3	−1.3 to −0.3		0.6 to 1.6	> 1.6
	Central	< −1.5	−1.5 to −0.2		0.7 to 1.5	> 1.5
	Northern	< −1.4	−1.4 to −0.4		0.6 to 1.6	> 1.6
March	Southern	< −1.3	−1.3 to −0.4		0.5 to 1.3	> 1.3
	Central	< −1.5	−1.5 to −0.3		0.6 to 1.4	> 1.4
	Northern	< −1.4	−1.4 to −0.3		0.6 to 1.3	> 1.3
April	Southern	< −1.1	−1.1 to −0.4		0.4 to 1.0	> 1.0
	Central	< −1.2	−1.2 to −0.4		0.4 to 1.0	> 1.0
	Northern	< −1.1	−1.1 to −0.3		0.5 to 0.9	> 0.9
May	Southern	< −0.9	−0.9 to −0.4		0.3 to 0.7	> 0.7
	Central	< −0.9	−0.9 to −0.4		0.3 to 0.7	> 0.7
	Northern	< −0.8	−0.8 to −0.2		0.4 to 0.6	> 0.6
June	Southern	< −0.8	−0.8 to −0.3		0.3 to 0.8	> 0.8
	Central	< −0.7	−0.7 to −0.3		0.2 to 0.7	> 0.7
	Northern	< −0.6	−0.6 to −0.3		0.2 to 0.5	> 0.5
July	Southern	< −0.8	−0.8 to −0.3		0.2 to 0.9	> 0.9
	Central	< −0.8	−0.8 to −0.3		0.3 to 0.8	> 0.8
	Northern	< −0.6	−0.6 to −0.3		0.1 to 0.5	> 0.5
August	Southern	< −0.9	−0.9 to −0.3		0.3 to 0.9	> 0.9
	Central	< −0.9	−0.9 to −0.3		0.4 to 0.8	> 0.8
	Northern	< −0.7	−0.7 to −0.3		0.2 to 0.7	> 0.7
September	Southern	< −0.9	−0.9 to −0.3		0.2 to 0.8	> 0.8
	Central	< −0.9	−0.9 to −0.3		0.3 to 0.8	> 0.8
	Northern	< −0.9	−0.8 to −0.3		0.3 to 0.8	> 0.8
October	Southern	< −0.9	−0.9 to −0.3		0.3 to 0.8	> 0.8
	Central	< −0.9	−0.9 to −0.3		0.3 to 0.8	> 0.8
	Northern	< −0.8	−0.8 to −0.3		0.3 to 0.9	> 0.9
November	Southern	< −1.0	−1.0 to −0.3		0.4 to 0.9	> 0.9
	Central	< −0.9	−0.9 to −0.3		0.3 to 0.8	> 0.8
	Northern	< −0.8	−0.8 to −0.3		0.3 to 0.9	> 0.9
December	Southern	< −1.1	−1.1 to −0.3		0.6 to 1.2	> 1.2
	Central	< −1.1	−1.1 to −0.3		0.5 to 1.1	> 1.1
	Northern	< −0.9	−0.9 to −0.3		0.4 to 1.1	> 1.1

direction in the afternoon when temperatures are higher. Daily as well as annual variations of temperature are therefore important when structural theory is applied to specific pavement design problems.

9.13 Measurements of temperature in flexible pavements have been made in connection with a number of full-scale experimental roads. The most complete data are available from a site on the Al trunk road near Alconbury in Cambridgeshire. This is in the central climatic zone referred to in Para. 9.8. Details of the pavements and the positions of the thermocouples used to make the measurements are shown in Fig. 9.2. The thermocouples were connected to recording galvanometers which have been operating continuously for several years. Measurements of air temperatures have also been made at the site.

9.14 The analysis given below is based on the 12-month period from March 1969 to February 1970. This period was chosen because the mean monthly air temperatures were close to the long-term means for the central temperature zone given in Table 9.1.

9.15 Figure 9.3 shows the relationship between mean monthly air temperature and the corresponding mean temperature recorded at a depth of 38 mm in flexible pavements. (Between depths of 38 and 203 mm, depth had only a small effect on the mean pavement temperature.) The relationship shows some hysteresis between the heating and cooling conditions of the pavement. This arises from the shape of the temperature–depth distribution curves considered over a depth of several metres.

9.16 Table 9.3 shows the average hourly variations of temperature for the months of January, April, July, and October 1969 for depths of 38, 127, and 203 mm. During these months the average air temperatures were generally close to the average values for the central zone given in Table 9.1. Where there were small differences a correction was made to the values shown in Table 9.3 using the relationship given in Fig. 9.3. The values shown in the table can be taken therefore as

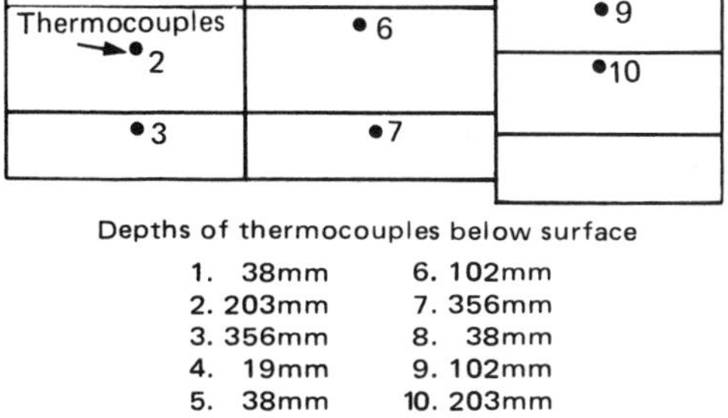

Depths of thermocouples below surface

1.	38mm	6.	102mm
2.	203mm	7.	356mm
3.	356mm	8.	38mm
4.	19mm	9.	102mm
5.	38mm	10.	203mm

Figure 9.2 Pavement structures used for temperature measurements and position of thermocouples (Alconbury Bypass)

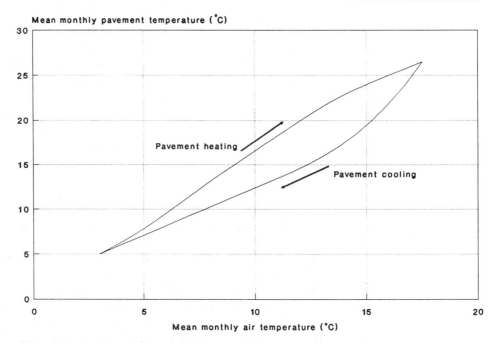

Figure 9.3 Relationship between mean monthly air temperature and pavement temperature 38 mm below surface—bituminous pavement

applying generally to the central zone. The values can be adjusted using Table 9.1 to obtain similar figures for the northern and southern zones. Comparison of temperatures measured at the same depth in asphalt and bitumen macadam showed differences of less than 1 °C and this difference is too small to take into account in structural analysis.

9.17 The information given in Table 9.3 can be used in conjunction with the material properties to estimate the elastic modulus and fatigue properties of bituminous roadbases and surfacings over the daily temperature cycle and during the various seasons. In conjunction with traffic/time data such estimates provide information basic to the structural analysis of flexible pavements.

9.18 Because these curves are averages for particular months they do not give special weight to the short periods of high and low temperature which occur and which may be very relevant to pavement performance. To provide this information the measurements made at this site have been analysed to show, on an annual basis, the percentage of each of the 24 hours when the pavement is operating within specified temperature bands. This information is given in Tables 9.4–9.7, which refer to depths between 19 and 356 mm. Again the figures relate to the central temperature zone.

9.19 The high temperatures, which are likely to be most important, occur exclusively in the months of June, July and August for which the northern

Table 9.3 **Average monthly temperatures (°C) measured at three depths in bituminous surfacings: southern Britain**

Time span from midnight	January			April			July			October		
	Depth below surface, mm											
	38	127	203	38	127	203	38	127	203	38	127	203
0–1	5.3	5.3	5.0	9.8	11.0	11.7	19.4	20.8	21.0	9.0	10.1	10.2
1–2	5.7	5.4	5.1	9.2	10.9	11.4	18.8	20.6	20.6	9.1	9.9	10.2
2–3	5.9	5.5	5.2	8.6	10.7	10.9	18.1	20.0	19.8	9.1	9.7	10.2
3–4	5.7	5.4	5.3	8.3	10.0	10.5	16.8	19.8	19.2	8.8	9.5	10.0
4–5	5.7	5.6	5.3	7.9	9.8	10.3	16.1	19.4	19.0	8.6	9.3	10.0
5–6	5.4	5.6	5.2	7.6	9.5	10.0	15.9	18.9	18.9	8.4	9.0	10.0
6–7	5.0	5.5	5.1	7.8	9.2	9.7	16.2	18.7	18.8	8.6	8.9	9.9
7–8	4.8	5.4	5.0	9.2	9.5	9.4	17.3	18.8	18.8	8.5	9.0	9.6
8–9	4.6	5.2	5.0	10.8	10.6	9.8	18.8	19.3	18.9	8.8	9.1	9.5
9–10	4.8	5.1	5.0	13.7	11.8	10.2	21.6	20.2	19.1	10.0	9.4	9.6
10–11	5.1	5.3	5.0	16.4	13.3	10.7	23.8	21.7	19.3	11.8	10.7	10.0
11–12	5.2	5.7	5.0	18.5	15.0	11.7	26.9	23.2	19.9	13.2	11.5	10.3
12–13	5.5	5.8	5.1	20.2	16.2	12.7	28.6	25.0	20.7	14.4	12.5	10.8
13–14	5.6	6.0	5.3	21.5	17.4	13.6	30.2	26.2	21.5	15.2	13.5	11.6
14–15	5.6	6.0	5.3	22.4	18.4	14.6	31.4	27.2	22.6	16.0	14.0	12.2
15–16	5.6	6.2	5.5	22.5	19.2	15.1	31.7	28.0	23.5	15.8	14.0	12.5
16–17	5.5	6.0	5.4	22.0	19.2	15.7	31.0	28.3	24.0	14.7	13.8	12.7
17–18	5.4	6.0	5.4	20.0	18.9	15.7	29.4	28.3	24.4	14.0	13.3	12.7
18–19	5.1	5.8	5.4	17.8	17.8	15.5	27.8	27.7	24.5	13.0	12.7	12.6
19–20	5.0	5.7	5.3	16.0	16.6	15.1	26.0	26.5	24.2	12.0	12.2	12.3
20–21	4.8	5.6	5.1	14.3	16.0	14.5	23.8	25.1	23.4	11.0	11.7	12.0
21–22	5.1	5.6	5.0	13.6	15.0	14.4	21.8	23.9	22.5	10.3	11.3	11.7
22–23	5.3	5.8	5.0	12.1	13.8	13.0	21.0	23.0	21.8	9.6	11.0	11.2
23–24	5.6	6.0	5.1	11.2	13.0	12.5	20.2	22.3	21.1	9.7	10.8	10.7
Mean over 24 hours	5.3	5.6	5.2	14.2	13.9	12.5	23.0	23.0	21.1	11.2	11.1	10.9
Mean over 24 hours of full depth	5.4			13.5			22.4			11.1		

temperature zone has an average temperature 1.8 °C lower than the central zone. This will correspond to a reduction of pavement temperatures of about 3 °C (Fig. 9.3), and it should be sufficiently accurate for the purpose of structural design to reduce the temperature values for each of the temperature bands by 3 °C when applying the measurements to the northern zone. The summer temperatures in the central and southern temperature zones are not sufficiently different to require a similar adjustment.

Table 9.4 Percentage of each hour for which the temperature of a bituminous pavement is within specified ranges—calculation on an annual basis (depth 19 mm below surface)

Hour ranges headed: "Percentage of the hour for which the bituminous material at a depth of 19 mm is within the specified range". The final column is "Percentage of year within temperature range".

Temperature range, °C	0–1	1–2	2–3	3–4	4–5	5–6	6–7	7–8	8–9	9–10	10–11	11–12	12–13	13–14	14–15	15–16	16–17	17–18	18–19	19–20	20–21	21–22	22–23	23–24	Percentage of year within temperature range
48–51																									0.1
45–48													0.4	0.2	0.5	0.7	0.2	0.3							0.3
42–45												0.4	2.5	2.0	2.1	1.9	1.4	1.4	0.1						0.7
39–42											0.3	2.8	3.3	3.0	3.0	3.4	2.0	2.7	1.3						0.8
36–39											1.5	3.3	2.5	3.0	1.7	1.4	2.7	2.8	2.1	1.2					0.9
33–36										0.6	3.6	2.6	2.8	2.6	2.1	1.9	2.3	2.7	4.1	1.3	0.7	0.7			1.4
30–33									0.1	2.4	3.3	4.4	5.4	3.1	3.9	4.5	3.4	3.1	2.9	3.6	1.8	2.2			2.0
27–30									1.3	4.5	6.1	7.1	8.5	5.8	5.9	4.5	3.9	4.2	4.4	4.3	4.1	4.1	1.5	0.7	3.2
24–27	2.3	1.2	0.3				0.1	0.8	4.4	7.1	7.4	7.3	9.0	8.4	7.2	6.9	6.2	8.3	5.3	3.9	3.9	5.4	4.4	2.9	4.5
21–24	5.0	3.8	3.6	1.9	1.2	0.8	1.5	4.9	7.0	7.0	8.2	9.8	7.1	6.1	7.6	7.6	7.2	7.4	8.5	7.4	5.1	6.4	6.1	5.5	5.7
18–21	7.5	6.9	8.1	8.6	8.3	8.2	8.6	9.9	12.5	10.6	9.8	7.4	5.9	8.8	10.2	8.7	9.8	7.9	8.6	10.6	5.6	7.9	7.0	8.8	8.8
15–18	12.6	15.2	11.3	9.3	9.6	8.7	9.9	12.6	11.6	10.0	8.6	8.9	9.8	8.5	8.1	8.2	8.7	10.9	10.1	9.9	9.8	11.7	10.9	12.4	10.6
12–15	9.6	10.2	12.3	13.9	15.4	15.6	15.3	11.5	7.0	7.9	7.4	5.4	5.0	4.7	6.0	6.5	6.6	7.5	9.5	10.8	11.7	9.8	13.8	11.8	9.6
9–12	14.6	16.5	16.3	14.2	14.5	13.5	12.0	10.1	11.1	9.5	7.8	7.3	9.7	10.2	10.5	10.5	10.3	9.6	9.7	9.9	9.8	14.3	14.2	14.2	11.8
6–9	20.7	16.8	17.5	18.1	19.6	19.9	18.5	18.5	13.9	15.1	13.9	14.9	13.2	11.7	11.3	12.1	12.7	14.4	13.6	15.2	13.6	14.8	16.1	17.0	15.8
3–6	14.5	15.9	15.7	16.5	16.3	16.8	17.6	17.4	17.4	13.4	12.4	10.9	10.1	9.7	9.5	9.3	9.4	11.2	13.5	13.1	13.2	15.0	15.2	15.8	13.6
0–3	10.4	11.0	12.5	14.8	12.3	13.1	12.2	11.5	10.2	8.4	8.8	7.2	4.9	4.2	3.0	3.4	4.9	5.4	5.5	7.7	8.5	8.6	9.3	9.3	8.6
−3 to 0	2.7	2.5	2.5	2.7	2.9	2.9	3.7	2.4	2.9	3.0	0.8	0.2						0.4	0.8	1.1	1.0	1.6	1.8	2.2	1.6
−6 to −3					0.2	0.4	0.5	0.5	0.5	0.6	0.1													0.1	0.1

Table 9.5 Percentage of each hour for which the temperature of a bituminous pavement is within specified ranges—calculation on an annual basis (depth 38 mm below surface)

Percentage of the hour for which the bituminous material at a depth of 38 mm is within the specified range

Temperature range, °C	0–1	1–2	2–3	3–4	4–5	5–6	6–7	7–8	8–9	9–10	10–11	11–12	12–13	13–14	14–15	15–16	16–17	17–18	18–19	19–20	20–21	21–22	22–23	23–24	Percentage of year within temperature range
45–48															0.2	0.6	0.7	0.1							0.1
42–45															0.6	1.9	2.0	1.4	0.1						0.4
39–42												0.3		0.2	1.3	2.8	1.9	1.7	1.5	0.1	0.1				0.8
36–39												1.6	2.0	1.3	2.3	2.8	2.9	3.6	2.0	1.6	1.6		0.3		1.0
33–36											1.5	4.2	3.5	3.1	2.8	3.7	2.4	2.3	4.0	2.7	1.8	0.2	0.1		1.3
30–33											3.3	2.7	3.1	3.3	3.0	3.7	3.0	3.7	3.0	3.8	2.3	1.6	1.5	0.1	1.6
27–30	0.8	4.4							1.9		5.1	5.3	2.0	3.9	3.8	7.5	3.5	4.3	3.3	5.0	4.3	3.5	5.4	1.3	3.2
24–27	2.8	5.6	1.7	0.5				0.5	2.7	0.1	6.8	7.7	7.6	7.8	9.0	7.5	6.3	8.2	6.4	5.1	4.8	5.1	6.3	4.6	4.7
21–24	5.8	7.1	4.4	4.1	3.2	2.4	2.9	4.8	7.1	0.7	9.3	10.7	9.2	8.3	7.9	9.0	8.1	9.0	10.0	11.6	7.4	6.1	8.3	5.7	6.9
18–21	8.4	13.8	7.0	7.7	7.8	7.7	7.8	7.8	10.4	3.3	10.7	9.1	9.7	11.4	8.1	9.7	8.0	8.0	7.6	10.9	11.0	8.7	13.7	8.3	8.5
15–18	13.8	14.5	14.5	12.7	11.2	10.9	10.4	13.3	14.2	4.5	9.3	8.3	6.2	6.1	8.2	8.0	10.1	10.9	10.6	10.1	8.7	14.5	9.1	13.2	11.4
12–15	10.8	10.2	10.0	12.8	13.1	13.7	14.8	12.1	7.9	9.2	8.7	8.4	9.6	9.8	9.3	9.3	8.9	7.2	8.5	8.0	10.1	7.6	12.7	10.4	10.2
9–12	13.2	14.6	15.1	14.9	13.4	13.7	12.6	11.8	10.7	11.4	7.8	7.0	7.3	5.9	5.2	9.3	6.2	8.3	9.2	9.2	10.0	12.1	17.4	11.5	10.9
6–9	14.7	14.9	16.2	14.9	18.0	18.1	17.6	16.4	16.3	13.4	13.2	13.7	7.4	9.0	9.5	13.8	9.2	14.2	14.7	17.9	17.5	17.3	17.3	19.4	15.7
3–6	17.3	16.7	17.5	17.4	18.0	18.2	18.6	18.7	16.8	14.3	14.0	12.8	15.4	14.4	14.3	8.8	14.1	12.4	12.8	10.0	12.6	13.6	14.9	14.3	14.2
0–3	9.8	10.4	11.7	12.7	6.9	12.5	12.4	11.5	10.5	10.3	9.1	7.9	11.2	9.2	9.4	4.3	10.1	5.1	5.9	7.7	8.7	9.0	9.1	9.3	8.5
−3 to 0	2.5	2.4	2.1	2.4	3.2	2.7	2.8	2.9	3.0	2.8	1.1	0.5	5.8	4.4	4.0		4.7	0.3	0.4	0.6	0.8	0.9	1.3	1.9	1.4
−6 to −3						0.1	0.2	0.3	0.3	0.1															0.04

93

Table 9.6 Percentage of each hour for which the temperature of a bituminous pavement is within specified ranges—calculation on an annual basis (depth 102 mm below surface)

Percentage of the hour for which the bituminous material at a depth of 102 mm is within the specified range

Temperature range, °C	0–1	1–2	2–3	3–4	4–5	5–6	6–7	7–8	8–9	9–10	10–11	11–12	12–13	13–14	14–15	15–16	16–17	17–18	18–19	19–20	20–21	21–22	22–23	23–24	Percentage of year within temperature range
39–42														0.2											0.2
36–39														0.9	2.5	1.2	1.5	1.1	0.7	1.6	0.2	0.7			0.5
33–36												0.1	1.4	3.2	3.7	1.8	2.2	2.0	1.8	2.1	2.1	2.1	0.2		1.3
30–33												1.8	4.3	4.4	3.3	4.4	4.4	5.0	4.1	4.0	2.8	2.8	1.1	0.6	1.4
27–30	0.7	0.7	0.3							0.2	0.3	4.3	4.3	3.2	4.2	2.7	2.3	2.0	2.9	4.4	4.9	4.5	3.5	2.8	2.5
24–27	3.4	2.7	2.2	2.0	1.1	0.8	0.8	1.2	1.8	4.5	4.0	6.0	6.9	8.4	9.8	4.3	5.6	4.5	4.1	4.7	4.6	5.1	5.4	4.9	4.9
21–24	7.5	7.5	6.8	6.6	6.8	5.8	4.6	5.4	6.3	7.2	8.9	8.8	10.5	11.6	10.0	9.9	7.9	8.7	5.6	8.0	7.1	6.8	6.1	7.6	7.6
18–21	8.0	7.9	7.9	7.6	6.2	6.4	6.9	6.4	8.3	9.4	11.6	12.1	10.6	10.8	10.4	8.6	8.6	9.8	10.3	11.0	11.6	9.4	8.4	9.1	9.1
15–18	13.4	14.3	14.2	14.4	14.1	14.6	14.9	14.4	16.3	14.7	11.2	10.3	8.9	7.9	9.3	10.9	10.9	8.6	8.3	9.5	10.0	12.8	13.7	13.6	12.2
12–15	9.7	9.8	10.9	11.3	11.6	11.3	11.4	11.7	8.6	7.7	8.9	10.0	9.6	8.0	8.3	9.9	9.8	10.2	11.1	9.5	9.8	9.2	10.9	8.8	9.5
9–12	14.0	12.5	12.5	12.0	12.2	12.3	12.3	11.5	11.4	11.7	12.5	9.7	8.9	8.5	8.9	7.2	7.2	7.5	8.2	8.0	8.0	10.1	11.0	11.9	10.7
6–9	18.6	18.2	18.0	17.8	17.2	17.1	16.0	16.2	16.8	16.7	16.2	15.8	15.1	15.5	14.1	15.3	15.5	14.9	16.2	15.8	18.4	17.8	18.1	19.3	16.7
3–6	15.4	16.6	17.3	18.0	19.8	19.4	20.5	20.9	18.3	16.7	14.9	12.7	13.7	12.3	11.9	12.2	11.2	13.2	14.2	15.1	15.3	15.3	13.8	14.4	15.5
0–3	8.7	9.0	9.0	9.4	9.9	10.9	10.5	9.6	9.4	8.9	8.9	8.0	5.8	5.0	2.0	2.7	3.5	3.8	3.9	4.3	4.7	6.1	7.3	7.5	7.2
−3 to 0	0.6	0.7	0.9	0.9	1.0	1.4	2.0	2.7	2.8	2.4	1.1	0.5						0.1	0.1	0.2	0.3	0.3	0.5	0.6	0.8

Table 9.7 Percentage of each hour for which the temperature of a bituminous pavement is within specified ranges—calculation on an annual basis (depth 356 mm below surface)

Temperature range, °C	Percentage of the hour for which the bituminous material at a depth of 356 mm is within the specified range																								Percentage of year within temperature range
Hour	0–1	1–2	2–3	3–4	4–5	5–6	6–7	7–8	8–9	9–10	10–11	11–12	12–13	13–14	14–15	15–16	16–17	17–18	18–19	19–20	20–21	21–22	22–23	23–24	
27–30	1.9	1.4	1.0	0.8	0.8	0.7	0.6	0.5	0.2								0.2	0.6	1.0	1.2	1.4	2.3	2.0	2.0	0.8
24–27	6.0	6.6	7.1	7.2	6.7	6.4	5.4	5.2	5.1	4.6	4.1	4.8	4.8	4.7	5.3	5.8	6.3	7.0	7.2	6.8	6.6	5.9	5.4	5.4	5.9
21–24	7.9	8.0	7.7	7.3	7.5	7.2	7.6	6.4	6.8	6.6	7.4	7.9	6.8	7.3	7.6	8.3	8.5	8.4	8.2	9.2	9.1	8.7	9.3	8.4	7.8
18–21	10.9	11.3	11.0	10.3	10.0	10.1	9.4	9.7	10.0	10.9	11.1	10.4	10.9	11.1	11.0	10.8	10.5	11.1	11.6	11.4	10.9	10.2	10.8	10.7	10.7
15–18	12.4	11.3	12.2	12.7	12.5	12.6	14.5	14.8	14.8	16.2	14.3	14.4	14.0	14.5	14.0	13.3	12.8	11.7	12.2	13.2	13.7	13.8	13.9	14.2	13.5
12–15	11.2	10.3	9.7	10.1	9.4	10.0	9.4	9.3	9.5	8.9	9.2	8.4	9.4	9.1	9.1	9.2	9.5	10.1	9.3	8.0	7.6	8.3	8.2	7.6	9.2
9–12	13.9	15.0	14.2	14.6	14.8	14.3	15.5	14.6	14.4	14.8	14.2	13.7	13.8	14.9	14.8	14.3	13.9	13.4	12.7	11.7	12.6	12.6	12.4	12.7	13.9
6–9	21.8	21.4	17.2	21.1	22.4	22.3	21.1	22.9	21.4	20.6	22.9	23.4	23.9	21.3	23.3	23.5	23.3	22.7	22.6	23.0	22.9	22.9	24.2	24.6	22.4
3–6	13.1	13.9	14.3	15.0	15.0	15.5	15.6	15.4	16.5	16.0	15.4	14.9	14.5	15.2	13.7	13.4	13.3	14.4	14.4	15.0	14.5	14.5	12.8	13.7	14.6
0–3	0.8	0.9	0.9	0.8	0.8	0.8	0.9	1.2	1.2	1.5	1.6	2.0	1.8	1.7	1.3	1.3	0.9	0.8	0.8	0.9	0.8	0.8	0.9	0.8	1.1

9.20   This method of presentation of temperature data is particularly applicable to the computer analysis of flexible pavement behaviour, when used in conjunction with the traffic data given in Tables 8.8–8.15.

Temperatures of concrete pavements

9.21   Temperature measurements have been made in concrete pavements at a large number of sites, mainly in the central temperature zone. Over the period March 1969 to February 1970, referred to above in connection with flexible pavements, continuous measurements were made in the top, centre, and bottom of a concrete slab 254 mm thick at Long Bennington on the A1 trunk road 12 km north of Grantham. Figure 9.4 shows the relationship between mean monthly air temperature and the mean monthly slab temperature, which can be compared with Fig. 9.3 giving similar information for bituminous pavements. The curves follow the same general slope as those for flexible pavements but the hysteresis effect previously noted is smaller.

9.22   Table 9.8 gives the hourly variation of temperature at mid-depth of the slab for the months of January, April, July, and October. Figure 9.4 was used to correct the results to the long-term mean air temperatures for the central temperature zone given in Table 9.1. Table 9.8 can thus be compared directly with Table 9.3, which includes the same information for the same depth in the flexible pavements at

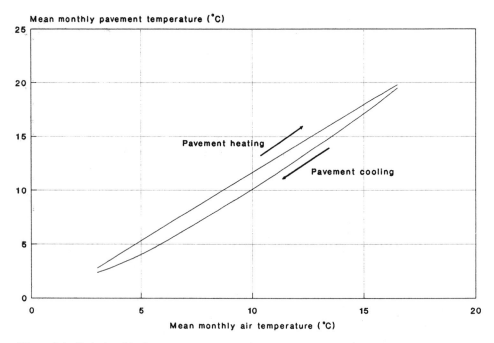

Figure 9.4   Relationship between mean monthly air temperature and pavement temperature 38 mm below surface—254-mm concrete slab

Table 9.8 Average monthly temperature (°C) measured 127 mm below the surface of a 254-mm road slab for the months of January, April, July and October

Time span from midnight	January	April	July	October
0–1	3.3	9.9	21.5	9.9
1–2	3.2	9.8	21.0	9.8
2–3	3.1	9.4	20.8	9.7
3–4	3.0	9.0	20.4	9.5
4–5	2.9	8.8	19.8	9.4
5–6	2.8	8.5	19.4	9.2
6–7	2.7	8.4	19.2	9.1
7–8	2.7	8.4	19.1	9.0
8–9	2.6	8.5	19.4	9.0
9–10	2.6	8.7	19.8	9.2
10–11	2.8	9.2	20.5	9.6
11–12	3.0	10.0	21.2	9.9
12–13	3.1	10.8	22.2	10.3
13–14	3.4	11.6	23.0	10.9
14–15	3.5	12.2	23.8	11.2
15–16	3.6	12.5	24.1	11.6
16–17	3.6	12.8	24.8	11.8
17–18	3.6	12.6	24.9	11.7
18–19	3.5	12.4	24.7	11.3
19–20	3.5	12.2	24.2	11.1
20–21	3.3	11.8	23.8	11.0
21–22	3.2	11.4	23.2	10.8
22–23	3.2	10.8	22.5	10.4
23–24	3.3	10.5	22.0	10.3

Alconbury. The January temperatures are on average 2 °C colder than in the flexible construction, and because of the tendency for the concrete surface to reflect rather than absorb heat, the afternoon temperatures at all seasons of the year tend to be several degrees lower in the concrete. As with flexible pavements, adjustments can be made to Table 9.8 to obtain equivalent data for the southern and northern temperature zones, using in this case Fig. 9.4 in conjunction with Table 9.1.

9.23 In order to calculate warping stresses in concrete slabs (see Chapter 22) it is necessary to know the magnitude of the temperature gradients acting over the depth of the slab. Table 9.9 shows temperatures measured in slabs at Long Bennington throughout the 24 hours for 27 January 1970, 16 April 1969, 17 July 1969, and 31 October 1969. These days were selected as having average air temperatures reasonably close to the long-term means for those months in the central zone. It is shown in Chapter 22 that warping stresses are additive to traffic stresses when the upper surface of the concrete is hotter than the lower surface. Temperature gradients throughout the 24 hours can be calculated using the temperatures given in Table 9.9.

Table 9.9   Temperature measurements in a concrete road pavement 254 mm thick at four times a year

Time from midnight, h	27 January 1970				16 April 1969				17 July 1969				31 October 1969			
	Temperature (°C) at depths shown (mm) and air temperature (°C)															
	0	127	254	Air	0	127	254	Air	0	127	254	Air*	0	127	254	Air
1	5.5	5.7	6.0	5.4	5.4	7.0	8.3	4.2	22.1	25.0	26.0		10.2	10.3	10.7	9.9
2	5.0	5.6	5.9	5.0	5.0	6.6	8.1	4.2	21.0	24.0	25.6		10.0	10.3	10.6	9.9
3	4.7	5.4	5.8	4.8	5.2	6.4	7.7	3.7	19.8	23.1	24.9		10.0	10.3	10.7	9.9
4	3.6	5.0	5.5	3.4	4.7	6.1	7.4	4.0	19.3	22.7	24.3		10.0	10.3	10.8	9.9
5	3.5	4.8	5.4	3.2	4.5	5.9	7.2	4.0	18.8	22.0	21.7		10.4	10.5	10.8	10.0
6	3.0	4.4	5.0	2.7	4.3	5.7	7.0	3.3	18.5	21.5	23.2		10.4	10.5	10.7	10.4
7	3.2	4.0	4.9	3.6	4.4	5.4	6.9	4.0	18.6	21.0	22.0		10.4	10.5	10.7	10.4
8	3.2	4.0	4.8	2.9	4.9	5.4	6.7	4.7	19.7	20.7	22.4		10.1	10.5	10.7	9.9
9	3.2	4.0	4.8	3.1	5.4	5.5	6.7	5.1	21.4	20.7	22.1		10.0	10.4	10.7	10.0
10	3.3	3.9	4.7	3.5	6.8	6.0	6.8	6.7	22.7	21.2	22.0		10.6	10.4	10.7	10.5
11	3.9	4.0	4.7	4.0	9.0	6.6	6.9	7.7	24.2	22.0	22.2		11.2	10.7	10.7	11.0
12	4.3	4.2	4.7	4.7	10.1	7.5	7.1	8.5	25.1	23.0	22.5		11.5	10.9	10.9	11.5
13	4.8	4.4	4.6	5.6	11.0	8.1	7.5	9.0	25.5	23.3	22.7		11.8	10.1	10.0	12.3
14	5.9	4.8	4.8	6.5	12.0	9.0	8.0	9.2	26.8	23.7	23.0		12.7	11.4	11.3	12.7
15	7.0	5.1	4.9	8.0	12.7	9.5	8.4	9.7	27.1	24.4	23.3		12.6	11.8	11.4	12.4
16	7.1	5.6	5.1	7.9	12.4	10.1	8.9	10.4	28.0	25.0	23.6		12.4	11.9	11.8	11.8
17	6.0	5.6	5.3	7.2	12.5	10.4	9.2	10.5	27.4	25.5	24.0		12.1	11.9	11.8	11.7
18	5.0	5.4	5.3	6.0	12.0	10.5	9.6	10.2	27.3	25.6	24.4		11.8	11.8	11.8	11.4
19	4.5	5.0	5.2	5.1	11.0	10.5	9.8	9.0	25.5	25.5	24.5		11.6	11.7	11.8	11.0
20	3.7	4.7	5.1	4.0	10.0	10.1	9.9	8.4	24.5	25.0	24.5		11.3	11.6	11.7	10.5
21	3.5	4.4	5.0	3.6	9.0	9.7	9.8	7.4	22.6	24.1	24.2		11.3	11.5	11.7	10.2
22	2.8	4.1	4.8	3.5	8.0	9.1	9.6	5.0	21.0	23.4	24.0		10.4	11.2	11.6	9.8
23	2.5	4.0	4.7	2.0	7.0	8.6	9.4	4.9	20.0	22.6	23.7		10.2	11.0	11.4	9.4
24	2.0	3.5	4.4	1.0	6.3	7.8	9.0	4.5	19.0	21.8	23.1		9.5	10.8	11.4	8.8

*Air temperatures for 17 July 1969 are not available.

Table 9.10   Temperature gradients in concrete slabs

Date	Temperature gradient, °C per mm						
	8 h	10 h	12 h	14 h	16 h	18 h	20 h
27.01.70		−0.003	0	+0.007	+0.003	−0.003	
16.04.69	−0.004	+0.008	+0.013	+0.018	+0.011	+0.004	−0.003
17.07.69	−0.005	+0.008	+0.010	+0.015	+0.014	+0.007	−0.007
31.10.69		+0.002	+0.002	+0.005	+0.002	−0.001	

Table 9.11   Relation between mean daily slab and air temperatures

Date	Mean temperature of concrete slab, °C	Mean air temperature, °C
27.01.70	4.8	4.4
16.04.69	8.0	6.8
17.07.69	23.2	20.5
31.10.69	11.4	10.8

9.24   Table 9.10 shows the magnitude of the temperature gradients in °C per mm. A negative gradient indicates that the surface is cooler than the bottom of the slab and a positive gradient that it is hotter.

9.25   The magnitude of the gradients is determined largely by the difference between the maximum and minimum air temperature, and not by the mean air temperature. There is therefore unlikely to be any systematic difference between temperature gradients in the three temperature zones previously considered, and for the purpose of calculating warping stresses the values given in Table 9.10 can be taken as typical of the three zones.

9.26   Table 9.11 shows the mean slab temperatures and the mean air temperatures for the four days considered in Table 9.9. It is significant that these points lie on the curves for the heating and cooling conditions given in Fig. 9.4, which were based on mean monthly slab and air temperatures. It appears therefore that Fig. 9.4 can also be used with acceptable accuracy to obtain mean slab temperatures from mean daily air temperatures.

References

1. Roads and Transportation Association of Canada, Soils and Materials Committee and Pavement Design and Evaluation Committee: Low-temperature pavement cracking studies in Canada, *Proceedings, 3rd Conf. on the Structural Design of Asphalt Pavements, London, 1972,* vol. 1, University of Michigan, Ann Arbor, Michigan, 1972, 581–9.
2. Meteorological Office: *Monthly Weather Survey and Prospects* (monthly publication), MO, Bracknell, Berks.

PART THREE Pavement Materials—Specification and Properties

10. The soil foundation

Introduction

10.1   When a loaded wheel moves over the surface of a multilayer pavement, the magnitude of the generated stresses decreases from layer to layer, and at the same time the duration of the stress pulse increases with depth. The stress reduction effected by any layer depends on the stiffness and thickness of that layer. A major function of the pavement is to reduce the stresses transmitted to the subgrade to a level which the soil will accept without significant deformation or shear. In the fulfilling of this function the stresses induced in each layer must also be within the limits necessary to control deformation and tensile cracking within that layer.

10.2   This chapter is concerned with those aspects of soil mechanics which are of particular concern in relation to road subgrades and road embankments. These include those properties of importance in the structural design of pavements, namely modulus of elasticity and deformation under repeated loading.

The constitution of soil

10.3   Soil is the most variable material with which the civil engineer has to deal; large changes can occur in the type and condition of the soil over distances of only a few metres. The comparatively low unit cost of road pavements does not permit the detailed soil testing and evaluation usual with other, more compact civil engineering projects, such as high-rise buildings and dams. The pavement engineer must generally be content with an average assessment of the soil conditions over a long length of carriageway. He must accept that this may lead eventually to some areas of the finished road requiring structural maintenance before the end of the design life, or before general strengthening by an overlay is necessary. On a small job, closely under the control of the engineer, it may be possible to vary the design to take into account soil changes found during the progress of the work but on major projects the design must be based largely on the preliminary soil survey. If the engineer requires changes to be made during construction, and the contract does not make provision for this, then it must be expected that the contractor will make claims.

10.4   Soil consists of a mass of weathered mineral particles of various shapes and sizes, between which there is water and generally some air. Near the surface most soils contain organic matter derived from the decomposition of vegetation, but in poorly drained areas, strata consisting almost entirely of vegetable matter may occur at various depths below the surface. This material which is loosely described as peat presents many problems to the road engineer.

10.5   In thinking of soil, the mind almost inevitably concentrates on the solid particles. However, it cannot be too strongly emphasized that the engineering properties of soils depend on all three constituents—solid matter, water, and air. Generally speaking, the type of soil can be defined in terms of size and shape of particles, but the state of the soil, which determines the engineering characteristics, can be defined only in terms of the solid, liquid, and air contents.

10.6   Since in all foundation problems a knowledge of the type and state of the soil is necessary, it is essential that these terms should be defined as concisely as possible.

Particle size distribution

10.7   The type of soil is generally specified in terms of the particle sizes present. The particles in soil range from stones several centimetres across down to colloidal material too fine to be susceptible to direct measurement. The normal method of representing the particles in a soil (sometimes called the grading) is in terms of the percentages of particles by weight finer than specified sizes, as shown in Fig. 10.1. Since the small particles play a particularly important part in determining the properties of soil, it is usual, as shown on the figure, to use a logarithmic scale for particle size. This has the effect of spreading the smaller sizes.

10.8   The normal procedure used to determine the particle size distribution of soil

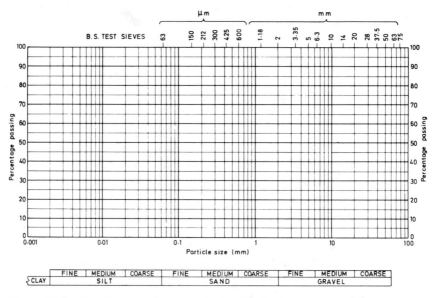

Figure 10.1   Chart for recording particle size distribution

involves sieving for the particles larger than 0.06 mm and sedimentation for the smaller particles. These procedures are described as Tests 7A–7D of BS 1377:1975 and in AASHTO Designation T88–86. The sedimentation process is too complex for most site laboratories and the properties of the silt and clay fractions are generally assessed by plasticity tests as described in Para. 10.40.

10.9   Certain broad terms are used to describe the shape of the particle distribution curve. A well-graded soil is characterized by a wide range of particle sizes in proportions which give a smooth curve for the particle size distribution. In poorly graded soils, although a wide range of sizes may be present, the soil is deficient in certain intermediate particle sizes, resulting in a 'stepped' distribution curve. A uniformly graded soil (sometimes referred to as a single-size soil) contains only a very narrow band of particle sizes. Examples of well-graded, poorly graded, and uniformly graded soils are shown in Fig. 10.2.

10.10   The particle size spectrum is divided into four arbitrary groups: gravel, sand, silt, and clay. The maximum and minimum particle sizes included in each of these groups are as follows:

gravel   particles between 60 mm and 2 mm;
sand   particles between 2 mm and 0.06 mm;
silt   particles between 0.06 mm and 0.002 mm;
clay   all particles smaller than 0.002 mm.

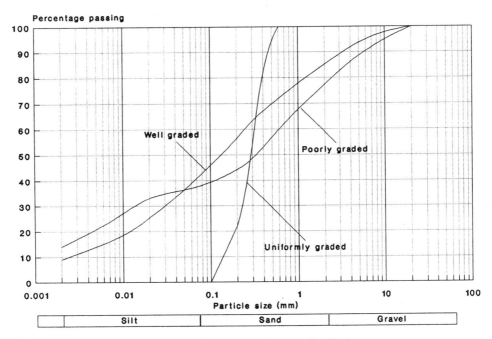

Figure 10.2 Description of soils by shape of particle size distribution curves

The sand and silt groups are further subdivided into coarse, medium, and fine fractions as shown below:

coarse sand	particles between 2 mm and 0.6 mm
medium sand	particles between 0.6 mm and 0.2 mm
fine sand	particles between 0.2 mm and 0.06 mm
coarse silt	particles between 0.06 mm and 0.02 mm
medium silt	particles between 0.02 mm and 0.006 mm
fine silt	particles between 0.006 mm and 0.002 mm

These subdivisions are shown beneath Fig 10.1.

10.11 Although these subdivisions of the particle size spectrum are in some measure based on observed differences in the behaviour of the groups, it is best to regard them as purely arbitrary.

Description of soils in terms of particle groups

10.12 Most soils have particle size distribution which span several of the grading groups referred to in Para. 10.10. Thus a soil whose grading included all particle sizes would be referred to as a gravel-sand-clay. Where the particles fall predominantly in two groups, ambiguities can arise in the descriptions used in different countries. In the USA the main grading group is given first followed by the secondary group. Thus, if we refer to Fig. 10.3, a soil with grading curve A would be classified as a

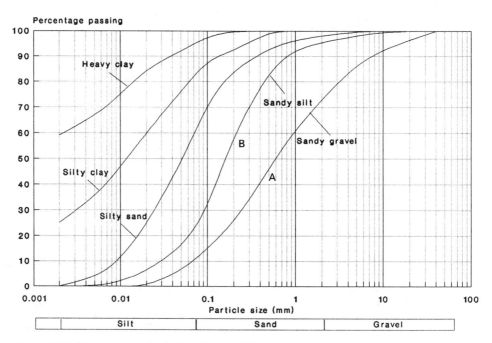

Figure 10.3 Description of soils by their particle size components

sand-gravel and the other grading curves included in the figure would be classified in the manner indicated on the diagram.

10.13   In the UK the terms sandy gravel and silty sand are often used. When this procedure is used the adjective should be formed from the lesser size group, e.g., curve A in Fig. 10.3 would be described as a gravelly sand and curve B as a sandy silt. A more precise indication of the constitution of the soil can of course be given if the proportions by weight in each size group are tabulated.

Relative size and surface area of particles

10.14   The behaviour of soils, particularly in relation to changing moisture conditions, depends to a great extent on the relative sizes of the particles present and their surface areas. A clearer picture of these factors than is given by a mere statement of equivalent particle diameters can be obtained by considering the number of particles of different sizes which can be contained in a given volume, and their surface areas, assuming them to be spherical. In Table 10.1 the number of such particles which can be contained in a 2-mm cube is given together with the corresponding total surface area of the particles. The particle sizes selected are the minimum of the gravel group (2 mm), the means of sand and silt groups (approximately 1 mm and 0.03 mm) and the maximum of the clay group (0.002 mm). The loosest degree of packing consistent with contact between the particles and the enclosing cube is assumed.

Since the clay particles tend to be flat and elongated rather than spherical the number and surface area of particles in this group quoted in Table 10.1 will be an underestimate.

Nature of the soil particles

10.15   *Inorganic material*   The gravel, sand, and silt arise from the disintegration of the parent rocks by weathering. They are roughly cubical in shape and may be transported from their place of origin by water or wind. The clay particles differ from the other particle fractions both in chemical composition and in their physical properties. Chemically, they consist of hydrated aluminio-silicates which are formed during the leaching processes to which the coarser particles of the rock minerals are subjected. Among the minerals which occur in clay particles are forms of kaolinite, montmorillonite, and mica.

Table 10.1   Size and surface area of soil particles

Particle group	Equivalent diameter mm	Approximate number of particles in a 2-mm cube	Total surface area of particles in a 2-mm cube, mm^2
Gravel	2	1	12.5
Sand	1	8	25
Silt	0.03	340 000	950
Clay	0.002	8 000 M	24 000

10.16   Physically, the clay particles are elongated and lamellar, which together with their small size and large specific surface area (see Table 10.1) imparts to clay soils their properties of plasticity and compressibility referred to in Paras 10.37 and 10.43.

10.17   The specific gravity of soil particles is generally between 2.6 and 2.8; lower values usually indicate the presence of organic matter and higher values the presence of metallic ores. The particle specific gravity of fine-grained soils is determined by the specific gravity bottle method, whilst the pycnometer method is used for coarse-grained soils. Both methods are described in British Standard 1377, AASHTO T100-86, or ASTM (American Society for Testing and Materials) D854-83.

10.18   *Organic material*   The organic material is derived mainly from the plant residue and is generally concentrated in the top 30 cm of the soil. However, leaching in sandy soils may cause soluble constituents to be extracted and deposited lower down. The distribution of organic deposits such as peat is conditioned by geological factors and may extend to much greater depths.

10.19   The composition of the organic matter is dependent on the plant cover and on the extent to which decomposition has progressed. Thus the organic constituents of forest soils are derived largely from leafmould, whereas in pasture soils the organic matter is derived from grass leaves and roots. In some cases the plant materials can be recognized visually, while in other cases the decomposition may have proceeded so far that the original plant structure has largely disappeared, leaving a dark, amorphous material called humus. Freshly decomposed organic matter and humus have different characteristics in that the former consists of macroparticles and fibres which are relatively inert, whereas humus is acidic and colloidal in nature and absorbs water readily.

10.20   The organic content of soil immediately below road structures should not exceed four per cent. A method of measuring the organic content of soil is described in British Standard 1377:1975, Test 8, or AASHTO T267-86.

The solvent action of soil water

10.21   In addition to its important influence on the properties of soil, which is discussed later in this chapter, the soil water is of concern to the engineer because of its action as a solvent. The principal materials in solution are (1) soluble salts, generally in the form of sulphates of sodium, magnesium, and calcium, and (2) finely divided organic matter.

Sulphates in the soil water affect the properties of the soil and of structures in contact with it, by

1. attacking concrete and other materials containing cement,
2. disrupting the soil structure by crystallization,
3. corroding metals and particularly iron pipes buried in the soil.

In Britain, only (1) and (3) are likely to be important. Special precautions such as the use of sulphate-resistant cements, and the protection of iron pipes with an impervious coating, have to be taken when the sulphur trioxide content of the ground water exceeds 50 parts in 100 000. The determination of the sulphur trioxide content is described in British Standard 1377:1975, Test 9.

10.22   The organic matter in soil water is probably not in a true state of solution, but rather consists of colloidal matter in suspension. In this way, organic matter can be leached out of the topsoil and deposited in the subsoil below, resulting in dark zones. It is possible that soluble organic matter also influences the redistribution of mineral elements of the soil, since iron is known to form soluble complexes with certain organic compounds. Thus iron may be removed from some parts of the soil mass and deposited lower down in the form of concretions round siliceous particles, giving rise to an iron pan.

The state of the soil

10.23   The strength properties of soil which are of importance to the engineer can be only very loosely related to the type of soil as defined above in terms of the particle size distribution. They are much more related to the manner in which the particles are packed together (the density) and the amount of water between the particles (the moisture content). These factors define the state of the soil.

10.24   An engineer preparing a specification either for the construction of earthworks or to give the condition which is required in the subgrade must carry out sufficient testing, as part of the site investigation, to ensure that the specification not only can be achieved under the prevailing climatic conditions using the type of plant normally available to a civil engineering contractor, but will also give the strength and stability required by the design. The required state of the soil may be expressed by limits of (1) the moisture content, (2) the dry density, or (3) the maximim air content in the compacted material. It is important for the engineer to understand the interrelation of these factors. This is considered in the following paragraphs in conjunction with Fig. 10.4, which shows the weights and volumes of dry solids, water, and air in a volume V of wet soil of weight W.

Dry density

10.25   The weight of dry material in unit volume of wet soil is defined as the dry density, ρ_d, and is usually expressed in Mg/m^3. If we refer to Fig. 10.4, which shows the weights and volumes of dry solids, water, and air in a volume V of wet soil of weight W, then

$$\rho_d = \frac{W_s}{V} = \frac{W_s}{V_s + V_w + V_a} \tag{10.1}$$

Moisture or water content

10.26   The weight of water expressed as a percentage of the weight of dry solids is termed the moisture or water content, w. In both these definitions the weight of dry solids is defined as the weight of the soil after drying for 24 hours at a temperature

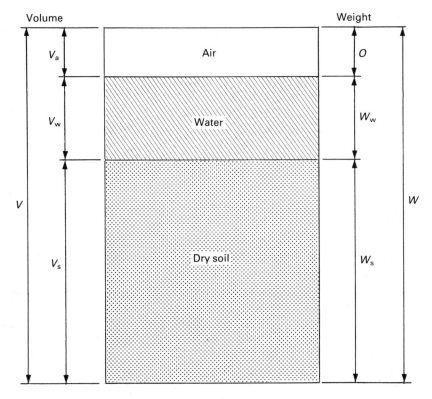

Figure 10.4 Component parts of soil mass. (The volumes and weights shown are defined in the text starting at Para. 10.25)

of 105 °C. Hence,

$$w = \frac{W_w}{W_s} \times 100 \tag{10.2}$$

Percentage air voids (air content)

10.27   The space in soil not occupied by solid material is termed the voids, and the space occupied by air is referred to as the air voids. The percentage ratio of the volume of air to the total volume of soil is defined as the percentage air voids or air content, a and it follows that

$$a = \frac{V_a}{V} \times 100 = \frac{V_a}{V_s + V_w + V_a} \times 100 \tag{10.3}$$

Relationship between dry density, moisture content, and percentage air voids

10.28   The relation between these quantities can be deduced from Eqs (10.1) to

(10.3):

$$\rho_d = \frac{W_s}{V_s + V_w + V_a}$$

hence

$$\frac{1}{\rho_d} = \frac{V_s}{W_s} + \frac{V_w}{W_s} + \frac{V_a}{W_s}$$

$$= \frac{1}{\rho_s} + \frac{w}{100\rho_w} + \frac{V_a}{V\rho_d}$$

where ρ_w and ρ_s are the densities of water and of the soil particles,

and

$$\frac{1}{\rho_d}\left[100 - \left(\frac{V_a}{V} + 100\right)\right] = \frac{100}{\rho_s} + \frac{w}{\rho_w}$$

hence

$$\frac{1}{\rho_d}(100 - a) = \frac{100}{\rho_s} + \frac{w}{\rho_w}$$

or

$$\rho_d = \frac{\rho_w\left(1 - \dfrac{a}{100}\right)}{\dfrac{1}{G_s} + \dfrac{w}{100}}$$ (10.4)

where G_s is the particle specific gravity.

In a saturated soil the voids are completely filled with water and $a = 0$. For such a soil,

$$\rho_d = \frac{\rho_w}{\dfrac{1}{G_s} + \dfrac{w}{100}}$$ (10.5)

The above definition of a saturated soil should be noted carefully. The term 'saturated' does not imply that the soil will not take up any more water, since soils containing clay particles may, even in the saturated condition, absorb more water by the process of swelling. The term 'saturated' is therefore not sufficient to define the state of a soil.

10.29   The relationship between dry density, moisture content, and percentage air voids given in Eq. (10.4), can be represented graphically by a family of curves as in Fig. 10.5, which refers to a particle specific gravity of 2.70, i.e., $\rho_w = 1$ Mg/m^3, $\rho_s = 2.70$ Mg/m^3. Each curve represents a different air content. The limiting curve corresponding to zero air content is often referred to as the saturation line or the zero air voids line.

10.30   The state of any soil can be represented by a point on a diagram such as

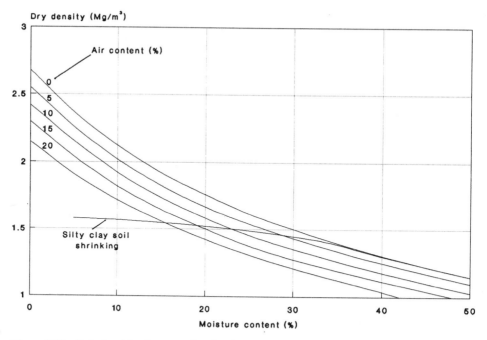

Figure 10.5 Relationships between dry density, moisture content, and percentage air content

Fig. 10.5 drawn to the appropriate particle specific gravity. Every point on the diagram to the left of the saturation line will represent a different state of the soil. It will be seen that if any two of the factors—dry density, moisture content, and percentage air voids—are known, then the third is established. Further, a change in the state of the soil can be represented by a line or curve on the diagram. Thus if the particles of a soil are made to move closer together without any change of moisture content (defined as the process of compaction), then the corresponding change of state is represented by a straight line parallel to the axis of dry density, which will cross the family of curves representing different air voids conditions, showing that as the dry density is increased the air content must in this case decrease. Similarly, if water is removed from a saturated clay soil by the application of a compressive load (defined as the process of consolidation), then the change of state is represented by the saturation line. The curve actually shown on Fig. 10.5 represents a silty clay soil shrinking because of the removal of water by evaporation. In this case both the dry density and the air content of the soil increase as the moisture content decreases. It is important to realize that in a diagram such as Fig. 10.5 the state of the soil cannot be represented by a point to the right of the saturation line, since this would imply compressibility either of the water or of the soil particles.

10.31   For the convenience of engineers, a set of charts relating dry density and moisture content for air voids of 0, 5, 10, 15, and 20 per cent and particle specific gravities of 2.6, 2.65, 2.7, 2.75, and 2.8 is included as an appendix to this chapter.

Bulk or wet density

10.32   Both the moisture content and the dry density of soil can be defined on a wet weight basis, the water content being expressed as a percentage of the wet weight and the density as the weight of wet mineral in unit volume. In civil engineering practice it is most unusual to express moisture content in this way, but the bulk or wet density is often required, as for example, in the calculation of overburden pressures. If we refer back to Fig. 10.4, the bulk density is given by the following:

$$\rho_w = \frac{W}{V} = \frac{W_s + W_w}{V_s + V_w + V_a} \tag{10.6}$$

Relationship between bulk density and dry density

10.33   The relation between these quantities follows from their definitions:

$$\frac{\rho_w}{\rho_d} = \frac{W}{V} \times \frac{V}{W_s} = \frac{W}{W_s} = \frac{W_s + W_w}{W_s} = 1 + \frac{w}{100}$$

Therefore

$$\rho_w = \rho_d\left(\frac{100 + w}{100}\right) \tag{10.7}$$

Voids ratio

10.34   Another term sometimes used in expressing the state of soil is the voids ratio, e, defined as the volume of voids per unit volume of matter. Hence, if we refer again to Fig. 10.4,

$$e = \frac{V_w + V_a}{V_s} \tag{10.8}$$

or, in a saturated soil,

$$e = \frac{V_w}{V_s} = \frac{\rho_s W_w}{\rho_w W_s} = \frac{G_s W_w}{W_s} = \frac{G_s w}{100} \tag{10.9}$$

Relationship between voids ratio and dry density

10.35   It follows from the definitions that dry density and voids ratio are simply related:

$$\frac{1}{\rho_d} = \frac{V_w + V_a}{W_s} + \frac{V_s}{W_s}$$

$$= \frac{e \cdot V_s}{W_s} + \frac{V_s}{W_s}$$

$$= \frac{(1 + e)}{\rho_s}$$

$$\text{or} \qquad\qquad \rho_d = \frac{\rho_s}{1+e} \qquad\qquad (10.10)$$

Thus the state of the soil can be expressed in terms of voids ratio and moisture content as an alternative to dry density and moisture content.

Porosity

10.36   The porosity, n, of a soil is defined as the ratio of the volume of voids to the total volume of the soil. Thus:

$$n = \frac{(V_w + V_a)}{V} \qquad\qquad (10.11)$$

Plasticity of clay soils

10.37   The particles in soil are normally covered by a layer of water the thickness of which will increase as the soil is wetted from the dry condition. In the case of clay particles the thickness of the water films is also influenced by the particular types of clay mineral involved. Further, some clay minerals have an expanding lattice structure into which water can enter to cause expansion of the clay mineral itself. Montmorillonite is the commonest form of such minerals likely to be found in Britain.

Liquid and Plastic Limits

10.38   Because of the very large number of water films associated with the small, flat clay particles (Table 10.1), any soil with a clay content exceeding about 15 per cent exhibits the properties of plasticity and cohesion. Over a certain moisture range the particles will slide over each other, the action being to shear rather than break the interconnecting water films. This gives rise to an appearance of plasticity when the soil is 'worked'. At higher moisture contents the clay will deform under its own weight and take on the behaviour of a viscous liquid.

The moisture content at which the soil changes from the plastic to the liquid state is termed the liquid limit, LL. As the moisture content is reduced below the plastic range the soil becomes friable owing to breaking of the moisture bonds as the soil is worked. The moisture content at which this change occurs is referred to as the plastic limit, PL. The moisture content range between the liquid and plastic limits is termed the plasticity index, PI. Hence,

$$\text{LL} - \text{PL} = \text{PI} \qquad\qquad (10.12)$$

10.39   Two other relations are sometimes used to define the moisture content, w, in terms of the plasticity properties:

The liquidity index, LI, is defined as follows:

$$\text{LI} = \frac{w - \text{PL}}{\text{PI}} \qquad\qquad (10.13)$$

The consistency index, CI, is defined as follows:

$$CI = \frac{LL - w}{PI} \qquad (10.14)$$

Determination of the liquid and plastic limits

10.40   The determination of the liquid and plastic limits (sometimes called the Atterburg limits or the index tests) is discussed in detail in BS 1377:1975. The soil is first mixed to a high moisture content and a pat is placed in the cup of the liquid limit machine. The cup is raised by a cam, and allowed to fall sharply onto the hard rubber baseplate as the handle of the machine is turned. The number of turns or 'blows' required to close a groove, cut through the soil from front to back, is observed. The test is repeated at decreasing moisture contents and the moisture content at which the groove is closed by 25 blows is arbitrarily defined as the liquid limit. After further drying the soil is rolled out on a glass plate using the palm of the hand. The lowest moisture content at which the soil can be rolled into a thread of 3 mm diameter without breaking is termed the plastic limit. Full details of the sample preparation and the test procedures to measure the index tests are given in British Standard 1377:1975, Tests 2 and 3, and in AASHTO Standards T89-86 and T90-86.

Cohesion

10.41   A granular soil has little strength in tension, but the water bonds between the clay particles which give a clay soil its plasticity also bond the particles together and give a significant strength in tension. This strength is termed the cohesion, c.

Relation between the plasticity index and clay content of soils

10.42   Table 10.2 shows values of the clay content of a wide range of soils, together with the plasticity properties and the particle specific gravity. The table includes both British and overseas soils. The data are shown graphically in Fig. 10.6. There is a great deal of scatter which arises mainly from the different clay minerals present in the soils. Soils with very active clay minerals such as montmorillonite tend to fall below the line and those with less active minerals are above the line. The mean relation indicated is useful as an approximate guide to the clay content of soils of known plasticity index.

Swelling and shrinkage of clay soils

10.43   Increase in thickness of the water films between the clay particles in soils results in an increase in volume, and there is therefore a relation between volume and moisture content for all soils with a significant clay content.

10.44   Shrinkage is expressed as the observed change of volume per 100 g of dry soil as indicated in Fig. 10.7. As the soil dries in the saturated condition, the relation follows the zero air voids or saturation line. As the larger particles come into contact, air enters the soil structure and a further change in moisture content results in a

Table 10.2   Clay content, particle specific gravity, and results of index tests on various soils

Soil description	Place of origin	Clay content (%)	Results of index tests			Particle specific gravity
			PL (%)	LL (%)	PI (%)	
British soils						
Lias Clay	Shipton, Oxon.	39	24	60	36	2.71
Weald Clay	Ditchling, Sussex	62	25	68	43	2.74
Oxford Clay	Cumnor, Berks.	56	24	72	48	2.74
Kimmeridge Clay	Sunningwell, Berks.	67	24	77	53	2.74
London Clay	Heathrow, Middx.	60	26	78	52	2.73
Gault Clay	Steyning, Sussex	56	25	70	45	2.68
Gault Clay	Stoke Mandeville, Bucks.	57	29	81	52	2.68
Gault Clay	Aylesbury, Bucks.	69	34	102	68	2.70
Gault Clay	Shaves Wood, Sussex	60	32	121	89	2.65
Silty clay	Harmondsworth, Middx.	34	24	43	19	2.70
Silty clay	Harmondsworth, Middx.	33	10	43	24	2.72
Sandy clay	Harmondsworth, Middx.	24	19	27	8	2.70
Clay silt	Rippon, Yorks.	19	17	28	11	2.67
Clay silt	Wellington, Som.	12	19	33	14	2.75
Overseas soils						
Decomposed granite	Pretoria, South Africa	20	42	65	23	2.75
Silty clay	Habbaniya, Iraq	45	28	58	34	2.78
Sandy, silty clay	Thornhill, Zimbabwe	40	25	57	32	2.71
Silty clay	Heany, Zimbabwe	20	20	41	21	2.76
Silty clay	Heany, Zimbabwe	32	22	48	26	2.76
Clay	Kumalo, Zimbabwe	58	27	60	33	2.77
Sandy, silty clay	Kumalo, Zimbabwe	34	24	51	27	2.60
Clay	Sudan	54	26	95	69	2.72
Silty clay	Trinidad	19	27	40	13	2.72
Silty clay	Trinidad	26	17	36	19	2.68
Clay	Trinidad	45	16	51	35	2.73
Clay	Trinidad	60	24	71	47	2.80
Clay	Kenya	63	34	81	47	2.65
Clay	Kenya	75	44	101	57	2.65
Sandy, silty clay	Grenada	24	23	63	40	2.78
Silty clay	Ghana	36	21	65	44	2.83
Clay	Kenya	79	70	104	34	2.79
Clay	Kenya	83	44	87	43	2.85
Clay	Uganda	59	21	57	36	2.76
Silty clay	Kenya	22	23	38	15	2.56

volume change smaller than the volume of water removed. Close to zero moisture content the rate of shrinkage tends to zero.

The shrinkage limit

10.45   The moisture content at which the saturation line meets the horizontal, corresponding to the volume at zero moisture content, is arbitrarily termed the

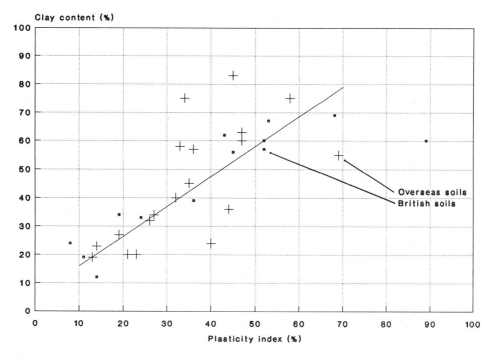

Figure 10.6 Relationship between clay content and plasticity index

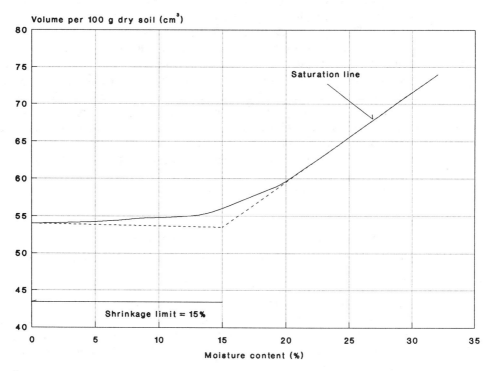

Figure 10.7 Shrinkage of soil

shrinkage limit, although it does not represent a limiting condition with regard to shrinkage.

Measurement of shrinkage

10.46   The shrinkage curve for soils is often measured by a mercury displacement method (AASHTO T92-86), but a preferable procedure, because is imposes no external loading on the soil, is to use an optical profile projector operating at a magnification of 50 times.[1] The outline of a cylindrical sample of the soil about 15 mm in diameter and 15 mm high is projected on the screen and the mean height and mean diameter are deduced by direct measurement. The soil is allowed to dry slowly on the rotating stage of the projector and a series of measurements of weight and volume obtained. The moisture contents are subsequently deduced from the dry weight of the sample.

10.47   Figure 10.8(a) shows the shrinkage curves for a gault clay, for a London Clay, and for a silty clay determined in the above manner. In Fig. 10.8(b) the curves are plotted in an alternative form to show the change in dry density with moisture content. Provided the soil is wetted or dried slowly, there is no significant hysteresis between the wetting and drying conditions.

10.48   The shrinkage limits for the three soils considered in Fig. 10.8(a) and (b) are as follows: the gault clay 10.5 per cent, the London Clay 18.3 per cent, and the silty clay 21 per cent. This shows that the shrinkage limit tends to decrease with the clay content, although the clay minerals present are also important.

10.49   The significance of shrinkage depends in practice on the moisture range over which the soil is likely to fluctuate. For the silty clay under a road pavement a typical moisture content fluctuation would be between 13 and 20 per cent, which from the shrinkage curve would correspond to a volume change of less than 2 per cent. For the London Clay the range could be 24–30 per cent, giving a volume change of 13 per cent. For the gault clay the range could be 30–45 per cent, corresponding to a volume change of 25 per cent. Thus the engineer would anticipate no shrinkage problems with the silty clay, but potentially serious problems from the gault clay. To minimize such problems the engineer should specify that vegetation should be kept away from the verges of pavements laid on heavy clays, or consideration should be given to the use of impermeable shoulders.

Soil classification

10.50   Various methods of soil classification have been developed to relate soil types to civil engineering properties. The oldest is the Casagrande system, which dates from the forties. Soils were classified into groups, based in the case of non-cohesive soils on the particle size distribution and for cohesive soils on the values of liquid and plastic limits. At best, a classification system can give only the broadest indication of the engineering behaviour, and attempts which have been made to introduce further subdivisions into the Casagrande system have led to further complications without improving its validity. The problems arise from the fact that the state of the soil is often much more important than its type. In the last

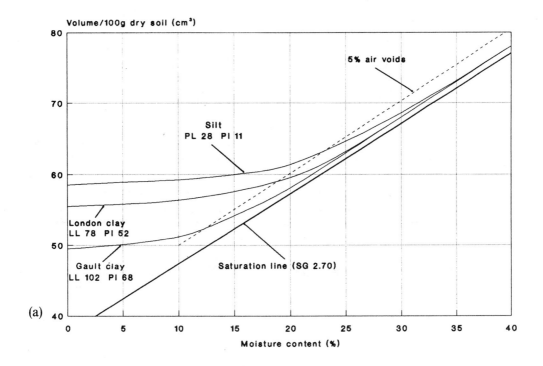

(a)

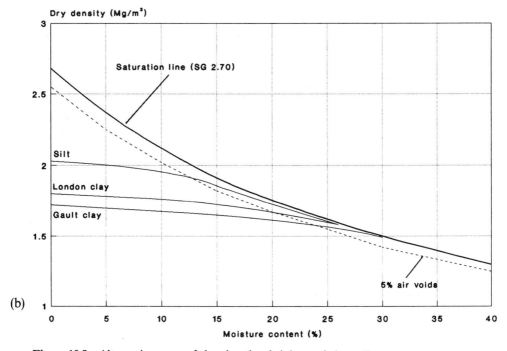

(b)

Figure 10.8 Alternative ways of showing the shrinkage of clay soils

119

15 years the tendency both in the USA and Europe has been to revert to classification procedures not directly linked to soil behaviour.

10.51   In the USA the use of the Casagrande system has largely been superseded by AASHTO Designation M145-82, Recommended practice for the classification of soils and soil aggregate mixtures for highway construction purposes. This is simpler than the Casagrande method and involves seven main soil groupings (A-1 to A-7), as described in Table 10.3. These are divided into subgroups shown in Table 10.4. The various groupings are defined in terms of the soil gradings, and the liquid and plastic limits. The information given relating to the engineering properties of the soils is less comprehensive than is the case of the Casagrande system.

10.52   British Standard 5930:1981, *Code of Practice for Site Investigation*, uses essentially the Casagrande classification system with some further subdivision of the soil types as indicated in Table 10.5 (Table 8 of the British Standard). Cohesive soils are classified in terms of the slightly modified plasticity chart shown here as Fig 10.9 (Fig. 31 of the British Standard). BS 5930 contains a great deal of important information relating to soil sampling and the visual classification of core samples.

Compaction of soil

10.53   Compaction is the process by which air is excluded from a soil mass to bring the particles closer together and thus increase the dry density. The effect is generally, but not necessarily, to increase the strength of the soil. Distinction must be drawn between the meaning of the terms compaction and consolidation. The latter, already referred to in more detail earlier, is the process by which water is excluded from a saturated clay soil by the action of a sustained load.

10.54   Under the application of a small stress, soil may behave elastically, any strain being fully recovered when the stress is removed. With greater stresses, compaction occurs which increases the strength of the soil to a level where further strain is resisted. At still higher stresses, the soil compacts to a state where no further strength can be mobilized and this is followed by shearing at constant volume.

10.55   If a loose soil is compacted by the application of a fixed amount of energy then the dry density achieved is related to the moisture content of the soil. The curve relating the two factors shows a maximum dry density at a particular moisture content generally referred to as the 'optimum moisture content' for that method of compaction or that amount of compacting energy. The shape of the curve relating compaction and moisture content can be deduced from the strength properties of the soil. Figure 10.10(a), shows the relationship between unconfined compressive strength, determined on compacted cylinders of a cohesive soil of known dry density, and the moisture content. If it is assumed that energy is applied to initially loose samples of the same soil to produce maximum strengths of 100, 200, 300, and 400 kN/m² the dry density–moisture content curves corresponding to each compaction condition would be as indicated in Fig. 10.10(b). In each case the curve reaches a peak at the moisture content corresponding to saturation. A qualitative explanation of the shape of dry density–moisture content relationship curves often put

Table 10.3 Classification of soils and soil—aggregate mixtures

	General classification						
	Granular materials (35% or less passing 0.075 mm)			Silt–clay materials (more than 35% passing 0.075 mm)			
Group classification	A-1	A-3*	A-2	A-4	A-5	A-6	A-7
Sieve analysis. Percentage passing:							
2.00 mm (No. 10)	—	—	—	—	—	—	—
0.425 mm (No. 40)	50 max.	51 min.	—	—	—	—	—
0.075 mm (No. 200)	25 max.	10 max.	35 max.	36 min.	36 min.	36 min.	36 min.
Characteristics of fraction passing 0.425 mm (No. 40)							
Liquid limit	—	—	—	40 max.	41 min.	40 max.	41 min.
Plasticity index	6 max.	N.P.	†	10 max.	10 max.	11 min.	11 min.
General rating as subgrade	Excellent to good			Fair to poor			

*The placing of A-3 before A-2 is necessary in the 'left-to-right elimination process' and does not indicate superiority of A-3 over A-2.

†See Table 10.4 for values.

Table 10.4 Classification of soils and soil—aggregate mixtures

	General classification										
	Granular materials (35% or less passing 0.075 mm)							Silt–clay materials (more than 35% passing 0.075 mm)			
	A-1		A-3	A-2				A-4	A-5	A-6	A-7
Group classification	A-1-a	A-1-b	A-3	A-2-4	A-2-5	A-2-6	A-2-7	A-4	A-5	A-6	A-7-5, A-7-6
Sieve analysis. Percentage passing:											
2.00 mm (No. 10)	50 max.										
0.425 mm (No. 40)	30 max.	50 max.	51 min.								
0.075 mm (No. 200)	15 max.	25 max.	10 max.	35 max.	35 max.	35 max.	35 max.	36 min.	36 min.	36 min.	36 min.
Characteristics of fraction passing 0.425 mm (No. 40)											
Liquid limit				40 max.	41 min.	40 max.	41 min.	40 max.	41 min.	40 max.	41 min.
Plasticity index	6 max.	6 max.	N.P.	10 max.	10 max.	11 min.	11 min.	10 max.	10 max.	11 min.	11 min.*
Usual types of significant constituent materials	Stone fragments, gravel and sand		Fine sand	Silty or clayey gravel and sand				Silty soils		Clayey soils	
General rating as subgrade	Excellent to good							Fair to poor			

*Plasticity index of A-7-5 subgroup is equal to or less than LL minus 30. Plasticity index of A-7-6 subgroup is greater than LL minus 30.

Table 10.5 British soil classification system for engineering purposes. (Extract from BS5930:1981 reproduced with permission of BSI)

Soil groups				Subgroups and laboratory identification				
GRAVEL and SAND may be qualified sandy GRAVEL and gravelly SAND, etc., where appropriate				Group symbol	Subgroup symbol		Fines (% less than 0.06 mm)	Liquid limit %	Name

Soil groups	Group symbol	Subgroup symbol	Fines (% less than 0.06 mm)	Liquid limit %	Name
COARSE SOILS (less than 35% of the material is finer than 0.06 mm) — **GRAVELS** (more than 50% of coarse material is of gravel size (coarser than 2 mm)) — Slightly silty or clayey GRAVEL	G — GW	GW	0 to 5		Well-graded GRAVEL
	GP	GPu GPg			Poorly graded/uniform/gap-graded GRAVEL
Silty GRAVEL	G-F — G-M	GWM GPM	5 to 15		Well-graded/poorly graded silty GRAVEL
Clayey GRAVEL	G-C	GWC GPC			Well-graded/poorly graded clayey GRAVEL
Very silty GRAVEL	GF — GM	GML, etc.	15 to 35		Very silty GRAVEL; subdivide as for GC
Very clayey GRAVEL	GC	GCL GCI GCH GCV GCE			Very clayey GRAVEL (clay of low, intermediate, high, very high, extremely high plasticity)
SANDS (more than 50% of coarse material (finer than 2 mm) of sand size (finer than 2 mm)) — Slightly silty or clayey SAND	S — SW	SW	0 to 5		Well-graded SAND
	SP	SPu SPg			Poorly graded/uniform/gap-graded SAND
Silty SAND	S-F — S-M	SWM SPM	5 to 15		Well-graded/poorly graded silty SAND
Clayey SAND	S-C	SWC SPC			Well-graded/poorly graded clayey SAND
Very silty SAND	SF — SM	SML, etc.	15 to 35		Very silty SAND; subdivided as for SC
Very clayey SAND	SC	SCL SCI SCH SCV SCE			Very clayey SAND (clay of low, intermediate, high, very high, extremely high plasticity)
FINE SOILS (more than 35% of the material is finer than 0.06 mm) — Gravelly or sandy SILTS and CLAYS (35% to 65% fines) — Gravelly SILT	FG — MG	MLG, etc.			Gravelly SILT; subdivide as for CG
Gravelly CLAY	CG	CLG CIG CHG CVG CEG		<35 35 to 50 50 to 70 70 to 90 >90	Gravelly CLAY of low plasticity of intermediate plasticity of high plasticity of very high plasticity of extremely high plasticity
Sandy SILT	FS — MS	MLS, etc.			Sandy SILT; subdivide as for CG
Sandy CLAY	CS	CLS, etc.			Sandy CLAY; subdivide as for CG
SILTS and CLAYS (65% to 100% fines) — SILT (M-SOIL)	F — M	ML, etc.			SILT; subdivide as for C
CLAY	C	CL CI CH CV CE		<35 35 to 50 50 to 70 70 to 90 >90	CLAY of low plasticity of intermediate plasticity of high plasticity of very high plasticity of extremely high plasticity
Organic soils	Descriptive letter 'O' suffixed to any group or subgroup symbol.				Organic matter suspected to be a significant constituent. Example MHO: Organic SILT of high plasticity.
Peat	Peat soils consist predominantly of plant remains which may be fibrous or amorphous.				

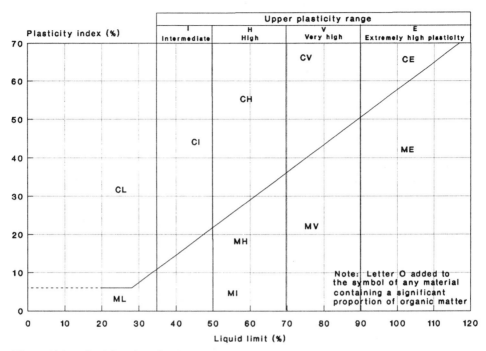

Figure 10.9 Plasticity chart for the classification of fine soils and the finer part of coarse soils (From BS5930:1981, reproduced with the permission of BS1)

forward is that on the dry side of the optimum moisture content the soil water acts as a lubricant, while on the wet side it acts as a displacer.

10.56 The form of the curves shown in Fig 10.10(b) illustrates the basic properties of relationships of this type, viz. that the maximum dry density increases and the the optimum moisture content decreases with increasing compactive effort.

Laboratory compaction tests

10.57 To provide an indication of the compactability of soils in the field, standardized laboratory compaction tests were developed in the USA some 50 years ago. In the first of these tests the soil is compacted in three approximately equal layers in a cylindrical mould 101.6 mm (4 in) in diameter and 116 mm (4.58 in) in height. A rammer having a 51-mm (2-in) diameter end-face and a weight of 2.5 kg (5.5 lb) is used to compact the soil. It is allowed to fall a distance of 305 mm (12 in) 25 times on each layer of the soil, a uniform distribution over the area of the mould being obtained as far as is practicable. The weight of the soil, after the top surface has been struck off level with the top of the mould, is obtained and the dry density is calculated from the volume of the mould and the measured moisture content of the soil. Tests are normally carried out at a range of moisture contents to give the density–moisture content relationship. This test was originally referred to as the

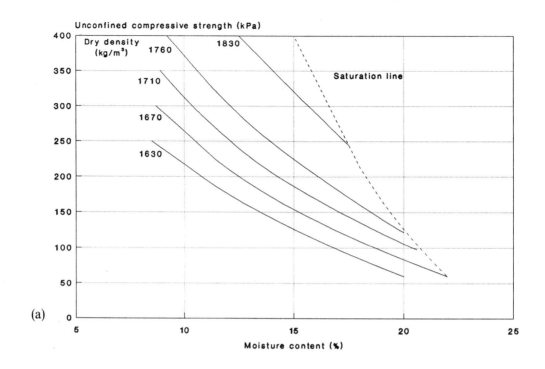

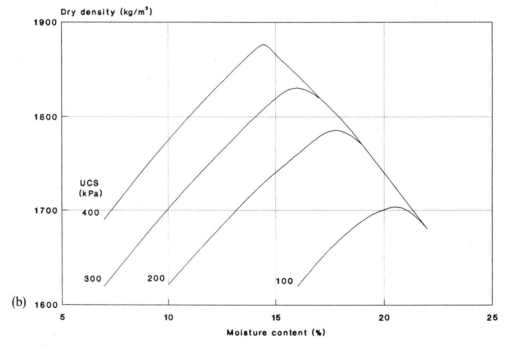

Figure 10.10 Relationship between (a) strength and moisture content and (b) density and moisture content for the same soil

Proctor test, after the originator, but it is now designated as AASHTO Test T99-86, as ASTM Test D698, or as British Standard 1377:1975, Test 12.

10.58   The advent of heavier compaction plant led to the need for a test which would produce greater densities. In this test the same size of mould is used but the soil is compacted in five layers using a rammer of weight 4.54 kg (10 lb), dropped 25 times on the surface of each layer from a height of 457 mm (18 in). This test is designated as AASHTO Test T180-86, as ASTM Test D1557, or as British Standard 1377:1975, Test 13.

10.59   The two compaction tests are generally distinguished by the adjectives 'normal' and 'heavy'. As would be expected from Fig. 10.10(b), the maximum dry density for the heavy compaction test is greater than for normal compaction and the optimum moisture content is lower. In the field the two compaction tests are carried out using hand rammers, but in the laboratory it is usual to use a mechanized form of the equipment.

10.60   The optimum moisture contents derived from these laboratory tests provide a useful indication of the range of moisture content suitable for field compaction, for most soils. However, a third compaction test has in recent years been introduced in the UK which relates laboratory and field compaction more closely in the case of granular soils with only a small silt and clay content. This is the vibrating hammer test in which the soil is compacted in three layers in a larger steel mould (152 mm in diameter and 127 mm high). The compaction equipment is a vibrating hammer operating at a frequency of 25–45 Hz. The hammer is applied to each layer of soil using a circular steel tamper of diameter 145 mm for a period of 60 s. Full details of the test procedure are given in BS 1377:1975, Test 14. This test is particularly useful in developing moisture content and density targets for granular road base and sub-base materials.

The performance of compaction plant

10.61   In the UK since the early 'fifties, new and existing compaction plant have been evaluated using four typical British soils having the gradings shown in Fig. 10.11. The relationship between dry density, moisture content, and the number of passes of the plant has been studied and comparison made with the results of the laboratory compaction tests referred to in Paras 10.57–10.60. Typical results are shown in Fig. 10.12 (a) (b) (c) and (d).

10.62   Derived from this work, Table 10.6 shows the number of passes and thickness of compacted layer necessary to give approximately 90 per cent of BS 'heavy' compaction (AASHTO 'modified' compaction) at the field moisture content for a wide range of plant when compacting (1) cohesive soils, (2) well-graded granular and dry cohesive soils, and (3) uniformly graded soils and granular materials. The table refers to the natural moisture content of the soils under British conditions of climate.

10.63   Table 10.6 is reproduced from the Department of Transport *Specification for Road and Bridge Works* (1976 edition). In the 1986 edition the table is expanded to cover the compaction of granular subbase and roadbase materials. For the

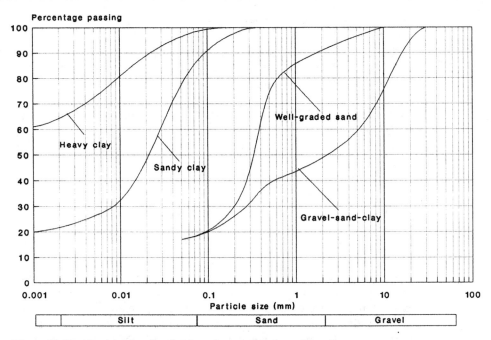

Figure 10.11   Particle size distributions for compaction trial soils

compaction of subgrades, as distinct from bulk earthworks, it is recommended that the number of passes of suitable plant should be doubled. With this type of specification, control on site is largely by observation of plant movements, but some density measurements *in situ* are desirable.

The moisture condition value (MCV) of soil

10.64   In Para. 10.54 it is stated in effect that if compactive energy is applied to a soil at a fixed moisture content then the strength of the soil will increase as a result of the increased density until the soil is incapable of mobilizing further strength at that moisture content. Any additional energy will then cause shear at constant volume and density. In field compaction, the effort expended in shearing the soil will be wasteful and in the case of clay soils it may destroy the soil structure and lead eventually to a long-term increase in moisture content and reduction in strength. It is therefore desirable that soils should not be overcompacted.

10.65   In the late seventies A. W. Parsons developed a simple field test which assesses the limit of compactibility of soils, which he termed the moisture condition value (MCV) test.[2,3] The test has proved most useful in assessing the suitability of cohesive soils for use in earthworks, (2) in providing a rapid field method for determining moisture content during the progress of works without the need for oven drying, and (3) in assessing the trafficability of soil by civil engineering plant and vehicles. (This latter function is referred to later in this book in relation to the

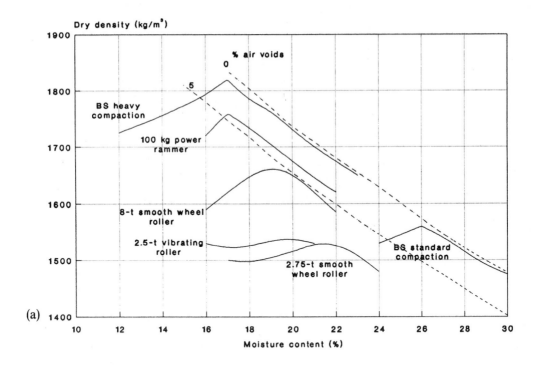

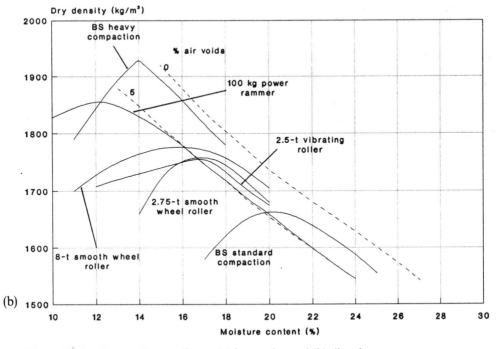

Figure 10.12 Compaction studies on (a) heavy clay and (b) silty clay

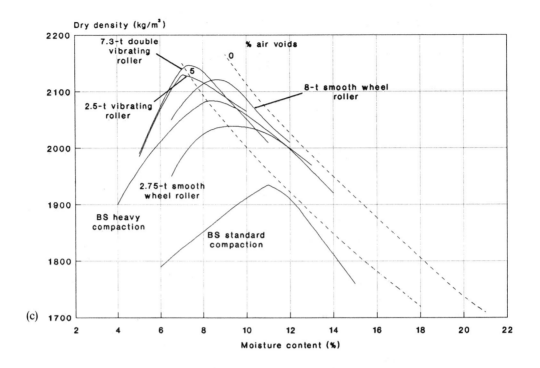

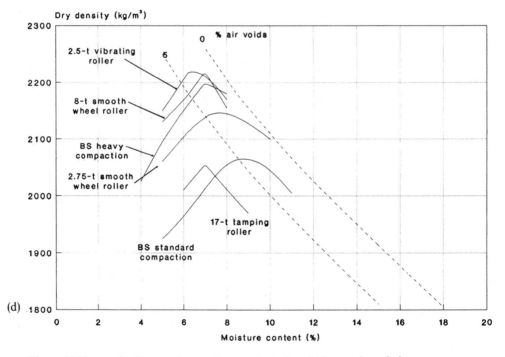

Figure 10.12–*contd.*–Compaction studies on (c) sand and (d) gravel-sand-clay

128

Table 10.6 Performance of compaction plant

Type of compaction plant	Category	Cohesive soils		Well-graded granular and dry cohesive soils		Uniformly graded material	
		D*	N*	D	N	D	N
Smooth-wheeled roller	Mass per metre width of roll						
	over 2 100 kg up to 2 700 kg	125	8	125	10	125	10[†]
	over 2 700 kg up to 5 400 kg	125	6	125	8	125	8[†]
	over 5 400 kg	150	4	150	8	Unsuitable	
Grid roller	over 2 700 kg up to 5 400 kg	150	10	Unsuitable		150	10
	over 5 400 kg up to 8 000 kg	150	8	125	12	Unsuitable	
	over 8 000 kg	150	4	150	12	Unsuitable	
Tamping roller	over 4 000 kg	225	4	150	12	250	4
Pneumatic-tyred roller	Mass per wheel:						
	over 1 000 kg up to 1 500 kg	125	6	Unsuitable		150	10[†]
	over 1 500 kg up to 2 000 kg	160	5	Unsuitable		Unsuitable	
	over 2 000 kg up to 2 500 kg	175	4	125	12	Unsuitable	
	over 2 500 kg up to 4 000 kg	225	4	125	10	Unsuitable	
	over 4 000 kg up to 6 000 kg	300	4	125	10	Unsuitable	
	over 6 000 kg up to 8 000 kg	350	4	150	8	Unsuitable	
	over 8 000 kg up to 12 000 kg	400	4	150	8	Unsuitable	
	over 12 000 kg	450	4	175	6	Unsuitable	
Vibrating roller	Mass per metre width of a vibrating roll:						
	over 270 kg up to 450 kg	Unsuitable		75	16	150	16
	over 450 kg up to 700 kg	Unsuitable		75	12	150	12
	over 700 kg up to 1 300 kg	100	12	125	12	150	6
	over 1 300 kg up to 1 800 kg	125	8	150	8	200	10[†]
	over 1 800 kg up to 2 300 kg	150	4	150	4	225	12[†]
	over 2 300 kg up to 2 900 kg	175	4	175	4	250	10[†]
	over 2 900 kg up to 3 600 kg	200	4	200	4	275	8[†]
	over 3 600 kg up to 4 300 kg	225	4	225	4	300	8[†]
	over 4 300 kg up to 5 000 kg	250	4	250	4	300	6[†]
	over 5 000 kg	275	4	275	4	300	4[†]
Vibrating-plate compactor	Mass per unit area of base plate:						
	over 880 kg up to 1 100 kg	Unsuitable		Unsuitable		75	6
	over 1 100 kg up to 1 200 kg	Unsuitable		75	10	100	6
	over 1 200 kg up to 1 400 kg	Unsuitable		75	6	150	6
	over 1 400 kg up to 1 800 kg	100	6	125	6	150	4
	over 1 800 kg up to 2 100 kg	150	6	150	5	200	4
	over 2 100 kg	200	6	200	5	250	4
Vibro-tamper	Mass:						
	over 50 kg up to 65 kg	100	3	100	3	150	3
	over 65 kg up to 75 kg	125	3	125	3	200	3
	over 75 kg	200	3	150	3	225	3
Power rammer	Mass:						
	100 kg up to 500 kg	160	4	150	6	Unsuitable	
	over 500 kg	275	8	275	12	Unsuitable	
Dropping-weight compactor	Mass of rammer over 500 kg:						
	Height of drop: over 1 m up to 2 m	600	4	600	8	450	8
	over 2 m	600	2	600	4	Unsuitable	

*D = maximum depth of compacted layer (mm); N = minimum number of passes.

[†]Indicates that the number of passes specified must be applied by a roller and towed by a track-laying tractor not by self-propelled machine.

design of haul roads.) Since the test will not be incorporated in BS 1377 until the next edition is published in 1991 it is described in some detail here.

10.66   The equipment for the moisture condition test is shown in Fig. 10.13. The soil is compacted by a falling rammer as in the standard compaction tests discussed in Paras 10.57 and 10.58. The difference is that in the MCV equipment the cyclindrical rammer has a diameter of 97 mm and it operates in a heavy steel mould of diameter 100 mm and height 200 mm, with a plastic sealing disc 99 mm in diameter between the rammer and the soil. Significant shear of the soil after compaction is thus prevented by the confining conditions. The mass of the rammer is 7 kg and the height of the drop between the soil and the underside of the rammer is controlled at 250 mm using the Vernier scales fixed to the rammer and the side rails. The mass of soil used is normally 1.5 kg and it is broken down through a 20-mm sieve.

10.67   The soil to be tested is placed in the mould with the plastic disc lying on its surface. The mould is mounted in the machine and the rammer lowered to the surface of the soil; the penetration of the rammer into the mould is noted from the scale engraved on the rammer surface and the automatic release mechanism is adjusted to give a drop of 250 mm. The additional penetration of the rammer for various numbers of blows is recorded as indicated in the table above Fig. 10.14. The height of drop is corrected to 250 mm as is necessary during the application of the blows.

10.68   In the interpretation of the test, the penetration of the rammer at any given number of blows is compared with the penetration for four times as many blows and the difference in penetration determined. This 'change in penetration' is plotted against the lower number of blows in each case. This is shown in the table in Fig. 10.14 and in the graph, which shows the number of blows on a logarithmic scale. To avoid predicting the point in the plotted relation when the change in penetration reaches zero, a change in penetration of 5 mm has been arbitrarily accepted as indicating the point beyond which no significant change of density occurs. The MCV is defined as 10 times the logarithm (to the base 10) of the number of blows corresponding to a change of penetration of 5 mm on the plotted curve. In the example shown in Fig. 10.14 the number of blows for 5 mm change in penetration is 9.8; this would correspond to an MCV of $10 \times \log 9.8 = 9.9$.

10.69   Figures 10.15 and 10.16 show this procedure carried out for a heavy clay of liquid limit 78 per cent and plastic limit 27 per cent and for a sandy clay of liquid limit 40 per cent and plastic limit 20 per cent. In each case tests were made over a wide range of moisture contents. The number of blows corresponding to a change of penetration of 5 mm gives MCVs which can be read off the scale shown at the top of the diagrams. Because the lower scale showing the initial number of blows is logarithmic, the MCV scale becomes linear. For both soils the relationship between the moisture content of the soil and the MCV is shown to be closely linear. This means that the MCV test can be used in the field as a very rapid method of checking the moisture content of the soil, since tests can be performed in a few minutes from the back of a site vehicle.

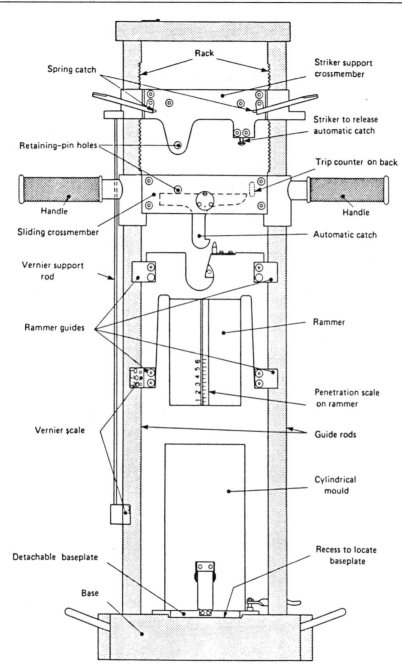

Figure 10.13   Prototype moisture condition apparatus

Soil:- Heavy clay   Moisture content: 26.3 per cent

Number of blows of rammer (n)	Penetration of rammer into mould (mm)	Change in penetration with additional 3 n blows of rammer (mm)
1	41	33.5
2	57.5	33
3	67	33.5
4	74.5	26.5
6	84	17
8	90.5	10.5
12	100.5	0.5
16	101	
24	101	
32	101	
48	101	

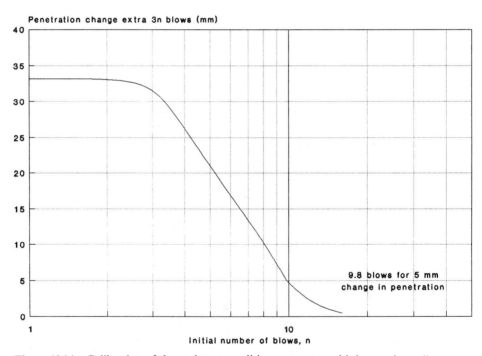

Figure 10.14 Calibration of the moisture condition apparatus with heavy clay soil

10.70   It is current British practice in the case of cohesive soils under UK climatic conditions to specify an upper limit of moisture content of 1.2 times the plastic limit at the time of compaction. For the two soils referred to in Figs 10.15 and 10.16 this would correspond to moisture contents not greater than 32.5 per cent and 24 per

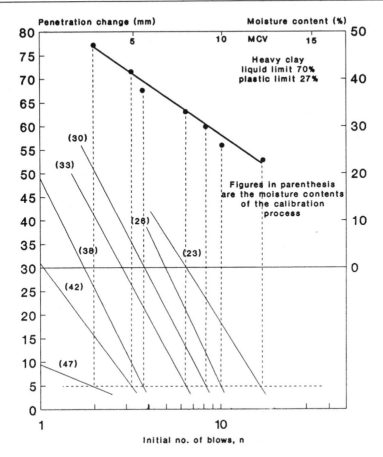

Figure 10.15 Calibration chart for the prototype moisture condition apparatus with heavy clay

cent respectively. The figures show that for the heavy clay the minimum MCV would be 8 and for the sandy clay 6.2. For a site where a variety of clays were likely to be encountered, a mean value of 7 would be appropriate and this would be included in the contract documents to define the required state of compaction of the earthworks.

10.71   As part of the development of the MCV test procedure a study was made of the relationship between undrained shear strength, c_u (determined by the vane test, see Para. 10.102) and MCV for the two soils referred to in Figs 10.15 and 10.16.[2] The results shown in Fig. 10.17 confirm that there is a linear relationship between $\log c_u$ and MCV. Since both scales of the diagram are logarithmic, it follows that shear strength and number of blows required to give full compaction are linearly related. This confirms the statement implied in Para. 10.54 that compaction is effected by repetitions of a compactive effort until a shear strength sufficient to resist further compaction is created at the prevailing moisture content. This relationship

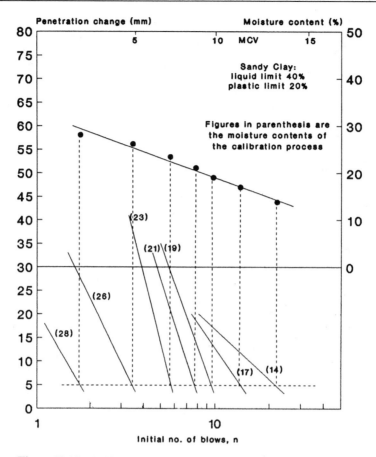

Figure 10.16 Calibration chart for the prototype moisture condition apparatus with sandy clay

between shear strength and MCV is important because it indicates that the MCV of cohesive soils is a reliable guide to their ability to support the passage of site traffic, i.e., to their traffickability. This subject is discussed in detail in relation to the design of haul roads in Chapter 24.

10.72   MCV tests have also been carried out on granular soils.[4] Figures 10.18 and 10.19 show results for a uniformly graded fine sand and for a well-graded sand. For such soils in the UK the upper limit of moisture content permitted in earthworks is 1.5 per cent above the optimum moisture content for the standard compaction test (see Para. 10.57). For the two soils to which Figures 10.18 and 10.19 refer, this would correspond to maximum moisture contents of 16.5 and 10.5 respectively. The diagrams show that the corresponding MCVs would be 7 and 8, i.e., very similar to those deduced for the cohesive soils. No data are given in the published papers for

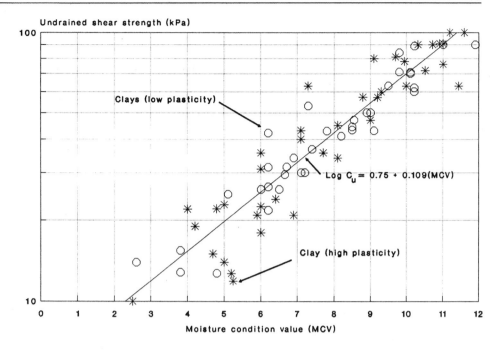

Figure 10.17 Relationship between undrained shear strength and MCV for clays of intermediate and high plasticity

the relationship between shear strength and MCV for the granular soils, but it seems probable that the relationship would be very similar for all the soils.

The engineer's responsibility for defining the suitability of soils for use in earthworks

10.73 Certain materials such as peat, highly organic soils from swamps and bogs, materials susceptible to spontaneous combustion, and soils contaminated with hazardous chemicals should be excluded from earthworks. In wet climates it may also be prudent to exclude clays of very high liquid limit (e.g. >90 per cent), which may prove impossible to handle under such circumstances. Normally only small quantities of soil unsuitable for these reasons will be involved in a major road contract.

10.74 In preparing the design and specification for a major road scheme the engineer must as far as is possible balance the quantities of cut and fill, by his choice of the vertical alignment. At one time this was considered to be a primary requirement only in developed countries. It is now accepted that economic development in Third-World countries depends much on the speed and capacity of trucks,[5] and permissible gradients are accordingly being reduced. The engineer has therefore for any contract to set limits of acceptability which will enable an experienced

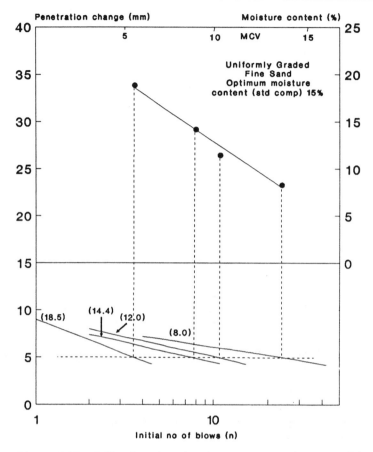

Figure 10.18 Calibration chart for the prototype moisture condition apparatus with uniformly graded fine sand

contractor to make use of the majority of the excavated material in the construction of the embankments. These limits will vary from contract to contract and they cannot therefore be defined in the form of a standard specification. In a wet climate, the best that a contractor can achieve is to move the soil from the embankment with no change of moisture content. In practice, the engineer will be wise to assume that there will be a small increase in moisture content of 1–2 per cent involved in this operation. In a dry climate, loss of moisture may be a problem and the engineer may need to set a limit of moisture content which will involve artificial wetting of the soil during the compaction process.

10.75   The upper limit of moisture content which the engineer selects for fill will influence the permissible slopes of the embankments and the strength of the soil used in designing the pavement. These decisions have to be made at the design stage and

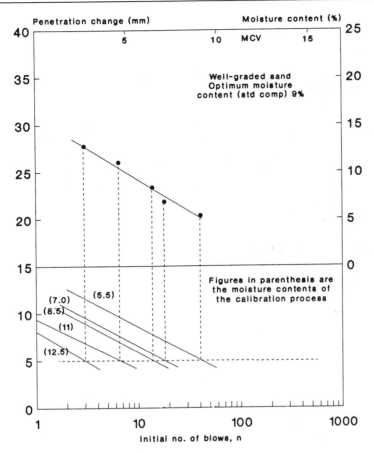

Figure 10.19 Calibration chart for the prototype moisture condition apparatus with well-graded sand

emphasize the need for a thorough site investigation supported by an adequate test programme on the materials involved.

10.76   A county or local-authority engineer working in a comparatively limited area soon develops expertise in specifying moisture content and density requirements for soils with which he is familiar. However, civil engineering is now international and engineers are increasingly putting in bids for design and supervision contracts in locations of which they have little or no experience. Under these circumstances it is the responsibility of the engineer to become thoroughly familiar with all aspects of the climate and geology of the site and to organize a site investigation which will give all the information necessary to the production of a workable earthworks specification. Failure to recognize this has led to some very expensive cases of litigation in recent years.

The distribution and movement of water in soil

The suction of soil

10.77   Water is held in soil by surface tension and adsorption forces, which impart to it a negative pressure or suction with respect to atmospheric pressure. The magnitude of this suction increases rapidly as the soil dries out to give a relationship between suction and moisture content which can be investigated at low suctions by the apparatus shown in Fig. 10.20. A small sample of the soil is placed on a ceramic plate sealed into a water-filled reservoir, connected to a flow tube to which a vacuum can be applied. The ceramic plate has a porosity which allows water to pass, but not air, at the range of suctions used. In this way the suction of the soil moisture is balanced by the applied suction, and, by testing soils over a range of moisture contents, the relation between the two factors is explored. Typical suction–moisture content relations for granular and cohesive soils are shown in Fig. 10.21. The soils were tested in the drying condition.

Pore water pressure and suction

10.78   If the surface of soil is covered to prevent the effects of rainfall and evaporation an equilibrium moisture distribution is reached with respect to the position of the water table. The pore water pressure which can be measured directly

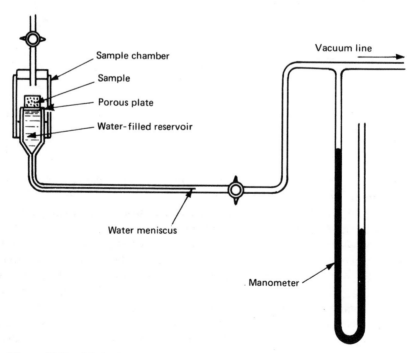

Figure 10.20   Method of measuring soil suction

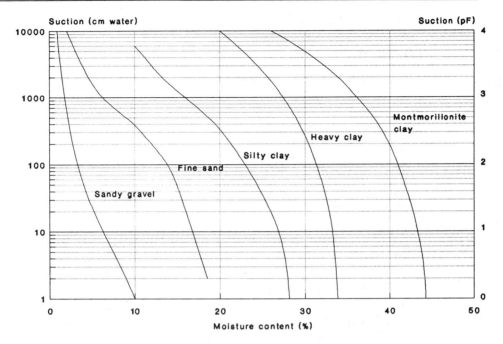

Figure 10.21   Relation between suction and moisture content for cohesive and non-cohesive soils (drying condition)

by piezometers is zero (i.e., atmospheric) at the level of the water table, and increases linearly with depth below the water table. Above the water table there is a similar linear decrease of pore water pressure, which means that it is negative with respect to atmospheric pressure. The soil water at a particular depth is also subject to overburden pressure from the wet soil above. In heavy clay soils the whole of the overburden pressure acts on the soil water, but in granular soils intergranular contacts support the overburden and no part is carried by the soil water. For intermediate soil types part only of the overburden pressure is imparted to the soil water. The suction of the soil, as defined above, acts to retain the water in the soil and the overburden pressure acts to exclude it. Thus if u is the pore water pressure, s is the suction, P is the overburden pressure, and α is the proportion of the overburden pressure acting on the soil water (the compressibility factor), then

$$u = s + \alpha P \qquad\qquad (10.15)$$

The suction s will be negative and the overburden pressure P will be positive. Above the water table, s will numerically exceed αP and the pore water pressure will be negative. Below the water table the reverse will be the case. In heavy clays all the overburden pressure is carried by the soil water and $\alpha = 1$. In purely granular soils all the overburden pressure is taken by intergranular contacts and $\alpha = 0$. For other

Table 10.7   Relationship between compressibility factor and the plasticity index of cohesive soils

Plasticity index (%)	Compressibility factor (α)
10	0.15
15	0.27
20	0.40
25	0.55
30	0.70
35	0.80
>35	1.00

soils its value is between 0 and 1, depending on the plasticity index as indicated in Table 10.7.

10.79   The density of wet soil is close to twice the density of water. Thus if u and s in Eq. (10.15) are also expressed in centimetres of water, the equation can be used in conjunction with the appropriate soil suction curve to deduce the equilibrium moisture content above the water table. Such calculations have been made in Fig. 10.22 for all the five soils referred to in Fig. 10.21, assuming the water table to be at

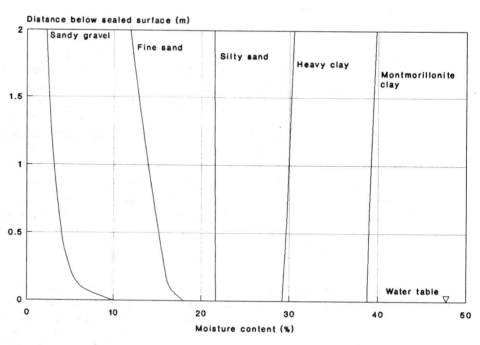

Figure 10.22   Equilibrium moisture distribution deduced from suction curves in Fig. 10.21 (water table depth 2 m)

a depth of 2 m below the surface. For the sands α was assumed to be 0 and for the two heavy clays a value of 1 was taken. For the silty clay 0.5 was assumed.

10.80   For the sands the moisture content increases with depth as the level of the water table is approached. With the heavy clays the moisture content decreases with depth owing to compression of the soil structure, while for the silty clay the moisture content is substantially constant with depth. These moisture distribution curves show that soils with very different moisture contents would be able to coexist in close proximity to one another.

Subsoil drainage

10.81   It is important to realize that subsoil drains placed above the level of the water table cannot effect the reduction in moisture content. Such a reduction can be achieved only by lowering the water table. The suction–moisture content relationship for a soil used in conjunction with Eq. (10.15) can be used to calculate the effect of lowering the water table on the moisture distribution. Figure 10.23 shows the effect of lowering the water table in the heavy clay referred to in Figs 10.21 and 10.22 from the surface to depths of 1 and 2 m. The first increment produces a substantial reduction of moisture content close to the surface but for the second increment the effect is much smaller. In general, subsoil drainage needs to be considered if there is any danger of the water table rising closer to the surface than 1–1.5 m.

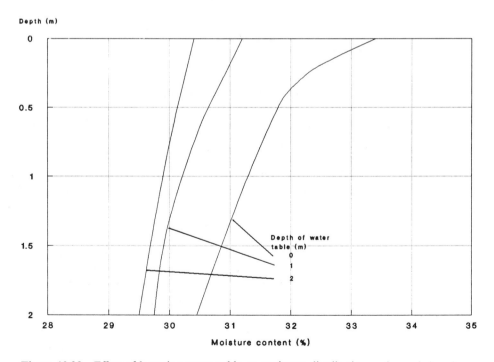

Figure 10.23   Effect of lowering water table on moisture distribution under sealed surface—London Clay

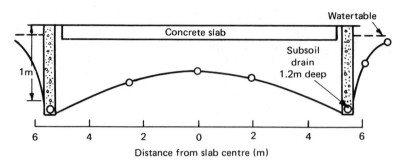

Figure 10.24   Measured draw-down curve in London Clay

10.82   Various methods of calculating the draw-down effect of subsoil drains laid in road verges are available.[6] They depend on a knowledge of the permeability of the soil which in practice is likely to be variable because of fissuring. Figure 10.24 shows actual measurements of draw-down from side drains placed close to the edge of a concrete pavement built in a very high water table situation, on a heavy clay soil. In this case side drains 1.5 m deep would have been required to ensure that the water table was maintained at least 1 m below the underside of the pavement. To prevent silting-up of the subsoil drainage system by fines washed in from the surrounding soil the pipes should be laid in a selected filter material. This should be continuously-graded and the grading curve should satisfy the following requirements.

$$\frac{15 \text{ per cent size of filter material}}{85 \text{ per cent size of the subgrade soil}} < 5$$

$$\frac{15 \text{ per cent size of filter material}}{15 \text{ per cent size of the subgrade soil}} > 5$$

(By the 15 per cent size is meant that size of particle corresponding to the 15 per cent ordinate of the particle size distribution chart; see Fig. 10.1.)

Consolidation of clay soils

10.83   It follows from Para. 10.78 that if a heavy clay soil in moisture equilibrium with a water table is loaded at the surface then the overburden pressure at any point within the soil will be increased by the loading pressure applied and as a consequence the suction will be increased in accordance with Eq. (10.15), and the moisture content will be decreased by an amount which can be deduced from the moisture content–suction curve. This process is termed consolidation. Taking again the example of the heavy clay referred to in Fig. 10.23, if an embankment 10 m high were constructed on the surface of the soil, with the water table maintained at a depth of

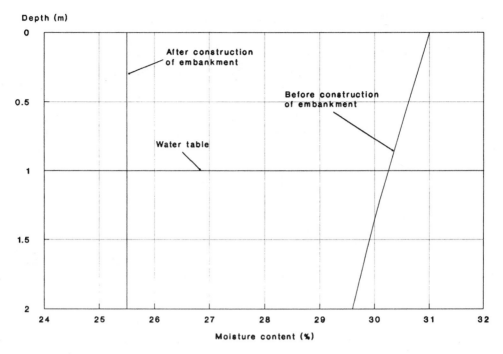

Figure 10.25 Change in moisture distribution in clay soil due to a 10-m embankment construction

1 m, then the average suction in the soil would increase to 2200 cm of water, and Fig. 10.25 indicates a fall in moisture content from about 31.0 per cent to 25.5 per cent. The corresponding reduction of 5 per cent would result in a settlement of about 200 mm in the 2 m of soil.

10.84 Consolidation can be estimated more simply from the laboratory consolidation test in which a disc of the soil mounted between ceramic porous plates is progressively loaded and the change of thickness measured. Full details of the method are given in BS 1377:1975, Test 17, AASHTO T216-83, and ASTM D2430-80. An indication of the rate of consolidation can also be obtained from this test by studying the consolidation–time relationship. However, such one-dimensional tests generally overestimate the settlement time when compared with field observations. In the case of embankments placed on compressible soils, most of the settlement occurs during the construction phase and settlement after paving is small. However, it may become apparent where embankments meet piled structures such as bridge abutments. Surcharging is sometimes used to accelerate settlement at such points. The construction of cuttings in heavy clay soils results in a release of overburden and some upward movement due to swelling of the soil must be expected. This can affect measurements during setting-out.

The effect of climate on the moisture distribution of soil

Influence of rainfall and evaporation

10.85   The two factors evaporation and rainfall largely determine the moisture condition of a soil in the field. Figure 10.26, which relates (a) and (b) to an area of grassland in southern England, close to London Airport (Heathrow) illustrate this point. For a number of years in the fifties the moisture condition of the silty clay, both exposed and beneath concrete pavements, was studied in relation to climatic factors and the level of the water table.[1] The results shown refer to two consecutive years, 1954 and 1955. The first was one of unusually high summer rainfall and the second was normal in this respect. Throughout 1954, rainfall exceeded evaporation except for a short period between mid-June and mid-July, and there was very little seasonal drying and the water table remained at a depth of 3 m. During 1955 evaporation exceeded rainfall during the period June to September and the moisture content of the top 0–600 mm of soil was reduced by about 12 per cent and at a depth of 900–1200 mm the reduction was 3 per cent. This reduction of moisture content was accompanied by a fall of the water-table of about 300 mm. This illustrates that even in temperate climates the annual moisture balance between rainfall and evaporation can have a major effect on earthwork construction and subgrade preparation. Figure 10.27 shows the distribution of moisture content with depth in February 1955 and September 1955 under grass cover and for comparison is shown the distribution in November 1955 under an adjacent concrete slab laid several years earlier. A similar distribution was reached under another concrete slab laid when the soil was very dry, as in September 1955. However, in this case the change in moisture content to the equilibrium condition was very slow and was completed only after 5–6 years. This was attributed to the very low permeability of the dry soil.

10.86   In an attempt to generalize the conclusions from this work to a wide range of climatic conditions a concurrent programme of tests was started at 10 airfields widely distributed in tropical and semitropical situations. Monthly measurements of moisture content were made at different depths both in uncovered soil and under runways or taxiways for a period of about 2 years.[7] Details were obtained of rainfall, evaporation, and temperature at all the sites. It was found that where the water table was within 10 m of the surface the theoretical methods of calculating the equilibrium moisture distribution under the pavement could be applied, and the moisture distribution in uncovered soil was determined by the moisture balance between rainfall and evaporation. Where the water table was deeper, generally in very arid areas, the moisture distribution with depth was similar under the pavement and in the uncovered soil, and both appeared to be controlled by the atmospheric humidity. Two cases of a high water table (1–2 m) were found where the rainfall was negligible. In these cases the high water table was found to arise from the proximity of the sea or of a river. No conclusive evidence emerged to indicate a buildup of moisture beneath pavements as a result of water vapour movements caused by temperature differences. The depth of the water table affected the magnitude of 'edge effects' resulting from the migration of water from the verges of paved areas and confirmed

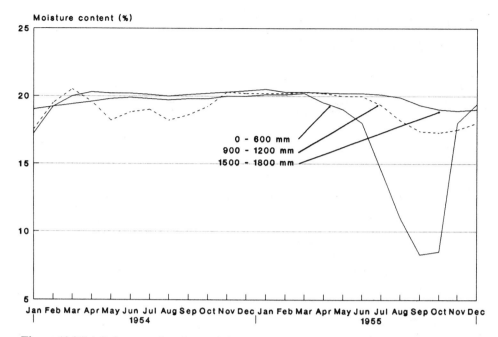

Figure 10.26(a) Influence of moisture balance on the moisture distribution in a silty clay soil—moisture content variation

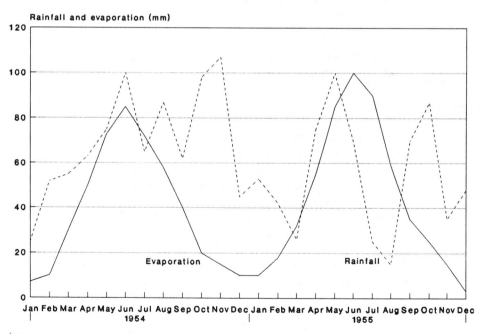

Figure 10.26(b) Influence of moisture balance on the moisture distribution in a silty clay soil—moisture balance

145

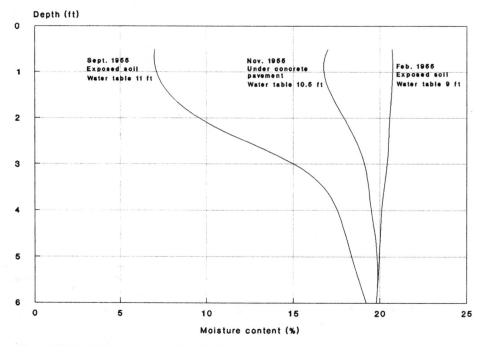

Figure 10.27 Moisture content distribution with depth in silty clay soil at a site near London Airport (Heathrow)

the importance of impermeable shoulders in maintaining equilibrium moisture conditions under pavements.

Frost heave in soils

10.87 Some soils and certain granular materials are susceptible to frost heave as the zero isotherm passes through the road structure into the subgrade. This heave, particularly if it is not uniform over the area of the pavement, is likely to cause cracking. However, more important is the fact that after the thaw the pavement foundation may be left in a very weak state and be subject to rapid breakup under traffic. The thermodynamics of the freezing process in moist porous materials are now fairly clearly understood.[8] At temperatures above freezing point, the water in such materials has a negative pressure or suction which results from the surface tension and adsorption forces by which the water is retained (see Paras 10.82–10.85). This suction increases rapidly with decreasing moisture content, and for this reason it is often expressed in terms of the logarithmic pF scale on which the common logarithm of the suction expressed in centimetres of water is equivalent to the pF value. If the temperature of the material is reduced a little below the freezing point of free water, water within the pores freezes until the suction of the water left unfrozen rises to a value which inhibits further freezing at that temperature. There is thus a relation between the temperature depression below 0°C and the suction of the unfrozen water. This relation, in terms of the pF scale, is

$$pF = 4.095 + \log t \qquad (10.16)$$

where t is the temperature depression. This relationship is shown in Fig. 10.28.

10.88   It follows that if soil or any other porous material in hydrostatic equilibrium with its surroundings is affected by local freezing then the equilibrium will be disturbed and there will be a tendency for water to move towards the freezing zone, defined as the zone in which temperatures are below 0°C. The significance of the moisture movement can best be discussed in terms of the physical properties of typical road foundations.

10.89   Figure 10.29(a) shows the distribution of temperature with depth in late January 1963, beneath a concrete pavement in southern England. The water table at this site was at a depth of about 1.8 m, and prior to freezing the negative pore-water pressure of the soil below the pavement was in approximate equilibrium with this level of water table. The equilibrium suction expressed on the pF scale is shown in Fig. 10.29(b). The relationship shown in Fig. 10.28 can be used to estimate the effect on the pore-water pressure distribution of the temperature gradient of Fig. 10.29(a), as shown in Fig. 10.29(b). Above the level of the zero isotherm there is a rapid increase in suction to a value between 10 and 100 times that below the freezing zone. This suction gradient will tend to draw water from the unfrozen soil into the freezing

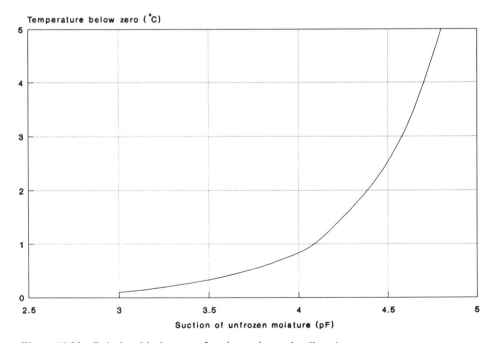

Figure 10.28   Relationship between freezing point and soil moisture suction

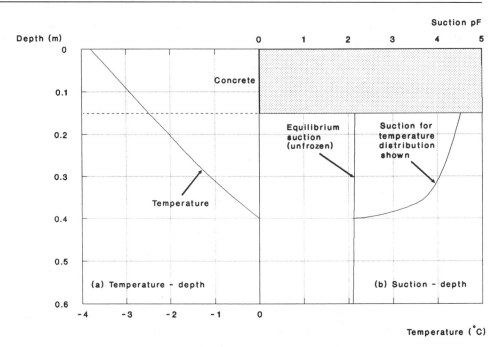

Figure 10.29   Temperature distribution and suction beneath a concrete road, January 1963

zone to form ice lenses and give rise to frost heave. The distribution of suction below the freezing zone shown in Fig. 10.29(b) would of course be modified by any flow of moisture arising from the suction gradients.

10.90   In the frost heave process the suction developed in the freezing zone provides the necessary pressure gradient to cause moisture flow. The rate at which the associated moisture migration occurs depends on the resistance to flow and hence on the prevailing permeability. Two permeabilities are involved: that of the unfrozen material through which the water must pass and that of the freezing front, defined arbitrarily as the thin boundary layer of the frozen zone. The exact mechanism involved in the formation of ice lenses is still a matter of conjecture. However, it is generally agreed that ice crystals form in the soil pores close to the boundary of the frozen zone and that these crystals grow from water drawn through what has been defined here as the freezing front. If the permeability of the unfrozen material is too low to permit any significant movement of water under the pressure gradient prevailing, heave cannot occur. Within the freezing front the permeability is controlled by the amount of water unfrozen at the prevailing temperature. Figure 10.21 shows relationships between suction and moisture content for two granular and three clay soils. For the suction between pF 3 and pF 4 prevailing in the proximity of the zero isotherm the heavy clay would contain about 25 per cent of unfrozen water, the silty clay 12 per cent and the sand about 2 per cent. The very small amount of unfrozen water in clean granular soils renders those materials virtually impermeable to moisture flow through the freezing front, so that frost heave in such materials is inhibited. In heavy clays, despite the relatively large proportion of unfrozen water, the natural permeability is in general too low to allow significant upward migration of water through the material during the relatively short periods of freezing associated with British winters.

10.91   Therefore, it would be expected that if clay fines were added to a clean granular material then the liability of the composite material to frost heave would increase up to an optimum fines content. Beyond this point the addition of more clay would decrease the permeability in the soil below the zero isotherm and cause a progressive reduction of heave. The results of experiments to verify this are shown in Fig. 10.30. A clay soil, with a clay content of 60 per cent and liquid and plastic limit values of 78 and 26 per cent respectively, was dried and ground and mixed with a fine, single-size sand to give the required proportions. Moisture was added during the mixing and the samples were compacted to the maximum dry density and optimum moisture content for standard compaction (2.5-kg rammer). The samples were tested for frost heave using the procedure described below. The heave shows a marked peak when plotted either against the percentage in the mix passing the 75-μm sieve or the percentage of clay particles (finer than 0.002 mm).

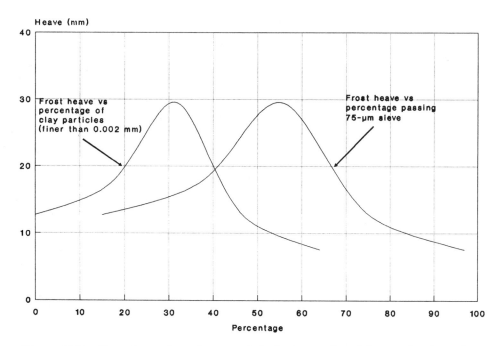

Figure 10.30 Frost heave for mixtures of single-size sand and heavy clay in various proportions

The British test for frost susceptibility

10.92   The test used in Britain to assess frost susceptibility[10] is based on one originally developed in the United States by Taber.[9] Compacted cylindrical samples, 102 mm in diameter and 152 mm long, of the material under test are frozen from one end while the other is in contact with water maintained at a constant temperature of +4°C. The samples are usually compacted at the optimum moisture content and maximum dry density of the standard compaction test (see Para. 10.57), although for some clays the natural (as-dug) moisture content is used with compaction to five per cent air voids.

10.93   Figure 10.31 shows the test cabinet, which is designed to accommodate nine specimens. After compaction and extrusion the curved surface is covered with waxed paper, end faces being left uncovered. The specimens are than placed in metal carriers provided with a porous ceramic base, which is in contact with water in a base tank when the samples are lowered into the test cabinet. The water in this tank is maintained at 4°C during the test. The samples are surrounded by dry sand which extends to the upper face of the samples. The top face of each sample is covered by a waxed disc, supporting a light brass pushrod operating through a metal bar fixed to the top of the cabinet. The heave is recorded from the movement of the top of the pushrod.

10.94   After equilibriating at room temperature for 24 hours, the cabinet is transferred to a cold room operating at a constant temperature of −17°C. Heave is recorded daily for a total period of not less than 250 hours, and the heave–time curve is plotted for each sample. It is important to realize that this test is not intended to simulate practice. The high water-table (approximately 70 mm below the level of the zero isotherm) represents a very severe condition. Furthermore, the specimens are allowed during freezing to rise above the level of the surrounding sand fill and for this reason the zero isotherm is falling throughout the test with respect to the top of the samples. (However, heaving is stopped immediately if the sand level is brought up to the level of the samples at any time during the test period.) Therefore, the test, as normally carried out, is assessing the combined permeability through the freezing front and in the unfrozen part of the specimen. These are the factors which control whether or not heave will occur in practice in relation to the length of the cold spell. Typical test results are shown in Fig. 10.32. The silty clay soil (brickearth) has sufficient fines to depress the freezing point in the freezing front and allow water to pass through to form ice lenses, and the soil beneath the freezing zone is sufficiently permeable to permit an upward movement of water from the water table. The result is considerable heave after 250 hours. The London Clay, on the other hand, will permit water to pass through the freezing front but the low permeability in the bulk of the material severely restricts the upward movement of water. The importance of the bulk permeability is illustrated in this example by the inclusion of a comparatively thin layer of London Clay between the brickearth and the water table. This considerably reduces the heave in the composite sample.

10.95   During very severe British winters, which occur on average at 10-yearly intervals, the test has been applied to soils and granular materials which have been

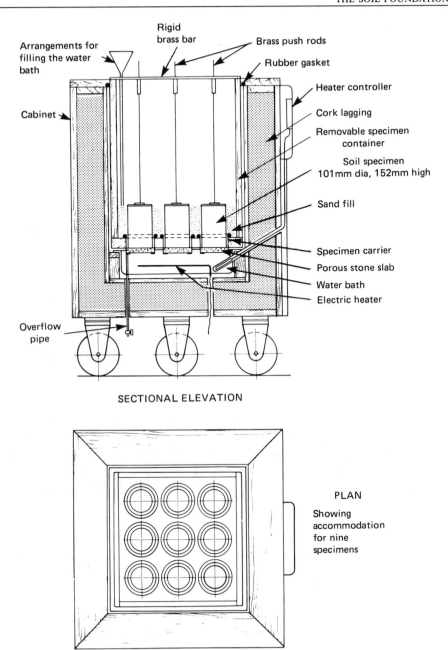

Arrangements for filling the water bath

Rigid brass bar

Brass push rods

Rubber gasket

Cabinet

Heater controller

Cork lagging

Removable specimen container

Soil specimen 101mm dia, 152mm high

Sand fill

Specimen carrier

Porous stone slab

Water bath

Electric heater

Overflow pipe

SECTIONAL ELEVATION

PLAN

Showing accommodation for nine specimens

Figure 10.31   Details of frost heave cabinet

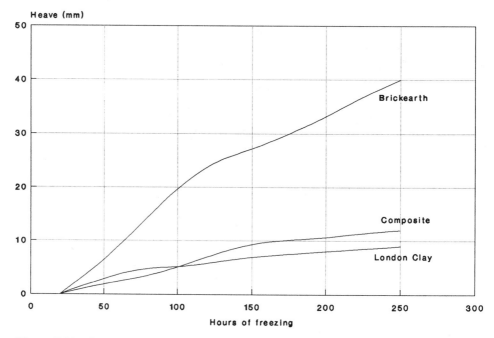

Figure 10.32   Comparison of heaves in silty clay and heavy clay soils with heave in composite sample

involved in cases of severe frost damage to roads, and to others where there has been little or no heave or damage. From this work it was concluded that materials which heaved 13 mm or less during a 250-hour test period were satisfactory, that materials which heaved between 13 mm and 18 mm were marginally frost-susceptible, and that those which heaved more than 18 mm should be classified as frost-susceptible. Since a main function of a sub-base is to replace frost-susceptible soil the same criteria were subsequently applied to sub-base and road base materials.

10.96   Table 10.8 shows the frost heaves recorded at 250 hours on five heavy clay soils of plasticity index within the range 35–54 per cent. These measurements and others obtained for silty and sandy clay soils with plasticity indices between 8 and 20 per cent have been used to relate frost heave with plasticity index as shown in Figure 10.33. In the case of non-cohesive soils, frost heave has been related to the percentage of fine particles present. Table 10.9 relates the frost heave at 250 hours with the percentage of particles passing the 75-μm and 600-μm sieve for eight silty sand soils. Figure 10.34 shows there is good correlation with the percentage passing the 75-μm sieve but none in the case of the 600-μm sieve. Figures 10.33 and 10.34 will permit a preliminary judgement to be made as to whether a soil is likely to be frost-susceptible, but in the case of materials which appear to be marginal a test should be carried out.

Table 10.8   Frost heave measured on five heavy clay soils

Soil	Index tests			Particle size		Sample compaction		
	LL %	PL %	PI %	Passing 75 µm sieve %	Clay content %	Dry density kg/m³	Moisture content %	Heave at 250 hours mm
Keuper marl	63	29	34	—	—	1 520	29	12.5
London Clay (2)	78	24	54	98	58	1 568	24	9.7
Oxford Clay	69	23	46	99	66	1 360	32	10.2
Black cotton soil	103	43	60	91	67	1 120	45	8.4
London Clay (1)	75	23	52	99	62	1 664	20	5.1

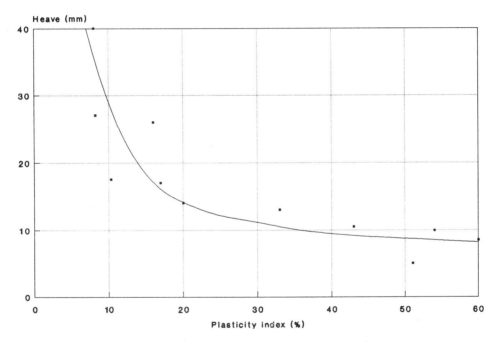

Figure 10.33   Relationship between frost heave and plasticity index for cohesive soils

10.97   Chalks and soft oolitic limestones are liable to be frost-susceptible, owing to the high permeability of the parent rock, and their use at depths likely to be affected by frost must be avoided. Various additives including cement have been found to reduce frost heave. Chemicals such as calcium lignosulphonate and sodium tripolyphosphate will inhibit frost heave with concentrations of 0.5 per cent by weight. However, the use in practice of such chemicals is unlikely to be economic.

Table 10.9 Frost heave measured on eight non-cohesive soils

Soil number	Percentage by weight passing		Frost heave mm
	75-μm sieve	600-μm sieve	
1	2	96	2.5
2	3	18	5.1
3	2	36	6.4
4	11	40	18
5	18	77	18
6	17	99	22
7	14	93	25
8	26	67	41

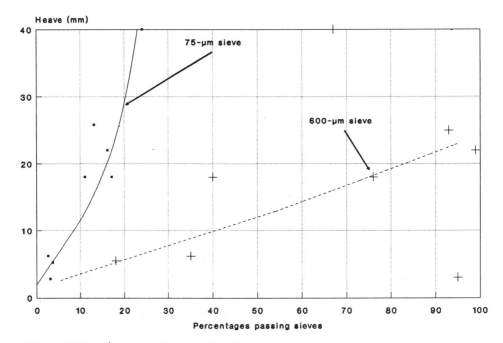

Figure 10.34 Relationship between frost heave and percentages passing the 75- and 600-micron sieves

Frost penetration

10.98   The magnitude of frost heave depends on both the depth and the rate of frost penetration. Figure 10.35 compares the frost penetration at Ottawa, Illinois, during the winter 1958–9 with the penetration measured near Heathrow, London, in the winter of 1962–3. The Illinois measurements were made in connection with the

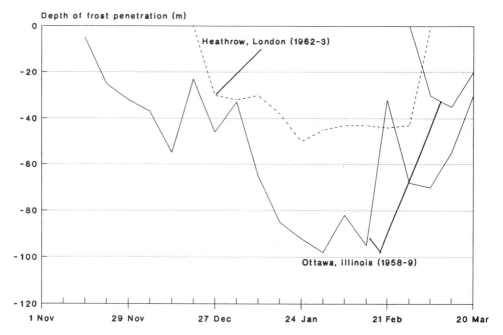

Figure 10.35   Frost penetration under concrete at Ottawa, Illinois, 1958–9, and at Heathrow, London, 1962–3

AASHO road test (1958–60) conducted at that site. The winter of 1958–9 at that site was somewhat colder than average, but the Heathrow measurements were made during what proved to be the coldest winter for about 15 years. The rate of frost penetration is slower and the frost penetration much deeper at the Illinois site than at Heathrow. The soils at the two sites were not dissimilar (Illinois: liquid limit 30 per cent, plastic limit 13 per cent; Heathrow: liquid limit 28 per cent, plastic limit 18 per cent). The water table level at the Illinois site was about 1.2 m below pavement level and at the Heathrow site it was about 2.7 m. At neither site would the soil be regarded as other than marginally frost-susceptible. The heave measured at Illinois was about 11 mm, compared with about 7 mm at Heathrow, and in this respect the results appear to be consistent. At neither site would the heave have caused any apparent deterioration of the pavement, but at both sites a marked loss of strength was indicated by deflection measurements made after the thaw.

10.99   In the UK frost penetration very rarely exceeds 450 mm and for some years it has been normal practice to replace any frost-susceptible soil within that depth range with non-frost-susceptible sub-base material. However, consideration is now being given to modifying this requirement for areas where less severe frost penetration is expected. Whether the construction cost savings justify the risks which may be involved remains to be seen.

10.100   Since the fifties the concept of frost index has been used to express the severity of very cold periods. The frost index is defined as the product of the number of freezing days and the average daily air temperature below 0 °C. Thus two consecutive days each with an average daily air temperature of −2 °C would represent a frost index of 4 °C days. A summation of this type based on daily 24-hour air temperatures during a continuous cold spell will give the frost index for that period. A paper by Johnson, Beck, *et al.* of the US Army Corps of Engineers quoted by Sherwood and Roe[11] has related the frost penetration to the frost index for a range of different types of soil (see Fig. 10.36). This gives a useful broad guide to possible frost penetrations. The frost index for the cold period in the winter of 1962–3 referred to in Fig. 10.35 has been calculated from available meteorological data to be approximately 102. Figure 10.36 indicates that for this index the frost penetration in the silty sand at the site would be 390 mm. This does not agree very well with the measured value of 500 mm. The latter figure corresponds more closely with the anticipated penetration in gravel and sand. However, it may well be that the penetration at the site was increased by the presence of the 150-mm concrete pavement.

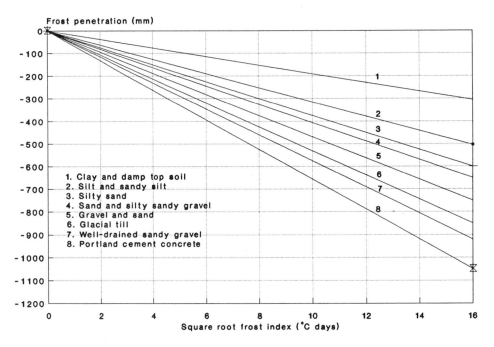

Figure 10.36 Relationship between frost index and frost penetration into snow-free homogenous materials

The strength of soil

General

10.101   The shear strength of soil is generally expressed in the following form:

$$s = c + \sigma_n \tan \phi$$

where $s =$ the shear strength,
  $c =$ the cohesion
  $\phi =$ the angle of shearing resistance
  $\sigma_n =$ the stress normal to the shear plane

For cohesive soils the shear strength is determined indirectly by triaxial compression tests carried out under the appropriate conditions of drainage. Such tests are described in AASHTO Test T234-85 (ASTM Designation D2850-70), and in less detail in BS 1377:1975, Test 21.

10.102   In clay soils free of stones, direct measurements of shear strength can be made using the rotating field vane, in which a small cruciform vane is pushed into the soil and the shear stress calculated from the torque required to rotate it. This test is described in ASSHTO Designation T233-76 (1981) or BS 1377:1975, Test 18. For coarse cohesive soils large shear boxes are generally used.

Stability of slopes of cuttings and embankments

10.103   In designing slope angles for cuttings and embankments, it is normally assumed that failure occurs on a circular arc, and that it develops when the moment tending to cause rotation of the soil mass cannot be resisted by the shear strength of the soil acting round the slip circle. In considering the stability of earth dams, where the risks involved in failure are so great, a great deal of analytical work relating to safe slopes is essential. The number of cuttings and embankments in modern road projects precludes a similar detailed analysis, particularly where soil conditions are far from homogeneous. Slopes are therefore based on experience and the generalized findings of research.

10.104   In 1937 Taylor produced a simple design procedure for slope angles in terms of c and ϕ. This was based on total stress and the role of the water table was not considered. In 1960 Bishop and Morgenstern[12] produced a similar analysis based on effective stress, in a form particularly suited to computer analysis. Symons[13] has since published a relation between life and critical slope for clay cuttings of various heights. The results, which provide a useful basis for the design of clay slopes, are shown in Fig. 10.37. A recent survey of slope behaviour on the motorway system of the UK[14] has enabled a number of useful conclusions to be reached relating long-term slope stability and soil type. The conclusions relating to slope angles and soil types are summarized in Table 10.10.

10.105   Cuttings and embankments in granular soils present no serious problems and slopes of 1:1.5 will normally be adequate for all heights. For sandy and silty

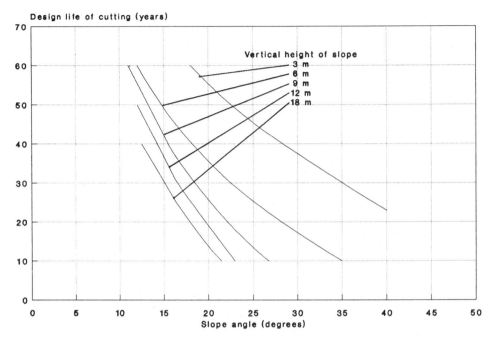

Figure 10.37   Relations between design life and slope angle for overconsolidated clay cuttings

Table 10.10 Geologies with a high percentage of failure

Geology	Percentage of failure	Predominant slope angle
Embankments		
Gault Clay	8.2	1:2.5
Reading Beds	7.6	1:2
Kimmeridge Clay	6.1	1:2
Oxford Clay	5.7	1:2
Lower Keuper Sandstone	4.9	1:1.5
London Clay	4.4	1:2
Cuttings		
Gault Clay	9.6	1:2.5
Enville Beds	5.8	1:2.5
Oxford Clay	3.2	1:2
Reading Beds	2.9	1:3
Bunter Pebble Beds	2.3	1:2
Lower Old Red Sandstone—St Maughan's Group	1.7	1:2

clay soils the slope angle widely used is between 1:2 and 1:1.5, depending on the plasticity of the soil and the height.

10.106   Although cuttings in chalk and soft limestones give the appearance of stability when nearly vertical, such slopes are subject to frost errosion. Slopes in such materials should not be steeper than $50°$, to allow vegetation to establish itself. Even with such a slope, provision should be made by fencing to catch any debris loosened by frost. Most slips which occur in highway embankments are surface slides which arise mainly from water entering poorly compacted soil on the face of the slopes. In the construction of embankments particular care should be taken in the edge compaction as the layers of the embankment are constructed. Vegetation helps to stabilize all slopes, but on clay embankments the vegetation should not be deep-rooted.

10.107   Where an area has a history of landslides, or where roads are to be cut in side-long ground, the engineer is advised to have a thorough geological examination of the site made before deciding on the line and level of the road.

The strength of subgrades

10.108   A well-designed flexible road pavement would be expected to show a permanent deformation of little more than 20–30 mm after a life of 20 years. The deformation in the subgrade would then be less than 10 mm corresponding perhaps to the passage of 100 million standard axles. It follows that under the imposed stress regime the soil needs to behave elastically, and that shear strength is not directly the factor which defines a satisfactory subgrade. In designing a pavement structurally the elastic modulus of the subgrade and its Poisson ratio are the foundation properties needed. However, these are complex properties to measure, and, bearing in mind the variability of soils over comparatively small distances, it would not be economically feasible to use them directly to assess subgrade suitability. It follows therefore that if pavements are designed empirically on past experience or fundamentally using elastic theory, a relatively simple test procedure is needed, the results of which can be related by experiment to the structural properties.

The California bearing ratio test

10.109   Various penetration type tests were developed in the USA for evaluating soils, the most enduring of which has been the California bearing ratio (CBR) test, which dates from the twenties and was adapted by the US Corps of Engineers for airfield design in the early forties. The CBR test seems to have been first used in the California State Highways Department by O. J. Porter, Engineer to the Department. Like many tests developed and modified over a long period, the method of sample preparation and testing varied considerably in the early years and Mr Porter's papers are not precise, particularly relating to when and whether samples were soaked prior to testing and at what stage and under what conditions measurements *in situ* were permitted to be used.

10.110   During the Second World War the method was introduced into Britain in connection with airfield construction and immediately after the war it began to be used in road design. From Britain its use has spread to a number of European countries. Because of ambiguities in the test procedure, the decision was taken in the UK to test samples at the dry density and moisture content likely to be achieved in the field, without soaking. For clay soils, where the mould confinement had little effect on the measured value, an *in situ* rig was developed to monitor *in situ* the subgrade during construction. Where time allowed the relationships between CBR, dry density, and moisture content were studied for the principal soils of a contract.

10.111   The equipment and test procedure are described in detail in BS 1377:1975, Test 16, and under AASHTO Designation T193-81 (1986). The equipment is of the form and dimensions shown in Fig. 10.38. The soil under test is compacted into the mould at the moisture content and dry density which it is estimated will be achieved in the prepared subgrade, and the penetration test is carried out at the standard rate. A loading frame is used to give the necessary reaction and a proving ring measures the load.

10.112   Typical load–penetration curves are shown in Fig. 10.39. The loads required to cause penetrations of 2.5 mm and 5 mm are recorded and expressed as ratios of the loads to cause the same penetrations in a 'standard' crushed rock material, the load–penetration curve for which is also included in Fig. 10.39. For

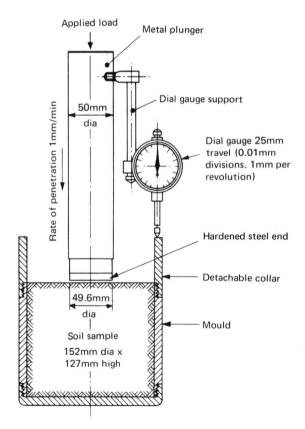

California bearing ratio test equipment

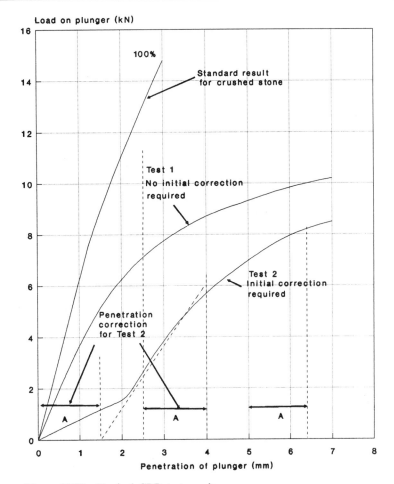

Figure 10.39   Typical CBR test results

various reasons the initial part of the penetration curve may be concave, as shown
for Test 2 in the diagram. In such a case the load–penetration curve is projected back
to the horizontal axis, as shown on the figure, to give the intercept A. This intercept
is added to the standard penetrations of 2.5 and 5 mm when evaluating the loads
equivalent to those penetrations for the material under test. No such addition is of
course made in obtaining the corresponding loads for the standard crushed stone
material. The larger of the ratios corresponding to the 2.5 and 5 mm penetrations is
normally taken as the CBR value of the material for the test conditions used. The
test is usually carried out on materials with a maximum particle size of 20 mm. If
the material to be tested contains 10 per cent or less by weight coarser than 20 mm
then this fraction can be removed without seriously underestimating the strength of
the soil. The test is not really suitable for soils or other materials containing more

than 10 per cent coarser than 20 mm. However, under such circumstances tests on the fraction passing 20 mm carried out at a range of moisture contents will give an indication of whether the material as a whole will lose strength markedly if the moisture content is raised.

10.113   The use of a standard curve for crushed rock arises from the fact that the test was originally designed to assess the quality of fine crushed-rock base materials in the state of California. At a later stage, when the test was used on subgrades, this method of expressing the results was continued, so that the majority of clay soils in their natural conditions have a CBR value less than 10 per cent.

10.114   Just before the Second World War two tentative design thickness curves for pavements with crushed stone bases were in use in the USA in conjunction with the CBR test. These were based on tests made on a variety of existing pavements judged to have reached a critical structural condition. The two existing curves represented 'heavy' and 'light' traffic conditions, expressed in terms of the maximum wheel loads likely to use the two categories of road. A few years later this enabled the Boussinesq equations for vertical stress to be used to extrapolate these design curves to cover the much higher wheel loads associated with military aircraft. These curves were modified after full-scale experimental checks.

10.115   After the war it was decided to adopt the CBR test as the basis for the design of flexible pavements in Britain. Because of uncertainties relating to the exact test procedure and to the method used to ascribe wheel loads to the original curves, the decision was taken to prepare new design curves linked to CBR tests carried out at the equilibrium moisture content and dry density conditions expected under the road pavement. A programme of testing on existing roads together with a measure of extrapolation led to the curves shown in Fig. 10.40 based on the traffic intensity expected to use the road. These curves were used to give the total thickness of pavement required, the constitution in terms of sub-base, roadbase, and surfacing being established from a comprehensive programme of full-scale road experiments. This procedure remains the basis of the current design for flexible pavements used in the UK.

10.116   A study has been made by E. H. Davis of the influence of dry density and moisture content on the CBR of a wide range of soils from a heavy clay to a sandy gravel.[15] The gradings of the soils are shown in Fig. 10.41 and the results of classification tests in Table 10.11. The relations between CBR, moisture content, and dry density for soils A, B, C and D are given in Fig. 10.42.

10.117   Figure 10.42 shows that the relationship between log CBR moisture content is linear over the likely field moisture content range. Exactly what shapes the curves are, as they approach the saturation line, is difficult to explore experimentally. They appear to join the saturation line but it is more likely that they drop vertically as the pore water pressure becomes positive with respect to atmospheric pressure. This is not a matter of particular concern.

10.118   An engineer preparing designs for pavement thickness should, at the site investigation stage, have CBR–moisture content–dry density curves such as those shown in Fig. 10.42, prepared for the principal soils on the site. Then, on the basis

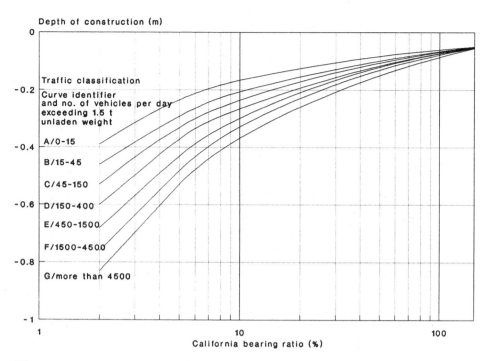

Figure 10.40 CBR design curves for different classes of road

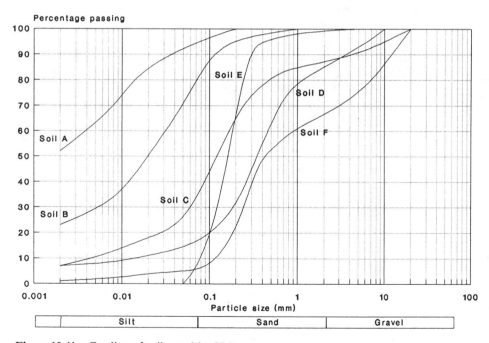

Figure 10.41 Grading of soils used in CBR test programmes

163

Table 10.11   Details of four soils used in CBR investigation

Soil	Location	Liquid limit, %	Plasticity Index %	Specific gravity of soil	BS compaction test	
					Maximum dry density, kg/m³	Optimum moisture content, %
Heavy clay	Staines, Middx.	75	42	2.76	1554	26
Sandy clay	Harmondsworth, Middx.	31	11	2.76	1794	16
Silty clay	Rippon, Yorks.	24	3	2.62	1874	13
Well-graded sand	Heritingforbury, Herts.		Non-plastic	2.70	2002	10

of the moisture content and density requirements specified by the engineer for the subgrade, it will be possible to deduce the CBR value and design the pavement accordingly.

Estimation of the CBR from soil properties

10.119   Black, regarding the CBR test as a bearing capacity test using a small plate,[16,17] produced a method for relating the CBR of soils with their bearing capacity and for cohesive soils with the consistency index and the suction. From the suction curves for a wide range of British soils he related the consistency index (see Para. 10.39) of remoulded soils with the suction in the manner shown in Fig. 10.43. Using the bearing capacity approach, he then related the plasticity index and the consistency index as in Fig. 10.44.)

10.120   To illustrate the use of these graphs the case will be considered of a pavement 550 mm thick on a soil of plasticity index 30 per cent with a water table 600 mm below formation level. The average density of the pavement material is assumed to be twice that of water. If we refer to Table 10.7 for a soil of plasticity index 30 per cent, then the value of the compressibility factor α will be 0.7. From Eq. (10.15),

$$u = s + \alpha P$$

at formation level, with the water table 60 cm below, $u = -60$ cm of water,

$$\alpha P = 2 \times 55 \times 0.7 \text{ cm of water}$$
$$\text{thus } s = 77 + 60 = 137 \text{ cm of water.}$$

From Fig. 10.43, for a suction of 137 cm of water the consistency index is 0.92, and from Fig. 10.44 the CBR is approximately 3 per cent.

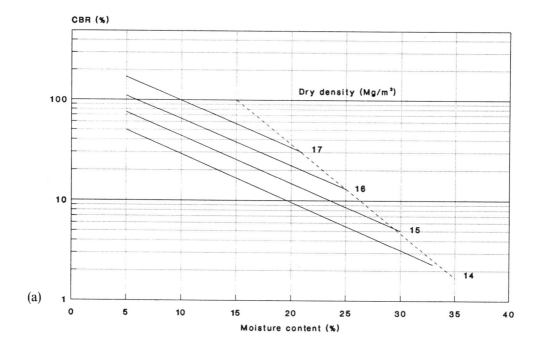

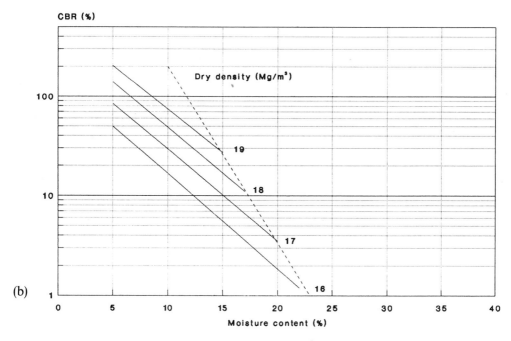

Figure 10.42 Laboratory measurements relating CBR, moisture content, and dry density for (a) a heavy clay (soil A); (b) a silty clay (soil B)

165

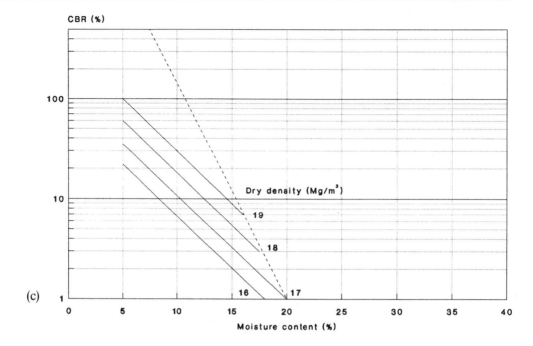

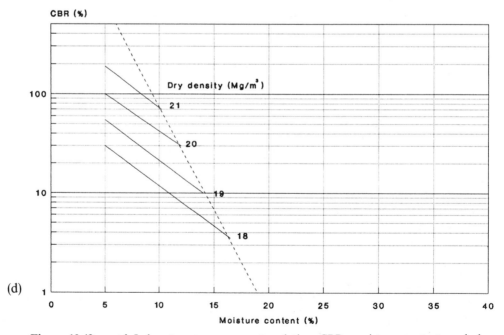

Figure 10.42–*contd*–Laboratory measurements relating CBR, moisture content, and dry density for (c) a silty sand (soil C) and (d) a well-graded sand (soil D)

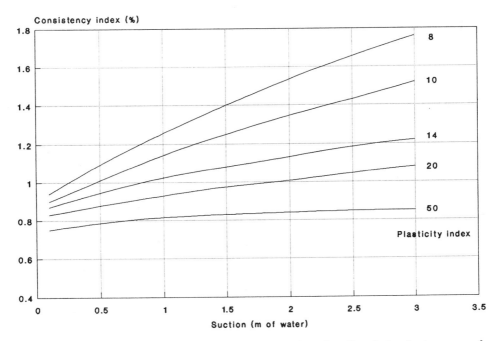

Figure 10.43 Variation of consistency index with suction of undisturbed soil at a range of plasticity indexes

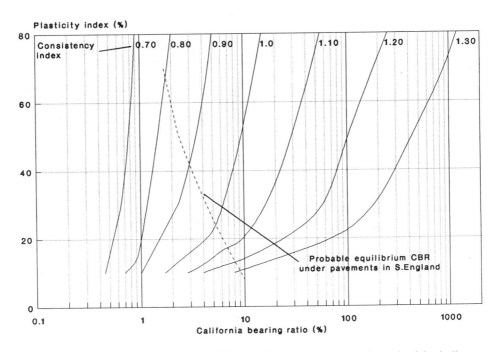

Figure 10.44 Relationship between CBR and plasticity index at various plasticity indices

167

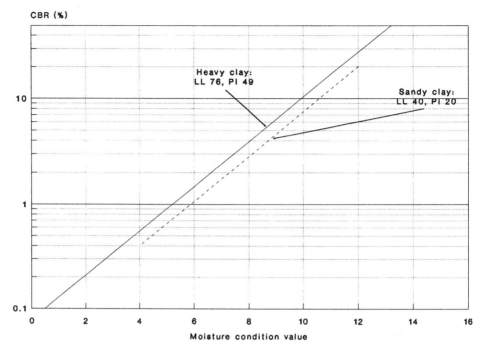

Figure 10.45 Theoretical relationship between CBR and moisture condition value

In situ CBR tests

10.121 The CBR test can be carried out *in situ* and rigs to fit at the rear of suitably loaded site vehicles are available. The degree of confinement of the soil in laboratory tests and in those conducted *in situ* is clearly different. This influences the stress distribution under the plunger, and the load–penetration curves. For heavy clays and for other cohesive soils having an air content of 5 per cent or more, the difference between the results of laboratory tests and those of tests *in situ* is small. For other cohesive soils and most granular materials the difference is much larger and tests *in situ* should not be used to verify the quality of workmanship in relation to specification requirements.

Relationship between CBR and moisture condition value MCV

10.122 Parsons has published the relationships shown in Fig. 10.45 between CBR and MCV (see Paras 10.64–10.72).[18] They relate only to cohesive soils. Where MCV tests are included in a site investigation report these relationships give a useful indication of the CBR values likely to be achieved in subgrades.

Plate bearing test

10.123 Plate loading tests are sometimes specified, particularly in connection with the evaluation of subgrades for concrete pavements. The load–deformation relation-

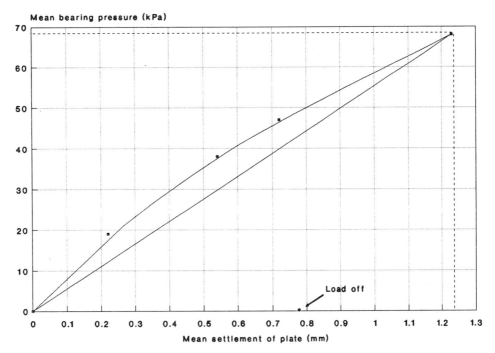

Figure 10.46   Typical result of plate bearing test

ship using a 760 mm diameter plate was used by Westergaard[19] to define what he called the modulus of subgrade reaction, k.

10.124   The standard 760-mm diameter plate is normally about 16 mm thick. To increase the stiffness, plates of 660- and 560-mm diameter are often used on top of the standard plate. A movable trailer, loaded up to 30 tonnes, provides a suitable reaction against which the plate is loaded hydraulically. Care is necessary to seat the plate accurately and hand levelling using a straight-edge is necessary on clay soils. On granular soils which are difficult to level, a thin layer of well-graded sand is used as a bedding. Alternatively, a quick-setting plaster bed a few millimetres thick can be used. Gantries, located as far as possible outside the zone of influence of the plate and the trailer wheels, support dial gauges set to record the plate settlement at four equally spaced locations round the perimeter of the plate. A proving ring, or alternatively the pressure in the hydraulic system, is used to measure the load. Figure 10.46 shows a typical test result. The modulus of subgrade reaction, k, is normally calculated for a mean plate deflection of 1.25 mm. The load–deformation curve is not in general linear and on removal of the load at the completion of a test the greater part of the deflection is found to be non-recoverable, as is indicated on Fig. 10.46. Therefore the test, as normally carried out, is not an elastic one and it cannot be closely related to the elastic modulus of the soil. There is an approximate relationship between the k-value and CBR when the soil is uniform in depth. This empirical relation is shown in Fig. 10.47.

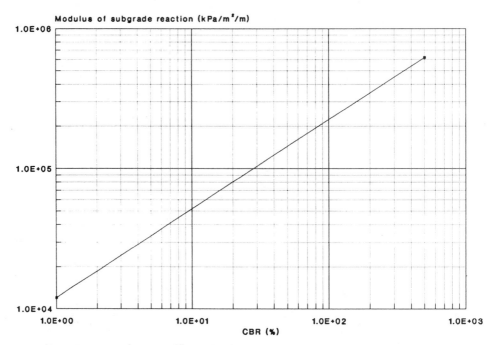

Figure 10.47 Empirical relationship between k-value and CBR

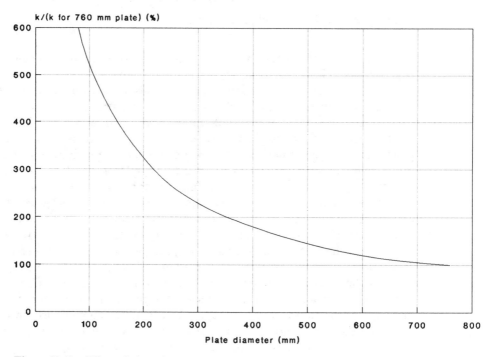

Figure 10.48 Effect of plate size on apparant modulus of subgrade reaction

170

10.125   The value of the modulus of subgrade reaction depends critically on the size of plate used. Clearly, plates smaller than the standard diameter of 760 mm are easier to use and require a smaller loading rig. Figure 10.48 shows a curve based on American experimental evidence relating the measured k-value with plates of various sizes.[20]

The elastic properties of soil

10.126   The thickness requirements which form part of a road construction contract must be specified in terms of subgrade strength tests which can be carried out by both the engineer and the contractor, using equipment which will be normally available in a site laboratory and which can be operated by trained site staff. For this reason pavement design procedures throughout the world have been developed around such tests as the CBR. Such procedures need to be validated by long-term experience before they are adopted. In the UK since the Second World War numerous pavement design experiments have been constructed on heavily trafficked in-service highways and some of these experiments are now more than 30 years old. Such a method of developing pavement design procedures is highly reliable, but it does not lend itself to detailed studies of the influence of changes of subgrade support or of pavement material specifications, beyond those incorporated in the original experiments. For this reason efforts have been made since the twenties to generalize available experience using elastic theory.

10.127   The structural analysis of pavements based on elastic theory requires a knowledge of the elastic modulus and Poisson's ratio of soil foundations and of sub-bases, bases, and surfacing materials. The remainder of this chapter summarizes present knowledge regarding the elastic properties of soils. Similar discussions at the close of Chapters 11–16 deal with the elastic properties of the other constituents of pavements.

Vibration techniques

10.128   In the forties experiments were conducted at the Road Research Laboratory in the UK to measure the elastic modulus of soils by an induced vibration technique. Samples of the soils tested, of 25 mm square section and 100 mm length, were cut using a compression cutter from the soils after compaction by the standard laboratory test (2.5-kg rammer) at a suitable range of moisture contents. The sample beams so prepared were coated with paraffin wax to stop evaporation, and were tested suspended vertically. Vibration was excited by a steel ball falling from a fixed height onto the upper end face and the frequency, n, of the fundamental longitudinal vibration was measured by a pickup coupled electromagnetically to a steel plate stuck to the lower flat face. Young's modulus was calculated from the formula[21]

$$E = \frac{4l^2 n^2 \rho}{\left(1 - \pi^2 v^2 \dfrac{K^2}{2l^2}\right)^2} \qquad (10.17)$$

where ρ = the density of the material

l = the length of the rod

v = Poisson's ratio

K = the radius of gyration of the cross-section of the rod about the longitudinal axis

10.129   Figure 10.49 shows results obtained using this technique on three British clay soils having the plasticity properties indicated. Because of the compaction procedure and the various moisture contents used, the tests do not correspond to constant conditions of dry density. Relationships between CBR and elastic modulus for the same three soils are shown in Fig. 10.50. The CBR values were deduced using Black's method (See paras 10.119 and 10.120).

Wave velocity techniques

10.130   A vibratory impulse acting at a point on the surface of a material infinite and homogeneous with respect to area and depth gives rise to a complex system of vibrations throughout the material. These include Rayleigh waves which are propogated close to the surface. The velocity of the Rayleigh waves in such a material is related theoretically to the shear modulus of the material and this in turn to the Young's modulus, E, and Poisson's ratio, v, of the material. These relation-

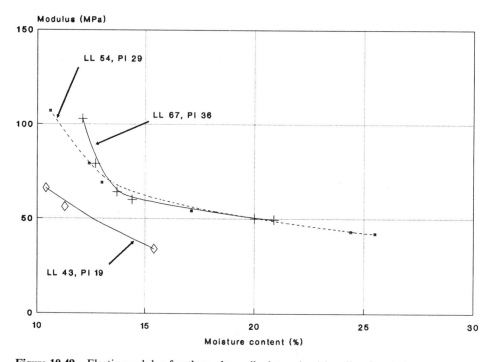

Figure 10.49   Elastic modulus for three clay soils determined by vibration tests

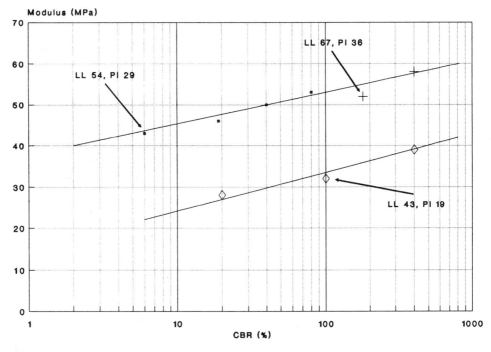

Figure 10.50 Relationship between modulus and CBR for three soils

ships are:

$$V_R^2 = p^2 \cdot g \frac{G}{\rho} \qquad (10.18)$$

where V_R = the velocity of the Rayleigh wave
  ρ = the density of the material
  p = a constant depending on Poisson's ratio, but close to 0.95
  g = the acceleration due to gravity

The modulus of elasticity, E, is obtained from the shear modulus using the equation

$$E = 2(1 + v)G \qquad (10.19)$$

10.131 Jones in the early fifties pioneered the use of this method of testing sub-grades and subsequently roadbases and sub-bases.[22,23] Vibrations are produced by an electromagnetic vibrator driven by a variable-frequency oscillator and a power amplifier of suitable gain. The vibrator is placed on a prepared area of the surface soil, so that close contact is obtained, and a straight line is established extending from the vibrator for a distance of about 10 m. With the vibrator running at a frequency above 40 Hz, a seismic geophone pickup is moved away from the vibrator and successive positions are established along the test line for which the vibrations from the pickup are in phase with those from the vibrator. This condition is indicated on a cathode ray display. The distance between successive points located in this manner is equal to one wavelength and the wave velocity is established from the equation

$$V = nL \qquad (10.20)$$

where n is the frequency of vibrations being used in the test. At frequencies below about 150 Hz the wavelength and phase velocity measured in this way may be distorted by vibration waves other than surface Rayleigh waves. However, as the frequency of the vibrator is increased the phase velocity assumes a constant value corresponding to that of the Rayleigh wave.

10.132   Figure 10.51 shows results obtained between June 1955 and May 1956 on an area of sandy clay which was exposed to the weather, but free of vegetation. The E-values calculated from four sets of measurements are shown in the figure. The suction at the time of the May 1956 measurements was equal to approximately 180 cm of water (pF 2.3). For the earlier three sets of measurements, the suction varied between 30 and 60 cm of water (pF 1.5–1.8).

10.133   More comprehensive tests of this type were subsequently carried out by Jones using the facility, and the four soils, used at the TRRL in the UK for the

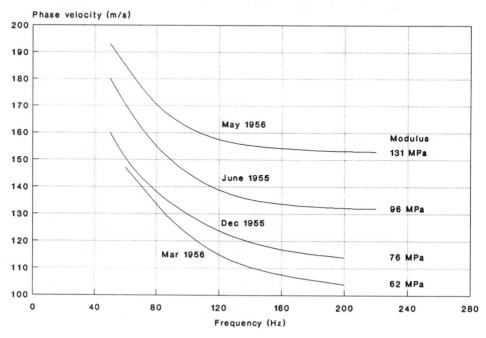

Figure 10.51   Elastic modulus of soil determined from velocity of Rayleigh waves

testing of compaction plant (see Para. 10.61). In this work the elastic modulus deduced using the test procedure described above was related to CBR tests carried out *in situ* on the surface of the soils. The results are shown in Fig. 10.52. The procedure was subsequently used at a number of sites where full-scale pavement design experiments were being constructed. The intention was to provide information on the elastic properties of the soils for use in subsequent structural analyses. Fig. 10.53 shows results from one such experiment. The soil at this site was predominately a heavy clay which included pockets of boulder clay of the same type but with a variable content of stone. The liquid limit of the clay was 62 per cent and the plasticity index 41 per cent. This clay was from the same geological source as soil A in Figs 10.49 and 10.50 and the index test results very similar. The relationship between elastic modulus and CBR shown in Fig. 10.50 is also shown on Fig. 10.53 for comparison.

10.134   Figures 10.52 and 10.53 show that the relationship between CBR *in situ* and modulus of elasticity determined by the wave velocity method falls between straight lines represented by $E = 100$ CBR and $E = 200$ CBR, when E is expressed in kg/cm^2 or approximately $E = 10$ CBR and $E = 20$ CBR when E is expressed in MN/m^2. However, the relationship for more granular soils, again determined in this manner, is not linear and falls below the $E = 100$ CBR line. This applies to the gravel-sand-clay of Fig. 10.52 and to the more stoney boulder clay in Fig. 10.53.

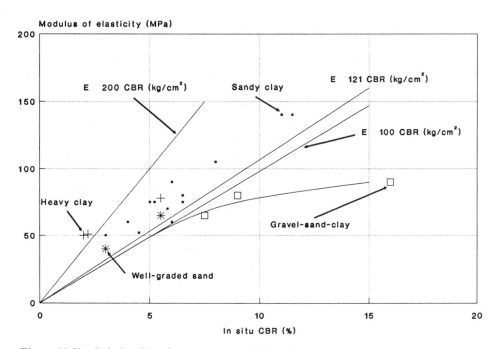

Figure 10.52 Relationships between *in situ* CBR values and modulus of elasticity (wave velocity measurements)

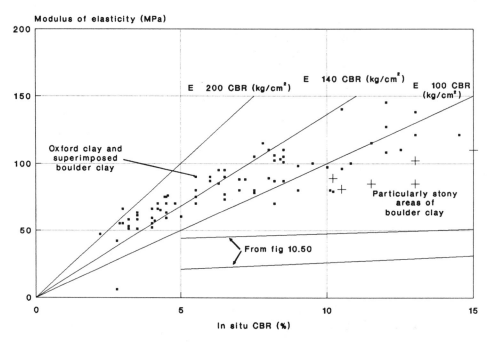

Figure 10.53 Relationship between *in situ* CBR values and modulus of elasticity (wave velocity)—Alconbury Hill

10.135   The comparison included in Fig. 10.53, of the relationship between CBR and elastic modulus determined by the longitudinal vibration and the wave velocity methods on the same cohesive soil, shows no agreement between the two methods despite the fact that the underlying theory is basically similar. The difference probably originates in the much greater strain induced in the longitudinal-vibration technique and suggests that the value of *E* measured decreases with increasing strain. This to a large extent questions the value of wave velocity measurements in the application of elastic theory to the structural design of pavements and has focused attention on the measurement of the elastic properties under strain conditions likely to occur in practice. This is most easily done under triaxial loading conditions.

Repeated loading triaxial tests

10.136   In the early sixties a relatively simple repeated loading triaxial machine was constructed at the Transport and Road Research Laboratory.[24] Both the deviator stress and the cell pressure were pulsed in phase, to simulate the stress conditions in road subgrades. The machine was purely mechanical and was based on the loaded lever and lifting-cam principle.

10.137   Figure 10.54 shows the results of a test made with this machine on remoulded London Clay of liquid limit 76 per cent and plastic limit 27 per cent. The clay was mixed at a moisture content of 40.4 per cent and then recompacted to zero

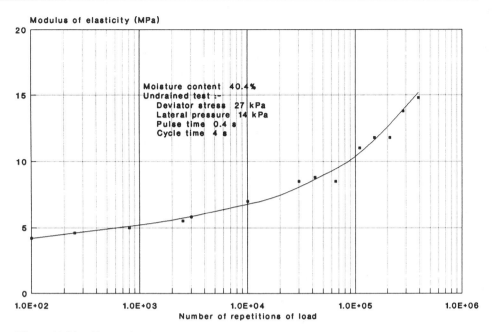

Figure 10.54 Change in elastic modulus of remoulded London Clay with repeated loading

air voids in a standard triaxial mould. As would be expected, the material was very weak when set up in the machine. The test conditions were as shown on the figure. Although the test was undrained, there was a more than threefold increase in the measured modulus between 100 and 400 000 stress applications. The corresponding axial permanent deformation is shown in Fig. 10.55.

10.138 This test was carried out to illustrate some of the difficulties which can arise in interpreting repeated loading triaxial tests on soils unless very careful attention is given to the sample preparation and the stress regime used in the tests. The comparatively large permanent deformation after 400 000 applications of stress, shown in Fig. 10.55, was not due to compaction, since the clay was fully saturated. The sample deformed laterally due to the low cell pressure used. Had such a weak soil been used as a subgrade then the total thickness of the pavement would have been very considerable and a higher cell pressure would have been appropriate.

10.139 The increase in the elastic modulus of the soil with repetitions of stress arises from the rather complex changes which would have occurred in the suction of the soil during the test. The suction of soil and its relationship to moisture content and soil type has been discussed in Paras 10.77–10.80. For the London Clay used in the repeated loading test, Fig. 10.56 shows relevant relationships between suction and moisture content. Because of the rapid increase in suction which arises when a soil dries to a low moisture content, it is usual to express suction levels on a logarithmic scale. The scale which has been used by agricultural scientists is the pF

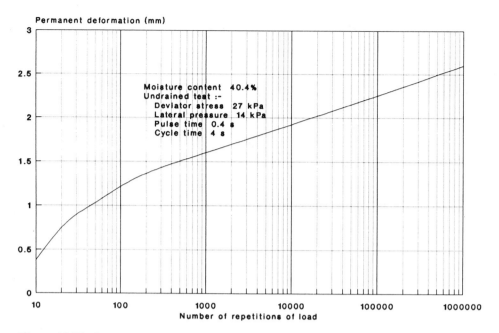

Figure 10.55 Permanent axial deformation of remoulded London Clay during repeated loading test

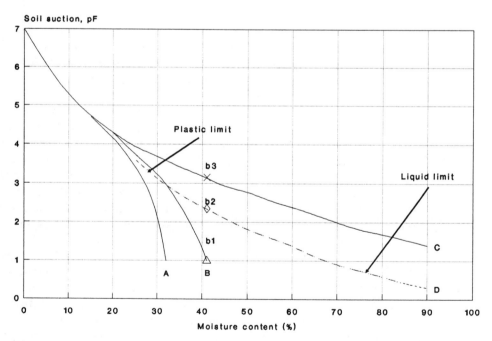

Figure 10.56 Relationship between suction and moisture content for London Clay used in repeated loading tests

178

scale (already referred to in Para. 10.87). On this scale the pF value is the common logarithm of the suction expressed in cm of water, i.e., pF 1 equals 10 cm of water and pF 2 equals 100 cm of water. Curve A in Fig. 10.56 refers to undisturbed London Clay drying from its natural moisture content. Curve C refers to the same soil slurried with water to the sedimentary condition, and then allowed to dry naturally. Curve B relates to the remoulded soil used in the repeated-loading test. This was a field sample remoulded with additional water to a moisture content of 40–42 per cent before being extruded for the triaxial test. It will be noted that all three curves come together at a suction between pF 4 and 5, which relates to the preconsolidation pressure to which the soil has been subjected in its past history.

10.140   Figure 10.56 also includes curve D. This is not a suction–moisture content relationship, but defines the suction which a sample of the soil, at a given moisture content, will assume on shearing. Research at the TRRL[25] has shown that when a sample of soil is sheared at constant moisture content its suction will be represented by curve D irrespective of its suction prior to shearing. There is a 'unique' line of this type for every cohesive soil. Thus, if the soil prepared for the repeated loading triaxial test had a suction of pF 1 at its initial moisture content of 41 per cent then its condition would be represented by point b_1 on curve B. On shearing at constant moisture content the condition would be represented by point b_2 on curve D. If the same soil were drying from a slurried condition, the suction at a moisture content of 41 per cent would be represented by point b_3 on curve C. On shearing the suction in this case would also fall to point b_2 on curve D. Since both the liquid and plastic limit tests involve shearing the soil, the corresponding suctions lie on the curve D as shown in the Figure.

10.141   In the repeated loading test on London Clay, Fig 10.55 shows that the significant deformation of the sample occurred as a result of repeated loading and although the sample did not exhibit shear failure the suction progressively increased towards the value represented by the curve D, with a resulting increase in shear strength and modulus of elasticity. (Further tests on cubical samples of wet heavy clays subject to shear between opposite faces showed that a progressive increase in suction occurred as the shear angle increased. A shear angle of about 30° was necessary to increase the suction to the curve D.)

10.142   In practice, the determination of the elastic modulus of a soil would be carried out on samples remoulded to the moisture content and density conditions likely to be present in a prepared subgrade, and the interpretation of the results would be less difficult than in the case illustrated above. However, it is normal to make determinations at several moisture contents and densities to explore the sensitivity of the results to these factors.

10.143   In the last 20 years servo-controlled electrohydraulic loading frames have become available for soil testing, permitting the use of a wide range of wave forms and pulse times for both vertical and radial loading conditions. Figure 10.57 shows such equipment currently in use at the Transport and Road Research Laboratory.

10.144   Under a modern flexible pavement designed to carry heavy traffic, the soil formation is subject to a vertical stress arising from the loading imposed by the

Figure 10.57 Repeated loading triaxial equipment for studying the elastic properties of soil

pavement. This vertical stress will be of the order of 15–$20 \, kN/m^2$, and it will give rise to a horizontal component of about one half this magnitude. The passage of a loaded wheel will impose additional vertical and radial stresses. In studying the stress–strain relations for soil in triaxial tests it is impractical to model all the conditions exactly because of the wide range of axle loads and vehicle speeds contained in the traffic. A reasonable compromise is to use a cell pressure of 10–$15 \, kN/m^2$ to simulate the dead load of the pavement and to pulse the deviator stress within the range 15–$20 \, kN/m^2$. A realistic pulse time for the transient stress system is about 0.5–0.8 s.

10.145   Axial strain is recorded during repetitive loading. As in the example above in Paras 10.136–10.142, initial strain may result from changes in suction within the soil, even in undrained tests, but if the soil has been compacted at the appropriate moisture content to model the subgrade condition, and the applied stress conditions are appropriate, the apparent modulus should stabilize after a few thousand stress applications.

10.146   Much valuable work relating to the repeated loading of soils has been carried out by Professors Seed and Monismith and their associates at the University of California. In Britain such work has been mainly concentrated at the University of Nottingham and at the TRRL. However, the research has been mainly directed at specific problems, and there has not been a sufficiently systematic approach to differentiate clearly between elastic moduli in terms of soil types, as is the case with the wave velocity approach.

10.147   Table 10.12 summarizes test results which have been reported, and in which the cell pressures and deviator stresses used are not very different from the ranges quoted in Para. 10.144. The sources are acknowledged in the table. The

Table 10.12   Summary of test data relating to the determination of elastic modulus of soils using repeated triaxial loading

Soil	LL %	PI %	Moisture content, %	CBR, %	Cell pressure, kN/m^2	Deviator stress, kN/m^2	M_r, MN/m^2	Source reference
Oxford Clay	56	37	28.2	2*	13.5	15	22	26
			13.5	30*	13.5	15	195	
London Clay	75	42	40	2[†]	14	27	12	24
Silty clay (AASHO road test)	30	17	16	4*	24	69	14	27
Silty clay (Marl)	32	14	19.6[§]	14[‡]	38	15	70	28
			19.6[§]	20[‡]	38	15	140	
Fine sand	—	—	10.5	10*	15	30	86	26

*Based on site measurements.
[†]Calculated using Black's method; see Paras 10.119 and 10.120.
[‡]Based on suction measurements.
[§]Drained tests.

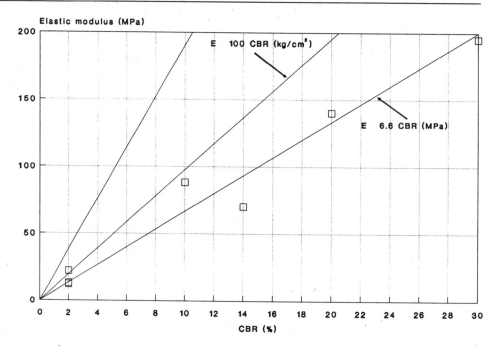

Figure 10.58 Relationship between CBR and elastic modulus determined by repeated loading triaxial tests

relationship between CBR and elastic modulus represented by the tests is shown in Fig. 10.58. The results show a considerable amount of scatter and there is clearly a need for further research, under more closely controlled conditions. The relationship proposed from these data is $E = 6.6$ CBR, where the E value is in MN/m^2. Figures 10.52 and 10.53 showed that the modulus measurement made using the wave velocity method fell largely between $E = 100$ CBR and $E = 200$ CBR (when expressed in kg/cm^2). These relationships are included in Fig. 10.58 and this confirms that tests involving significant strain give lower values than the wave velocity method.

10.148   The stresses induced in pavement materials are not very sensitive to small errors in subgrade modulus. It is proposed therefore that for fine-grained cohesive and non-cohesive soils the relationship $E = 6.6$ CBR (MN/m^2) should be used in estimating subgrade modulus. The elastic modulus of coarse-grained materials suitable for sub-bases is considered separately in Chapter 12.

10.149   Measurement of Poisson ratios for soils is also carried out using triaxial testing, but it is essential to have the facility for very accurate measurements of radial strain. Hicks and Finn,[27] using fine grained soil from the San Diego road test site reported values for the untreated soil of 0.32 to 0.5, with a tendency for the value to increase with increasing deviator stress. More recent tests at the Transport and Road

Research Laboratory[28] also show a small increase between 0.45 and 0.52 for a clay soil, as the deviator stress increases from 20 to 80 kN/m². Again, stress calculations within pavements are not very sensitive to small variations in Poisson ratio and it is proposed that 0.45 should be used in structural analyses.

Appendix to Chapter 10

The following charts relate dry density and moisture content for soils of particle specific gravity 2.60–2.80.

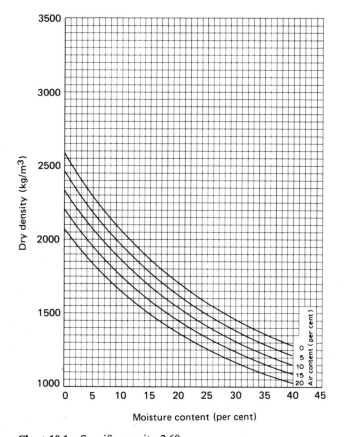

Chart 10.1   Specific gravity 2.60

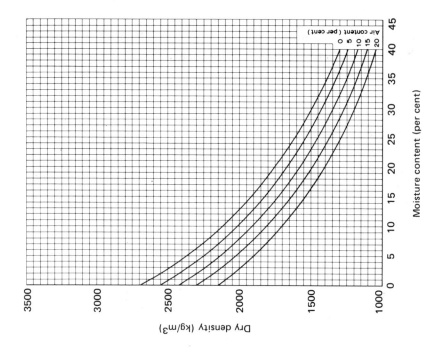

Chart 10.3 Particle specific gravity 2.70

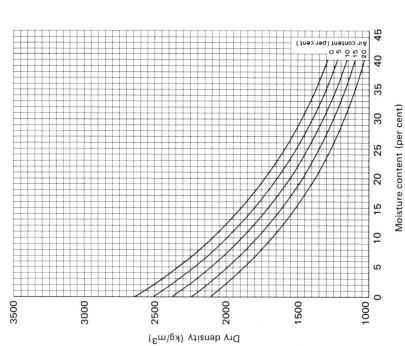

Chart 10.2 Particle specific gravity 2.65

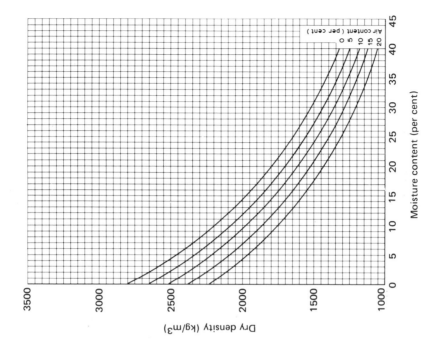

Chart 10.5   Particle specific gravity 2.80

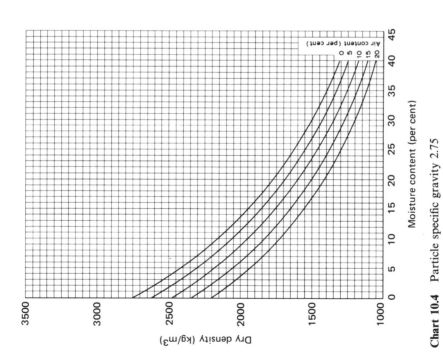

Chart 10.4   Particle specific gravity 2.75

185

References

1. Croney, D., J. D. Coleman, and W. P. M. Black: *Movement and Distribution of Water in Soil in Relation to Highway Design and Performance*, Highway Research Board Special Report 40, Water and its conduction in soils. National Academy of Science – National Research Council, Washington, D.C., pp. 226–52, 1958.
2. Parsons, A. W.: *The Rapid Measurement of the Moisture Condition of Earthwork Material*, Transport and Road Research Laboratory Report LR750, TRRL, Crowthorne, 1976.
3. Parsons, A. W. and J. B. Boden: *The Moisture Condition Test and its Potential Applications in Earthworks*, Transport and Road Research Supplementary Report SR522, TRRL, Crowthorne, 1979.
4. Parsons, A. W. and A. F. Toombs: *The Precision of the Moisture Condition Test*, Transport and Road Research Laboratory Research Report 90, TRRL, Crowthorne, 1987.
5. *Developing World Land Transport*, Grosvenor Press International, London, 1987.
6. Russam, K.: *Sub-soil Drainage and the Structural Design of Roads*, Transport and Road Research Laboratory Report LR110, TRRL, Crowthorne, 1967.
7. Russam, K.: *The distribution of moisture in soils at overseas airfields*, Road Research Technical Paper No. 58, HMSO, London, 1962.
8. Scofield, R. K.: The pF of the water in soil, *Trans. 3rd Int. Congr. Soil Science, 1935*, vol. 2, 37–48.
9. Croney, D. and J. C. Jacobs: *The Frost Susceptibility of Soils and Road Materials*, Transport and Road Research Laboratory Report LR90, TRRL, Crowthorne, 1967.
10. Taber, S.: Freezing and thawing of soils as factors in the destruction of road pavements. *Publ. Rds Wash.*, **11** (6), 113–32, 1930.
11. Sherwood, P. T. and P. G. Roe.: *Winter Air Temperatures in Relation to Frost Damage in Roads*, Transport and Road Research Laboratory Research Report 45, TRRL, Crowthorne, 1986.
12. Bishop, A. W. and N. Morgenstern: Stability coefficients for earth slopes, *Geotechnique, Lond.*, **10** (4), 129–50, 1960.
13. Symons, I. F.: *The Application of Residual Shear Strength to the Design of Cuttings in Over Consolidated Fissured Clays*, Transport and Road Research Laboratory Report LR277, TRRL, Crowthorne, 1968.
14. Perry, J.: *A Survey of Slope Conditions on Motorway Earthworks in England and Wales*, Transport and Road Research Laboratory Research Report 199, TRRL, Crowthorne, 1989.
15. Davis, E. H.: The California Bearing Ratio method for the design of flexible roads and runways, *Geotechnique, Lond.*, **1** (4) 249–63, 1949.
16. Black, W. P. M.: The calculation of laboratory and *in situ* values of California bearing ratio from bearing capacity data, *Geotechnique, Lond.*, **11** (1), 14–21, 1961.
17. Black, W. P. M.: A method of estimating the California bearing ratio of cohesive soils from plasticity data, *Geotechnique, Lond.*, **12** (4), 271–82, 1962.
18. Parsons, A. W.: Moisture Condition Test for assessing the engineering behaviour of earthwork material, *Conference on Clay Fills*, Institution of Civil Engineers, London 1979.
19. Westergaard, H. M.: Stresses in concrete pavements computed by theoretical analysis, *Publ. Rds Wash.*, **7** (2), 23–25, 1926.
20. Stratton, J. H.: Construction and design problems. Military airfields a symposium. *Proc. Amer. Soc. Civ. Engrs*, **70** (1), 28–54, 1944.
21. Love, A. E. H.: *The Mathematical Theory of Elasticity*, 4th edn, Cambridge University Press, Cambridge, 1927.
22. Jones, R.: Non-destructive testing of roads and structures, *Publ. Wks Munic. Services Congress, 1956, Final Report*, 450–73.
23. Jones, R.: In situ measurement of the dynamic properties of soil by vibration methods, *Geotechnique Lond.*, **8** (1), 1–21 (1958).

24. Grainger, G. D. and N. W. Lister.: A laboratory apparatus for studying the behaviour of soils under repeated loading, *Geotechnique, Lond.*, **12** (1), 3–14 (1962).
25. Croney, D. and J. D. Coleman: Soil structure in relation to soil suction (pF), *J. Soil Sci.*, **5** (1), 1954.
26. Croney, P.: The structural design of road and airfield pavements using modern analytical technique, London University thesis, 1975.
27. Hicks, R. G. and E. N. Finn: Analysis of results from the dynamic measurements programme on the San Diego Test Road, *Proc. Assn Ashp. Pav. Technology, Michigan*, **39**, 153–85, 1970.
28. Chaddock, B. C. J.: *Repeated Triaxial Loading of Soil: Apparatus and Preliminary Results*, Transport and Road Research Laboratory Supplementary Report 711, TRRL, Crowthorne, 1982.

The numerous references in this chapter to BS 1377 are to the 1975 edition (*Methods of Test for Soils for Civil Engineering Purposes*). At the time of going to press this Standard is in the process of being revised and issued in a series of separate parts, under the title *British Standard methods of test for soils for civil engineering purposes*.

The extracts from BS 5930:1981 (*Code of Practice on Site Investigation*) referred to in Para. 10.52 are reproduced with the permission of the British Standards Institution.

Complete copies of all the British Standards referred to in this book can be obtained from: BSI Sales, Linford Wood, Milton Keynes, MK14 6LE.

11. Preparation and testing of the subgrade—capping layers

Introduction

11.1   The soil immediately below formation level is generally referred to as the subgrade. Specifications for the compaction of earthworks usually distinguish between the soil above and below a depth of 600 mm. It is convenient therefore to regard the subgrade as the upper 600 mm of the soil foundation.

11.2   Under a well-designed pavement, the stresses in the subgrade, induced by the passage of heavy wheel-loads, decrease only marginally with depth. The engineer is therefore more concerned with the average strength than with surface measurements liable to be influenced by the prevailing weather conditions.

11.3   Major rural roads are today built to a maximum gradient of about 1:25, so that a steady flow of mixed traffic can be maintained. This involves considerable amounts of cut and fill and it is not unusual for construction to be evenly divided between cut, fill, and existing ground level.

Preparation of the formation

11.4   Final preparation of the formation should be delayed as far as possible until the contractor is ready to lay the sub-base or capping layer (if required by the Specification). Ideally, the two processes should be closely linked to minimize the period when the formation is left exposed to the weather. Most specifications contain a clause requiring the contractor to keep earthworks protected from rain at all times, but this is quite impracticable in a wet climate. At best, earthworks can be scheduled for the drier periods of the year and left as smooth as is feasible so that much of the rainfall will run off. The use of plastic sheeting on major contracts is not really feasible on the scale necessary and bituminous seals have been shown to be largely ineffective.

11.5   The drawings will show the finished levels required for the road surface at the two edges of the carriageway. The corresponding levels of the formation are obtained by subtracting the nominal thicknesses of the pavement layers. As with the other pavement interfaces, the specification will define tolerances to be applied to the nominal levels. For the formation, a tolerance of about ± 25 mm is normal. The procedure adopted by the contractor to trim the formation must be decided by the contractor. However, the engineer should develop a systematic approach to checking levels. In the UK the method recommended is to install level pegs on each side of the formation at intervals of about 10 m. Transverse level measurements are made at 2-m intervals between each pair of pegs. If the pegs are left in position (relevelled as necessary) then measurements can be made at the same points after each successive pavement layer is completed so that thicknesses can be checked.

11.6   The repeated passage of heavily loaded scrapers and other earthmoving equipment over the ground connecting cuttings and embankments is very likely to cause intense disturbance and shearing of the soil. The consequent rise in the suction of cohesive soils (see Paras 10.140 and 10.141) will cause the rapid absorption of surface water and progressive softening of the soil to a considerable depth. This is a very common cause of localized early failure of flexible pavements. It is advisable therefore as part of the final preparation and shaping of the subgrade to remove the soil in these areas to a depth of about 500 mm and to replace it with freshly dug soil at the natural moisture content. The compaction will be that specified for the subgrade.

11.7   In clay cuttings the release of overburden will give rise to a progressive increase in moisture content of the underlying soil (see Para. 10.84), giving rise to apparent heaving of the formation. This is a common cause of dispute between contractors and engineers when levels passed as satisfactory are subsequently rejected as being too high. To economize in pavement materials, some contractors tend to work to the upper tolerance on subgrades and sub-bases. This is particularly unwise in clay cuttings where uplift of 50 mm or more is not uncommon.

The testing of subgrades   ·

General

11.8   In road construction projects the structural design, i.e., the thickness of the various layers, particularly in the case of flexible pavements, is based on the strength of the soil. The engineer, having had various tests carried out as part of the site investigation for the project, will have used them to estimate this strength. If, as is likely to be the case, an empirical design procedure has been used, based, for example, on the California Bearing Ratio (CBR) test, then the engineer will have, or should have, studied the relationships between CBR value and the density and moisture content of the soil or soils present at the site. On the basis of this laboratory work selections will have been made for the maximum moisture content and minimum dry-density values which will ensure the CBR value used in the design. Alternatively, if the engineer elects to use a method specification for compacting the subgrade, it will be assumed that the requirements have been so framed as to produce the CBR value on which the design has been based. In either case, if the contractor carries out the compaction requirements of the specification correctly and a lower strength is achieved, the responsibility is the engineer's and not the contractor's. The engineer must then either modify the design and accept any financial penalties involved or proceed according to the original design in the knowledge that the pavement may have a shorter life than was intended. The same arguments would apply if the engineer were using a fundamental design procedure based on the elastic properties of the soil. It would not in general be feasible for the engineer to specify a minimum CBR value or a minimum modulus of elasticity for the soil, since this would transfer to the contractor all the responsibility involved in organizing and overseeing the site investigation.

11.9   The above discussion does emphasize the need, when a method specification is used for the preparation of the subgrade, for the engineer to pay close attention to the compaction plant and the way in which it is operated, i.e., the number of passes and the layer thickness being used. The engineer should at the outset check that the plant on site and its operators are sufficient to provide adequate compaction, bearing in mind the rate of progress of the work, and should have enough inspectors on site to make frequent checks that the requirements of the specification are being completely met. There may well be a case, where a method specification is being used for the construction of the embankments, to change to an end-product specification based on moisture content and dry density for the compaction of the subgrade.

Moisture content and dry density tests on the subgrade

11.10   Where the required state of compaction of the subgrade is defined in the contract in terms of moisture content and dry density, both contractor and engineer should carry out continuous testing of those properties. In his own interest the contractor for a major road construction project should have on site a well-equipped and completely staffed laboratory. Long experience shows that disputes and delays are much less likely to occur when both contractors and engineers maintain efficient site laboratories between which there exists understanding and mutual respect. The assistant in charge of each laboratory should be made responsible for keeping records of every test made and its date and location. This information will be called for in the event of arbitration or litigation.

11.11   If in the contract the density of the subgrade is expressed as a percentage of the maximum dry density obtained in one of the standard laboratory compaction tests (see Para. 10.57) then the appropriate laboratory test should be carried out at least once daily by both the engineer and the contractor, using soil taken from the subgrade. In the early stages of the work frequent determinations of dry density and moisture content should be made using the sand replacement method (BS 1377:1975, Test 15, or AASHTO Designation T191–86), again by both the engineer and the contractor. During this stage a correlation should be established with the density measured by a nuclear density meter of the backscatter type (AASHTO Designation T238–86, Method A). This equipment gives the wet (or bulk) density and a separate measurement of moisture content at the same location is required to deduce the equivalent dry density. Once a reliable correlation between the two methods has been obtained, increasing reliance can be placed on the nuclear tests. However, a revised calibration will be needed if a significant change of soil type occurs in the subgrade.

11.12   If the specification for the subgrade is in terms of a maximum moisture content and maximum air content, in addition to the moisture content and dry density, the specific gravity of the soil particles will need to be measured (BS 1377:1975, Test 6, and AASHTO Designation T100–86). The maximum air voids content can then be read off the appropriate chart give in the Appendix to Chapter 10.

The strength of the subgrade

11.13   Empirically designed pavements, whether flexible or concrete, will in general employ the CBR test to define the strength of the subgrade. This test has been described in detail in Chapter 10 and it is covered by BS 1377, Test 16, and AASHTO Designation T193-81. In designing a pavement using the CBR value the engineer will, on the basis of laboratory testing at the site investigation stage, have defined the required moisture content and dry density of the finished subgrade in such a way that the design CBR will be achieved in the properly constructed subgrade.

11.14   In checking the subgrade the engineer will need to carry out further laboratory CBR tests on soil taken from the prepared subgrade and remoulded in the standard CBR mould. It will be remoulded to the moisture content and dry density measured in the finished subgrade at the point from which the soil was taken. The CBR determined in this way should be equal to or marginally greater than the value used in the design of the pavement. Compliance will in general be more critical for flexible pavements than is the case for concrete construction. Several CBR determinations should be made in this way each day and they would be coupled with the dry-density and moisture content determinations. The tests are of necessity slow, giving results with a delay of 24 hours. It is usual, therefore, to adopt supplementary CBR measurements *in situ* which can be carried out more quickly. Because of the mould restraint factor, laboratory CBR values tend to be greater than measurements *in situ* at the same density and moisture content. The engineer must therefore carry out checks to establish the relationship between laboratory tests and tests *in situ* for the soils in question. Some comparative tests from UK and US sources are shown in Table 11.1. For heavy and medium clays the results *in situ* are only a little lower than laboratory values, but for less cohesive soils with low air voids content the difference is larger and for coarse granular soils they can be very large. CBR tests can be carried out *in situ* from a rig attached to the back of a truck (Fig. 11.1). For weaker soils, where the reaction required is smaller, a light pickup vehicle can be used to avoid damage to the subgrade.

11.15   A valuable tool for assessing the uniformity of subgrades both in the horizontal and vertical direction is the hand-held Soil Assessment Cone Penetrometer shown in Fig. 11.2. Two scales, corresponding to different sizes of cone, give

Table 11.1 Comparison of laboratory (remoulded) and *in-situ* CBR values

Soil type	Source of data	Dry density lb/cu ft (kg/m³)	Moisture content (per cent)	CBR: (per cent)	
				Remoulded	*In situ*
Heavy clay (LL 69 PL 27)	Transport and Road Research Laboratory	95 (1522)	24.8	8.9	7.9
Clay (LL 59 PL 22)	Transport and Road Research Laboratory	96 (1538)	25.1	3.9	3.0
Silty clay (LL 37 PL 23)	US Waterways Experimental Station	109 (1746)	19.5	2.0	12
		107 (1714)	19.0	5.0	11
		104 (1666)	16.1	22	22
Sandy clay (LL 30 PL 18)	Transport and Road Research Laboratory	95 (1522)	19.2	2.2	3.1
Clayey sand	US Waterways Experimental Station	116 (1858)	12.2	14	7.0
		114 (1826)	12.6	10	9.0
		109 (1746)	10.0	12	18
Single-size sand	Transport and Road Research Laboratory	98 (1570)	8.0	24	7.5
Crushed slag	Transport and Road Research Laboratory	140 (2243)	4.8	412	44

Figure 11.1   Equipment for in situ measurement of CBR

Figure 11.2   Soil assessment cone penetrometer

the soil strength in terms of a 'cone index' or the equivalent CBR *in situ* over the range 0–15 per cent. The readings correlate fairly closely with the CBR *in situ* on fine-grained soils, but not for coarse soils. For all soils, calibration against laboratory or *in situ* CBR tests is necessary. With an extended shaft the instrument can be used satisfactorily to examine the variation of the CBR value with depth, for soils in the range CBR 0–5 per cent. This application is useful in exploring the depth of 'soft spots'. The cone is pushed at constant rate into the soil and the steady reading observed at the different depths scribed on the shaft. Proof rolling to locate soft spots is strongly to be deprecated. Very heavy rollers or vehicles cause unnecessary damage to the subgrade without giving any quantitative information. On weak soils of CBR <5 per cent an unloaded panel truck or a private car can sometimes be used to show weak areas by the depth of tyre marks.

11.16   When pavements are designed using multilayer elastic theory, the 'property' criterion for the subgrade is its modulus of elasticity, corresponding to its moisture and density condition after compaction. The determination of the modulus of elasticity (or resilient modulus as it is called in the USA) is much more complicated than the dermination of the CBR value. Various methods have already been considered in Chapter 10. Basically, it involves carrying out repeated-loading triaxial tests on the soil and determining the ratio of stress and strain for the range of stress conditions generated by traffic loading.

11.17   To carry out this complex test procedure on soil with a wide range of density and moisture content conditions is impracticable outside a research institution. The engineer is advised therefore to proceed as if designing the pavement empirically using the CBR design procedure, i.e., to follow the steps outlined in Para. 11.8 above to derive an appropriate level of CBR for design purposes based on a maximum moisture content and a minimum dry density. Using these values of moisture content and dry density, remoulded cylindrical triaxial test samples would be prepared and subjected to repeated loading tests using increasing deviator stresses and associated cell pressures to simulate the vertical and radial stresses induced by wheel loads. For each such combination of stresses the effective elastic modulus after several hundred stress applications would be calculated and the minimum value used as input into the computer program adopted to calculate the stresses in the pavement layers. This subject is discussed in detail in Chapter 21. With this approach the information to be derived from the site investigation would be the same for both the empirical and structural design procedures.

11.18   The equipment and test procedure for measuring resilient modulus is described in AASHTO Designation T274-82 (1986). However, current research is directed towards relating the elastic properties of soils to other simpler tests, such as the index properties, shear strength, and CBR. This has been discussed in Chapter 10.

The use of subgrade capping in earthworks

11.19   When the soil at formation level is weak (CBR 2–4 per cent), 400–600 mm of sub-base will be required in the construction of heavily trafficked flexible pavements.

Under these circumstances it is a common cost-cutting practice to subdivide the sub-base layer, the upper part normally being an angular crushed rock and the lower part a naturally occurring gravel or gravel sand. In the UK these are termed Type 1 and Type 2 sub-bases, and their specifications are discussed in Chapter 12

11.20   There is naturally a temptation to believe that if this process of gradation of materials is extended to a third layer between the formation and the road base material, then considerable savings in cost might be made. To provide such a third layer the concept of 'capping' the subgrade has been introduced. Whether it does in fact prove to be economic is very questionable in many cases, and there is no doubt that attempts by contractors in the UK to meet specifications for capping layers have led to expensive confrontations between clients and contractors. This is in part due to inadequate specifications.

11.21   If a soil is abnormally weak (CBR <2 per cent), owing either to its particle size distribution or to a high natural moisture content, tipping and rolling-in granular sub-base material eventually produces a measure of mechanical stabiliz-ation, but the effectiveness of much of the granular material will be lost as a result of contamination by the wet soil. The local use of geotextile fabrics to separate the soil and the granular material has been shown to be effective in reducing subsequent deformation under construction traffic.[1] Table 11.2 shows the results of tests carried out by the TRRL, where a crushed stone layer 200 mm thick was laid over a heavy clay soil of *in situ* CBR 2 per cent with and without separation of the materials by a non-woven polypropylene–nylon fabric with a specified strength of 10.5 kN/m and weight of 450 g/m^2. The two forms of construction were trafficked by repeated passes of a loaded truck with front wheel loading of 2.25 t and rear-wheel loading of 4.55 t (carried on a dual wheel assembly). There was no initial difference in elastic deflection of the two sections, but it is possible that such a difference would have developed with time. The difference in deformation was therefore largely attributable to the influence of the fabric in preventing intermixing of clay and stone.

11.22   In the United States subgrade improvement by the addition of cement and lime has for many years been used to provide a capping for weak subgrades. The much smaller road construction programmes in Europe have not favoured similar

Table 11.2   The influence on deformation of a geotextile fabric separation layer between the subgrade and a crushed stone base

	Permanent deformation at the surface, mm	
Number of passes of truck	Without fabric	With fabric
50	28	20
100	37	25
200	47	29
300	53	32

developments although specialist subcontractors with the necessary single- and multiple-pass processing equipment are now available to encourage this type of subgrade treatment when it is applicable, and where it can be shown to be economic.

11.23   Some broad conclusions can be drawn from the experience gained from capping subgrades in the UK, and there seems no reason why they should not apply generally. They are as follows:

1. Capping or subgrade improvement should be considered only when the *in situ* CBR of the formation when properly compacted is likely to be less than 4 per cent.
2. With prepared subgrades of *in situ* CBR less than 2 per cent, any imported capping material or sub-base should be separated from the subgrade by a geotextile membrane.
3. Capping with material other than normal sub-base should be required by the contract documents only when the engineer is satisfied that granular materials with relevant properties between those of the subgrade and those of normal sub-base are available and that their use as capping will be economically advantageous to the client.
4. Forming a capping layer by processing the soil with cement, lime, or other chemical additives will only be required or permitted when the engineer or the contractor have carried out laboratory or field trials to show the method can be economically and advantageously used.

11.24   The UK Department of Transport *Specification for Highway Works* (1986) permits the use of four capping materials or processes.[2] These include two unbound materials, designated Class F1 and Class F2, and two stabilized materials with very wide grading envelopes. The unbound materials, Class F1 and Class F2, must conform to the gradings shown in Table 11.3. The material suitable for cement stabilization must conform to the grading limits for class 6E materials and the material suitable for lime stabilization to the limits for class 7E materials also included in Table 11.2.

11.25   The grading limits for Class F1 material are virtually identical to those for

Table 11.3   Grading requirements for capping materials

			mm					BS sieve size						μm		
Class	125	90	75	37.5	28	20	14	10	6.3	5	3.35	2	1.18	600	150	63
	Granular materials															
6 F1			100	75–100				40–95		30–85				10–50		<15
6 F2	100	80–100	65–100	45–100				15–60		10–45				0–25		0–12
	Cement stabilized material															
6 E	100	85–100						25–100						10–100		0–10
	Lime stabilized material															
7 E			100		95–100											15–100

Type 2 sub-base. The only difference appears to be that softer aggregates such as chalk and soft limestone can be used and presumably unspecified waste materials which would not be permitted as sub-base. The grading for the Class F2 material overlaps with the grading requirements of both Type 1 and Type 2 sub-base. The maximum size of aggregate is greater for Class F2 material, and it is presumably intended for use where greater thicknesses of capping are specified.

11.26   For both Class F1 and F2 materials the specification permits the engineer to require that a stated CBR value is achieved in the compacted material. The value commonly selected is 14 per cent, although it is often not made clear to the contractor whether this is a laboratory-determined CBR or whether it is intended to be an *in situ* value. Few engineers or contractors have any clear idea how a CBR 14 per cent material will behave under construction traffic and frequent disputes arise when the resident engineer attempts to use deformation as a performance criterion.

11.27   The stabilization alternatives for capping are primarily intended for use where the soils at the site conform to the gradings shown in Table 11.3 for class GE and FE materials. The importation of soil to the site for this purpose would never be economic. The performance criterion used for lime- and cement-stabilized capping is the laboratory CBR value, which must be set by the engineer, who must therefore carry out sufficient laboratory testing to ensure that the required strength will be obtainable economically. In general, once work has started the contractor would also be required to carry out site trials to validate his methods of working. Cement stabilization is unlikely to be a cheap option. For soils with a grading close to the finer boundary of the grading envelope, cement contents in excess of 10 per cent by weight could be needed to meet the strength requirement.

11.28   There is little experience with lime stabilization of soils in the UK, beyond laboratory and small-scale field trials. The process is intended primarily for treating wet, heavy clays and its effect is gradually to reduce the plasticity of the clay and thereby increase its strength. A method of assessing the suitability of a clay for lime stabilization is given in AASHTO Designation M216-84 (ASTM Designation C977-83A). The method is based on the measurement of the pH of the soil–lime mixture. The determination of the strength of soil–lime mixtures is covered in AASHTO Designation T220-66 (1984).

References

1. Potter, J. F. and E. W. H. Currer: *The effect of a fabric membrane on the structural behaviour of a granular road pavement*, TRRL Report LR 996, TRRL, Crowthorne, 1981.
2. Department of Transport: *Specification for Highway Works*, Part 2, HMSO, London, Clauses 613–615, 1986.

12. Unbound sub-bases and roadbases

Introduction

12.1   The sub-base of a flexible pavement is the layer between the subgrade (or the capping layer if one is used) and the base. In a concrete pavement it is the layer separating the concrete slab from the subgrade. The base, or roadbase, is the layer immediately below the bituminous surfacing of a flexible pavement.

12.2   Sub-bases can be constructed from unbound compacted granular material, or similar material bound with a small amount of cement. Bases can also be made from unbound crushed rock, but more usually the aggregate is bound either with cement or bitumen.

12.3   This chapter deals exclusively with unbound sub-bases and bases. Subsequent chapters deal with cement-bound sub-bases and bases and with bituminous-bound bases.

12.4   The sub-base has three main functions, as follows:

1. It is a structural layer which will accept greater compressive stress than the subgrade and it thus reduces the deformation of the pavement under traffic loading.
2. It provides a working platform over which construction plant can operate when the layer above is being placed.
3. If thick enough it prevents frost from penetrating into frost-susceptible subgrades.

12.5   The main function of the base is to reduce the vertical compressive stress induced by traffic, in the sub-base and the subgrade, to a level at which no unacceptable deformation will occur in these layers. Unbound bases perform this function solely by virtue of their thickness and state of compaction. Bound bases perform the same function by a combination of thickness and stiffness.

British specifications for unbound sub-bases and roadbases

Types 1 and 2 sub-bases

12.6   The UK Department of Transport *Specification for Highway Works*, Part 3, Clauses 801–804, defines two unbound sub-base materials, Type 1 and Type 2. The gradings, determined by wet sieving are shown in Table 12.1 and the grading envelopes in Fig. 12.1.

Table 12.1   Grading limits for Type 1 and Type 2 sub-bases

BS sieve size	Percentage by mass passing	
	Type 1	Type 2
75 mm	100	100
37.5 mm	85–100	85–100
10 mm	40–70	45–100
5 mm	25–45	25–85
600 μm	8–22	8–45
75 μm	0–10	0–10

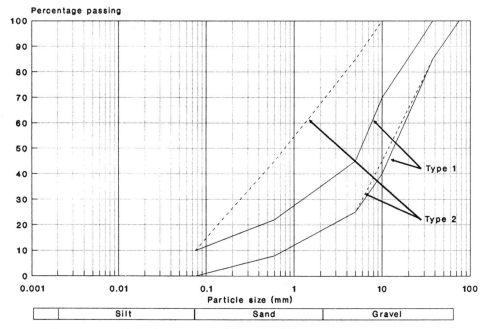

Figure 12.1   Grading limits for Type 1 and Type 2 sub-bases

12.7   The aggregate for Type 1 sub-base is restricted to crushed rock, crushed concrete, or well-burnt, non-plastic colliery shale, and the material passing the 425 μm sieve should be non-plastic. The aggregate for Type 2 sub-base additionally includes natural sand and gravel, and the plasticity index of the material passing the 425 μm sieve is limited to 6 per cent. For both types, to ensure that the aggregate is sufficiently hard, the 10 per cent fines value determined with the aggregate saturated but surface dry is required to be not less than 50 kN.[1]

12.8   Type 1 material is considered free-draining and no moisture content requirement for compaction is given. Compaction of Type 2 sub-base is now specified in terms of the optimum moisture content determined using the vibrating hammer test rig described in BS 5835:1980:Part 1. The state of compaction to be achieved corresponds to 5 per cent air voids at the optimum moisture content, $+1$ per cent to -2 per cent. To determine the air voids content, the particle specific gravity is additionally required. Such a specification makes field control very difficult, particularly if the material being supplied is of variable grading within the required limits. The earlier specification required that the moisture content of Type 2 material should be within the range $+1$ to -2 per cent of the optimum moisture content determined in accordance with the vibrating hammer compaction test of BS 1377:1975, Test 14. This is a comparatively simple test which can be carried out in a field laboratory. (See also Para. 10.60.)

12.9   Compaction of Type 1 and Type 2 sub-bases is normally carried out by vibrating rollers. The relationship between type of roller, number of passes, and thickness of compacted layer used in the British method-type specification is given in Table 12.2.

12.10   For type 2 sub-base material, the engineer is also required to specify the minimum CBR value for the compacted sub-base. This is to be determined in the laboratory using the field moisture content and dry density. This involves carrying out a series of CBR tests at various dry densities, using the field moisture content.[2] The field density must then be measured at a number of points using the sand replacement method[3] and the CBR deduced from the mean of the field density measurements. *In situ* and laboratory CBR values for coarse granular materials carried out at the same moisture content and dry density are likely to be very different (see Para. 11.14) and *in situ* tests cannot be used to assess compliance with the CBR requirements for sub-bases.

12.11   All sub-bases should be non-frost susceptible when subjected to the standard frost test (see Para. 10.95). Most materials which satisfy the 10 per cent fines test required by Para. 12.7, and the grading curves of Fig. 12.1 should be satisfactory from this point of view. However, some limestone gravels are marginally frost-susceptible and it is advisable to have the frost test carried out.

12.12   Types 1 and 2 sub-base are normally end-tipped and spread by grader. For major roads a sub-base thickness of between 200 and 600 mm will be required, depending on the strength of the subgrade. It is usual pratice in the UK to use Type 1 material for the upper 200 mm and Type 2 below. This can involve two layers of Type 2 and one layer of Type 1 if satisfactory compaction is to be achieved and means that loaded trucks will need to operate over both types of sub-base. Some deformation is inevitable particularly in Type 2 material during wet weather. Disputes between the engineer and contractor often arise when the former uses deformation as a means of assessing the quality of the sub-base. Deformation of the order of 25 mm must be expected from traffic and plant involved in sub-base and base laying. Over weak soils (CBR <2 per cent) the engineer should give serious consideration to the use of a textile membrane under the sub-base (see Para. 11.23).

Table 12.2 Compaction requirements for granular materials Types 1 and 2 and wet-mix macadam

Type of compaction plant	Category	Number of passes for layers not exceeding compacted thickness		
		110 mm	150 mm	225 mm
Smooth-wheeled roller (or vibratory roller operating without vibration)	Mass per m width of roll:			
	2 700–5 400 kg	16	u/s	u/s
	over 5 400 kg	8	16	u/s
Pneumatic-tyred roller	Mass per wheel:			
	4 000–6 000 kg	12	u/s	u/s
	6 000–8 000 kg	12	u/s	u/s
	8 000–12 000 kg	10	16	u/s
	over 12 000 kg	8	12	u/s
Vibratory roller	Mass per m width of roll:			
	700–1 300 kg	16	u/s	u/s
	1 300–1 800 kg	6	16	u/s
	1 800–2 300 kg	4	6	10
	2 300–2 900 kg	3	5	9
	2 900–3 600 kg	3	5	8
	3 600–4 300 kg	2	4	7
	4 300–5 000 kg	2	4	6
	over 5 000 kg	2	3	5
Vibrating-plate compactor	Mass per sq m of plate:			
	1 400–1 800 kg/m²	8	u/s	u/s
	1 800–2 100 kg/m²	5	8	u/s
	over 2 100 kg/m²	3	6	10
Vibro-tamper	Mass:			
	50–65 kg	4	8	u/s
	65–75 kg	3	6	10
	over 75 kg	2	4	8
Power rammer	Mass:			
	100–500 kg	5	8	u/s
	over 500 kg	5	8	12

Unbound roadbases

12.13 Two types of unbound road base are in use in the UK. These are wet-mix macadam and dry-bound macadam. The first is defined in the UK Department of Transport *Specification for Highway Works*, Part 3, Clause 805. The second is no longer included in the specification but it is widely used in various forms for the less heavily trafficked rural roads.

Wet-mix macadam

12.14 The grading of the aggregate for wet-mix macadam is given in Table 12.3 and Fig. 12.2. The aggregate consists of non-flakey crushed rock or crushed slag,

Table 12.3   Grading limits for wet-mix macadam

BS sieve size	Percentage of mass passing
50 mm	100
37.5 mm	95–100
20 mm	60–80
10 mm	40–60
5 mm	25–40
2.36 mm	15–30
600 μm	8–22
75 μm	0–8

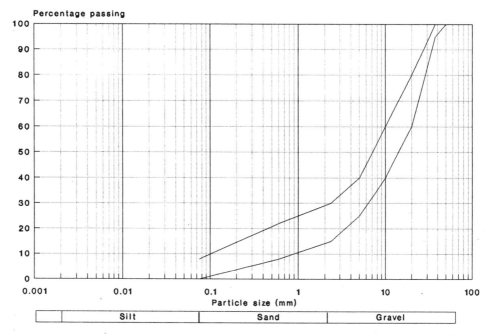

Figure 12.2   Grading limits for wet-mix macadam

with a 10 per cent fines value, when tested in the saturated surface dry condition of 50 kN, i.e., the same value as is required for Type 1 and Type 2 sub-bases. Apart from having a rather smaller maximum size of stone, the gradings for wet-mix macadam and Type 1 sub-base are very similar. The moisture content at laying is required to be within ±0.5 per cent of the optimum determined by the vibrating hammer test.[4] The material must be spread by a paving machine and compacted, normally by vibrating roller, in accordance with Table 12.2. The compacted material must be non-frost susceptible, and tests should be carried out if there is any doubt about the quality of the stone.

12.15   Wet-mix materials are often compacted drier than the specified moisture content, and this can result in comparatively low field densities and subsequent deformation under traffic. Figure 12.3 shows the relationship between moisture content and dry density for a limestone wet-mix material compacted in a 200-mm layer using a smooth-wheel roller weighing 8 tonnes. The results of the vibrating hammer compaction test carried out on the same material are also shown. Compliance with the specification with respect to moisture content, i.e., 3.4 ± 0.5 per cent in this case, would result in a compacted dry density of not less than $2350 \, \mathrm{kg/m^3}$. A decrease in moisture content to 2 per cent would mean a reduction of dry density to $2200 \, \mathrm{kg/m^3}$. This would eventually lead to the development of a poor riding quality.

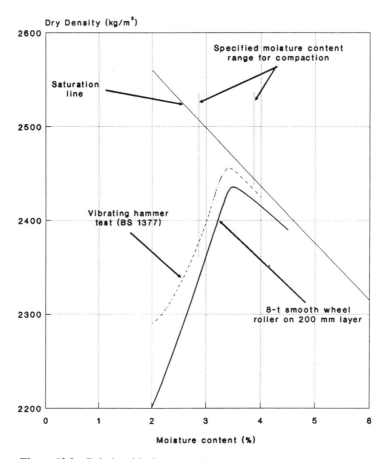

Figure 12.3   Relationship between dry density and moisture content for limestone wet-mix roadbase

Dry-bound macadam

12.16   In this process a layer of single-size crushed stone or crushed slag of nominal size 50 mm or 37.5 mm is uniformly laid to a thickness between 75 and 100 mm. The use of a box spreader or a bituminous paving machine is recommended. The spread material is given two passes of a smooth-wheel roller of weight 8–10 t. The stone is 'blinded' by progressive applications of fine aggregate of maximum size 5 mm and having less than 10 per cent passing the 75-μm sieve. This material is also crushed rock or crushed slag. Each application of fine aggregate is vibrated into the voids of the larger stone using a vibrating plate compactor having a static pressure under the base plate of at least 13.8 kN/m² or a vibrating roller having a static force per 100 mm width of at least 1.76 kN. The blinding operation is continued until no more fines are accepted and the surface is then brushed off. Acceptable gradings for the coarse and fine aggregates are shown in Fig. 12.4. This is essentially a dry-weather process and it is most important that the fines are kept dry before and during their application and vibration. The dry density of a dry-bound roadbase should be very similar to that obtained in a wet-mix roadbase using the same aggregate type, and the performance of the two types of roadbase has been shown to be very similar.

12.17   An economic form of road construction used by some road authorities for rural roads carrying comparatively few heavy vehicles employs crusher-run stone for both sub-base and base. The gradings of crusher-run materials cannot be closely

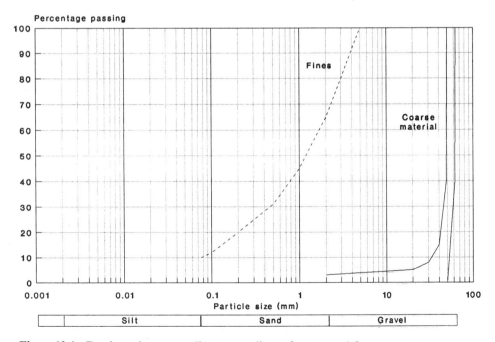

Figure 12.4   Dry-bound stone roadbases—gradings of coarse and fine aggregates

controlled, but it is not unusual for materials of maximum size 50 mm to give a grading within or close to the wet-mix specification. The material may, however, be gap-graded or have an excess of fines. The compaction used is the same as for wet-mix roadbases, but because the material is normally at a moisture content of less than one per cent a high state of compaction cannot be achieved. A dry density of about 90 per cent of the value for a wet-mix material using the same aggregate is normal. This can result in traffic compaction during the early life of the road and for this reason traffic should initially be run on a sealed temporary surfacing (e.g., the basecourse, surface dressed). The wearing course should be applied not more than one year later. The success of such work depends largely on local knowledge of the material and for this reason the method is most applicable to direct-labour jobs. Since high compacted densities are unlikely to be obtained, some traffic deformation must be expected.

US specifications for unbound sub-bases and bases

12.18   Both AASHTO and ASTM have issued specifications for unbound sub-base and base materials. These are briefly discussed below.

12.19   In AASHTO Designation M147–65 (1980) are specified the six gradings, A–F, shown in Table 12.4 and Fig. 12.5. Grading A is used primarily for bases and gradings B–D refer to sub-base materials. Gradings E and F are used as top courses for unsurfaced roads. Requirements in relation to plasticity of fines and aggregate durability are shown below Table 12.4.

12.20   The extremes of the grading envelopes of materials B, C, and D correspond quite closely with British Type 2 sub-base material and material A is very similar in grading to Type 1 sub-base and wet-mix road base. The subdivisions used in the

Table 12.4   Grading requirements for unbound sub-bases and base materials to AASHTO Designation M147-65 (1980)

Sieve size	Grading: percentage passing					
	A	B	C	D	E	F
50 mm	100	100				
25 mm	—	75–95	100	100	100	100
9.5 mm	30–60	40–75	50–85	60–100	—	—
4.75 mm	25–55	30–60	35–65	50–85	55–100	70–100
2 mm	15–40	20–45	25–50	40–70	40–100	55–100
425 μm	8–20	15–30	15–30	25–45	20–50	30–70
75 μm	2–8	5–20	5–15	5–20	6–20	8–25

Other requirements:
1. Coarse aggregate (>2 mm) to have a percentage wear by Los Angeles test not more than 50.
2. Fraction passing 425 μm sieve to have a liquid limit not greater than 25 per cent and a plasticity index not greater than 6 per cent.

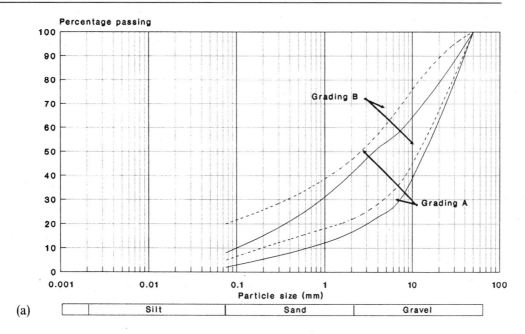

(a)

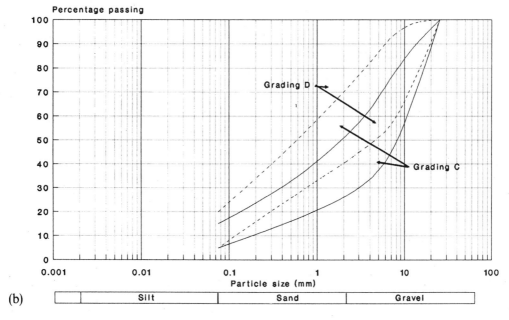

(b)

Figure 12.5   Materials for unbound bases and sub-bases. AASHTO Designation M147-65 (1980): (a) gradings A and B; (b) gradings C and D; (c) gradings E and F (overleaf)

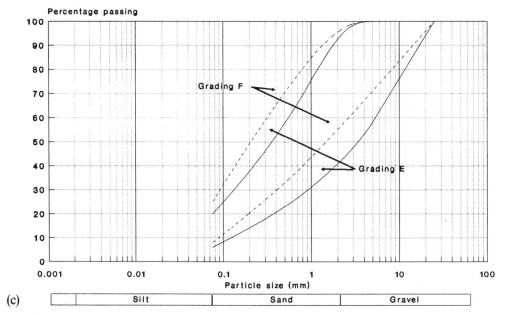

Figure 12.5 (*contd*)   (c) gradings E and F

AASHTO specification cover materials of different maximum sizes and this may have advantages when considering layer thickness.

12.21   Two gradings, one for sub-base and the other for base, are specified in ASTM Designation D2940-74 (re-approved 1985), and are shown in Table 12.5 and Fig. 12.6. Again, requirements in relation to plasticity of fines and durability of aggregate are shown under Table 12.5. The sub-base grading is more restrictive, particularly with regard to the finer grading limit, than Type 2 sub-base, but the grading for base material is very similar to the UK Type 1 sub-base and wet-mix gradings.

12.22   Neither the AASHTO nor the ASTM specifications give a strength criterion for the compacted materials, but the Asphalt Institute Thickness Design Manual[5] requires in its Table V-3 a CBR value of 20 per cent for sub-base and 80 per cent for base material. These are laboratory test results carried out at the appropriate moisture content and density conditions, and tested after four days' soaking.

Structural properties of unbound materials

12.23   Hicks and Monismith have published the results of comprehensive studies of the modulus of elasticity (resilient modulus) of a wide range of unbound granular materials and crushed rocks. Figures 12.7 and 12.8 are reproduced from their paper.[6]

12.24   Figure 12.7 shows the results from repeated loading triaxial tests on dry

Table 12.5   Grading requirements for bases and sub-bases for highways and airports to ASTM Designation D2940-74 (reapproved 1985)

Sieve size	Grading: percentage passing	
	Bases	Sub-bases
50 mm	100	100
37.5 mm	95–100	90–100
19 mm	70–92	—
9.5 mm	50–70	—
4.75 mm	35–55	30–60
600 μm	12–25	—
75 μm	0–8	0–12

Other requirements:
1. Coarse aggregate to be hard and durable.
2. Fraction passing the 75-μm sieve not to exceed 60 per cent of the fraction passing the 600-μm sieve.
3. Fraction passing the 425-μm sieve shall have a liquid limit no greater than 25 per cent and a plasticity index not greater than 4 per cent.

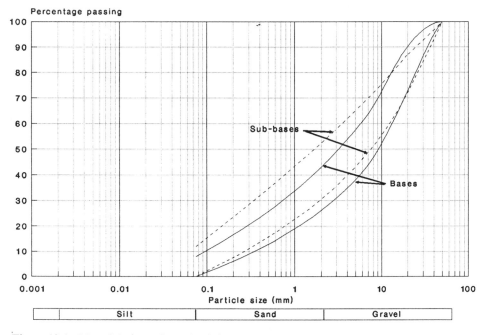

Figure 12.6   Materials for unbound sub-base and base—ASTM Designation D2940-74

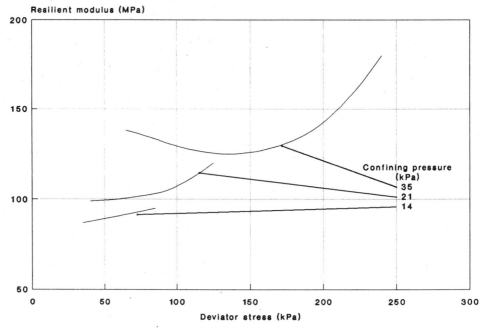

Figure 12.7 Relationships between resiliant modulus, deviator stress, and confining pressure for dry crushed gravel

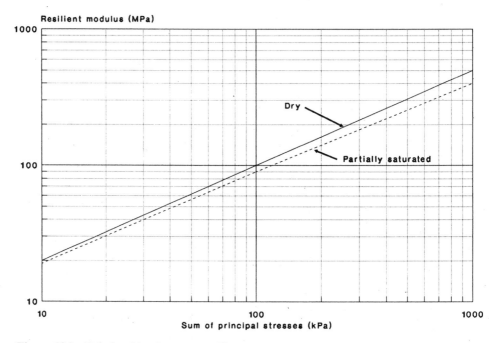

Figure 12.8 Relationships between resiliant modulus and stress conditions for granular materials

210

crushed gravel of a type suitable for sub-bases. The samples were conditioned by about 1000 applications of a medium-stress regime before the commencement of each series of tests. It was found possible to characterize the resilient modulus after 50–100 applications of stress. As would be expected, the modulus varied widely with confining stress. Figure 12.8 shows that plotted on a log–log basis the relationships between resilient modulus and confining pressure and between resilient modulus and the sum of the principal stresses are linear, and moisture content has little influence on the relationships. The tests showed that the grading and state of compaction of crushed rock and crushed gravel have only a small influence on the modulus.

12.25 The results given above provide useful target values for the elastic properties of sub-base and unbound base materials to be adopted in the structural analysis of pavements. An initial modulus of 150 MPa with a Poisson ratio of 0.3 is usually selected for the unbound base and a modulus of 100–150 MPa for the sub-base. Except when the subgrade is unusually stiff the use of such high modulus values leads to the prediction of significant tensile stresses in the unbound material (> 10 kPa). A stress-dependant modulus must therefore be used so that tensile stresses in excess of 10 kPa are not predicted.

References

1. British Standards Institution: *Methods for Sampling and Testing of Mineral Aggregates, Sands and Fillers*, British Standard 812:Part 3:1975, BSI, London, 1975.
2. British Standards Institution: *Methods of test for soils for engineering purposes*, British Standard 1377:1975, Test 16, BSI, London, 1975.
3. British Standards Institution: *Methods of Test for Soils for Engineering Purposes*, British Standard 1377:1975, Test 15, BSI London, 1975.
4. British Standards Institution: *Testing of aggregates: Part 1:Compatability test for graded aggregates*, British Standard 5835:Part 1:1980, BSI, London, 1980.
5. *Thickness Design—Pavements for Highways and Streets*, Asphalt Institute Manual Series No. 1 (MS-1), Asphalt Institute, College Park, Maryland, 1984.
6. Hicks, R. G. and C. L. Monismith: *Factors Influencing the Resilient Response of Granular Materials*, Highway Research Board Record 345, National Research Council, pp. 15–31, Washington, D.C., 1971.

13. Cement-bound sub-bases and roadbases

Introduction

13.1 The concept of increasing the strength of granular materials by the addition of cement has been approached on the one hand as an extension of soil mechanics and on the other as a development from concrete technology. During the past 50 years the soil cement process has attracted enthusiasts worldwide. The notion that the natural soil can be converted into a stable road base without the importation of materials other than cement is clearly attractive. Multiple- and single-pass machines to distribute the cement, mix it, and finally compact the product have been developed and used with success. However, two questions must be answered before such a process can be adopted, as follows:

1. Will the process be economical, compared with the importation of traditional materials?
2. How will the material behave long-term as part of the road pavement?

13.2 It does not follow that a small amount or cement added to a soil or to a granular material will necessarily improve its performance. Unbound materials will tend to compact under traffic stresses and become stronger, but cemented materials may crack and produce a gradation not susceptible to such traffic compaction. This is an aspect of pavement behaviour which is particulary susceptible to theoretical analysis. The liability of a cemented material to crack under the prevailing stress regime can be investigated and the consequences for the pavement structure as a whole assessed. This subject is discussed in detail in Chapter 21.

Soil cement as a sub-base or capping layer

13.3 There is no doubt that the mixing of cement with a soil which is free of deleterious organic matter will increase the strength and render the soil more capable of carrying construction traffic. The question the engineer must answer is whether the improvement is economic when considered in relation to:

1. the cost of additional sub-base material necessary to effect the same increase in pavement strength, and
2. the cost of the cement and the processing operations.

212

13.4   In Britain the soil cement process is not applied to soils of the sandy gravel classification, it being considered that these should be sufficiently strong for sub-base use without the additional cement. The UK Department of Transport *Specification for Highway Works* defines a coarse grading limit only, as indicated in Table 13.1 and in Fig. 13.1(a). Any soil with a finer grading can be considered for cement stabilization. However, experience shows that two other requirements should be met

Table 13.1   Coarse grading limit for soil cement

BS sieve size	Percentage by mass passing
50 mm	100
37.5 mm	95
20 mm	45
10 mm	35
5 mm	25
600 μm	8
300 μm	5
75 μm	0

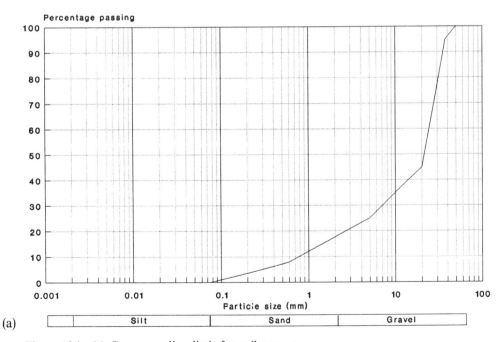

(a)

Figure 13.1   (a) Coarse grading limit for soil cement

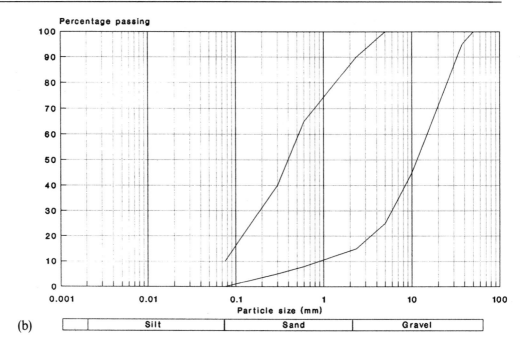

(b)

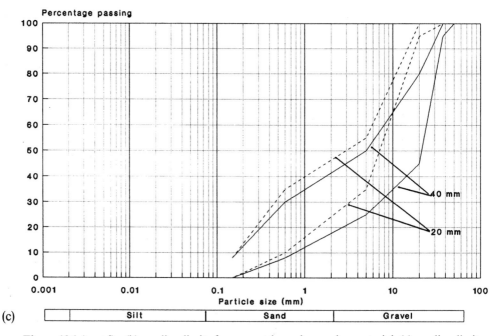

(c)

Figure 13.1 (*contd*)   (b) grading limits for cement-bound granular material; (c) grading limits for lean concrete

if the process is likely to be economic. These are as follows:

1. The soil should be well graded with a coefficient of uniformity of 5 or more. (The coefficient of uniformity is obtained from the grading curve: it is the ratio of the particle sizes corresponding to summation percentages of 60 per cent and 10 per cent.)
2. The plastic material passing the 425-μm sieve should have a liquid limit not greater than 45 per cent and a plastic limit not greater than 20 per cent. This requirement will exclude all heavy clays, but permit the use of sandy and silty clays.

13.5 When the soil cement process is used for improving the subgrade or providing a sub-base, the field operations must be preceded by a programme of laboratory testing. This will be aimed at determining the cement and water contents to be used to obtain the required strength. The latter is measured using 150-mm cubes. To determine the optimum moisture content to be used, the soil is compacted in three layers in the cube mould, without any cement. A vibrating hammer with a foot approximately 100 mm square is applied to each layer for a period of one minute with a downward force of 300–400 N. The wet density is obtained for a range of moisture contents and the optimum moisture content for maximum density deduced. A moisture content of about 1 per cent higher than this value is used for the mixing of the soil cement. A number of cubes are then made using this moisture content and a range of cement contents, the same compaction being used. After 7 days' curing in a saturated atmosphere, crushing strengths are determined and the cement content which gives the strength requirement for soil cement shown in Table 13.2 is selected.

Table 13.2 Strength and density requirements for cemented sub-bases and bases

Cement-stabilized material		Mixing method	Minimum compressive strength at 7 days, N/mm^2	
			Av. of 5	Individual
Soil cement	(CBM 1)*	in-place or plant	4.5	2.5
Cement-bound granular	(CBM 2)*	Plant	7.0	4.5
Normal-strength lean concrete	(CBM 3)	Plant	10.0	6.5
Higher-strength lean concrete	(CBM 4)	Plant	15.0	10.0

Note: Minimum field compaction 95 per cent cube density, based on mean of five field measurements and five cubes

*Description used in the Department of Transport *Specification for Highway Works*, Cl. 1036–1039.

13.6   When soil cement is used in a contract, a field trial should always be carried out in advance of the main work. This should involve an area of not less than 50 m by 10 m, particularly when the mix-in-place method is to be used. The equipment used for the trial should be the same as that for the main works. After spreading, and prior to compaction, batches of five cubes should be made up using the spread material. The wet density should be calculated and the cubes stored in the curing room. A few hours after the compaction of the trial area, batches of five determinations of wet density should be made using the sand replacement method. These tests should also be used to calibrate a nuclear density meter if it is intended to adopt this method of controlling density during the construction phase. The plant used for the compaction of the soil cement and the number of passes in relation to layer thickness should be the same as is recommended for unbound sub-bases and bases in Table 12.2. The strength and density of the soil cement as laid in the trial should be compared with the requirements given in Table 13.2.

13.7   If plant mix is used for the soil cement process, it is essential to use a paddle or pan-type mixer, and not a drum mixer. Where it is proposed to use the mix-in-place method consideration should be given to using a specialist subcontractor with the necessary plant and expertise. Such a contractor should also be able to carry out the preliminary laboratory testing described above.

13.8   For soil cement made with predominantly fine-grading soils (sand-silt-clays) used as capping layer or sub-base the CBR value after 7 days' curing is sometimes specified as an alternative to the crushing strength requirement. Target values in the range 30–70 per cent are generally used. Full details of the preparation of the samples and the test procedure are given in BS 1924. Where this method of specification is used, *in situ* CBR tests can be used for site testing.

Cement-bound granular material

13.9   This is exclusively a plant-mixed material, using a paddle or pan-type mixer, but otherwise it can be regarded as a rather stronger form of soil cement made with granular (crushed rock or gravel) aggregate. The grading should fall between the limits shown in Table 13.3 and Fig 13.1(b). The seven-day crushing strength requirements are included in Table 13.2.

13.10   The preliminary laboratory testing to determine the optimum moisture content and the strength and density are exactly the same as those described for soil cement in Para. 13.5 above.

13.11   When used as a sub-base for flexible pavements this material can be hand laid, but when it provides the base for such a pavement, or the sub-base for concrete roads, it should be laid by paver.

Lean concrete

13.12   This material is normally made from batched coarse and fine aggregates, although naturally occurring all-in washed aggregate can also be used. The aggre-

Table 13.3 Grading limits for cement-bound granular material

BS sieve size	Percentage by mass passing
50 mm	100
37.5 mm	95–100
20 mm	45–100
10 mm	35–100
5 mm	25–100
2.36 mm	15–90
600 μm	8–65
300 μm	5–40
75 μm	0–10

Table 13.4 Grading limits for lean concrete

BS sieve size	Percentage by mass passing nominal maximum size	
	40 mm	20 mm
50 mm	100	—
37.5 mm	95–100	100
20 mm	45–80	95–100
5 mm	25–50	35–55
600 μm	8–30	10–35
150 μm	0–8*	0–8*

*0–10 for crushed rock fines.

gate will be crushed rock, gravel, or crushed air-cooled blast furnace slag or a combination of these materials. Natural aggregates should comply with the requirements of BS 882 and slag with BS 1047. The grading limits are shown in Table 13.4 which caters for nominal maximum sizes of 40 mm and 20 mm. The limiting grading curves are shown in Fig. 13.1(c).

13.13 The Department of Transport specification provides for normal and higher-strength lean concrete as indicated in Table 13.2. The preparatory laboratory work to determine the moisture content and cement content is the same as that described in Para. 13.5. Some adjustment to the moisture content may be necessary to improve workability. Compaction should be in accordance with Table 12.2.

13.14 Lean concrete can be mixed in drum mixers as well as the pan and paddle types. On larger jobs it should always be laid by paver. Preliminary field density measurements should be made within 24 hours of compaction, by the sand replacement method. These tests can be used to calibrate the nuclear density meter if one is being used for control purposes.

US practice in relation to cemented sub-bases and bases

13.15   In the United States cemented sub-base and roadbase materials are not subdivided in terms of grading limits as is the case in Britain. Cement contents are recommended for the various soil types classified under AASHTO Designation M145-82 (see Para. 10.51). These cement contents, on a mass basis, vary from 3.5 to 7 per cent for A1–A3 soils (granular materials) to 7–10 per cent for A4–A7 soils (silt-clay materials). They are expected to give seven-day strengths of not less than 2 MN/m^2, and provide a starting point for the laboratory work necessary to establish the strength required.

13.16   Much more use is made in the United States of *in situ* soil stabilization than is the case in Europe. A wide range of multiple and single-pass plant has been developed and this has led to cost savings from this process which cannot in general be realized in smaller countries.

Influence of sample dimensions on the measured strength of cemented materials

13.17   Laboratory samples prepared in connection with the design of cement-stabilized materials are sometimes made in cylindrical moulds or, in the case of fine-grained soils, in 100 mm cubical moulds. In addition, to establish the actual strength of cured cemented sub-base and base materials it is common practice to test

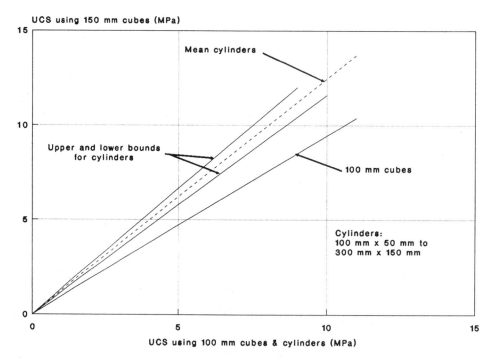

Figure 13.2   Relationship between crushing strength and sample size and shape

cores cut through the full depth of the material. To equate the results to strengths based on 150-mm cubes, it is necessary to know the relationship between the various types of test. Figure 13.2 shows the results of relevant tests carried out by the TRRL.

The structural properties of cemented base, sub-base, and capping materials

Increase in compressive strength with age

13.18   The increase in compressive strength with age for cemented materials with a wide range of compressive strengths has been studied over periods up to 10 years in the UK at the TRRL.[1,2] For lean concrete and soil cement the average relationship is given in Fig. 13.3. For pavement quality concrete the rate of increase of strength with age decreases slightly with increasing compressive strength. This is shown in Fig. 15.1.

Modulus of elasticity

13.19   The modulus of elasticity of cemented materials can be measured statically by loading 150 mm diameter cylinders fitted with extensometers, or dynamically using electrodynamic excitation on long beams of 150 mm square section. Both methods are described in BS 1881:Parts 121 and 203. The static method involves

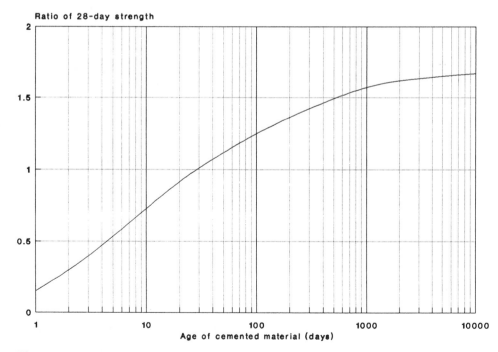

Figure 13.3 Influence of age on compressive strength of cemented materials

strains greater and more sustained than those experienced in pavements under the action of traffic. With the dynamic method the strains are less than occur under traffic, and of higher frequency. The comparative studies which have been made show the dynamic modulus to be consistently higher than the static value over a wide range of compressive strengths, as is indicated in Fig. 13.4. (The zones referred to on this figure are shown in Fig. 13.5). For weak cemented materials the ratio dynamic E:static E can be as high as 2:1, but for concretes it is much smaller.

13.20   Which value should be used for the structural analysis of pavements is not at present clear. Further research is required using dynamic loading tests which model traffic loading. For the time being it appears reasonable to use the mean between the two methods of measurement. Figure 13.6 shows the results of dynamic modulus tests carried out on a range of materials conforming to the grading zones shown on Fig. 13.4. These tests were carried out at the TRRL. Grading zones 2, 3, and 4 approximately cover the grading limits for cement-bound granular material (CMB 2) and grading zones 1 and 2 approximate to the grading limits for lean concrete (CMB 3 and 4). Grading zone 2 and finer correspond to the requirements for soil cement (CMB 1) and capping-layer material.

13.21   Figure 13.6 also includes measurements on two soil–cements made with cohesive soils (gradings 6 and 7). These would correspond to stabilized capping

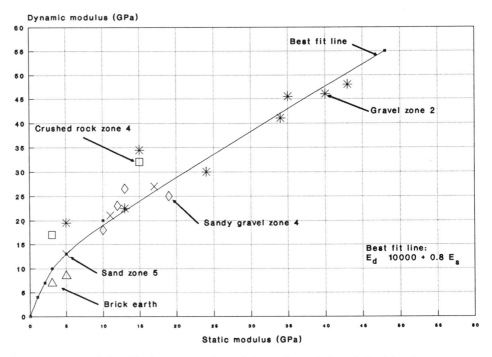

Figure 13.4   Relationship between static and dynamic modulus of elasticity for cemented materials

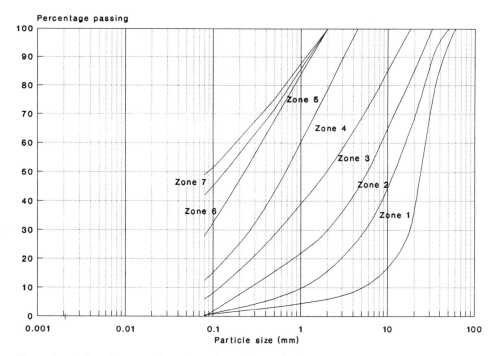

Figure 13.5 Grading zones for cement-bound materials

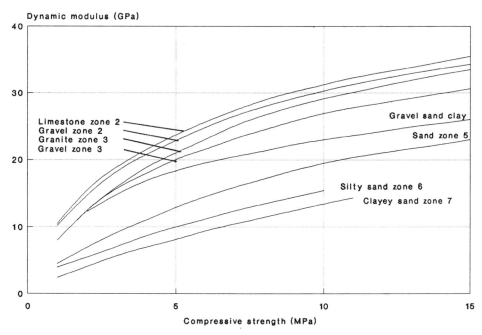

Figure 13.6 Relationship between dynamic modulus of elasticity and compressive strength at 28 days for cemented materials

material. For a more cohesive capping material of plasticity index 33 per cent, it has been found, using static tests, that the elastic modulus in tension was only about 10 per cent of the value in compression.[3] This is considered to be due to the development of microshrinkage cracks during curing. In computing tensile stresses in such materials a modulus of elasticity of not more than 25 per cent of the measured dynamic value would probably represent a reasonable estimate.

13.22   From the information given in Fig. 13.6 and on the basis of the discussion in Paras 13.19 and 13.20, Table 13.5 has been prepared.

Poisson's ratio

13.23   Kolias and Williams have studied Poisson's ratio for various cemented materials ranging from stabilized cohesive soil to lean concrete.[4] Static values close to 0.15 were found at an age of 28 days. Anson and Newman found a similar value for dense concrete.[5] It appears that, as with elastic modulus, dynamic values are rather higher, but it is suggested that this value should be used, since structural analyses are not sensitive to small changes in this factor.

Flexural and fatigue strength

13.24   Figure 13.7 shows the relations between compressive strength and dynamic modulus for a wide range of cemented materials with gradings within the limits for soil cement, cement-bound material, and lean concrete.

13.25   In the testing of concrete beams in flexure, the extreme fibre stress measured at the surface of the test beam is generally greater than the flexural strength as recorded by the standard test procedure. This extreme fibre stress is often referred to as the modulus of rupture. In the structural analysis of concrete pavements, the modulus of rupture, rather than the flexural strength, is used to

Table 13.5   Proposed values of elastic modulus of cemented materials for use in structural analyses

Stabilized material	Modulus of elasticity, GPa		
	Dynamic	Static	Mean
Soil–cement (CMB 1)			
Granular soils	18	10	14
Silty soils			
PI less than 10	7	4	5
Cement-bound granular (CMB 2)	23	13	18
Normal lean concrete (CMB 3)	27	19	23
Stronger lean concrete (CMB 4)	30	23	27
Capping layer			
Granular	18	9	14
Silty soil PI < 10	7	4	6
Clay soil PI > 10	1	0	0.5

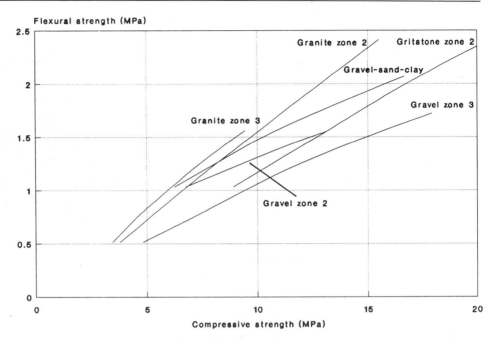

Figure 13.7 Relationship between compressive strength and flexural strength at 28 days for cemented materials

denote the onset of cracking. Sufficient information is not available for weaker cemented materials to allow this differentiation, and the flexural strength is used to define failure by cracking.

13.26   Symons has made a study of the fatigue strength of several cement-bound materials using the equipment shown in Fig. 13.8.[6] The frequency of oscillation was determined by the fundamental flexural resonance of the beams used, which was about 140 Hz, although this varied slightly with the cement content. The results are shown in Fig. 13.9. Galloway *et al.* have used a similar but more sophisticated loading procedure applied to concrete beams but they have included some tests on lean concrete of 7-day compressive strength 12 MN/m^2. The frequency of loading used was 20 Hz and tests were conducted on samples of different ages between 13 weeks and 2 years. The results of this work also are included in Fig. 13.9. Both sets of measurements indicate a failure stress of approximately 75–80 per cent of the flexural strength at 10^5 stress applications. This follows the generally accepted behaviour of pavement concretes.

13.27   In the above tests the failure was induced in a comparatively short period. The figure of 10^5 applications in the Symons tests was achieved in about 12 minutes, and in the Galloway tests in 80 minutes. The effects of ageing did not therefore influence the results. In the case of a road pavement, the incidence of very heavy wheel loads could be limited to about 10 per day, and 10^5 applications would be

Figure 13.8 Equipment used for repeated loading fatigue tests on beams of cemented materials

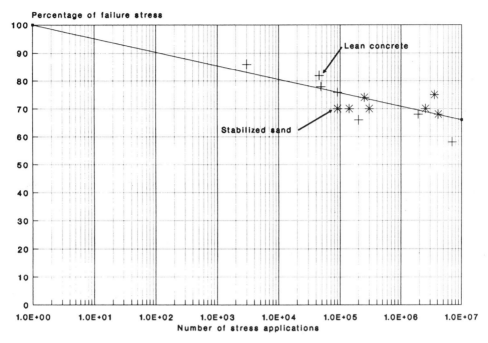

Figure 13.9   Fatigue of cement-stabilized materials

spread over a period in excess of 20 years; also, during the early life of the road the increase in flexural strength would tend to counteract the influence of fatigue. This matter is dealt with more fully in Chapters 21 and 22.

References

1. Road Research Laboratory: *Concrete Roads—Design and Construction*, p. 58, HMSO, London, 1955.
2. Galloway, J. W., H. M. Harding and K. D. Raithby: *Effects of Age on Flexural Fatigue and Compressive Strength of Concrete*, Transport and Road Research Laboratory Report LR 865, TRRL, Crowthorne, 1979.
3. Bofinger, H.E.: *The Measurement of the Tensile Properties of Soil-cement*, Transport and Road Research Laboratory Report No. LR 365, TRRL, Crowthorne, 1970.
4. Kolias, S. and R. I. T. Williams: Research on the Tensile Properties of Cement Stabilised Materials, University of Surrey.
5. Anson, M. and K. Newman: The effect of mix proportions and methods of testing on Poisson's ratio for mortars and concretes, *Magazine of Concrete Research*, **18** (56), 115–30 (1966).
6. Symons, I. F.: *A Preliminary Investigation to Determine the Resistance of Cement-stabilised Materials to Repeated Loading*, Transport and Road Research Laboratory Report LR 61, TRRL, Crowthorne, 1967.

14. Bituminous bases and surfacings

Introduction

14.1   The term bituminous material is applied to any mixture of aggregate and bituminous binder used in road construction. In the UK it also includes similar materials where tar is used as the binder; however, with the increasing use of natural gas, coal tar has ceased to be widely available.

14.2   In the USA all aggregate–bitumen mixtures are referred to as asphaltic concretes, but the term asphalt in Britain is reserved for dense, impervious mixes with a relatively high binder content. As already noted in Chapter 2, the first bituminous surfacings were laid in Paris in the eighteen-fifties. They consisted of natural rock, impregnated with asphalt, which was ground to a powder and consolidated with hot compacting irons. This process spread to England in the eighteen-seventies and subsequently to New York and other major American cities. Plant-mixed materials using tar and bitumen binders date from the beginning of the present century.

14.3   Until the nineteen-thirties, city and local-authority engineers developed their own specifications for bituminous materials largely on the basis of full-scale trials on their own road systems. Since then the responsibility of producing standard specifications has passed to organizations such as the British Standards Institution in the UK, the Laboratoire Central des Ponts et Chaussées in France, and the ASTM, AASHTO and the Asphalt Institute, in the USA.

14.4   In Europe, recipe-type specifications have been favoured in which aggregate grading, aggregate type, binder content, binder stiffness, mixing temperature, laying temperature and compaction procedure are all specified for mixes intended to fulfil particular requirements. In the USA recent developments have been towards laboratory design procedures aimed at producing specific stability properties in the mixes. This trend originated in the Second World War when airfield surfacings had to be designed for heavy wheel loads under a wide range of environmental conditions. Both the recipe and design approaches are considered in this chapter.

14.5   Bituminous materials should not be used as sub-base. To be effective all bituminous mixes need to be well compacted and this is not feasible on a weak foundation such as that provided by a subgrade of CBR 10 per cent or less. A granular sub-base modified if necessary by the addition of cement should normally be used, but an essential requirement is that the foundation will support the bituminous paver and its supply vehicles used to lay the base.

226

14.6 Bituminous materials are used for the base (or roadbase) and for the two layers of the surfacing, the lower of which is referred to as the basecourse (UK) or the binder course (USA) and the upper as the wearing course.

14.7 Bases may be wholly of bituminous material or they may consist of an upper bituminous base on a lower unbound or cemented base. An advantage of modern methods of structural analysis for pavements is that they allow alternative designs to be formulated for such composite bases which can each be costed.

Compaction of bituminous materials

14.8 Compaction of all bituminous materials is important both to increase their stiffness and to reduce subsequent compaction under traffic. This is particularly the case with bituminous base materials which may have a finished thickness of more than 300 mm and provide the main structural element of the pavement. The UK Department of Transport *Specification for Highway Works*[1] requires that the *minimum* thickness which should be laid in one pass of the paving machine should be 90 mm unless the design requirement for the layer is less than this thickness (e.g., a wearing course). It further states that compaction shall be by a smooth-wheel roller of 8–10 tonnes weight, with a roll width not less than 450 mm. Alternatively, a pneumatic-tyred or vibrating roller giving the same performance can be used.

14.9 For unbound and cement bound materials a *maximum* thickness of layer is normally specified to ensure deep compaction. The fact that the reverse appears to be the case with bituminous materials is related to their rate of cooling after spreading. Research has shown that a more uniform and generally greater density is obtained when thick-lift compaction is used in conjunction with sufficiently heavy plant. Figure 14.1 compares the density profile with depth for a dense bituminous base laid in one and three layers with a total thickness of 240 mm.[2] Heat retention in the thick layer obviates the large density changes at the interfaces of the three separate layers. However, where the sub-base is weak the laying of a thin lower layer may lead to an improved riding quality of the completed road.

14.10 Uniform compaction across the width of a pavement is also very important. Traditional methods of rolling concentrate compaction in the centre of the laid width, as shown in Fig. 14.2, giving a less than maximum density in the nearside wheel path, which is particularly important in relation to the slow traffic lane.[3]

British specifications for bituminous bases, basecourses, and wearing courses

Dense coated macadam roadbases (BS 4987:1988)[4]

14.11 Roadbase materials are made with aggregates of 40 mm maximum size and 28 mm maximum size. The gradings are shown in Table 14.1 and Fig. 14.3.

14.12 The binder contents for dense coated macadam roadbases are given in Table 14.2.

14.13 The 40-mm maximum size aggregate will normally be used where the

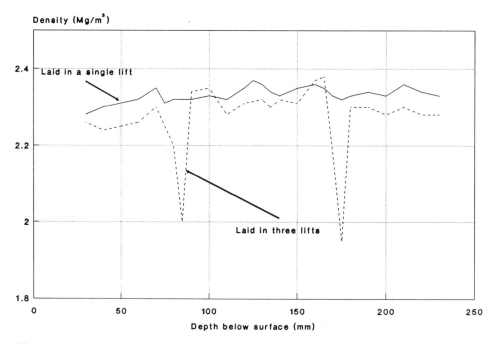

Figure 14.1 Typical density–depth profiles in dense bituminous roadbases compacted in one and three layers

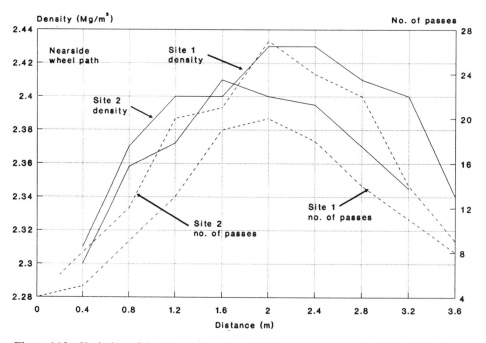

Figure 14.2 Variation of density and number of roller passes across the laid width of dense bitumen macadam at two sites

Table 14.1 Aggregate gradings for dense coated macadam bases of 40 mm and 28 mm maximum size

BS sieve	Percentage passing by mass	
	40 mm	28 mm
50 mm	100	—
37.5 mm	95–100	100
28 mm	70–94	90–100
20 mm	—	71–95
14 mm	56–76	58–82
6.3 mm	44–60	44–60
3.35 mm	32–46	32–46
300 μm	7–21	7–21
75 μm	2–9	2–9

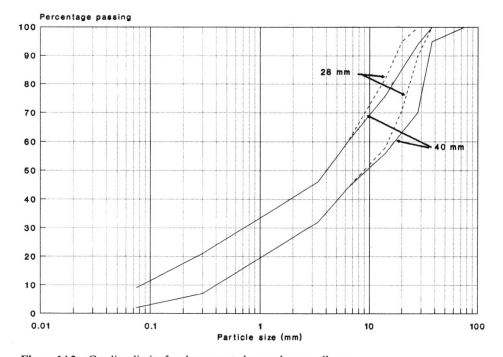

Figure 14.3 Grading limits for dense coated macadam roadbases

compacted layer thickness is 90–150 mm, and the 28-mm material where the layer thickness is 70–100 mm.

14.14 The limiting temperatures for mixing, laying, and compaction are shown in Table 14.3.

Table 14.2   Binder contents for dense coated bitumen macadam road bases

Aggregate	Percentage by mass of total mixture ($\pm 0.6\%$)			
	Bitumen binder 100 pen 200 pen		Tar binder C.58* C.54 C.50	
	40 mm	28 mm	40 mm	28 mm
Crushed rock	3.5	4.0	4.3	4.7
Blast furnace slag bulk density, kg/m^3				
1440	4.0	4.5	5.0	5.3
1360	4.2	4.8	5.3	5.6
1280	4.8	5.2	5.6	6.0
1200	5.4	5.8	6.0	6.4
1120	5.8	6.2	6.5	6.8
Steel slag	3.5	4.0	4.3	4.7
Gravel*	4.5	4.5	5.0	5.0

*C.58 tar should be used where the aggregate is wholly or partly flint gravel and traffic is heavy

Table 14.3   Limiting temperatures for mixing, spreading and compacting dense coated macadam

Bituminous material	Temperature, °C		
	Maximum mixing	Minimum spreading	Minimum rolling
Bitumen			
100 pen	160	120	75
200 pen	150	110	60
Tar			
C.58	125	90	70
C.54	110	80	60
C.50	105	80	60

Dense coated macadam basecourses (binder courses) (BS 4987:1988)[4]

14.15   Dense coated macadam basecourses are made with 40-mm, 28-mm and 20-mm maximum size aggregates. The gradings for the 40-mm and 28-mm materials are the same as those for the 40-mm and 28-mm roadbase materials shown in Table 14.1 and Fig. 14.3. The grading for the 20-mm material is shown in Table 14.4 and is compared with the grading envelopes for the 40-mm and 28-mm materials in Fig. 14.4.

Table 14.4 Aggregate grading for dense coated macadam basecourse material with 20-mm maximum size

BS sieve	Percentage passing by mass
28 mm	100
20 mm	95–100
14 mm	65–85
10 mm	52–72
6.3 mm	39–55
3.35 mm	32–46
300 μm	7–21
75 μm	2–9

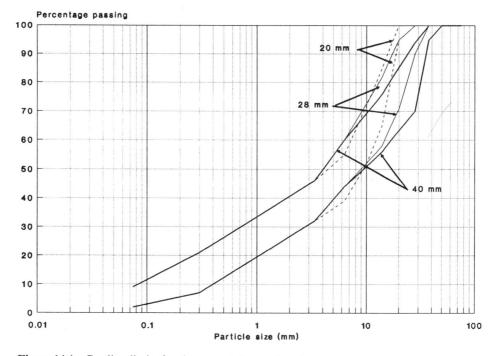

Figure 14.4 Grading limits for dense coated macadam basecourses

14.16 The binder contents for the three gradings are shown in Table 14.5.

14.17 The 40-mm maximum size aggregate will normally be used where the compacted thickness of the basecourse is 95–140 mm, the 28-mm maximum size for a thickness of 70–100 mm, and the 20-mm maximum size for a thickness of 50–80 mm.

Table 14.5   Binder contents for dense coated macadam basecourses

| | Percentage by mass of total mixture ($\pm 0.6\%$) | | | | | |
| | Bitumen binder 100 pen 200 pen | | | Tar binder C.58* C.54 C.50 | | |
Aggregate	40 mm	28 mm	20 mm	40 mm	28 mm	20 mm
Crushed rock	4.5	5.5	4.7	5.0	5.2	5.2
Blast furnace slag density kg/m³						
1440	5.2	5.5	5.5	5.5	5.7	5.7
1360	5.5	5.8	5.8	5.8	6.0	6.0
1280	5.8	6.2	6.2	6.2	6.4	6.4
1200	6.2	6.6	6.6	6.6	6.8	6.8
1120	6.6	7.0	7.0	7.0	7.3	7.3
Steel slag	4.1	4.3	4.2	5.0	5.2	5.2
Gravel*	4.8	5.0	5.0	5.3	5.5	5.5

*C.58 tar should be used where the aggregate is wholly or partly flint gravel and traffic is heavy

14.18   The limiting temperatures for mixing, laying, and compaction are the same as those shown in Table 14.3.

Dense coated macadam wearing course (BS 4987:1988)[4]

14.19   This material is made using 14-mm, 10-mm, or 6-mm maximum size aggregate. It is not recommended for use on other than comparatively lightly trafficked roads (less than 2.5 million standard axles in 20 years). For this level of traffic the 14-mm maximum size of aggregate only would be used, and the specification for that material alone is considered here.

14.20   The aggregate grading for dense coated macadam with 14-mm maximum size is shown in Table 14.6 below.

14.21   The binder content is given in Table 14.7. The use of tar binder and gravel aggregate is not recommended except for very light traffic.

14.22   Where this material is used the layer thickness will generally be between 40 and 55 mm. The material is pervious to water and it should be surface-dressed soon after laying.

14.23   The temperatures for mixing, spreading, and compaction are the same as those given in Table 14.3.

Pervious bitumen macadam (antisplash) wearing course (20-mm and 10-mm sizes)

14.24   These materials are highly pervious and they are intended to be laid on impervious surfacing materials to provide a reservoir and drainage layer to reduce

Table 14.6   Aggregate grading for dense coated macadam wearing course with 14-mm maximum size

BS sieve	Percentage passing by mass
20 mm	100
14 mm	95–100
10 mm	70–90
6.3 mm	45–65
3.35 mm	30–45
1.18 mm	15–30
75 μm	3–8

Table 14.7   Binder content for dense coated macadam wearing course with 14-mm maximum size

Aggregate	Bitumen binder 100 pen 200 pen % by mass of total mixture ($\pm 0.5\%$)
Crushed rock except limestone	5.1
Limestone	4.9
Blast furnace slag bulk density kg/m³	
1440	5.5
1360	6.0
1280	6.6
1200	7.0
1120	7.5
Steel slag	4.8

splash from fast-moving vehicles during periods of heavy rain. The aggregate gradings for the 20-mm and 10-mm maximum size materials are shown in Table 14.8 and in Fig. 14.5. Table 14.8 also includes the binder contents.

14.25   The mixing, laying, and rolling temperatures are given in Table 14.9.

14.26   The nominal layer thickness for the 20-mm material is 45–60 mm and for the 10-mm material 30–35 mm.

14.27   In addition to the materials discussed above, BS 4987 includes specification for a number of open-textured surfacing materials suitable for lightly trafficked roads.

Rolled asphalt (BS 594:1985)[5]

14.28   The bitumen macadam materials discussed above use a continuously graded aggregate mixed with bitumen in sufficient quantity to leave unfilled air voids within

Table 14.8 Grading of aggregate and binder content for previous wearing courses

| BS sieve | Aggregate Crushed rock or steel slag Percentage passing by mass | |
	20 mm	10 mm
28 mm	100	—
20 mm	90–100	—
14 mm	—	90–100
6.3 mm	20–30	40–50
3.35 mm	5–15	22–28
75 μm	3–7*	3–6
Bitumen content 100 pen and 200 pen	3.7 ± 0.3	5.2 ± 0.5

Note: bitumen content per cent by mass.
*To include 2 per cent by mass of aggregate of hydrated lime.

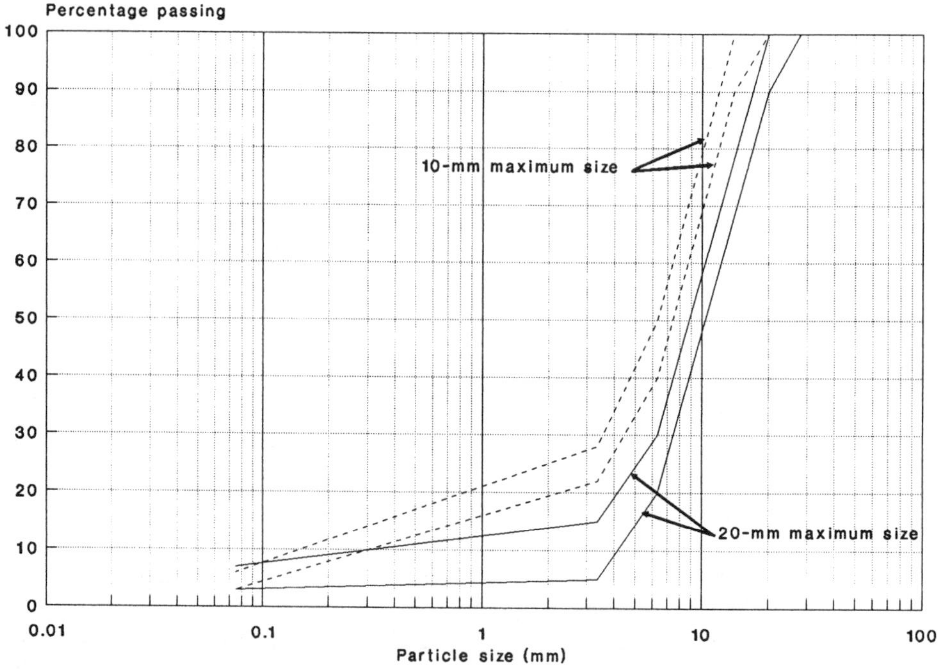

Figure 14.5 Grading limits for previous wearing course materials

the structure. Rolled asphalt differs, in that it employs a mixture of a coarse aggregate which is essentially of a single size mixed with a graded fine aggregate falling within the sand classification and containing some filler (finer than the 75-μm sieve size). The combined aggregate is markedly gap-graded. Figure 14.6 shows

Table 14.9 Mixing and laying temperatures for previous bitumen macadam surfacings

Grade of bitumen	Temperatures, °C		
	Maximum at any stage	Maximum laying	Maximum rolling
100 pen	135	120	85
200 pen	125	110	85

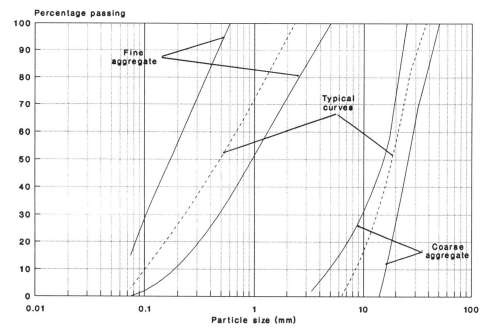

Figure 14.6 Grading limits for coarse and fine aggregates for rolled asphalt roadbases and basecourses

typical gradations for the coarse and fine aggregate and Fig. 14.7 shows the combined grading for the typical materials indicated on Fig. 14.6.

14.29 The concept is that the fine aggregate and filler form a mortar with the bitumen, which, during compaction, completely fills the voids between the coarser particles, and thus forms a dense impervious mixture. Although rolled asphalt is now regarded as a 'British' material it was in fact developed in the last years of the nineteenth century as a result of close cooperation between The Limmer Asphalt Paving Company of America and several local-authority engineers in London.

14.30 In earlier editions of BS 594 the mixes were defined in terms of proportions of coarse and fine aggregates, but in the latest revision the combined grading limits

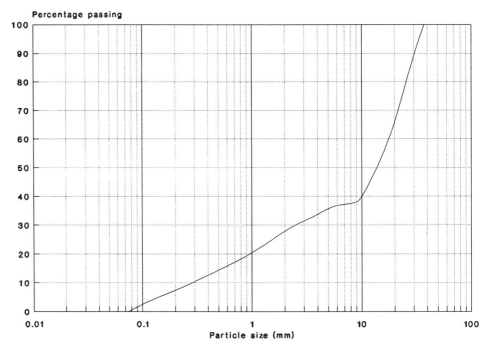

Figure 14.7 Grading of total aggregate based on typical gradings

are given and suppliers combine suitable aggregates to meet the requirements. This has led to a generally closer specification, which must be beneficial. Because the material is virtually saturated with bitumen after compaction, the properties of the sand are important in establishing the internal friction within the material.

Rolled asphalt roadbase materials (BS 594:1985)[5]

14.31   British Standard 594 now provides for three roadbase materials with increasing nominal size of aggregate, to suit increasing layer thickness. The gradings and binder contents are shown in Table 14.10 and the grading envelopes in Fig. 14.8.

14.32   The maximum temperature during mixing and the minimum temperature during rolling for rolled asphalt roadbases depends on the grade of the bitumen used, as indicated in Table 14.11.

Rolled asphalt basecourse (BS 594:1985)[5]

14.33   The grading limits and binder contents for rolled asphalt basecourse materials are shown in Table 14.12 and the grading envelopes in Fig. 14.9. The 50/10 and 50/14 materials will also be used as regulating layers.

14.34   The mixing and rolling temperature limitations are the same as those for rolled asphalt roadbases, shown in Table 14.11.

14.35   Where both rolled asphalt surfacing and rolled asphalt roadbases are used,

Table 14.10 Grading limits and binder contents of rolled asphalt roadbase materials

Designation*	60/20	60/28	60/40
Nominal layer thickness, mm	45–80	60–120	75–150
Percentage passing by mass			
50 mm	—	—	100
37.5 mm	—	100	90–100
28 mm	100	90–100	70–100
20 mm	90–100	50–80	45–75
14 mm	30–65	30–60	30–65
10 mm	—	—	—
6.3 mm	—	—	—
2.36 mm	30–44	30–44	30–44
600 µm	10–44	10–44	10–44
212 µm	3–25	3–25	3–25
75 µm	2–8	2–8	2–8
Binder content percentage by mass of total mix			
Crushed rock or steel slag	5.7	5.7	5.7
Gravel	5.5	5.5	5.5
Blast furnace slag bulk density kg/m³			
1440	5.7	5.7	5.7
1360	5.9	5.9	5.9
1280	6.0	6.0	6.0
1200	6.1	6.1	6.1
1120	6.3	6.3	6.3

*The mixture designation numbers (e.g., 0/3) refer to the nominal coarse aggregate content of the mixture/nominal size of the aggregate in the mixture respectively.

the basecourse can be replaced by additional roadbase, unless the engineer feels it desirable to retain the extra course in the interest of better riding quality.

Rolled asphalt wearing courses (BS 594:1985)[5]

14.36 Rolled asphalt wearing courses, like rolled asphalt basecourses, have been traditionally mixed using recipe specifications. In the 1973 edition of BS 594, a tentative design procedure was introduced to examine the stability of the fine aggregate–filler–binder content mixture. In the latest edition (1985) an alternative mix design procedure involving the total mix is included, together with the recipe specifications. Both the recipe and design procedures are now related to a fine (F) and coarse (C) set of grading requirements. The grading and binder contents for the recipe mixes are shown in Tables 14.13 and 14.14 for the fine (F) and coarse (C) mixes. Figure 14.10 compares the fine and coarse gradings suitable for a nominal

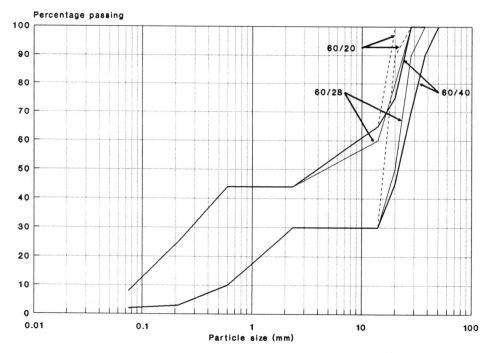

Figure 14.8   Grading envelopes for rolled-asphalt roadbase materials

Table 14.11   Mixing and rolling temperatures for rolled asphalt roadbase

| Grade of bitumen | Temperatures, °C | |
	Maximum at any stage	Maximum laying
35 pen	175	90
50 pen	170	85
70 pen	165	80

thickness of 35 mm of wearing course. It will be seen that the coarse grading is much less gap-graded than the finer grading. It will be noted that in Table 14.13 reference is made to Schedules 1A and 1B, 2A and 2B, and 3A and 3B in connection with the binder content. The quantities corresponding to the A schedules will normally be used, except where weather conditions are adverse, when the B schedules are to be used.

Table 14.12 Grading limits and binder contents of rolled asphalt basecourse materials

Designation*	50/10	50/14	50/20
Nominal layer thickness, mm	25–50	35–65	45–80
Percentage passing by mass			
50 mm	—	—	—
37.5 mm	—	—	—
28 mm	—	—	100
20 mm	—	100	90–100
14 mm	100	90–100	65–100
10 mm	90–100	65–100	35–75
6.3 mm	—	—	—
2.36 mm	35–55	35–55	35–55
600 µm	15–55	15–55	15–55
212 µm	5–30	5–30	5–30
75 µm	2–9	2–9	2–9
Binder content percentage by mass of total mix			
Crushed rock or steel slag	6.5	6.5	6.5
Gravel	6.3	6.3	6.3
Blast furnace slag bulk density, kg/m³			
1440	6.6	6.6	6.6
1360	6.7	6.7	6.7
1280	6.8	6.8	6.8
1200	6.9	6.9	6.9
1120	7.1	7.1	7.1

*The mixture designation numbers (e.g., 0/3) refer to the nominal coarse aggregate content of the mixture/nominal size of the aggregate in the mixture respectively.

Rolled asphalt wearing courses (design mixes)

14.37   The gradings used for rolled-asphalt wearing courses during design mixes are given in Tables 14.15 and 14.16. The gradings are in fact identical with those for the recipe mixes given in Tables 14.13 and 14.14 with the following exceptions: (1) for the fine mixes the grading for a nominal thickness of layer of 30 mm is omitted, and (2) an additional coarse grading suitable for a nominal thickness of layer of 25 mm has been added.

14.38   For the binder content a minimum target value for each mix is specified. The actual binder content is adjusted to give the values of stability and flow required by the contract. The terms of stability and flow are considered in detail in the next section dealing with USA specifications for bituminous materials. If the binder

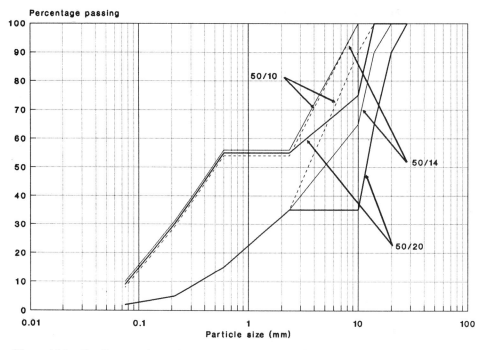

Figure 14.9   Grading envelopes for rolled-asphalt basecourse

content to achieve the required stability and flow is less than the minimum target binder content given in the appropriate Table 14.15 or 14.16 then the binder content used will be increased accordingly. The stability recommended for designed rolled asphalt wearing courses varies from 2–8 kN for traffic lanes carrying less than 1500 commercial vehicles per day, to 6–10 kN for traffic lanes carrying more than 6000 commercial vehicles per day.

14.40   Most rolled-asphalt wearing courses used in Britain have precoated chippings rolled into the surface as part of the laying operation. These must have a polished stone value capable of providing adequate low-speed skid resistance and they should be so inserted to give a texture depth which is adequate for high-speed skid resistance. This means that the chippings must stand proud of the matrix surface.

14.41   The chippings should be of nominal size 20 mm or 14 mm, the former being preferred for high-speed, heavily trafficked roads, for which a highly textured surface is necessary. The grading of the chippings should conform to the requirements of Table 14.17. They should be cubical in shape. This requirement is met by specifying a 'size and shape index' of 60 or less. The size and shape index is the sum of the percentage undersize and the flakiness index. The latter is determined in accordance with BS 63: one hundred representative chippings of the nominal size 20 mm or 14 mm are selected and the percentage which can be passed through a slot 6.5 mm wide is defined as the flakiness index.

Table 14.13   Composition of fine (type F) recipe wearing course mixtures

Designation*	0/3	15/10	30/10	30/14	40/14	40/20	55/20
Nominal layer thickness, mm	25	30	35	40	50	50	50
Percentage passing by mass							
28 mm	—	—	—	—	—	100	100
20 mm	—	—	—	100	100	95–100	90–100
14 mm	—	100	100	85–100	90–100	50–85	35–80
10 mm	—	95–100	85–100	60–90	50–85	—	—
6.3 mm	100	75–95	60–90	—	—	—	—
2.36 mm	96–100	75–87	60–72	60–72	50–62	50–62	35–47
600 µm	80–100	60–87	40–72	46–72	35–62	35–62	25–47
212 µm	25–70	20–60	15–50	15–50	10–40	10–40	5–30
75 µm	13–17	11–15	8–12	8–12	6–10	6–10	4–8
Maximum percentage aggregate passing 2.36 mm and retained on 600 µm BS sieve	—	18	14	14	12	12	9
Binder content percentage by mass of total mix							
Crushed rock or steel slag							
Schedule 1A1	10.3	8.9	7.8	7.8	7.0	7.0	5.8
Schedule 1B1	10.8	9.4	8.3	8.3	7.5	7.5	6.3
Gravel							
Schedule 2A1	10.3	8.9	7.5	7.5	6.5	6.5	—
Schedule 2B1	10.8	9.4	8.0	8.0	7.1	7.1	—
Blast furnace slag bulk density, kg/m³							
Schedule 3A1							
1440	—	9.0	7.9	7.9	7.2	7.2	—
1360	—	9.0	8.0	8.0	7.3	7.3	—
1280	—	9.2	8.1	8.1	7.4	7.4	—
1200	—	9.3	8.2	8.2	7.5	7.5	—
1120	—	9.4	8.3	8.3	7.6	7.6	—
Schedule 3B1							
1440	—	9.5	8.4	8.4	7.7	7.7	—
1360	—	9.6	8.5	8.5	7.8	7.8	—
1280	—	9.7	8.6	8.6	7.9	7.9	—
1200	—	9.8	8.7	8.7	8.0	8.0	—
1120	—	9.9	8.8	8.8	8.1	8.1	—

*The mixture designation numbers (e.g., 0/3) refer to the nominal coarse aggregate content of the mixture/nominal size of the aggregate in the mixture respectively.

14.42   The chippings are coated with a binder similar to that used in the wearing course; the mass of binder expressed as a percentage of the mass of coated chippings should be 1.5 ± 0.3. The chippings should be dried and fed into the mixer at temperature of 130–185 °C and the binder added at a temperature not exceeding 175 °C. To minimize the formation of insoluble material in the binder and to aid separation the chippings should be cooled quickly after discharge from the mixer.

Table 14.14 Composition of coarse (type C) recipe wearing course mixtures

Designation*	30/10	30/14	40/14	40/20
Nominal layer thickness, mm	35	40	50	50
Percentage passing by mass				
28 mm	—	—	—	100
20 mm	—	100	100	95–100
14 mm	100	85–100	90–100	50–85
10 mm	85–100	60–90	50–85	—
6.3 mm	60–90	—	—	—
2.36 mm	60–72	60–72	50–62	50–62
600 μm	25–45	25–45	20–40	20–40
212 μm	15–30	15–30	10–25	10–25
75 μm	8–12	8–12	6–10	6–10
Binder content percentage by mass of total mix				
Crushed rock	7.8	7.8	7.0	7.0
Steel slag	6.8	6.8	6.2	6.2
Blast furnace slag: bulk density, kg/m³				
1440	7.8	7.8	7.0	7.0
1360	7.9	7.9	7.2	7.2
1280	8.1	8.1	7.4	7.4
1200	8.3	8.3	7.8	7.6
1120	8.5	8.5	7.8	7.8

*The mixture designation numbers (e.g., 0/3) refer to the nominal coarse aggregate content of the mixture/nominal size of the aggregate in the mixture respectively.

This can be done by the application of clean water or by spreading the chippings out in a thin layer.

14.43   The chippings should be spread uniformly over the surface of the hot asphalt, after preliminary compaction by the paver. A mechanical chipping spreader is essential to obtain adequate uniformity. The rate of spread should be in accordance with Table 14.18. After spreading, the normal compaction procedure should be followed. If the chippings are laid to a lesser rate of spread than is given in Table 14.18 then an adequate texture-depth for the surfacing may not be obtained. If the rolling temperature is too low the chippings may pull out of the asphalt under the action of traffic.

US specifications for bituminous bases, binder courses, and wearing courses

14.44   The main difference between British dense-coated macadam materials and rolled asphalt lies in the grading of the aggregates. The gap grading of rolled asphalts provide sufficient space for a comparatively high binder content to be used without

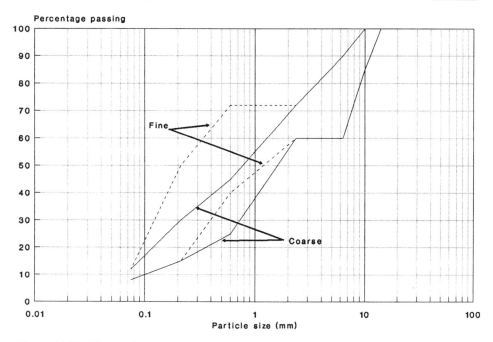

Figure 14.10 Fine and coarse gradings for recipe specification for rolled asphalt for 35 mm (nominal) wearing courses

the development of excess pore pressures in the hot binder during the compaction process. The high binder content gives increased cohesion, improved fatigue properties, and impermeability to water. However, it does increase cost and the use of rolled asphalt is generally confined to the major roads where the advantages are cost effective.

14.45   Rolled asphalt is not widely used in the United States. The term adopted there for every form of bitumen-bound material is asphaltic concrete, and although aggregates are compounded from coarse and fine fractions the gradings used are continuous as distinct from gap-graded. Figure 14.11 shows typical grading curves for asphaltic concrete binder and wearing courses. They are very similar to the gradings used in the UK for dense-coated macadam basecourses and wearing courses (see Tables 14.4 and 14.6).

14.46   The essential difference between British dense-coated macadam and US asphaltic concrete is that the binder content of the latter is designed in relation to the actual grading to ensure a required stability and flow accompanied by an appropriate air content in the fully compacted material.

The Marshall test procedure

14.47   The stability and flow of an asphaltic concrete mix are defined in terms of the empirical Marshall test. This is described in AASHTO Designation T245-82

Table 14.15 Composition of design type F wearing course mixtures

Designation*	0/3†	30/10	30/14	40/14	40/20	55/20
Nominal layer thickness, mm	25	35	40	50	50	50
Percentage passing by mass						
28 mm	—	—	—	—	100	100
20 mm	—	—	100	100	90–100	90–100
14 mm	—	100	85–100	90–100	50–85	35–80
10 mm	—	85–100	60–90	50–85	—	—
6.3 mm	100	60–90	—	—	—	—
2.36 mm	95–100	60–72	60–72	50–62	50–62	35–47
600 μm	80–100	45–72	45–72	35–62	35–62	25–47
212 μm	25–70	15–50	15–50	10–40	10–42	5–30
75 μm	13–17	8–12	8–12	6–10	6–12	4–80
Max. percentage aggregate passing 2.36 mm and retained on 600 μm sieve	—	14	14	12	12	9
Min. target binder content percentage by mass of total mixture‡	9.0	7.0	6.5	6.3	6.3	5.3

*The mixture designation numbers (e.g., 0/3) refer to the nominal coarse aggregate content of the mixture/nominal size of the aggregate in the mixture respectively.

†Suitable for regulating course.

‡In areas of the country where prevailing conditions are characteristically colder and wetter than the national average the addition of a further 0.5 per cent of binder may be beneficial to the durability of the wearing courses.

Table 14.16 Composition of design Type C wearing course mixtures

Column No.	13	14	15	16	17
Designation*	0/3	30/10	30/14	40/14	40/20
Nominal layer thickness, mm	25	35	40	50	50
Percentage passing by mass					
28 mm	—	—	—	—	100
20 mm	—	—	100	100	90–100
14 mm	—	100	85–100	90–100	50–85
10 mm	—	85–100	60–90	50–85	—
6.3 mm	100	60–90	—	—	—
2.36 mm	90–100	60–72	60–72	50–62	50–62
600 μm	30–66	25–45	25–45	20–40	20–40
212 μm	15–40	15–50	15–30	10–25	10–25
75 μm	13–17	8–12	8–12	6–10	6–10
Min. target binder content percentage by mass of total mixture†	9.0	7.0	6.5	6.3	6.3

*The mixture designation numbers (e.g., 0/3) refer to the nominal coarse aggregate content of the mixture/nominal size of the aggregate in the mixture respectively.

†In areas of the country where prevailing conditions are characteristically colder and wetter than the national average the addition of a further 0.5 per cent of binder may be beneficial to the durability of the wearing courses.

Table 14.17   Grading of precoated chippings for rolled asphalt wearing courses

BS sieve	Percentage passing by mass BS sieve	
	20 mm nominal	10 mm nominal
28 mm	100	—
20 mm	90–100	100
14 mm	0–25	90–100
6.3 mm	0–4	0–25
3.35 mm	—	0–4
75 μm	0–2	0–2

Table 14.18   Rates of spread of coated chippings on asphalt surfacings for major roads

	Rate of spread, kg/m^2					
	20-mm chippings, relative density			14-mm chippings, relative density		
Size and shape index	2.6	2.7	2.8	2.6	2.7	2.8
20	11.0	11.5	12.0	8.5	9.0	9.5
40	10.5	11.0	11.5	8.0	8.5	9.0
55	9.5	10.0	10.5	7.5	8.0	8.5

(1986),[6] or more fully in BS 598:Part 3:1985.[7] Briefly, the test is carried out on compacted samples of the mixture perpared in a steel mould 101.6 mm in diameter. Approximately 1100 g of the material at the appropriate mixing temperature is placed in the heated mould and compacted by a rammer with a circular foot of 98.5 mm diameter acted upon by a mass of 4585 g falling freely through a distance of 457 mm. Fifty blows are applied to each face of the sample at a rate of approximately one per second. After compaction the sample is stored at 20 °C for not more than 8 hours prior to testing.

14.48   Before testing, the weight of the dry sample in air is determined to an accuracy of 0.1 g. It is then weighed submerged in water at 20 °C to the same accuracy. The volume of the sample is numerically equal in cm^3 to the difference of the mass in air and water. The relative density of the specimen S_M, is equal to the mass in air divided by volume, and the aggregate density, S_A, is given by

$$S_A = \frac{S_M \times 100 - W_B}{100}$$

where W_B is the percentage by mass of the binder in the specimen.

14.49   For testing, the sample at a temperature maintained at 60 ± 0.5 °C is placed between the jaws of a testing head, shown in section in Fig. 14.12. The testing head

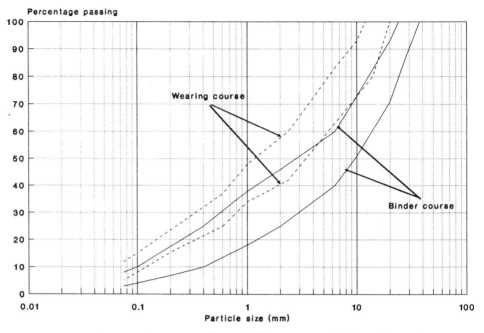

Figure 14.11   Typical grading curves for asphaltic concrete binder and wearing-course materials

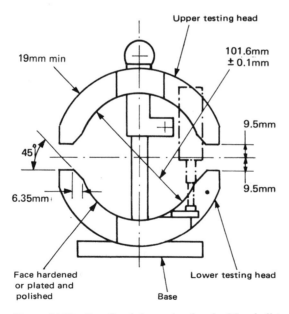

Figure 14.12   Details of the testing head—Marshall test

is mounted in a compression-testing machine capable of operating at a constant strain rate of 50 ± 3 mm per minute. Figure 14.13 shows a test in progress. The applied load–time curve is observed beyond the point where the maximum load has been recorded, in the manner indicated in Fig. 14.14.

14.50   From Fig. 14.14, the maximum load is 4.8 kN and this is defined as the stability. The time taken to reach this load is 4.5 s. At a strain rate of 50 mm/minute this corresponds to a deformation of $(50 \times 4.5)/60$, or 3.8 mm. This is termed the flow.

14.51   The design procedure involves making up and testing a number of samples of the bituminous material with different binder contents using the grade of bitumen intended for use. The results are plotted in the form shown in Fig. 14.15 (a)–(d), proposed in BS 598:Part 3:1985. The binder contents corresponding to maximum stability, maximum mix density, and maximum compacted aggregate density are meaned and the stability and flow at this mean binder content are recorded. This information provides the basis for the minimum stability and maximum flow values included in a contract specification. If the stability obtained is considered to be too low then an adjustment must be made to the grading or, more particularly, to the

Figure 14.13 Marshall test in progress

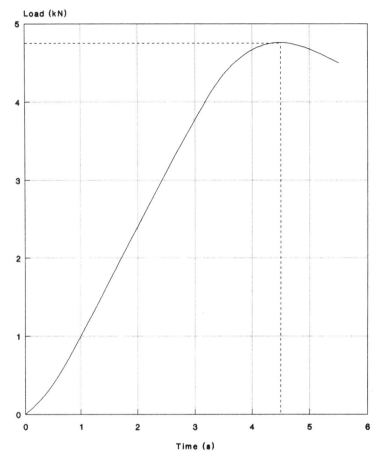

Figure 14.14   Relationship between load and time for Marshall test

penetration grade of the binder used. These tests will normally be conducted using bin aggregates. The contractors will subsequently have to carry out similar tests using the aggregate they propose to use to establish a job mix for the contract and, periodically, checks on the stability will also need to be made.

The structural properties of bituminous materials

14.52   The structural behaviour of bituminous materials in road pavements is much more complex than is the case with cemented materials. Some of the deformation which occurs in a pavement, owing to traffic, is within the bituminous materials. It is clear therefore that the materials do not behave completely elastically. The strain which occurs as a result of transient loading is dependent both on the temperature and the period for which the load is applied. There is no doubt that

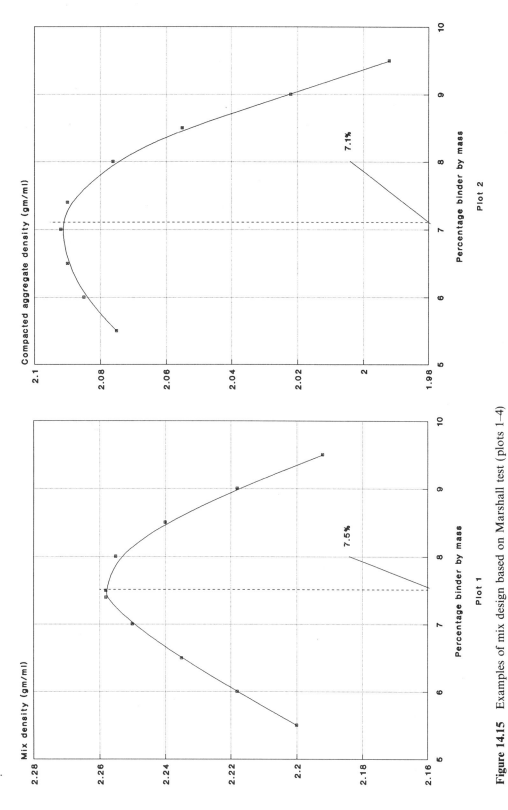

Figure 14.15 Examples of mix design based on Marshall test (plots 1–4)

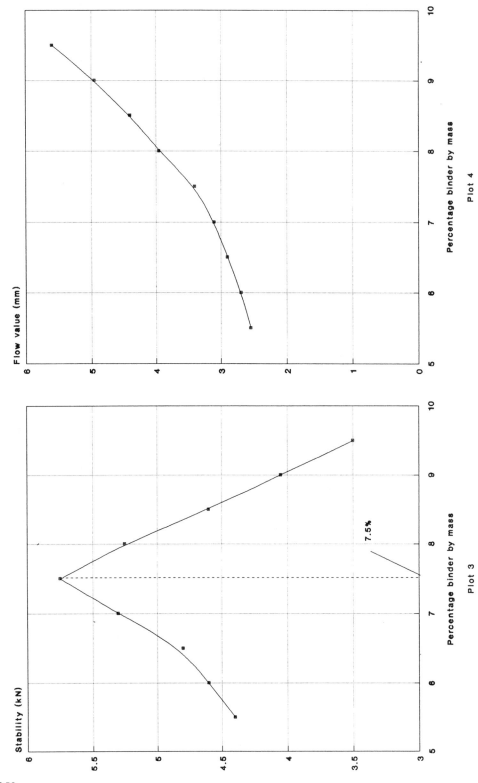

Figure 14.15 (*contd*)

bituminous road surfacings crack, but what proportion of the cracking is due to fatigue and what to thermal contraction is not easy to judge. With a wide range of experimental road pavements in Britain now reaching ages of 20–30 years, with complete histories of traffic, deformation, cracking, and transient deflection measured by the Deflection (Benkelman) Beam, there is a wealth of opportunity to model long-term behaviour using modern structural approaches. Attempts to do this are indicating large gaps in our present knowledge of the behaviour of bituminous roadbases, basecourses, and wearing courses. In particular, it is becoming clear that all bituminous materials in a situation where they are likely to have a moderately long life stiffen progressively with time and have an increasing rather than a decreasing life expectancy. This subject is considered in detail in later chapters dealing with full-scale road experiments, and the structural analysis of pavements. The reminder of the present chapter deals with what is now known about the structural properties of bituminous materials. The main centres of research into this subject during the past 30 years have been the Shell Laboratories in Amsterdam and London, the TRRL, the University of California, Berkeley (Professor Monismith and associates) and Nottingham University, England (Professor Pell and associates).

The elastic modulus of bituminous materials

14.53   If unit stress is applied to viscoelastic materials, such as bitumen or a mixture of bitumen and stone, a strain–time curve such as that shown in Fig. 14.16 is obtained. The total strain at any time can be subdivided into an irrecoverable component due mainly to viscous flow, an instantaneously recoverable component, and a retarded recoverable component. The magnitude of the latter component is time-dependent, and, as a consequence, if an oscillatory stress is applied to a bituminous material then the associated oscillatory strain reaches a maximum value a significant time after the maximum stress, i.e., the strain is out of phase with the stress. This is illustrated in Fig. 14.17(a). If the component of the strain in phase with the stress is J_1 and the component $90°$ out of phase is J_2 then the resultant strain will have a magnitude $\sqrt{(J_1^2 + J_2^2)}$. The ratio stress$/\sqrt{(J_1^2 + J_2^2)}$ is generally referred to as the dynamic complex modulus of elasticity, E^*, and it is this modulus which is generally used in the structural analysis of pavements. Measurements of J_1 and J_2 for various frequencies of sinusoidal loading, made on a typical bitumen,[8] are shown in Fig. 14.17(b). At high frequencies of loading the phase angle is small and the contribution of J_2 can be neglected. For the bitumen considered in Fig. 14.17(b) the value of J_2 tends to 3.5×10^{-7} m^2/kN, giving a limited upper value of E^* of 3 GPa. For a frequency of 10 cycles per second, which corresponds approximately to the speed of traffic loading at the surface, the values of J_1 and J_2 would be 1.5×10^{-6} and 2.5×10^{-6} m^2/kN respectively, giving a value of E^* of about 330 MPa at 10 °C. The effect of temperature on the stress–strain relationship can be expressed by a shift of the frequency scale. Thus at a temperature of 16 °C the modulus at a frequency of 10 cycles per second would be 10 MPa and, at a temperature of 4 °C, 140 MPa. This

Strain

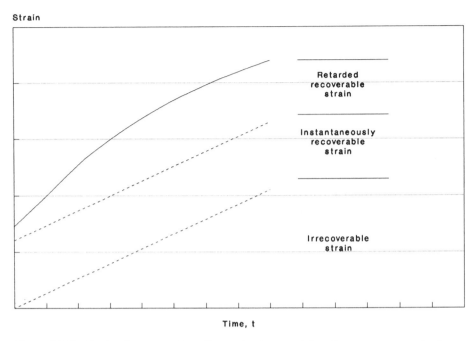

Retarded
recoverable
strain

Instantaneously
recoverable
strain

Irrecoverable
strain

Time, t

Figure 14.16 Strain–time curve for a linear elastic material under constant sustained stress

illustrates the large effect of temperature and rate of loading on the elastic modulus of bitumens and bituminous materials.

14.54 Because the stress–strain relationship for bituminous material depends on the time for which the load is applied, Fig. 14.16, the shape of the load–time curve and the manner in which the loading time is defined are much more important than is the case with other road materials. At a depth in a road structure the vertical stress–time curve generated by a wheel load approximates to half a sine curve, and this type of loading is generally used in investigations into the elastic modulus of bituminous materials. Particularly where bituminous materials are used at depth in a pavement, i.e., as roadbases, it is desirable to examine the shape and duration of the stress pulse from a structural analysis using estimated modulus values. Brown has examined theoretically the pulse lengths of the vertical, radial and tangential stress due to traffic at various depths,[9] and using the average pulse length has prepared the curves given in Fig 14.18.

14.55 Shook and Kallas have conducted an extensive research into the elastic modulus of asphaltic concretes using various frequencies of sinusoidal loading.[10] Samples 100 mm in diameter and 200 mm long were tested in unconfined compression using loading frequencies of 1, 4, and 16 cycles per second. They investigated the effects of asphalt content and state of compaction, as defined by air voids content. The aggregates used were continuously graded and in this respect the

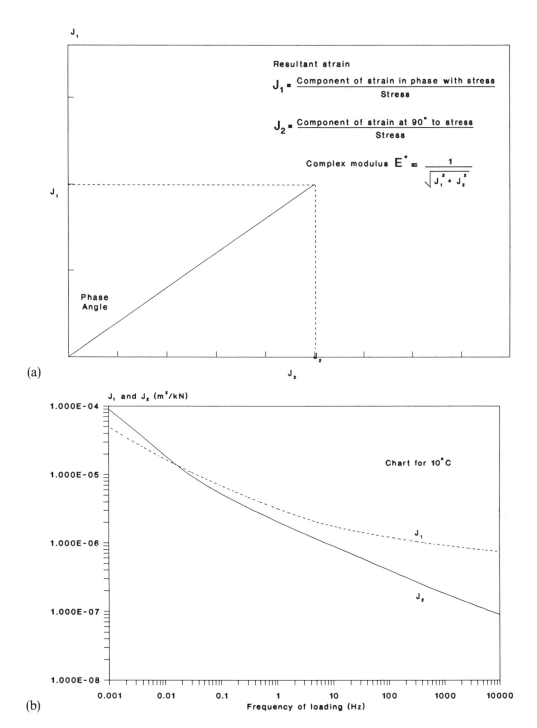

(a)

(b)

Figure 14.17 (a) Relationship between in-phase and out-of-phase strain components; (b) relationship between strain components and loading frequency

253

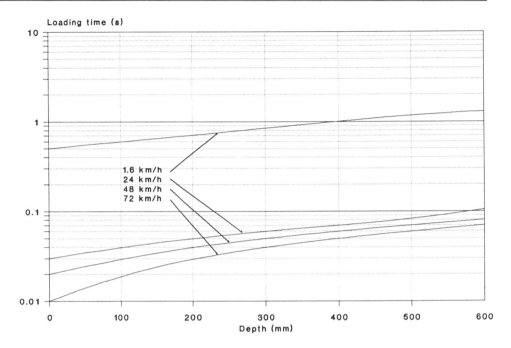

Figure 14.18   Relationships between loading time and depth for various vehicle speeds

mixtures resembled dense bitumen macadams as used in Britain. The binder used was generally of about 100 penetration but some tests were made with a harder binder of about 50 penetration. Figure 14.19 shows the relationship between E^*, air voids, and temperature for asphaltic concretes made with the 50 and 100 penetration binders at a loading frequency of 4 Hz. The harder binder produced a significantly higher modulus and for both materials a reduction of air voids content (i.e., an increase in compacted density) resulted in an increase in modulus. The large effect of temperature on modulus is apparent. Increasing the temperature from 4°C to 38°C reduces the modulus by a factor of about 12. Figure 14.20 shows the effect of binder content on elastic modulus. Increasing the binder content by about four per cent decreases the modulus for all the temperatures investigated. A further important finding was that the modulus in tension and compression were very similar over the practical stress range.

14.56   From their work Shook and Kallas produced several statistical equations relating complex elastic modulus of bituminous materials with the physical and mechanical properties of the mixes. The equation most applicable to British materials as they are currently specified is:

$$\log_{10} E^* = 3.12197 + 0.0248722\,(X_1) - 0.0345875\,(X_2)$$
$$- 9.02594\,(X_4)^{0.19}/(X_6)^{0.9} \tag{14.1}$$

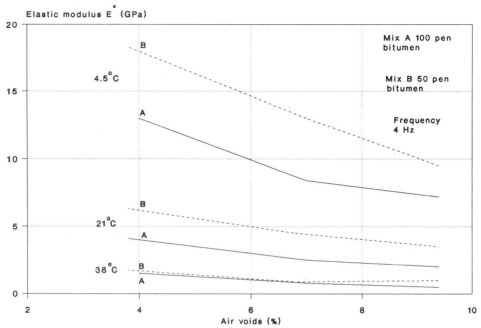

Figure 14.19 Relationship between complex modulus, air voids and temperature for asphaltic concretes

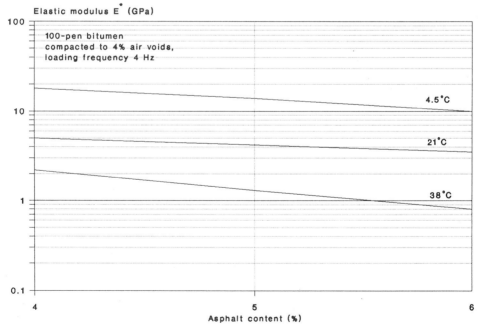

Figure 14.20 Relationship between complex modulus, asphalt content, and temperature for asphaltic concrete

where $E^* =$ dynamic modulus, 10^5 psi (4 cps loading frequency)

$X_1 =$ percentage of total aggregate finer than 75 μm

$X_2 =$ percentage air voids in compacted mix

$X_3 =$ asphalt viscosity at 70 °F, poises

$X_4 =$ percentage of binder by weight of mix

$X_6 = \log_{10}$ viscosity of binder at test temperature, poises.

In accordance with normal American practice Eq. (14.1) uses imperial units with temperature expressed in °F. Appropriate values of X_3 and X_6 can be deduced from Table 14.19 for various penetration grades of bitumen.

Table 14.19   Relationship between binder viscosity, temperature and penetration grade of bitumen

Temperature		Viscosity (poises) for bitumen of penetration (at 25 °C)			
°C	°F	20/30	40/50	80/100	100/200
0	32	4×10^{10}	5×10^9	3×10^8	5×10^7
10	50	1×10^9	2×10^8	2×10^7	5×10^6
20	68	8×10^7	1×10^7	1.5×10^6	4×10^5
30	86	6×10^6	1×10^6	2×10^5	5×10^4
40	104	7×10^5	1.5×10^5	3×10^4	1×10^4
50	122	1×10^5	4×10^4	9×10^3	3×10^3

14.57   The values obtained for E^* depend to some extent on the type of test adopted. A variety of test procedures have been used by research workers modelling to different degrees the practical condition in the pavement. Brown has made a useful summary of the information available,[9] and has used it to prepare average relationships between elastic modulus and loading time at temperatures of 0° and 20°C for dense bitumen macadam made with 100 penetration binder and for rolled asphalt made with 50-penetration binder. These are modifications of curves previously prepared by the Shell Laboratories. Curves derived from Brown's data are included in Fig. 14.21 which define the relationship between modulus and loading time for dense bitumen macadam and for rolled asphalt.

14.58   Bituminous materials in British roads operate for about 10 per cent of the year at temperatures above 20°C and that within the upper 40 mm they operate for about 5 per cent of the year at temperatures above 30°C. The results from full-scale road experiments show that the deformation of flexible pavements occurs mainly at road temperatures in excess of 20°C. Particularly in relation to subgrade and sub-base stresses it is necessary to consider the change of elastic modulus which occurs in bituminous materials at temperatures above 20°C. Unfortunately, owing to the difficulties which arise in high temperature testing, little information is available other than that reported by Shook and Kallas, already discussed. Their results at temperatures up to 20°C do not agree very closely with the average curves prepared by Brown, but the relationship they found between modulus and temperature

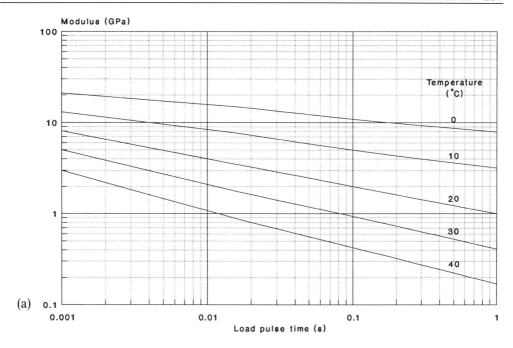

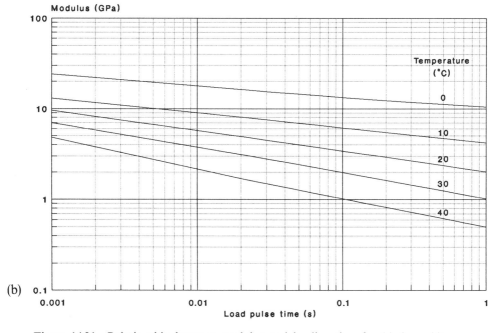

Figure 14.21 Relationship between modulus and loading time for (a) dense bitumen macadam, (b) rolled asphalt (*After* Brown[19])

between 4.5 and 38 °C can be used with moderate confidence to extend Brown's curves to temperatures of 30° and 40 °C and this has been done on Fig. 14.21. Figure 14.22 presents Brown's data as relationships between modulus and temperature. More recently the TRRL has published[11] the relationships shown in Fig. 14.22 which relate to a more restricted rate of loading. The temperature effect is however probably more refined.

14.59   The data given in Fig. 14.21 for both dense bitumen macadam and rolled asphalt and in Fig. 14.22 for dense bitumen macadam relate to freshly made materials. The data shown in Fig. 14.22 for rolled asphalt were obtained on cores cut from a full-scale experiment after at least 10 years. Recent research carried out by the TRRL based on long-term deflection studies shows that the stiffness of bituminous materials increases markedly with age. Although the process continues for 20 + years it is most pronounced in the first 5 years. This is accompanied by an equally marked decline in temperature sensitivity. Deflection measurements made at 1-hour intervals over a 24-hour period at the Nately Scures full-scale experiment at several times of the year also indicated that for mature bituminous materials there is an approximately 4-hour lag between temperature and measured deflection, i.e., the modulus is lowest about 4 hours after the maximum temperature. It was concluded that measured deflections correlated well with the mean temperature measured in the bituminous materials over the 24-hour period.

14.60   Based on a back analysis of a large number of sections from full-scale experiments with rolled asphalt and dense bitumen macadam bases, Fig. 14.24 has been produced showing the modulus temperature relationships for rolled asphalt surfacings on rolled asphalt bases and for rolled asphalt surfacings on dense bitumen macadam bases. From this data, together with the data shown in Figs 14.21–14.23, Fig. 14.25 has been prepared which shows, for UK conditions, modulus tempera-ture relationships for use in structural analysis for prediction of stresses, strains, and deflections under both slow-moving (deflection beam) vehicles and normal traffic.

14.61   The elastic modulus of tar-bound materials has not been studied in detail. Where, however, as is the case with UK dense-coated basecourses and roadbases, the specification for the aggregate grading is identical for bitumen macadam and tarmacadam then the modulus is likely to be determined almost entirely by the binder viscosity and the binder content. The binder contents used differ little for the two types of binder and viscosity is therefore the main factor determining modulus. Table 14.20 relates the viscosities of tar and bitumen at various temperatures. It follows from the table that a dense tarmacadam basecourse made with a 54-e.v.t. tar should have an elastic modulus similar to the equivalent dense bitumen macadam made with 100 penetration bitumen at temperatures below 15 °C. However, it would have a rather lower modulus at higher temperatures. Cooper and Pell confirmed that the modulus of a dense tarmacadam made with 54-e.v.t. tar was about twice that of dense bitumen macadam made with 200-penetration bitumen, for the same binder content and compacted density. The test temperature was 10 °C.[14]

14.62   The effect of aggregate type on the elastic modulus of bituminous materials

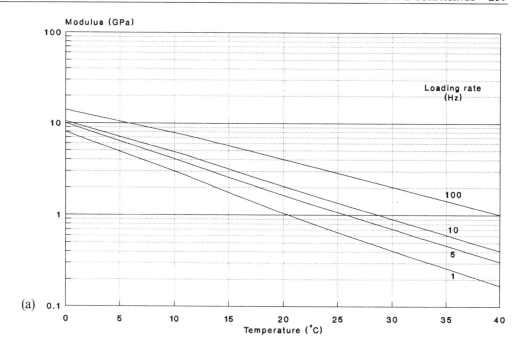

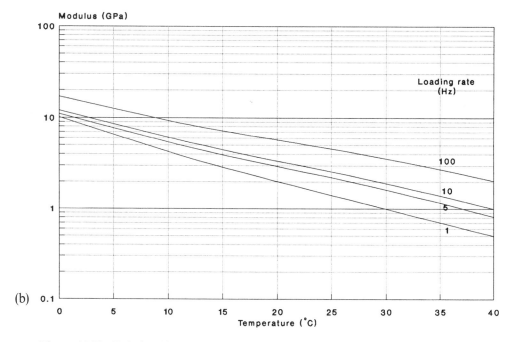

Figure 14.22   Relationship between modulus and temperature for (a) dense bitumen macadam, (b) rolled asphalt (*After* Brown[19])

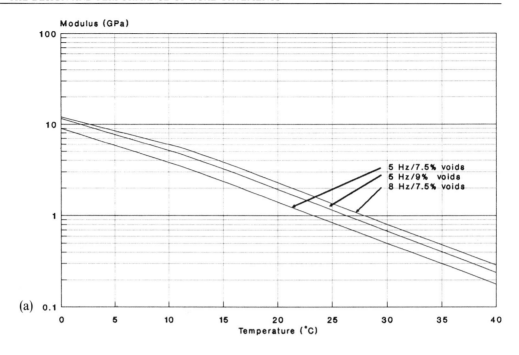

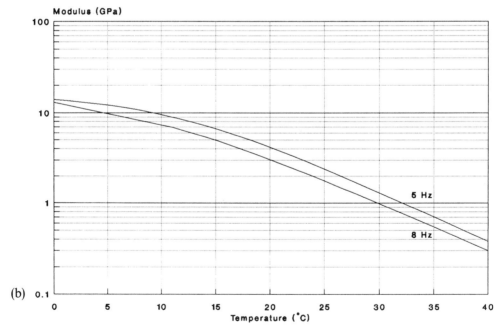

Figure 14.23 Relationship between modulus and temperature for (a) dense bitumen macadam; (b) rolled asphalt (*After* TRRL[11])

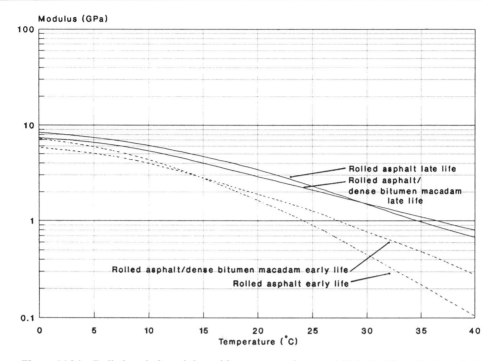

Figure 14.24 Rolled asphalt and dense bitumen macadam moduli derived from back analysis of deflection data

has not been studied as a primary variable. The evidence available from tests in which it was a secondary variable suggests that it is not a very important factor.

Poisson's ratio of bituminous materials

14.63   The value of Poisson's ratio for bituminous road materials is generally close to 0.4. Monismith and Secor show[12] that for extreme conditions of loading and temperature the value for asphaltic concrete mixes could vary between 0.3 and 0.5.

The fatigue of bituminous materials under repeated loading

14.64   The complicated nature of the relationship between stress and strain for bituminous materials—its dependence on the magnitude of the stress, the frequency of loading, and the duration of rest periods between load applications—means that the fatigue life measured depends to a large extent on the test procedure used. Pell has provided a very useful background discussion to the fatigue testing of bituminous materials.[13] This is summarized in the next two paragraphs.

14.65   If a sinusoidal stress of peak value σ is applied to a bituminous material (controlled stress test) then an approximately linear relationship is found between $\log \sigma$ and $\log N$ where N is the number of stress applications required to cause

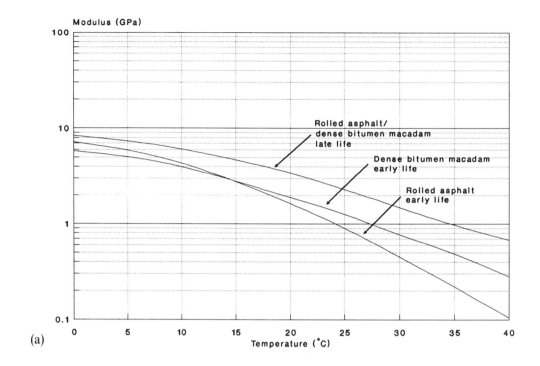

(a)

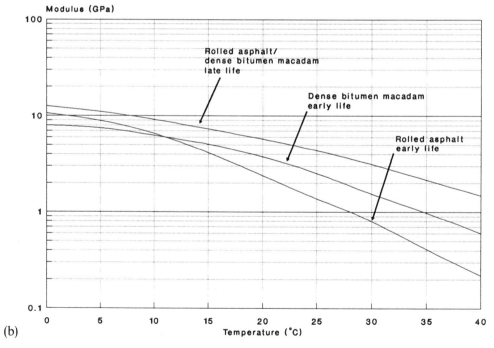

(b)

Figure 14.25 (a) 1-Hz (Deflection Beam) moduli for use in structural analysis; (b) 10-Hz (normal traffic) moduli for use in structural analysis

Table 14.20 Bitumens and tars of equivalent viscosities at various temperatures

Penetration of bitumen at 25 °C	e.v.t. of tar of same viscosity as bitumen		
	0 °C	25 °C	45 °C
25	71	76	82
50	61	68	75
100	52	60	68
200	42	52	61
300	37	47	56
400	33	44	53
500	30	41	50

fatigue failure. The application of such a controlled stress to bituminous materials of various stiffnesses (where stiffness is defined as the maximum stress divided by the maximum strain for the type of stress pulse applied) gives a family of fatigue relationships. If the logarithm of the measured strain (as opposed to stress) is plotted against $\log N$ then the curves relating to the various stiffnesses become superimposed. The fatigue life of bituminous materials is thus best examined in relation to strain.

14.66　The situation is rather different if the strain level is maintained constant during repeated loading fatigue tests (controlled strain test). Relationships for materials of different stiffnesses are not in general coincident, as is the case with the controlled stress test. This is because the process of crack propagation which leads to fatigue is less well defined, particularly in the less stiff materials, when controlled strain tests are used.

14.67　As with cemented materials, various methods of testing bituminous materials for fatigue have been used. These include beam and cylindrical flexural tests. Comprehensive data relating fatigue life with stress and strain levels have been published by Cooper and Pell,[14] Epps and Monismith,[15] and Kirk.[16]

14.68　Pell has pioneered the use of a controlled stress machine in which waisted cylindrical samples are fatigued in rotational bending.[13] The magnitude of the flexural stress is derived from the geometry of the machine and specimen, and from the load applied. The speed of rotation is variable but most of the tests have been carried out at a speed giving 16 stress reversals per second. A controlled strain machine, working on the same principle and using the same test specimens, is used to determine the dynamic stiffness of the materials under essentially the same test conditions. Figure 14.26(a) shows a typical result relating stress with the number of cycles of loading to failure for a rolled asphalt basecourse material. Figure 14.26(b) gives the measured dynamic stiffness for the various stress levels and this is used in Fig. 14.26(c) to give the fatigue life in terms of peak strain in the specimen.

14.69　Expressing the fatigue stress relationship in the form $N = K(1/\sigma)^n$, and the fatigue strain relationship in the form $N = C(1/\varepsilon)^m$, where K and C are coefficients

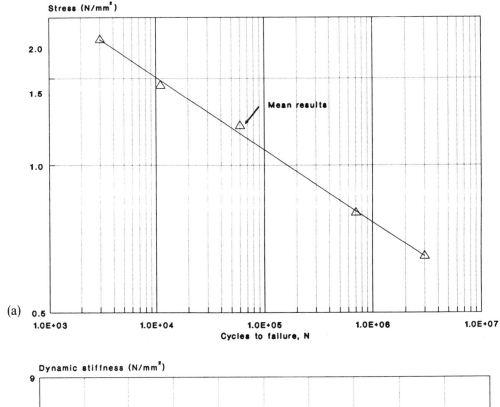

(a)

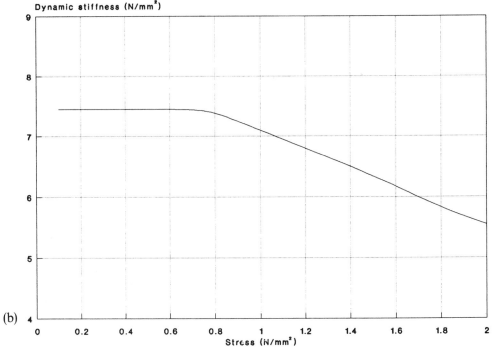

(b)

Figure 14.26 Typical fatigue test on rolled asphalt basecourse material—10°C, 1000 rev/min, 60 per cent stone, 6 per cent 43-pen bitumen. (a) stress–life relationship; (b) stiffness–stress relationship; (c) strain–life relationship

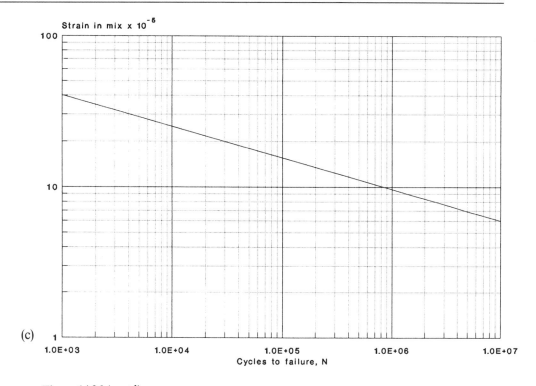

Strain in mix x 10^{-5}

Figure 14.26 (*contd*)

which vary between materials which are determined experimentally, Cooper and Pell have carried out an extensive research into the fatigue properties of the various bituminous materials currently in use in Britain and have published values of K, n, C, m, and stiffness applying to these materials.[14] Typical fatigue curves relating strain and fatigue life are shown in Fig. 14.27. The main conclusions reached by Cooper and Pell are that binder content and binder type are primary factors affecting the fatigue performance on the basis of applied strain. For all binders, increasing the binder content increases the fatigue life. This applies even over the range where increasing the binder content decreases the elastic modulus (see Para. 14.55). Decreasing the air voids content by compaction or by modifying the aggregate grading increases the stiffness of a bituminous material and thus decreases the strain for a given applied stress. However, it has little direct effect on the fatigue life of a bituminous material subjected to repetitions of a constant strain.

14.70   An important recent finding is that rest periods, between the applications of stress (such as will occur in practice between the passage of axles and of vehicles), have an important influence on fatigue life. This would be expected from the nature of the stress–strain relationship shown in Fig 14.16. Raithby and Sterling, using direct tensile and compressive loading on sawn beams of rolled asphalt surfacing,

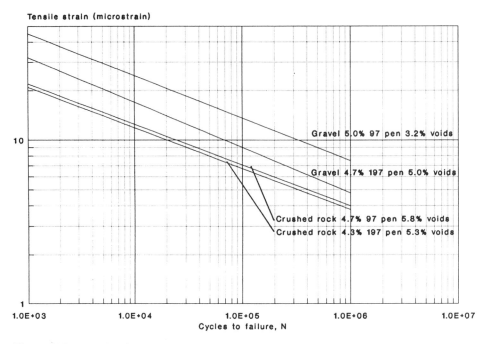

Figure 14.27   Strain life relationships for dense bitumen macadam

showed that rest periods of 0.3 s between load applications could increase the fatigue life by as much as 25 times in the temperature range 10–25 °C (see Fig. 14.28).[18] The rest periods between the passage of the axles of a large commercial vehicle over a particular point on the road surface will be of the order 0.1–0.3 s and between the axles of different vehicles will exceed 0.3 s. The fatigue life determined at a frequency of loading of 15–20 Hz will therefore underestimate the fatigue life under practical conditions. To cover this point and take into account other differences between laboratory and field loading, Brown has suggested that laboratory-determined fatigue lives should be arbitrarily increased by a factor of 100 and on this basis has proposed the use of the fatigue relationships shown in Fig. 14.29 for the bituminous materials used in Britain for surfacings and roadbases.[19] More recently, the Transport and Road Research Laboratory has issued a modified version of these curves shown in Fig. 14.30, which includes the effect of temperature.[11] Unless or until the fatigue lives of these materials can be more closely defined, estimates of flexible pavement lives based on fatigue tests must remain very conjectural.

Permanent deformation of bituminous materials under repeated loading

14.71   The permanent deformation of bituminous materials under repeated loading has not been as extensively studied as the fatigue properties. This is because

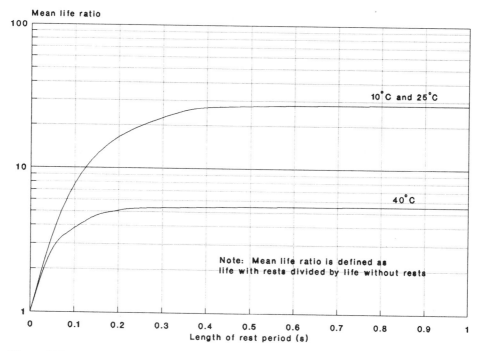

Figure 14.28 Effect of rest period on life ratio

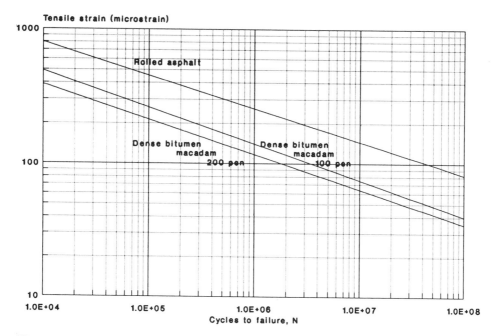

Figure 14.29 Approximate fatigue lives for typical bituminous mixes adjusted for *in situ* conditions

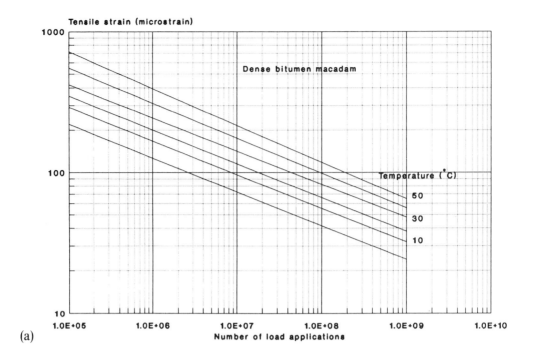

(a)

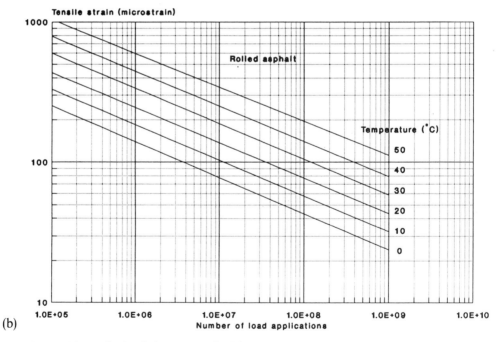

(b)

Figure 14.30 Effective fatigue curves for bituminous materials; (a) dense bitumen macadam; (b) rolled asphalt

268

in the USA permanent deformation has generally been regarded as unimportant. As with unbound materials, additional compaction under the action of traffic contributes to deformation, but the major cause of rutting within bituminous surfacings and roadbase materials appears to be plastic flow. Only under rare conditions, generally associated with high temperature, is sideways displacement of bituminous materials sufficient to cause a measurable upward movement of the pavement surface outside and between the wheel tracks. This suggests that plastic or viscous movements in such materials are generally small enough to be masked by other downward displacements in the immediate neighbourhood of the wheel tracks. Figure 14.31 shows the measured contributions of subgrade, sub-base, and roadbase plus surfacing to the permanent deformation of a pavement with a rolled asphalt surfacing and roadbase of combined thickness 250 mm. The increase of deformation during the summer months indicates the influence of temperature on the elastic modulus of the bituminous material.

14.72 Structural analysis shows that bituminous surfacings laid on less stiff roadbases (e.g., uncoated stone) will be subject to considerable tensile stress near the interface with the roadbase. The same applies to bituminous roadbases laid on granular sub-bases. In such cases the lower half of the roadbase will be subject to tension as a wheel passes over the pavement. Bituminous materials laid on uncracked cemented roadbases will be subject only to compressive stress. In studying

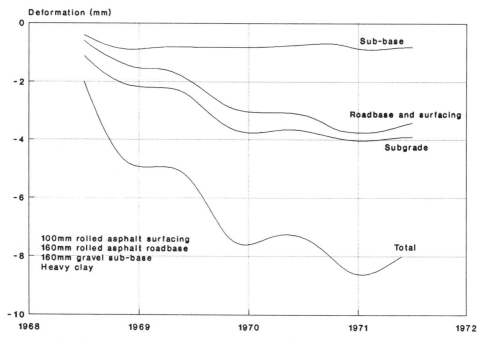

Figure 14.31 Permanent deformation of layer in nearside wheel track

the permanent deformation of bituminous materials under repeated loading, it is clearly desirable to use a test in which tensile stress can be applied to, or induced in, the sample under test. With the triaxial type of test this is not possible except for very modest levels of tensile stress. For this reason the work so far carried out has been restricted to zero or positive confining pressures.

14.73   Snaith, Brown, and Pell have made preliminary studies of the permanent deformation of a dense coated macadam roadbase material made to the current British specification, using a 100-penetration bitumen and a binder content of 4 per cent.[20] Latterly they have used an electrohydraulic servo-controlled triaxial testing machine in which both vertical and cell pressures can be independently pulsed. This machine has been used to study the effects on permanent deformation of vertical stress, temperature, confining pressure, binder content, voids content, frequency of loading and the length of rest periods between application of load.

14.74   It was found for all the tests that the rate of change of permanent deformation with load applications decreased at first with increasing number of applications and then began to increase. The condition at this change point was arbitrarily defined as 'failure' and the tests were not in general continued beyond this point, although in practice considerably larger deformations can occur. Figure 14.32 summarizes the preliminary results obtained by Snaith, Brown, and Pell, and they provide a useful basis for estimating the permanent deformation likely to occur in bituminous roadbases and surfacings. The procedure recommended is that the bituminous material be considered in horizontal slices and that the permanent deformation be estimated from the average stress conditions in each slice, the influence of temperature being particularly considered.

14.75   Figure 14.32(b) illustrates the considerable effect which temperature will have on the permanent deformation of bituminous materials and Fig. 14.32(c) shows the increased liability of rich mixtures of deformation. An inference from Fig. 14.32(f) is that near the surface of a bituminous layer, where the magnitude of the dynamic radial compressive stress is likely to be large, the permanent deformation will be smaller than in the region of the neutral axis. It is probable that the effect of a large dynamic tensile radial stress will be to increase the permanent deformation in material below the neutral axis. The magnitude of such an effect must remain conjectural until more experimental evidence is available.

14.76   In the last 10 years considerable research has been carried out by the Transport and Road Research Laboratory into the effect of the addition of organic polymers to bituminous materials. These include EVA (ethylene vinyl acetate) and SBS (styrene butadiene styrene block copolymers).[21,22,23] These appear to have a small beneficial effect on the early-life elastic modulus of the materials, but little effect on the fatigue properties. The main influence is on the early life deformation under traffic, which has been studied using the wheel-tracking test. Table 14.21 summarizes the results. It appears that the influence of the additives on the penetration value of the mixture is mainly responsible for the reduction in permanent deformation. Current research is investigating whether similar effects can be produced by changes in the filler type and content. A number of full-scale road experiments have been laid using EVA asphalt and early results appear promising.

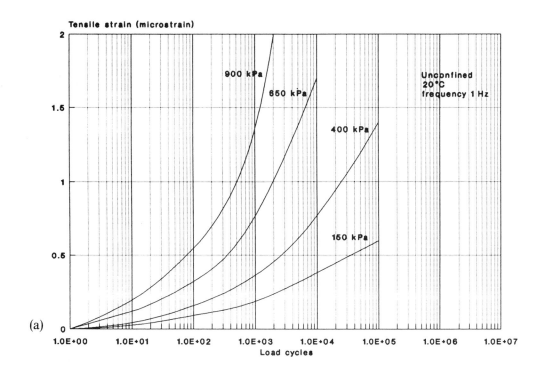

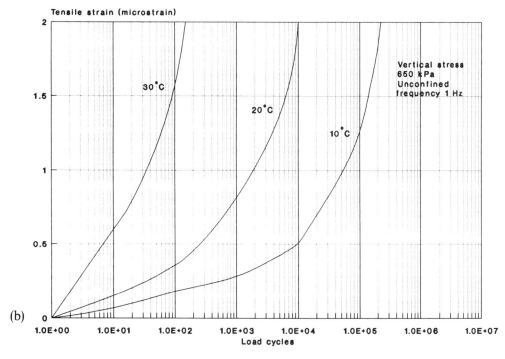

Figure 14.32 Permanent deformation of dense bitumen macadam roadbase under repeated loading. (a) effect of vertical stress; (b) effect of temperature

271

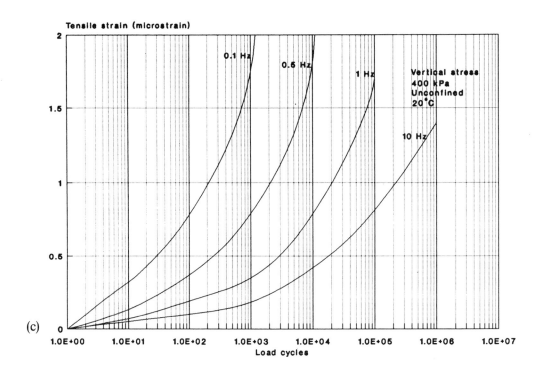

(c)

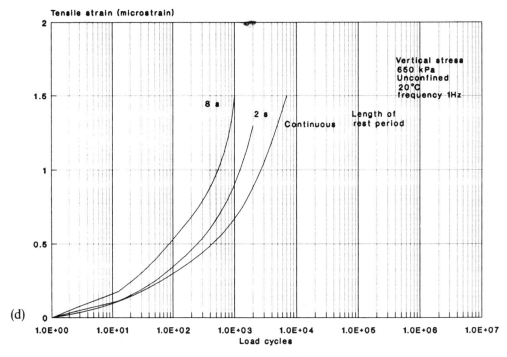

(d)

Figure 14.32 (*contd*) (c) effect of loading frequency; (d) effect of rest periods

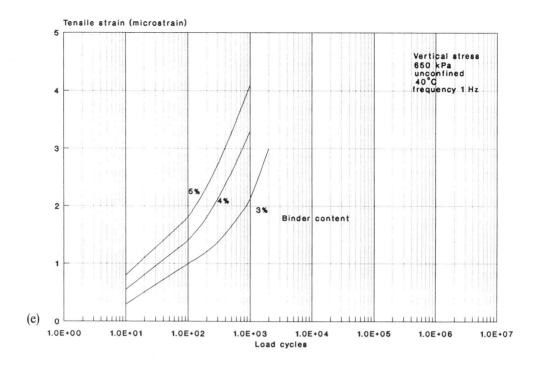

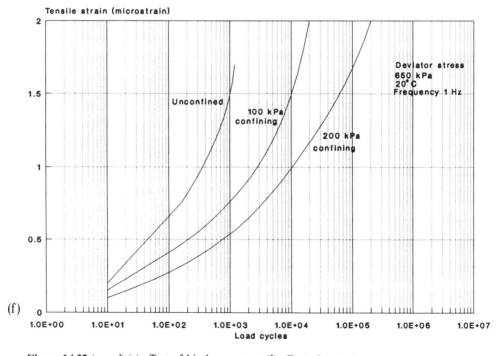

Figure 14.32 (*contd*) (e) effect of binder content; (f) effect of confining pressure

Table 14.21 Properties of binders and wheel-tracking rates of rolled-asphalt wearing courses

Binder		Pen 25 °C	R&B °C	Apparent viscosity at shear rate, 0.05 s^{-1}		Wheel-tracking rate at 45 °C, mm/h
	Description			10 °C	45 °C	
A	Conventional bitumen	56	52	1.2×10^8	7.5×10^4	3.2
B	A + 2% EVA	52	60	1.5×10^8	4.1×10^5	1.2
C	A + 2.5% EVA	46	63	1.0×10^8	3.0×10^5	—
D	A + 3.5% EVA	41	64	8.0×10^7	5.0×10^5	0.9
E	A + 5% EVA	35	70	8.0×10^7	1.3×10^6	0.4
F	(94% A + 6% 300 pen) + 5% EVA	42	68	6.4×10^7	7.2×10^5	0.7
G	Bitumen/SBS	158	80	1.8×10^6	1.8×10^5	2.8
H	Bitumen/SBS	84	90	1.9×10^7	7.7×10^5	0.7
I	100 pen-grade bitumen + 5% natural rubber	84	53	2.0×10^7	5.0×10^4	3.4
J	100 pen-grade bitumen	92	46	3.4×10^7	1.7×10^4	9.0
K	200 pen-grade bitumen	202	38	8.0×10^6	3.9×10^3	23
L	35 pen-grade bitumen	33	59	5.6×10^8	3.2×10^5	1.4
M	Heavy-duty bitumen	49	59	1.2×10^8	3.7×10^5	1.2
N	Heavy-duty bitumen	42	68	1.5×10^8	8.1×10^6	0.7
O	Oxidized bitumen	44	78	8.5×10^7	2.1×10^6	0.6

References

1. Department of Transport: *Specification for Highway Works*: Part 3, HMSO, London, August 1986.
2. Harland, D. G.: A radio-active method for measuring variations in density in concrete cores, cubes and beams, *Mag. Concr. Res.*, **18** (55), 95–101 (1966).
3. Lister, N. W. and W. D. Powell: Research into compaction of bituminous materials, *Asphalt and Coated Macadam Association, Seminar 74, London, 15 October, 1974*, ACMA, London, 1974.
4. British Standards Institution: *Coated Macadam for Roads and Other Paved Areas*, British Standard 4987:1988, BSI, London, 1988.
5. British Standards Institution: *Hot Rolled Asphalt for Roads and Other Paved Areas*, British Standard 594:1985, BSI, London, 1985.
6. American Association of State Highway and Transportation Officials: *AASHTO Materials*: Part II: Tests, 14th Edn, Designation T245-82 (1986), AASHTO, Washington D.C., p. 1006, 1986.
7. British Standards Institution: *Sampling and examination of Bituminous Mixtures for Roads and Other Paved Areas*. British Standard 598:Part 3:1985, BSI, London, 1985.
8. Road Research Laboratory: *Bituminous Materials in Road Construction*, HMSO, London, 113, 1962.
9. Brown, S. F.: *Determination of Young's Modulus for Bituminous Materials in Pavement Design*, Highway Research Record No. 431, National Research Council, Washington D.C. pp. 38–49, 1973.
10. Shook, J. F. and B. F. Kallas: Factors influencing dynamic modulus of asphalt concrete, *Proc. t. Sess. Ass. Asph. Pav. Technol., Los Angeles*, **38** (Feb.), 140–78, 1969.

11. *Fatigue Resistance of a Bituminous Roadpavement Design for Very Heavy Traffic. Transport and Road Research Laboratory Report 1050*, TRRL, Crowthorne, 1982.
12. Monismith, C. L. and K. E. Secor: Viscoelastic behaviour of asphalt concrete pavements. *Proc. of the 1st Int. Conf. on the Structural Design of Asphalt Pavements, Ann Arbor, Michigan, 1962*, University of Michigan, Ann Arbor, 1963.
13. Pell, P. S.: Fatigue of asphalt pavement mixes. *Proc. 2nd Int. Conf. on the Structural Design of Asphalt Pavements, Ann Arbor, Michigan, 1967*, University of Michigan, Ann Arbor, 1968.
14. Cooper K. E. and P. S. Pell: *The Effect of Mix Variables on the Fatigue Strength of Bituminous Materials*, Transport and Road Research Laboratory Report LR 633, TRRL, Crowthorne, 1974.
15. Epps, J. A. and C. L. Monismith: Influence of mixture variables on the flexural fatigue properties of asphalt concrete, *Proc. t. Sess. Asph. Pav. Technol., Los Angeles*, **38** (Feb.), 423–64, 1969.
16. Kirk, J. M.: Relations between mix design and fatigue properties of asphaltic concrete, *Proc. 3rd Int. Conf. on the Structural Design of Asphalt Pavements, London, 1972*, University of Michigan, Ann Arbor, pp. 241–7, 1972.
17. Pell, P. S. and I. F. Taylor: Asphaltic road materials in fatigue, *Proc. t. Sess. Ass. Asph. Pav. Technol., Los Angeles*, **38** (Feb.), 371–422, 1969.
18. Raithby, K. D. and A. B. Sterling: Laboratory fatigue tests on rolled asphalt and their relation to traffic loading. *Rds and Rd Constr., London*, **50** (596–7), 219–23, 1972.
19. Brown, S. F.: A simplified fundamental design for bituminous pavements, *The Highway Engineer* (*J. Instn Highw. Engrs*), **21** (8–9), 14–23, 1974.
20. Snaith, S. M., S. F. Brown, and P. S. Pell: *Permanent Deformation of Flexible Paving Materials*, University of Nottingham Report No. MSS/3, June 1973.
21. Denning, J. H. and J. Carswell: *Improvements in Rolled Asphalt Surfacings by the Addition of Organic Polymers*, Transport and Road Research Laboratory Report 989, TRRL, Crowthorne, 1981.
22. Carswell, J.: *An assessment of bituminous basecourses and roadbase materials containing EVA and Sulphur*, Transport and Road Research Laboratory Research Report 92, TRRL, Crowthorne, 1986.
23. Carswell, J.: *The effect of EVA-modified Bitumens on Rolled Asphalts Containing Different Fine Aggregates*, Transport and Road Research Laboratory Research Report 122, TRRL, Crowthorne, 1987.

15. Pavement quality concrete

Introduction

15.1   Although short lengths of experimental concrete road were constructed in Britain in the later part of the nineteenth century, serious use of the material as a riding surface for major roads dates from the twenties. By that time concrete was being widely used in the USA and early British practice was based on American experience. Over the past 60 years the performance of concrete roads has been rather unpredictable. Either they have performed excellently or they have given trouble from a very early stage. The main problem appears to have been non-compliance with the specification, and particularly the concrete strength requirement.

Concrete mix design—British practice

Aggregates

15.2   Concrete is traditionally made using a combination of coarse and fine aggregates, the gradings for which are given in BS 882:1983,[1] although if a suitable all-in gravel aggregate is available it can be used. The gradings for the coarse and fine aggregates are shown in Tables 15.1 and 15.2. The grading for the all-in aggregate is given in Table 15.3.

Table 15.1   Grading of coarse aggregate

Sieve size	Percentage by mass passing BS sieves for nominal sizes							
	Graded aggregate			Single-sized aggregate				
	40–5 mm	20–5 mm	14–5 mm	40 mm	20 mm	14 mm	10 mm	5 mm*
mm								
50.0	100	—	—	100	—	—	—	—
37.5	90–100	100	—	85–100	100	—	—	—
20.0	35–70	90–100	100	0–25	85–100	100	—	—
14.0	—	—	90–100	—	—	85–100	100	—
10.0	10–40	30–60	50–85	0–5	0–25	0–50	85–100	100
5.0	0–5	0–10	0–10	—	0–5	0–10	0–25	45–100
2.36	—	—	—	—	—	—	0–5	0–30

*Used mainly in precast concrete products.

276

Table 15.2   Grading of fine aggregate

| Sieve size | Percentage by mass passing BS sieve | | | |
| | Overall limits | Additional limits for grading | | |
		C	M	F
10.00 mm	100	—	—	—
5.00 mm	89–100	—	—	—
2.36 mm	60–100	60–100	65–100	80–100
1.18 mm	30–100	30–90	45–100	70–100
600 μm	15–100	15–54	25–80	55–100
300 μm	5–70	5–40	5–48	5–70
150 μm	0–15*	—	—	—

Note: Fine aggregate not complying with Table 15.2 may also be used provided that the supplier can satisfy the purchaser that such materials can produce concrete of the required quality.

*Increased to 20 per cent for crushed rock fines, except when they are used for heavy duty floors.

Table 15.3   Grading of all-in aggregate

| Sieve size | Percentage by mass passing BS sieves for nominal sizes | | | |
	40 mm	20 mm	10 mm	5 mm*
50.0 mm	100	—	—	—
37.5 mm	95–100	100	—	—
20.0 mm	45–80	95–100	—	—
14.0 mm	—	—	100	—
10.0 mm	—	—	95–100	100
5.00 mm	25–50	35–55	30–65	70–100
2.36 mm	—	—	20–50	25–100
1.18 mm	—	—	15–40	15–45
600 μm	8–30	10–35	10–30	5–25
300 μm	—	—	5–15	3–20
150 μm	0–8[†]	0–8[†]	0–8[†]	0–15

*Used mainly in precast concrete products.
[†]Increased to 10 per cent for crushed-rock fines.

15.3   The aggregates to be used are crushed rock, crushed air-cooled blast furnace slag, or gravel, or a combination of these materials. Limestone coarse aggregate in the upper part of the slab is permitted only if an accelerated wear test[2] shows the concrete to be acceptable.

15.4   The flakiness index[3] of the coarse aggregate shall not exceed 35, and the 10 per cent fines value shall not be less than 100 kN,[4] or, alternatively, the aggregate impact value[5] shall not exceed 30 per cent.

15.5   The coarse and fine aggregate are mixed with cement and water in an approved plant, in proportions necessary to produce the required compacted strength and the required levels of workability and water–cement ratio as discussed below.

Cement content

15.6   The grade of concrete required by the Department of Transport *Specification for Highway Works* is C.40. For this grade the minimum cement content is 240 kg per cubic metre of compacted concrete. The actual cement content is determined by the compressive strength requirement (see Para. 15.14).

Water–cement ratio

15.7   The water content should be the minimum necessary to maintain the required workability, but for pavement quality concrete the water–cement ratio by weight must not exceed 0.50.

Workability

15.8   The workability of the concrete at the time of placing should enable the concrete to be fully compacted and finished without undue flow. The compacting factor test should be used when the aggregate is crushed rock or gravel and the target value should be 0.8 to 0.85. The VeBe test is applicable where slag or pulverized fuel ash are used in the mix, when the target level should be 6 seconds. In the compacting factor test,[6] freshly mixed concrete is allowed to fall under gravity in a controlled manner into a steel mould, and the density obtained is expressed as a ratio of the fully compacted density. The VeBe Test[7] is a modified form of slump test in which vibration is used. The VeBe time is the time taken for the slump formed in a standard manner to collapse to the horizontal condition under vibration.

Density

15.9   The density of the concrete is required to be such that without air entrainment the total air voids are not more than 3 per cent. With air entrainment the total air voids should be 7–8 per cent. The air voids content is derived from the difference between the theoretical maximum dry density of the concrete, calculated from the specific gravities of the constituents of the mix and the average value of three direct density measurements made on 100-mm cores cut from the finished concrete.

Trial slabs

15.10   All major concrete road schemes in Britain require trial slabs to be constructed several weeks in advance of the main concreting work. This provides an opportunity for the mix proportions and strength to be adjusted where necessary. Some contractors are reluctant to comply with this requirement and this can be a major factor in subsequent slab failures.

Reinforcement and joints

15.11 Slip form paving favours the use of unreinforced slabs with contraction joints at 5-m intervals and expansion joints at 60 m. Train laying is used for both unreinforced and reinforced concrete pavements. For the latter the traffic intensity determines the weight of reinforcement, which in turn determines the joint spacing.[8]

Dowel bars

15.12 All joints are provided with dowel bars. For expansion joints in heavily-trafficked roads the bars are 30 mm in diameter and 750 mm long, and for contraction joints the diameter is 25 mm and the length 600 mm (see Chapter 19).

Sub-base for concrete roads

15.13 Heavily trafficked roads with concrete pavements are provided with a 225-mm sub-base of free-draining material, connected to the side drains. This is to prevent mud pumping. Alternatively, a rather thinner impervious lean concrete sub-base is used. A polythene slip layer is used between the sub-base and the concrete slabs.

The effect of age on compressive strength

15.14 The compressive strength of concrete is usually specified as a cube strength at an age of 7 or 28 days. The current UK Department of Transport requirement for pavement concrete is a compressive strength of 31 N/mm^2 at 7 days (44 N/mm^2 at 28 days). It is now normal practice to measure the strength at 7 days and 28 days by a series of preliminary laboratory tests at both ages using the cement and the aggregate to be used in the contract. In fact, the ratio of the 7-day and 28-day compressive strengths is not very significantly affected by the type of aggregate, although it is obviously affected by the rate of hardening of the cement. Figure 13.3 has shown the change of strength with time for lean concretes and weaker cemented materials stabilized with ordinary Portland cement. Research reported by the TRRL shows that over a period of 5 years the rate of increase of strength declines as the 28-day compressive strength increases from 20 N/mm^2 to 60 N/mm^2, as shown in Fig. 15.1. Beyond 5 years the gain in strength is small.[9]

The relationship between the compressive strength and modulus of rupture of concrete

15.15 Whether a concrete slab cracks under an applied tensile stress depends on the modulus of rupture of the concrete at the time the tensile stress is applied. The modulus of rupture is the stress which first initiates cracking. It is determined by the constitution of the concrete and its age and stress history in relation to fatigue. Research carried out in the early fifties showed that the modulus of rupture determined by slow flexural tests could be related to the compressive strength measured on cubes by relationships which were to an extent, influenced by the aggregate used in the concrete.[10] The equations for gravel aggregates and for crushed rock aggregates are given below, where the compressive strength, F_e, and

Figure 15.1   Relationship between age and compressive strength for pavement-quality concrete

the modulus of rupture, M_R, are expressed in N/mm^2:

$$\text{For gravel aggregate: } M_R = 0.49 \times F_e^{0.55} \tag{15.1}$$

$$\text{For crushed stone aggregate: } M_R = 0.36 \times F_e^{0.7} \tag{15.2}$$

15.16   These equations have been used in Table 15.4 to calculate the modulus of rupture for concrete made with crushed rock and gravel aggregates having a crushing strength of 10–60 N/mm^2. For a given crushing strength, the modulus of rupture of concrete made with crushed rock aggregate is considerably greater than gravel concrete. The lower cost of gravel may well at medium strengths justify on economic grounds the use of gravel concrete with a higher cement content and higher compressive strength.

The relationship between elastic modulus, compressive strength, and age

15.17   The elastic modulus of concrete is measured using both dynamic and static methods.[11,12] As with bituminous materials, the static method gives a lower value. The strains involved in static tests are greater than those which occur under wheel loading, while with the dynamic method they are smaller.

15.18   Table 15.5 shows the variation of dynamic modulus measured on two concretes, with compressive strength and age. The PQ1 material was made with

Table 15.4 Effect of age on the compressive strength and the modulus of rupture of concrete made with gravel and crushed rock aggregates (all units N/mm²)

Age of concrete	F_e	M_R		F_e	M_R		F_e	M_R		F_e	M_R		F_e	M_R		F_e	M_R	
		CR*	G*		CR	G		CR	G		CR	G		CR	G		CR	G
28 days	10.0	1.80	1.74	20.0	2.93	2.55	30.0	3.89	3.18	40.0	4.76	3.73	50.0	5.51	4.21	60.0	6.32	4.66
40 days	11.0	1.93	1.84	22.1	3.14	2.69	32.9	4.15	3.35	43.5	5.05	3.90	53.8	5.86	4.39	63.6	6.59	4.81
3 months	13.3	2.20	2.03	26.5	3.57	2.97	38.4	4.63	3.64	50.4	5.59	4.23	61.8	6.46	4.73	71.1	7.12	5.11
6 months	14.7	2.36	2.15	29.4	3.84	3.15	42.5	4.97	3.85	55.0	5.95	4.44	65.8	6.75	4.90	75.6	7.43	5.29
1 year	15.9	2.50	2.24	31.8	4.06	3.28	45.8	5.23	4.01	58.6	6.22	4.60	69.0	6.97	5.03	78.3	7.62	5.39
2 years	16.6	2.57	2.30	33.3	4.19	3.37	48.0	5.41	4.12	61.0	6.39	4.70	71.3	7.14	5.12	79.5	7.70	5.44
3 years	17.0	2.62	2.33	34.0	4.25	3.41	48.6	5.46	4.15	61.6	6.44	4.73	72.0	7.19	5.15	79.8	7.67	5.45
4 years	17.2	2.64	2.35	34.4	4.28	3.43	48.7	5.47	4.15	61.8	6.46	4.73	72.3	7.21	5.16	80.1	7.74	5.46
5 years	17.3	2.65	2.35	34.5	4.29	3.44	48.9	5.48	4.16	62.0	6.47	4.74	72.3	7.21	5.16	80.1	7.74	5.46

CR* = crushed rock; G* = gravel.

Table 15.5   Dynamic modulus of elasticity, density, and compressive strength

Concrete	Age, weeks	Dynamic modulus, kN/mm²			Density, kg/m³			Equivalent cube strength, N/mm²		
		Mean	No. of results	c.v.,* %	Mean	No. of results	c.v., %	Mean	No. of results	c.v., %
PQ1	4	43	20	1.8	2 344	20	0.5	41.20	20	3.3
	13	45	21	1.1	2 341	21	0.4	48.80	21	3.1
	26	45	47	1.5	2 331	47	0.5	49.83	40	4.1
	39	45.5	20	1.0	2 332	20	0.4	52.10	20	5.0
	52	46.5	27	1.6	2 344	32	0.4	54.23	31	4.9
	104	46	23	0.9	2 335	25	0.4	53.73	22	2.8
	156	47	20	1.1	2 348	20	0.4	56.75	19	3.3
	260	47.5	53	1.5	2 351	53	0.5	61.21	47	4.4
	520	48	10	1.1	2 350	10	0.35	61.95	10	4.6
PQ2	13	39	20	1.4	2 374	20	0.3	39.26	20	3.1
	26	39.5	54	1.2	2 367	55	0.4	43.09	50	2.6
	39	40.5	20	3.8	2 376	20	0.4	44.40	19	3.6
	52	40	20	1.1	2 373	20	0.5	44.43	20	4.8
	104	41	19	1.7	2 370	19	0.8	45.48	14	9.5

*c.v. = coefficient of variation.

gravel aggregate and PQ2 with crushed stone. The value increases with both age and strength, but the variation is small. Comparison between static and dynamic moduli measured on the same concretes indicate a ratio of about 0.8. Structural analyses carried out on concrete pavements show that computed stresses are not very sensitive to small changes in elastic modulus. It is proposed therefore that a constant modulus should be used in such analyses and that it should be the mean value between the two methods of determination. A value of $35–40 \times 10^3$ N/mm² is appropriate.

Poisson's ratio of pavement quality concrete

15.19   The value of Poisson's ratio for concrete has been discussed in Para. 13.23. The appropriate value is 0.15. There appears to be little change with the compressive strength of the material, or with the type of aggregate used.

Fatigue of concrete pavements

15.20   Concrete pavements are subject to fatigue under repeated loading, in the sense that they may crack under repeated applications of a stress less than the modulus of rupture. As with most brittle materials there is a linear relation between the applied tensile stress and the logarithm of the number of applications of that stress which will cause cracking. The fatigue of concrete pavements appears to have been first studied in detail by Kesler in the USA.[13] Using a repeated loading flexural test, operated at a frequency designed to obviate the effect of ageing on the tensile strength, he showed that the stress to cause failure after 10^5 applications was close to 0.74 times the modulus of rupture at 28 days. This compares with the value of about 0.77 shown in Fig. 13.9 referring to lean concrete and cement-bound materials.

15.21   Kesler used concrete beams approximately 1.5 m long and of 150×150 mm cross-section. These were freely supported near the ends and loaded between the third points as in the normal flexural strength test. The load was applied through a lever and cam system to give loading frequencies of 70, 230, and 440 cycles per minute. Typical results are shown in Fig. 15.2. Even with the lowest loading frequency the tests were completed within 24 hours. Kesler used the flexural strength measured on the free ends of the same beams to determine the static strength.

15.22   More recently Galloway, Harding, and Raithby have carried out fatigue tests on two concretes,[14] using the dynamic loading machine shown in Figs 15.3 and 15.4. Tests were made on a concrete PQ.1 of 28-day compressive strength 45 N/mm^2, and a concrete PQ.2 of 28-day compressive strength 33 N/mm^2. The tests were conducted with the materials at various ages between 28 days and 5 years. Figure 15.5 shows the results. It is clear that the strength of the concrete and its age have

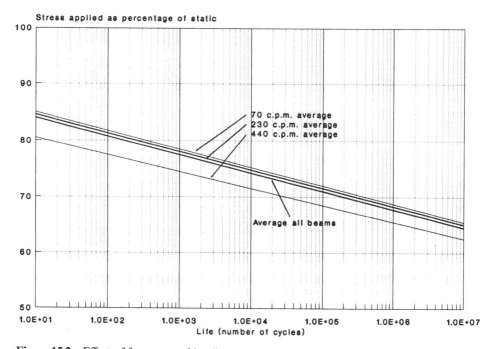

Figure 15.2   Effect of frequency of loading on fatigue of concrete

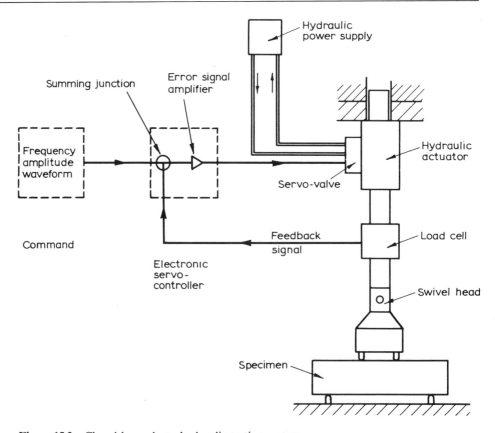

Figure 15.3 Closed-loop electrohydraulic testing system

little influence on the fatigue life expressed as a percentage of the flexural strength at the time of testing. The percentage of the flexural strength required to cause fatigue at 10^5 stress applications is close to 75. The relationship is less linear than that from the Kesler tests. This is due partly to the fact that a number of the tests were not continued to failure. There is likely to be little error involved in assuming a linear relationship with fatigue failure due to a stress of 80 per cent of the flexural strength at 10^5 applications.

Relationship between fatigue and age

15.23   Linear fatigue relations of this type can be drawn for any concrete at ages between 28 days and 5 years. The information given in Table 15.4 and in Para. 15.22 will enable a family of such relations to be prepared. The rupture envelope will cross the fatigue lines in a manner which depends solely on the rate at which the stress applications are repeated. This must be taken into account in the structural design of concrete pavements, and it is considered in detail in Chapter 22.

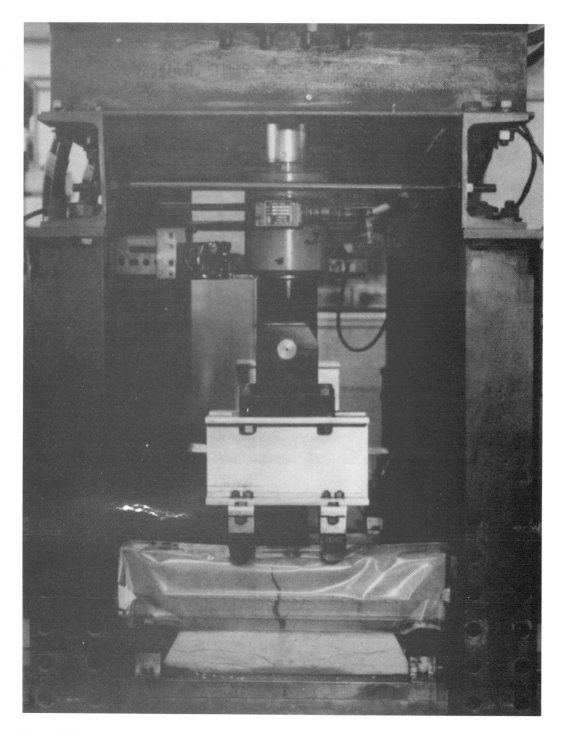

Figure 15.4 Method of loading

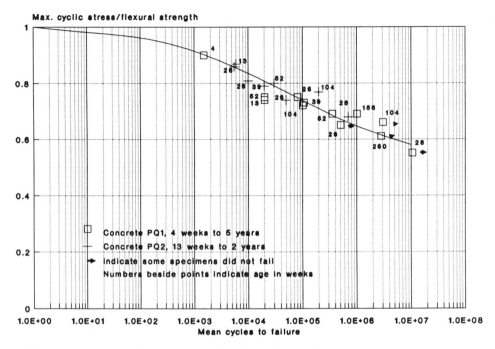

Figure 15.5 Fatigue performance related to flexural strength

References

1. British Standards Institution: *Aggregates from Natural Sources for Concrete*, BS 882:1983, BSI, London, 1983.
2. Department of Transport: *Specification for Highway Works*, Part 3, HMSO, London, Clause 1033, 1986.
3. British Standards Institution: *Testing Aggregates*, BS 812:Section 105.1:1985, BSI, London, 1985.
4. British Standards Institution: *Sampling and Testing of Mineral Aggregates, Sand and Fillers*, BS 812:Part 3:1975, Section 8, BSI, London, 1975.
5. British Standards Institution: *Sampling and Testing of Mineral Aggregates, Sand and Fillers*, BS 812:Part 3:1975, Section 6, BSI, London, 1975.
6. British Standards Insitution: *Testing Concrete. Method of Determining the Compacting Factor*, BS 1881:Part 103:1983, BSI, London, 1983.
7. British Standards Institution: *Testing Concrete. Method of Determination of VeBe Time*, BS 1881:Part 104:1983, BSI, London, 1983.
8. *A Guide to the Structural Design of Pavements for New Roads*, Road Note 29, HMSO, London, 1970.
9. Croney, D., E. W. H. Currer, and P. Croney: The structural design of concrete pavements, *Highways and Transportation*, **34**, 11, 1987.
10. Road Research Laboratory, *Concrete Roads—Design and Construction*, HMSO, London, p. 74, 1955.
11. British Standards Institution: *Testing Concrete: Recommendations for Measurement of Velocity of Ultrasonic Pulses in Concrete*, BS 1881:Part 203:1983, BSI, London, 1983.

12. British Standards Institution: *Testing Concrete: Method of Determination of Static Modulus of Elasticity in Compression*, BS 1881:Part 121:1983, BSI, London, 1983.
13. Kesler, C. E.: Effect of speed of testing on flexural fatigue strength of plain concrete, *Proc. Highw. Res. Bd., Wash.*, **32**, 251–8, 1953.
14. Galloway, J. W., H. M. Harding, and K. D. Raithby: *Effects of Age on Flexure, Fatigue and Compressive Strength of Concrete*, Transport and Road Research Laboratory Report LR865, TRRL, Crowthorne, 1979.

16. Block pavements

Introduction

16.1   Concrete and ceramic block pavements have enjoyed a considerable degree of popularity in recent years. They undoubtedly look attractive, particularly when new. In situations such as shopping malls and pedestrian precincts they can provide a pleasing architectural feature. An advantage frequently stressed is that they can be lifted when necessary to restore regularity, or to provide access to undergound services. However, it is to be deprecated that there is a growing tendency to infill areas which have been raised or damaged with concrete or bitumen as shown in Fig. 16.1. Because of changes in the shape and colour of blocks any authority using this form of construction should order sufficient spare blocks to permit adequate maintenance.

16.2   Hard-selling advertising claims that block pavements spread loads more effectively than continuous concrete and bituminous surfacings, or that 30-per-cent savings can be made by their use. These claims need to be treated with caution. There is no long-term full-scale evidence to support such claims.

History of block pavements

16.3   Block paving is far from a new concept. Stone setts, laid in a very similar manner to modern blocks, have been a feature of many European cities since medievel times. In the early nineteenth century interlocking wood blocks, generally hexagonal in shape, were introduced into the City of London, as a quieter alternative to stone setts. They were laid on a cemented base at least as thick as the blocks. In various forms, wood blocks remained a very popular form of paving in London until after the Second World War. Latterly they were surfaced dressed with hot tar and chippings to provide adequate skid resistance.

16.4   Brick pavements were used very widely in the USA in the last two decades of the nineteenth century, particularly in Ohio and Illinois. The bricks were fired at a high temperature to provide a vitreous appearance and high crushing strength. They were generally $9\,in \times 4\,in \times 3\,in$ deep with an alternative size for lightly trafficked situations where the depth was 2 in.

In 1899 a US Commission was set up to report on brick pavements. A major conclusion was that the bricks should be set on a bed of sharp sand 1 in thick, over a concrete base. It was recommended that the joints should be filled with a cement slurry.

16.5   In western Holland, which includes the cities of Amsterdam, Rotterdam,

Figure 16.1 Bituminous in-fill in block pavement

and The Hague, and where the subsoil is a well-compacted sand, brick pavements have been widely used for more than 80 years. The bricks are laid directly on the sand and experienced gangs are employed to relay the surface as deformation occurs. The frequency of the relaying operation depended on the type and constitution of the traffic. After the Second World War the increase in the loading of commercial traffic made the continued use of this form of construction on major roads uneconomic.

Modern block pavements

16.6   The blocks being used today for this type of paving are of either pressed concrete or fired clay. Thicknesses range from 50 to 100 mm and they are either rectangular or shaped to provide lateral interlock. The overall size is such that, when laid, each square metre contains about 40 blocks. Present thinking appears to prefer the rectangular shape as being less liable to crack during service. The blocks are produced in a variety of colours.

16.7   The manufacturers' recommendation is to use a base and sub-base thickness appropriate to an asphalt pavement designed for the traffic to be carried. In place of the asphalt, the blocks are laid on a bedding of sand of 50 mm compacted thickness. The sand, which should have a maximum size of 5 mm and less than 3 per cent by weight finer than 0.06 mm, is laid to an appropriate uncompacted thickness. After placement the blocks are surface-vibrated using an appropriate vibrating-plate machine. During compaction, sand is applied to the surface in an attempt to fill the spaces between the blocks.[1] The blocks are normally required to have a crushing strength in excess of 50 N/mm² at 28 days.

Load-spreading by block pavements

16.8   The manufacturers' recommendations as stated above imply that the load-spreading properties of block pavements are equal to those of an uncracked two-course asphalt pavement of equal total thickness. This would be possible only if the friction between the vertical faces of the blocks was sufficient to ensure load transfer without differential sliding between the blocks. This is a most unlikely situation. Seddon, working in New Zealand, appears to have been the first to investigate this matter using the blocks as part of a road structure, as distinct from laboratory tests in shallow tanks. He assessed the load spreading ability by a process of back calculation from measured deflection under a heavily-loaded wheel. He concluded that the effective modulus of elasticity of the combination of blocks and their bedding was similar to that of a compacted unbound material.[2]

16.9   Clark,[3] following earlier similar work carried out by the Cement and Concrete Association,[4] attempted to assess the load-spreading ability of block pavements using tank tests and a synthetic subgrade of expanded polystyrene. The blocks were laid on a 60-mm uncompacted sand bedding over 300 mm of well-compacted Type 1 crushed stone sub-base (see Chapter 12). The sub-base was instrumented with pressure cells; five were in the surface of the sub-base, close to the axis of loading, and one was in the lower surface of the sub-base. The last was on the axis of loading at the mid-depth of the sub-base. Loading was by a 300-mm-diameter plate and a hydraulic ram. The report states that a number of the pressure cells failed to operate satisfactorily, and as a result the observations were restricted to some measurements of compressive stress in the surface of the sub-base. These indicated a stress level of about 40–50 per cent of the applied stress at the surface. The Boussinesq stress analysis for circular loading indicates that this is consistent with a surfacing having an effective modulus of elasticity very similiar to the sub-base material. The report states:

> In the tests, the surface deformation of the paving had been confined solely to the blocks in direct contact with the loading plate and virtually no movement had been detected in adjacent blocks. This suggests that the level of load transfer across the boundary between the loaded and unloaded blocks was small.[3]

This indicates that there was relatively unimpaired vertical sliding between the loaded and unloaded blocks. A photograph in the paper shows this clearly.

16.10   A most comprehensive study of the load spreading of block pavements has recently been published by the TRRL.[5] The laboratory's new linear road testing machine was used for the tests (see Chapter 17 and Fig. 17.6). Various combinations were used. These included (1) brick paver blocks with sand bedding laid on 135 mm of Type 1 sub-base over a deep clay fill of CBR 5–8 per cent, compared with a dense bitumen macadam roadbase material laid on the same sub-base and to a thickness equal to that of the blocks and their bedding, and (2) a similar comparison, but with an additional layer of dense bitumen base material 60-mm thick laid beneath both the blocks and the bituminous material of equal thickness. Wheel loads of 40–80 kN were applied at speeds of 2.5 and 20 km/h to give cumulative traffic up to 8000 standard axles. The sections were instrumented for the measurement of vertial subgrade strain and the horizontal strain under the base.

16.11   The measured vertical strain in the subgrade beneath the block pavement was about three times that under the equivalent thickness of bituminous roadbase. The horizontal strain under the base was 2–3 times greater under the block pavement. Elastic deflection measurements were made on the pavements using the Falling Weight Deflectometer (see Chapter 29). These showed deflections of the block pavements three to five times greater than those observed on the bituminous pavements. When the permanent deformation had produced a rut depth of 10 mm, there was no indication from the strain measurements that a 'lock-up' effect had occurred.

16.12   These measurements appear to confirm Seddon's conclusion that the effective modulus of brick pavements is similar to that of an equivalent thickness of crushed stone, and that it does not compare in this respect with two-course rolled asphalt.

16.13   The inference from all the research work referred to above is that, to be

Figure 16.2   Examples of deformation in block pavement laid on a heavily-trafficked road

successful, blocks should be laid on a foundation which itself is strong enough to resist both deformation and cracking under the envisaged traffic loading.

16.14   Confirmation that block pavements spread traffic loads less adequately than asphalt of equivalent thickness is shown in Figs 16.2 and 16.3. These refer to the performance of blocks laid on a heavily trafficked A-class road. The original asphalt surfacing was removed and replaced by blocks on a sand bedding to restore

Figure 16.3   Displacement of blocks in an acceleration and braking situation

the original surface level. Considerable deformation is shown in Fig. 16.2 some 2 years after the work was completed. Figure 16.3 shows the tendency of the blocks to move in the direction of traffic flow in an area subject to braking and acceleration forces.

References

1. Cement and Concrete Association: *Concrete Block Paving: Model Specification Clauses for Roads Subject to Adoption*, C & CA, Wexham Springs, Slough, Bucks., 1978.
2. Seddon, P. A.: The behaviour of interlocking concrete block paving at the Canterbury Test Track, *Tenth Australian Road Research Board Conference, August 1980*, ARRB, Vermont South, Victoria 3133.
3. Clark, A. J.: *Further Investigations into the Load-spreading of Concrete Block Paving*, Cement and Concrete Association Technical Report 545, C & CA, Wexham Springs, Slough, Bucks., 1981.
4. Knapton, J.: *The Design of Concrete Block Roads*, Cement and Concrete Association Technical Report 415, C & CA, Wexham Springs, Slough, Bucks, 1976.
5. Addis, R. R., R. G. Robinson, and A. R. Halliday: *The Load-spreading Properties of Clay Brick Pavements*, Transport and Road Research Technical Report 234, TRRL, Crowthorne, 1989.

PART FOUR   Pavement Performance Studies and Empirical Design

17. Pavement performance studies using test track and controlled traffic conditions

Introduction

17.1   The various combinations of surfacing, base, and sub-base necessary to carry traffic during the design life of a pavement can be studied by long-term observations on experimental sections built into in-service highways. This has been the approach to pavement design adopted in the UK since the thirties. The advantage of this method is that it fully takes into account the effect of climatic changes, and the natural ageing and hardening of many of the materials used in pavements. However, it is clearly slow, although interim conclusions can be drawn in many instances after a few years of traffic.

17.2   As an alternative the trial sections can be constructed round a closed loop subjected to a high density of continuous traffic. In this way trafficking can be accelerated by a factor of more than 10. This accelerated form of testing was used in the USA for the WASHO (Western Association of State Highway Officials) and AASHO road tests, which have provided the basis for current American standards for flexible and concrete pavements.

17.3   In addition to these two approaches, circular or linear testing facilities (often referred to as 'road machines') have been built in Britain, the USA, and a number of countries in Europe. These are used primarily to compare the behaviour of different road materials under the passage of predetermined heavy wheel loads.

17.4   This chapter briefly considers the development of road machines and then discusses in detail the WASHO and AASHO road tests.

Road machines and their application

17.5   The interaction of wheel and pavement appears to have been studied as early as 1840 in a machine designed to assess the wear of stone setts. However, the first British road machine constructed for a systematic investigation of road deformation and wear was made at the National Physical Laboratory (NPL) in 1912 and was

Figure 17.1   Teddington road testing machine (1912)

operated there for many years.[1] A photograph of the machine before it was fitted with rubber tyres is shown in Fig. 17.1

17.6   This machine incorporated a number of desirable features, some of which have unfortunately been omitted from later machines of this type. It was, for example, operated in a building, permitting both control and variations of temperature. This is not possible in some later machines operated in the open. The eight loading wheels were individually driven by 2-hp (1.5 kW) electric motors and the load on each was separately adjustable. Practical details of the loading mechanism and the test track are shown in Fig. 17.2. The maximum wheel load of the NPL machine was 2800 lb (1270 kg), and the maximum speed 7 rev/min, giving approximately 80 000 wheel coverages per 24-hour day.

17.7   This machine, and a smaller one constructed later, were used primarily to test the performance of bituminous materials laid on a concrete foundation. Hence it was the stability of the mixtures (resistance to shear) that was studied. The possible influence of the tensile stresses which would have developed on a less stiff foundation was not at that stage appreciated. Nevertheless, the results from these machines considered in conjunction with field trials provided the basic information for the early British specifications for bituminious surfacing materials.

17.8   By the early thirties there was a need for a machine capable of imposing much heavier wheel loads. In the USA, the Bureau of Public Roads had constructed in the twenties a special circular test track on which experimental surfacings could be laid and trafficked by a manually driven truck (see Fig. 17.3).[2] In 1933 a similar test facility was constructed at the Harmondsworth site of the Road Research Laboratory, but the 'traffic' was provided by an electrically driven truck tethered by

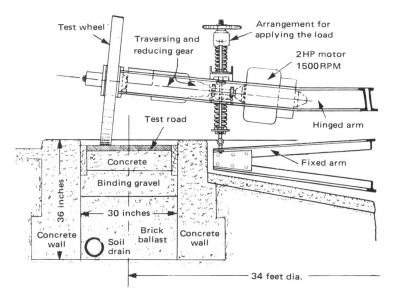

Figure 17.2 Details of wheel load adjustment used on the Teddington road testing machine (1912)

Figure 17.3 Bureau of Public Roads test track (1925)

Figure 17.4   Road Machine No. 3 as originally constructed

a radial arm 17 m long to the track centre (see Fig. 17.4).[3] The load range of the vehicle was 10–23 tons with a corresponding speed range 45–30 mile/h. A radial tracking mechanism was built into the machine.

17.9   As originally designed, this machine was used to test bituminous materials laid on a concrete foundation, but in 1963 major modifications were made to the track and the test vehicle. The track was excavated to a depth of more than 2 m, and provided with concrete walls between which complete road pavements (including the subgrade) could be constructed. The width of the test vehicle was increased so that the road wheels were supported by the concrete walls and a fifth wheel was introduced to run over the experimental pavement (see Fig. 17.5). The load on the test wheel in the modified machine is adjustable using a pair of hydraulic rams. Wheel loads up to 7 t can be used with the machine operating at 25 km/h. Pavements constructed in this machine have been fully instrumented for the measurement of stress, strain, and deformation and the facility has been principally used to compare measured and computed stress and strain distributions.[4]

17.10   All roads machines with circular tracks, and particularly those of small radius, impose on the road surface radial stress not normally present on roads in service. As early as 1905 designs were prepared for a linear road machine in which

Figure 17.5   Arrangement of test wheel of Road Machine No. 3

a loaded wheel moved in a straight line over an experimental length of pavement.[1] Provision was made in the design to move the wheel across the pavement to simulate the distribution of wheels in the nearside wheel tracks of normal roads. The machine was not built, the circular form being adopted in preference.

17.11   However, in 1985 a machine working on the linear principle was installed at the TRRL. The new facility consists essentially of a test pit 25 m long and 10 m wide which can accommodate up to 10 test pavements instrumented to measure stresses and deflections. The test wheel can apply loads up to 10 t as it traverses the test pavements at speeds up to 20 km/h. The machine is shown in Fig. 17.6.

17.12   A most interesting form of transportable linear road machine has been constructed by the National Institute for Road Research in South Africa.[5] The pavement is trafficked by a reciprocating wheel operated beneath a self-mobile road vehicle. The machine can be operated under temperature-controlled conditions on test sections constructed in a laboratory, or alternatively it can be used to traffic

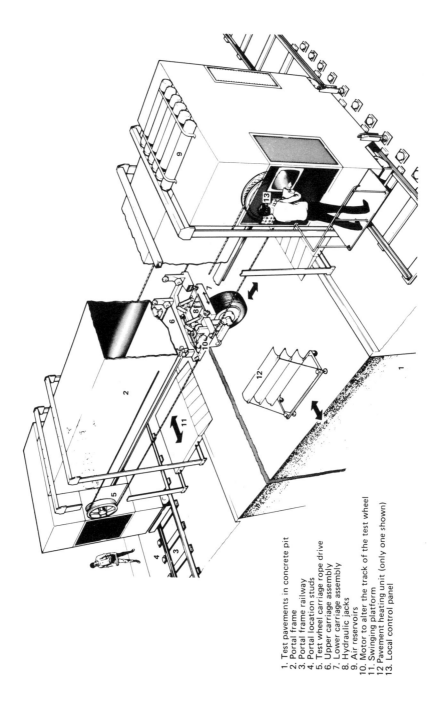

1. Test pavements in concrete pit
2. Portal frame
3. Portal frame railway
4. Portal location studs
5. Test wheel carriage rope drive
6. Upper carriage assembly
7. Lower carriage assembly
8. Hydraulic jacks
9. Air reservoirs
10. Motor to alter the track of the test wheel
11. Swinging platform
12 Pavement heating unit (only one shown)
13. Local control panel

Figure 17.6 The TRRL Road Tester

in-service roads. The wheel-load range is 2–8 t and the frequency of loading 800/h. The length of pavement loaded is 6 m and the applications are distributed over a width of about 1 m. Apart from its versatility, the very heavy wheel loads which the machine can impose permit a considerable acceleration of life-testing compared with normal road traffic.

The WASHO road test

17.13   The WASHO road test was sponsored by the Western Association of State Highway Officials in the USA and administered by the Highway Research Board of America. The object was to study the performance of experimental flexible road pavements constructed to a wide range of overall thicknesses, when they were trafficked by repetitions of known axle loads.

17.14   The site chosen for the experiment was in the south of the state of Idaho where the subgrade was a silty clay of average liquid limit 35 per cent and average plastic limit 25 per cent. The percentage passing the 75 µm sieve varied between 80 and 95. The average moisture content of the soil at the time of construction was 22.7 per cent, and the mean annual rainfall was 200 mm. Compared with Great Britain the climate is extreme, the maximum air temperature in July and August averaging 35°C and the minimum air temperature in December and January averaging −10°C.

17.15   Two identical test tracks were constructed, each consisting of two two-lane straight lengths of highway connected by turnabouts at the ends (Fig. 17.7). Five experimental sections each 100 m long were constructed on each straight length, the construction being the same for the two lanes. The experimental sections were separated by 30-m transition lengths in which any changes in thickness were made. On one straight length of each test track the pavements had a 100-mm asphaltic concrete surfacing, a 50-mm crushed stone roadbase and granular sub-bases of thickness 0, 100, 200, 300, and 400 mm. On the other straight length the sections had

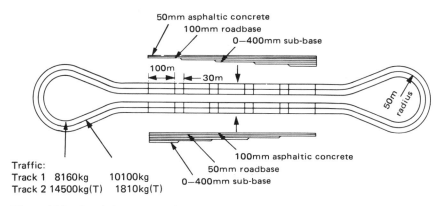

Figure 17.7   Track layout used for WASHO road test

a 50-mm asphaltic concrete surfacing, a 100-mm crushed stone roadbase, and the same range of sub-base thickness.

17.16   The inner lane of one test track was trafficked by three-axle trucks with two load axles each carrying 8160 kg. The outer lane of the same track carried similar vehicles with two load axles each carrying 10 100 kg. The inner lane of the second test track was trafficked by five-axle trucks with two pairs of tandem load axles, the load on each pair being 14 500 kg. The outer lane of this track carried similar vehicles with 18 100 kg on each pair of tandem axles.

17.17   The aggregate for the sub-base, the roadbase, and the asphaltic surfacings of the WASHO road test were obtained from a local borrow pit in which a crushing plant was installed, The material was predominantly limestone with some quartz, siltstone and basalt. The gradings for the three materials were closely controlled and showed little variation from the average particle size distribution curves shown in Fig. 17.8.

17.18   The subgrade was compacted at an average moisture content of 22.8 per cent to give an average dry density of 1528 kg/m^3. The average dry density obtained in the sub-base was 2102 kg/m^3 with a standard deviation of 74 kg/m^3 and the corresponding figures for the roadbase were 2127 kg/m^3 and 45 kg/m^3.

17.19   After a very short period of traffic in November 1952 the test tracks remained untrafficked until June 1953. Trafficking at a uniform rate was commenced in mid-June and continued until the end of May 1954, with a break of two months

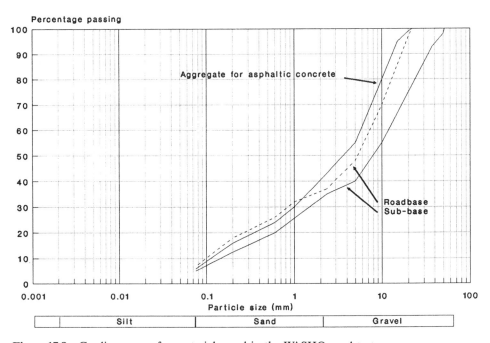

Figure 17.8   Grading curves for materials used in the WASHO road test

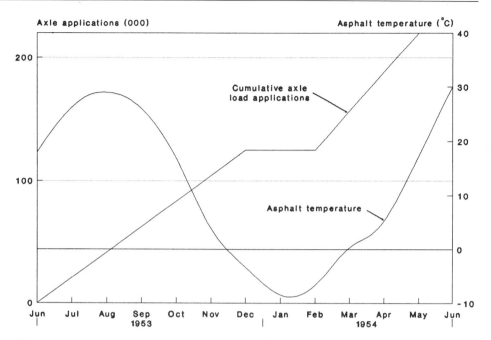

Figure 17.9   WASHO road test—trafficking in relation to time and pavement temperature

between mid-December 1953 and mid-February 1954 while the subgrade was frozen (see Fig. 17.9).

17.20   The performance of the pavements was assessed mainly in terms of the permanent deformation which occurred under the action of traffic. Measurements were made in the wheel tracks and between the wheel tracks at monthly intervals. As is usually found, the deformation tended to be greatest in the outer wheel track. Observations were also made of the amount of cracking which occurred and of the elastic deflection measured by the Benkelman Beam. Where excessive deformation and cracking occurred patching was undertaken to keep the sections serviceable and to minimize sympathetic deterioration in adjacent sections.

17.21   Results from all but the thinnest sections (those without any sub-base) are shown in Fig. 17.10. The thinnest sections deformed rapidly under all the axle loads and little other useful information was obtained from them. The deformation curves are characterized by a steep initial portion associated with the first 30 000 applications of axle loads, followed by comparatively little deformation during the subsequent 100 000 applications. When traffic resumed after the thawing of the subgrade in February 1954 the sections with the 50-mm asphalt surfacing deformed comparatively rapidly but under the 100-mm surfacing there was little apparent acceleration of deformation which could be attributed to a weakened foundation.

17.22   The initial rapid deformation under traffic coincided with the highest summer temperature conditions, when the elastic modulus of the asphalt would be expected to be low and the stresses transmitted to the roadbase, sub-base, and subgrade correspondingly higher. Much of this initial deformation would have been due to compaction of the materials by the traffic. However, it is unfortunate that the tests were not continued through another summer to determine whether further deformation would have occurred in July and August 1954. (In the later AASHO road test, traffic was continued for two complete years to give more information on seasonal effects.)

17.23   Figure 17.10 shows that the performance of the sections with the 100-mm asphalt surfacings was much superior to that of the sections of the same total thickness but with a 50-mm surfacing. Increasing the thickness of the sub-base in all cases reduced the permanent deformation, although the influence of sub-base thickness is less under the 100-mm surfacing than under the 50-mm surfacing.

17.24   For the sections with 100-mm surfacings, the deformation increased with the total axle load. The performance of the sections with 50-mm surfacings was more random, suggesting that small differences in the quality of the roadbase, sub-base and foundation were more important than the axle load, where the surfacing was thin.

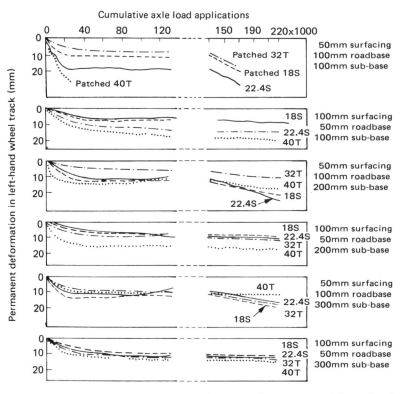

Figure 17.10   WASHO road test. Development of permanent deformation in the left-hand wheel tracks

17.25   If the fourth-power damaging relationship referred to in Para. 8.43 is used, the damaging effects of the four axle loads used in the WASHO road test can be expressed in terms of 'standard' 8160-kg axles as indicated in Table 17.1. The results for the test section with 100-mm asphalt surfacings are reasonably consistent when this table is used to relate deformation with the cumulative number of standard axles applied by the traffic. However, the 10 100-kg single axle does appear to be rather less damaging than the 14 500-kg tandem axle.

Table 17.1   Axle loads used in the WASHO road test expressed in terms of 'standard' 1860-kg axles

Axle load, kg	Equivalent 8160-kg standard axles
8 160 (single)	1
10 100 (single)	2.4
14 500 (tandem)	1.2
18 100 (tandem)	3

17.26   The fact that pavements with as little construction as 50 mm of road-base and 100 mm of sub-base were capable of carrying more than 200 000 applications of the maximum axle load permitted in Britain may appear surprising to British engineers. However, due account must be taken of the subgrade and environmental conditions of the WASHO test site. The average *in situ* CBR of the soil in the outer wheel tracks was 16.5 per cent in November 1953, immediately before the frost period, and 14.5 per cent in June 1954. These values are several times higher than would be expected in the same soil in Britain. This is probably explained by the low rainfall at the WASHO site (250 mm per year) and the high summer temperatures. With such a low rainfall it is unlikely that a water table would have been present even during the winter (none is recorded in the site investigation reports) and a large reduction in subgrade strength on thawing would not be expected.

The AASHO road test[†]

17.27   The AASHO road test was conceived as early as June 1952, i.e., 2 years before the completion of the WASHO test. The principal stated objective was

> To determine the significant relationship between the number of repetitions of specified axle loads of different magnitude and arrangement, and the performance of different thicknesses of uniformly designed and constructed asphaltic concrete, plain Portland cement concrete and reinforced Portland cement concrete surfacings on different thickness of base and sub-base when laid on a basement soil of known characteristics.[6]

17.28   Planning the project continued until 1955 so that lessons learned from the

---

[†]The AASHO Road Test was conducted and analysed in terms of imperial units and these have been retained in this discussion to avoid modification of the statistical equations.

WASHO test could be incorporated in the proposals. The site selected was at Ottawa, Illinois, about 100 km southwest of Chicago. Construction started in August 1956 and was completed in 1958. Trafficking occupied two complete years from October 1958 to November 1960 and was continuous over that period. The results were first discussed at a special meeting of the Highway Research Board held at St Louis in May 1962. The total cost of the project was equivalent to about £10 m.

17.29   As with the WASHO test, experimental pavements were laid on loops consisting of straight lengths of normal two-lane, dual-carriageway highway connected at the ends by circular turnabouts. The materials used for the pavements were broadly similar to those of the earlier test, but the thicknesses adopted covered a wider range as also did the axle loads of the test vehicles.

17.30   Continuation of the test for 2 years allowed the influence of climatic factors to be studied more completely than in the WASHO test but it is unfortunate that different performance criteria were used to interpret the results of the two tests. The concept of 'present serviceability' was introduced to assess the changing condition of the AASHO pavements under the action of traffic.

17.31   This concept is based on the principle that the road user is not directly interested in the amount of cracking or deformation present in the pavements over which he drives; he is primarily interested in the ability of the road to provide a comfortable and safe ride. However, riding quality is not necessarily related to the structural condition of the pavement; it may, for example, be influenced by the original laying standards achieved or by deep-seated foundation movements. Performance expressed in terms of present serviceability is not therefore directly relatable to structural condition defined by rutting and cracking.

Present serviceability rating and present serviceability index

17.32   Subjective serviceability measurements could not be made on the comparatively short sections planned for the AASHO test, and as preliminary to the test itself subjective measurements were made on a total of 99 selected lengths of road in the states of Illinois, Minnesota, and Indiana. The selected sites were almost equally divided between flexible and concrete construction. A subjective assessment panel was constituted of drivers of a wide range of private and commercial vehicles and they were asked to rate the serviceability of the pavement sections using their own guidelines and judgement of what was meant by serviceability, using a scale of 0–5 as defined in Fig. 17.11. They were further asked to say whether the sections were acceptable or not. In this way a level of acceptability on the rating scale was to be established. The mean rating of the panel and the mean opinion on acceptability was used to define the present serviceability rating (PSR) of each section. A conclusion from this study was that a PSR value of 2.5 represented the critical condition of a pavement likely to require an overlay in the near future and a value of 1.5 represented the condition of a pavement unfit to carry further traffic.

17.33   Physical observations were made on the same sections of highway, including measurements of the longitudinal surface irregularity, the degree of cracking, the extent of any patching and subsequently for flexible pavements, the

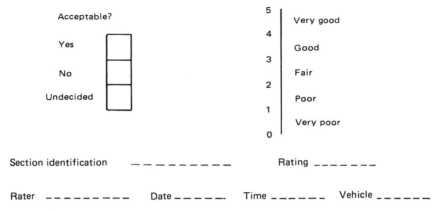

Figure 17.11   Present serviceability rating form used in the WASHO road test

depth of rutting in the wheel paths. These observations were combined statistically to give a present serviceability index (PSI) on a scale of 0–5, in closest agreement with the subjective PSR.[6]

17.34   The equation finally used to evaluate the PSI of the flexible pavements included in the AASHO road test was:

$$\mathrm{PSI} = 5.03 - 1.91 \log(1 + \overline{\mathrm{SV}}) - 1.38 \overline{\mathrm{RD}}^2 - 0.01\sqrt{C + P} \qquad (17.1)$$

where $\overline{\mathrm{RD}}$ = the rut depth measured in inches over a 4-ft span embracing each wheel
          track (average for both wheel tracks)
  $\overline{\mathrm{SV}}$ = the slope variance × 10^6 (average of both wheel tracks)
    C = the cracking, expressed as the area of pavement in square feet exhibiting
          grid-pattern cracking or other cracking leading to the breakout of the
          bituminous surfacing, measured over an area of 1000 ft^2
    P = the area of patching per 1000 ft^2

Slope variance was measured by the CHLOE profilometer in which the pavement slope over a 9-in baseline was measured with respect to the average slope of the pavement at intervals of 1 ft. (Since the slope is generally less than $\pm 3°$ the angle in radians is approximately equal to the slope.) The slope variance is defined as follows:

$$\overline{\mathrm{SV}} = \left\{ \frac{\left[\sum_{i=1}^{i=n} X_i^2 - \dfrac{1}{n} \left(\sum_{i=1}^{i=n} X_i \right)^2 \right]}{n-1} \right\} \times 10^6 \qquad (17.2)$$

where X_i is the ith slope measurement and n is the total number of measurements made.

17.35   In Eq. (17.1) the value of $\overline{\mathrm{SV}}$ is much more important than the other factors in determining the level of PSI. For example, two pavements with the same value of

$\overline{SV}$, one of which showed no cracking or patching and the other with a surface covered by cracking or patching, would vary in PSI by only 0.3. Similarly, a difference in rut depth between 0 and 0.5 in would affect the PSI by only 0.4. Because of the statistical nature of the equations this does not mean that cracking and rutting are not important, since they will react on the value of $\overline{SV}$. However, it does mean that Eq. (17.1) cannot be directly used in comparing the AASHO road test results with those from other experiments in which rutting and cracking have been used as the criterion of structural performance. However, information is given in the AASHO test report which enables rut depth to be directly related to PSI both for the preliminary investigations in the three states and also for the road test itself. These relationships are shown in Fig. 17.12. For the road test and the measurements made in Illinois the correlation was strong. It was less strong for Minnesota and no correlation was found for the Indiana observations. It is surprising that the slopes of the relationships are so different. For the new pavements of the AASHO road test, rutting would appear to be a major factor affecting riding quality while for the presumably older pavements investigated in the three states surface movements, due for example to differential settlement and subgrade moisture changes, may be more important.

17.36   Before Fig. 17.12 can be used to compare the performance of British flexible pavements with those of the AASHO road test, more consideration must be

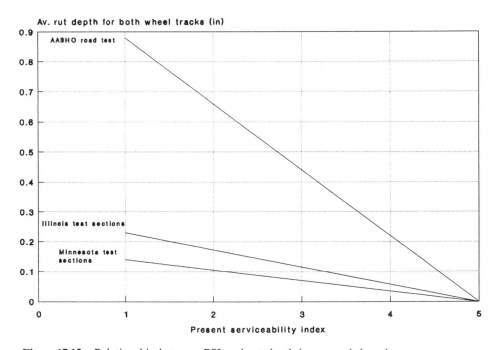

Figure 17.12   Relationship between PSI and rut depth in one and three layers

given to the relationship between rut depth and total deformation measured from original road level. The criterion of structural performance used in Britain is based on the deformation from original level measured in the left-hand (nearside) wheel track and a deformation of 25 mm has been adopted on the basis of experience to define 'failure'. If deformation is measured by placing a straight-edge transversely across the wheel tracks then the apparent deformation is less than the total deformation from original pavement level by an amount which depends largely on the length of the straight-edge. In Para. 4.9 it is stated that a total deformation of 25 mm would be observed as a deformation of about 20 mm under a 2-m straight-edge, for the types of flexible pavement commonly used in Britain. In the AASHO road test a 4-ft (1.2-m) straight-edge was used to assess rut depth. A study of transverse deformation measurements made on British roads with crushed stone, bituminous, and cemented road bases shows that the proportion of the total deformation which would be observed using such a straight-edge would be about 0.6. Another factor which needs to be taken into account is that British performance criteria are based solely on the condition of the pavement in the nearside wheel tracks, while in the AASHO test the mean rut-depth for the two wheel tracks was recorded. British experience, to a large extent confirmed by the ASSHO test, is that the deformation measured in the wheel track closer to the road verge is about 1.3 times the deformation in the other wheel track, when the road is straight. Taking these factors into account, it is necessary to multiply the average rut depth as measured in the AASHO test by 1.9 to obtain the equivalent permanent deformation in the nearside wheel track. The relationship between permanent deformation and PSI obtained in this way from Fig. 17.12 is shown in Fig. 17.13. It follows from this relationship that the British definition of failure for flexible pavements corresponds to a present serviceability index of about 2.5. It will be appreciated that in view of the large number of approximations involved in obtaining this relationship it can be used only as a guide.

17.37   The equation used to evaluate the PSI of the concrete pavements included in the AASHO road test was:

$$\text{PSI} = 5.41 - 1.78 \log(1 + \overline{\text{SV}}) - 0.09\sqrt{C + P} \qquad (17.3)$$

In this equation C has a different meaning from the same symbol used in Eq. (17.1); C is here defined as the total linear footage of Class 3 and Class 4 cracks (cracks opened or spalled to a width of $\frac{1}{4}$-inch or more) per 1000 square feet of lane area. On some of the concrete sections of the AASHO experiment it was not possible to use the CHLOE profilometer, so to determine $\overline{\text{SV}}$ the Bureau of Public Roads Roughometer was employed at a speed of 10 mile/h and the alternative formula given below was used to determine PSI:

$$\text{PSI} = 5.41 - 1.8 \log(0.4R - 33) - 0.99\sqrt{C + P} \qquad (17.4)$$

where R is the roughness index in inches per mile.

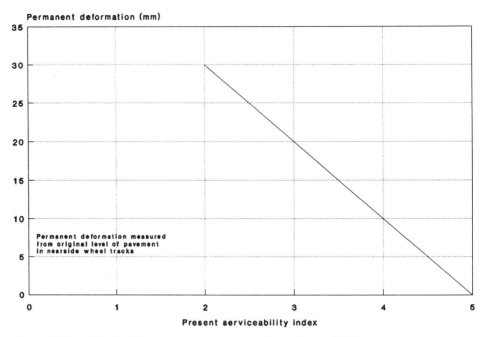

Figure 17.13   Relationship between permanent deformation and PSI

17.38   As for flexible pavements the value of PSI obtained from Eq. (17.3) or (17.4) is determined almost entirely by the riding quality of the road and the value of C and P are secondary, except in so far as they influence riding quality. The criterion used in Britain to assess the performance of experimental concrete roads is based entirely on the amount and severity of cracking and to relate British experience with the results of the AASHO road test it is necessary to examine more closely the relationship between PSI and cracking. In the preliminary tests on state roads from which Eq. (17.3) was established (see Para. 17.32) measurements of crack length were made and this enables the relationships between degree of cracking and PSI to be examined directly. Figure 17.14 shows the mean relationship between the total length of cracking (projected in either the longitudinal or transverse directions) per 100 ft of traffic lane and PSI derived from Eq. (17.3). (In this case the measurements made in the three states fitted the same curve reasonably well.)

17.39   The 'failure' criterion used for experimental reinforced concrete roads in Britain is 250 m of total crack length per 100 m of traffic lane. Experience shows that when such pavements are approaching the end of their lives about one-third of the total cracking falls into the class 3 and class 4 categories as defined in relation to the AASHO road test. It follows from Fig. 17.14 that the British failure condition would correspond to a PSI level of about 2.

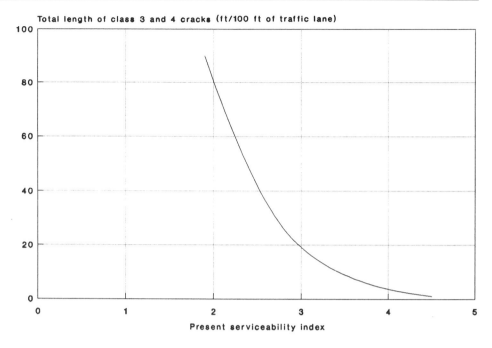

Figure 17.14 Relationship between the degree of cracking and PSI

Scope of the AASHO experiment

17.40 The road was built at Ottawa, Illinois, at a site where the climatic and soil conditions were regarded as typical of large areas of the northern United States. The construction was entirely on embankment, the top 3 ft of which were a uniform sandy clay (liquid limit 30 per cent, plastic limit 13 per cent). The average depth of frost penetration during the two winters of the test was 35 in. The laboratory CBR of the soil, as placed, appears to have been about 4 per cent. The *in situ* CBR after the spring thaw was about 2 per cent. The depth of the water table varied seasonally between 2 and 7 feet below the finished road level.

17.41 The experiment consisted of 6 loops (1–6) of which all were trafficked with the exception of loop 1, which was used for special climatic and other studies. Each loop had two traffic lanes 12 feet wide independently trafficked. The two straight tangential lengths of each loop were used for the experimental flexible and concrete pavements and one turnabout in each loop was in flexible construction and the other in concrete. Experimental bridges were incorporated in loops 5 and 6. Test traffic operated in rigidly controlled lanes at 35 mile/h, and was running over the sections for about 19 hours per day for slightly more than 2 years. The total number of axle loads was about 1 114 000 over each section. The axle loads ranged from 2000 lb on single axles to 48 000 lb carried on tandem axles. (In the AASHO road test reports axle loads are generally quoted in kips, i.e., units of 1000 lb.)

Thickness combinations and materials used for flexible pavements

17.42 The axle loads and combinations of surfacing, roadbase, and sub-base used on flexible lengths of each of the loops 2–6 are shown in Table 17.2.

Table 17.2   Axle loads and pavements used: main flexible-pavement experiment

	Loop 2		Loop 3		Loop 4		Loop 5		Loop 6	
	Lane 1	Lane 2	Lane 1	Lane 2	Lane 1	Lane 2	Lane 1	Lane 2	Lane 1	Lane 2
Axle load, lb	2000	6000	12 000	24 000	18 000	32 000	22 400	40 000	30 000	48 000
	S*	S	S	T*	S	T	S	T	S	T
Sub-base, in	0 and 4		0, 4, and 8		4, 8, and 12		4, 8, and 12		8, 12, and 16	
Roadbase, in	0, 3, and 6		0, 3, and 6		0, 3, and 6		3, 6, and 9		3, 6, and 9	
Surfacing, in	1, 2, and 3		2, 3, and 4		3, 4, and 5		3, 4, and 5		4, 5, and 6	

*S = carried on single axles; T = carried on tandem axles.

17.43 Each loop comprised a complete factorial design in the sense that each thickness of surfacing, roadbase, and sub-base was used in combination with every other thickness, i.e., on loop 2 there was $2 \times 3 \times 3 = 18$ sections on each lane plus some duplicates and on loops 3–6 $3 \times 3 \times 3 = 27$ sections on each lane. The sections were arranged in statistically random order around the loops, although some change of order was made to avoid too close a juxtaposition between thin and thick sections.

17.44 The sub-base used was a local sandy gravel modified by plant mixing with a fine sand and a slightly cohesive soil. The roadbase was a crushed limestone wet-mix. The gradings of the roadbase and sub-base are compared in Fig. 17.15 with British specifications of type 2 sub–base (see Para. 12.6) and wet-mix roadbase (see Para. 12.14). On loops 3–6 a subsidiary experiment was also included to compare the performance of crushed limestone, gravel, cement-bound, and bituminous-bound roadbases. A sloping subgrade and sub-base were used to give a varying thickness of roadbase along these sections. These experiments used only one thickness of surfacing in each loop, as shown in Table 17.3. The grading of the crushed-stone roadbase was identical with that used in the main experiment; the same grading was used for the gravel roadbase. The bituminous and cemented roadbases were made by mixing binder with the gravel sub-base material used for the main and subsidiary tests. The binder content for the bituminous roadbase was 5.2 per cent, and the cement content for the cemented roadbase was 4 per cent, giving a 7-day (cylinder) compressive strength of 840 lbf/in² (5.8 MN/m²), corresponding to a 28-day (cube) compressive strength of 1450 lbf/in² (10 MN/m²). Details of the surfacing materials used for all the flexible sections are given in Fig. 17.16.

Evaluation of the performance of the flexible pavements

17.45 During the period of trafficking the present serviceability index of each of the sections was measured at 14-day intervals and the relationship between axle-load

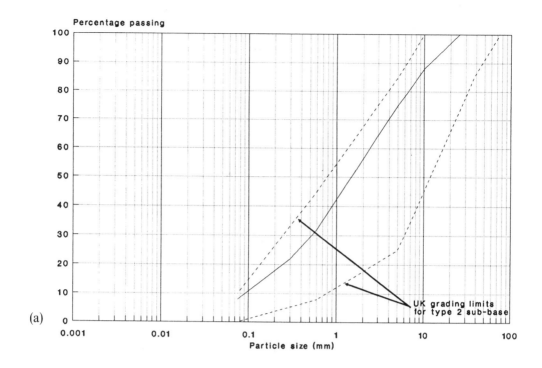

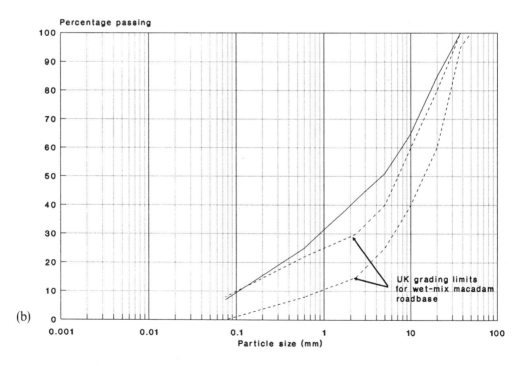

Figure 17.15 Gradings of (a) sub-base and (b) roadbase used in the AASHO road test compared with UK specifications

Table 17.3   Axle loads and pavements used: subsidiary flexible-pavement experiments

	Loop 3		Loop 4		Loop 5		Loop 6	
Axle load, lb	Lane 1	Lane 2	Lane 1	Lane 2	Lane 1	Lane 2	Lane 1	Lane 2
	12 000	24 000	18 000	32 000	22 400	40 000	30 000	48 000
	S*	T*	S	T	S	T	S	T
Sub-base, in	0		4		4		4 and 8	
Roadbase, in	2–14		2–16		3–18		3–19	
Surfacing, in	3		3		3		4	

*S = carried on single axles; T = carried on tandem axles.

applications and PSI obtained. Because of the seasonal effects, and particularly the weakening of the subgrade after the winter thaw, load applications at certain times of year were more damaging than at others. A concept of 'weighted' load applications was developed to enable deterioration to be assessed in terms of 'average' load applications. Coefficients, above and below unity were derived from observations made at regular intervals of the elastic deflection of the pavements under a standard wheel load. These were applied to the performance data before analysis.

17.46   The shapes of the curves relating PSI and W (the number of weighted applications of axle loads) for all the flexible sections in the main factorial experiment

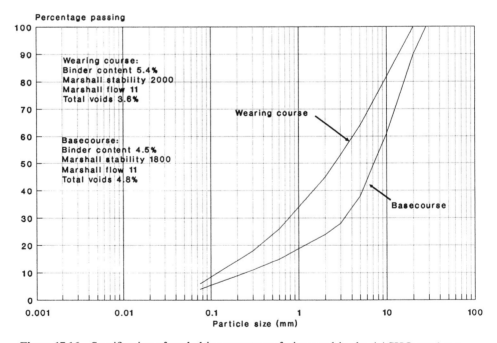

Figure 17.16   Specification of asphaltic concrete surfacing used in the AASHO road test

were analysed statistically in relation to the coordinates at the various levels of PSI and a model to fit the data was sought. The model finally chosen was as follows:

$$\text{PSI} = 4.2 - 2.7 \left(\frac{W}{\rho} \right)^{\beta} \tag{17.5}$$

where β and ρ are functions of the design variables D_1, D_2, and D_3 (thickness of surfacing, roadbase, and sub-base respectively) and the load variables L_1 (axle load in kips) and L_2 (unity for single axles and 2 for tandem axles).

The equations β and ρ for the materials tested and the range of axle loads used were:

$$\beta = 0.4 + \frac{0.081(L_1 + L_2)^{3.23}}{(D+1)^{5.19} \cdot L_2^{3.23}} \tag{17.6}$$

$$\rho = \frac{10^{5.93}(D+1)^{9.36} L_2^{4.33}}{(L_1 + L_2)^{4.79}} \tag{17.7}$$

and

$$D = 0.44D_1 + 0.14D_2 + 0.11D_3 \tag{17.8}$$

D is defined as the thickness index and suggests that unit thickness of surfacing was three times as effective as the same thickness of wet-mix roadbase and four times as effective as the same thickness of gravel sub-base in improving pavement performance.

For any value D_1, D_2, and D_3 the thickness index D is calculated from Eq. (17.8) and using the appropriate values of L_1 and L_2, ten discrete values of β and ρ are obtained from Eqs (17.6) and (17.7). These are substituted in Eq. (17.5) and for any value of PSI between 1 and 5 an appropriate value of W is obtained. Thus for any value of PSI, ten curves relating D and W are obtained. These relationships are shown in Fig. 17.17 for terminal PSI values of 2.5 and 1.5. The sections of the curves shown as full lines refer to the range of variables actually investigated and the broken portions represent extrapolation outside the experimental variables.

17.47   From Fig. 17.17 equivalence factors can be obtained relating the damage caused by applications of one axle load to the corresponding damage caused by applications of a 'standard' axle. The standard axle-load normally adopted is 18 000 lb, so that the equivalence factor is the ratio of the number of applications of an 18 000-lb axle to the number of applications of the test axle to give the same terminal PSI value. Equivalance factors of this type, derived from the AASHO road test, were first published by Liddle[7] and they are reproduced in Table 17.4. It will be noticed that as the thickness index increases the equivalence factor tends to decrease, particularly for the higher axle loads. The equivalence factor for tandem axles is rather less than twice the factor for half the total axle load, suggesting that the use of tandem axles is rather less damaging than uncoupled, more widely spaced,

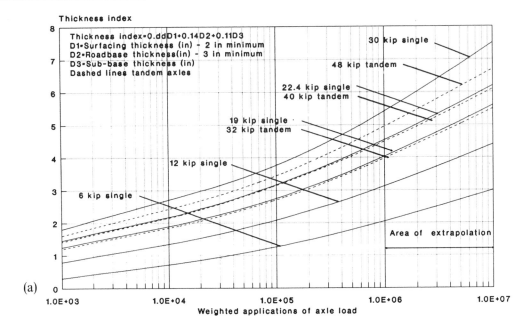

(a)

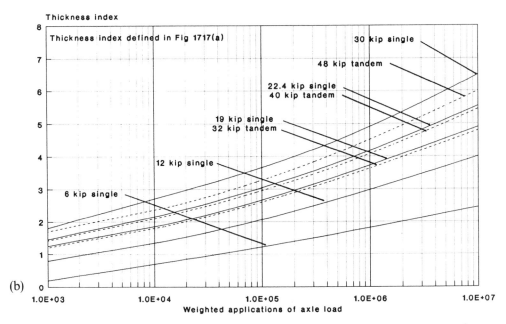

(b)

Figure 17.17 AASHO road test: relationship between pavement thickness and number of load applications for (a) PSI 2.5 and (b) PSI 1.5. (From *AASHTO Guide for Design of Pavement Structures*. Copyright © 1986, the American Association of State Highway and Transportaton Officials, Washington, DC; used by permission)

Table 17.4 Axle load equivalence factors for flexible pavements

Single axles, PSI = 2.0

Equivalence factors

Gross axle load, kips*	Thickness index					
	1	2	3	4	5	6
2	0.0002	0.0002	0.0002	0.0002	0.0002	0.0002
4	0.002	0.003	0.002	0.002	0.002	0.002
6	0.01	0.01	0.01	0.01	0.01	0.01
8	0.03	0.04	0.04	0.03	0.03	0.03
10	0.08	0.08	0.09	0.08	0.08	0.08
12	0.16	0.18	0.19	0.18	0.17	0.17
14	0.32	0.34	0.35	0.35	0.34	0.33
16	0.59	0.60	0.61	0.61	0.60	0.60
18	1.00	1.00	1.00	1.00	1.00	1.00
20	1.61	1.59	1.56	1.55	1.57	1.60
22	2.49	2.44	2.35	2.31	2.35	2.41
24	3.71	3.62	3.43	3.33	3.40	3.51
26	5.36	5.21	4.88	4.68	4.77	4.96
28	7.54	7.31	6.78	6.42	6.52	6.83
30	10.38	10.03	9.24	8.65	8.73	9.17
32	14.00	13.51	12.37	11.46	11.48	12.17
34	18.55	17.87	16.30	14.97	14.87	15.63
36	24.20	23.30	21.16	19.28	19.02	19.93
38	31.14	29.95	27.12	24.55	24.03	25.10
40	39.57	38.02	34.34	30.92	30.04	31.25

Tandem axle sets, PSI = 2.0

Equivalence factors

Gross axle load, kips	Thickness index					
	1	2	3	4	5	6
10	0.01	0.01	0.01	0.01	0.01	0.01
12	0.01	0.02	0.02	0.01	0.01	0.01
14	0.02	0.03	0.03	0.03	0.02	0.02
16	0.04	0.05	0.05	0.05	0.04	0.04
18	0.07	0.08	0.08	0.08	0.07	0.07
20	0.10	0.12	0.12	0.12	0.11	0.10
22	0.16	0.17	0.18	0.17	0.16	0.16
24	0.23	0.24	0.26	0.25	0.24	0.23
26	0.32	0.34	0.36	0.35	0.34	0.33
28	0.45	0.46	0.49	0.48	0.47	0.46
30	0.61	0.62	0.65	0.64	0.63	0.62
32	0.81	0.82	0.84	0.84	0.83	0.82
34	1.06	1.07	1.08	1.08	1.08	1.07
36	1.38	1.38	1.38	1.38	1.38	1.38
38	1.76	1.75	1.73	1.72	1.73	1.74
40	2.22	2.19	2.15	2.13	2.16	2.18
42	2.77	2.73	2.64	2.62	2.66	2.70
44	3.42	3.36	3.23	3.18	3.24	3.31
46	4.20	4.11	3.92	3.83	3.91	4.02
48	5.10	4.98	4.72	4.58	4.68	4.83

1 kip = 1000 lb

319

Table 17.4—*continued*

Single axles, PSI = 2.5

Equivalence factors

Gross axle load, kips*	Thickness index					
	1	2	3	4	5	6
2	0.0004	0.0004	0.0003	0.0002	0.0002	0.0002
4	0.003	0.004	0.004	0.003	0.003	0.002
6	0.01	0.02	0.02	0.01	0.01	0.01
8	0.03	0.05	0.05	0.04	0.03	0.03
10	0.08	0.10	0.12	0.10	0.09	0.08
12	0.17	0.20	0.23	0.21	0.19	0.18
14	0.33	0.36	0.40	0.39	0.36	0.34
16	0.59	0.61	0.65	0.65	0.62	0.61
18	1.00	1.00	1.00	1.00	1.00	1.00
20	1.61	1.57	1.49	1.47	1.51	1.55
22	2.48	2.38	2.17	2.09	2.18	2.30
24	3.69	3.49	3.09	2.89	3.03	3.27
26	5.33	4.99	4.31	3.91	4.09	4.48
28	7.49	6.98	5.90	5.21	5.39	5.98
30	10.31	9.55	7.94	6.83	6.97	7.79
32	13.90	12.82	10.52	8.85	8.88	9.95
34	18.41	16.94	13.74	11.34	11.18	12.51
36	24.02	22.04	17.73	14.38	13.93	15.50
38	30.90	28.30	22.61	18.06	17.20	18.98
40	39.26	35.89	28.51	22.50	21.08	23.04

Tandem axle sets, PSI = 2.5

Equivalence factors

Gross axle load, kips	Thickness index					
	1	2	3	4	5	6
10	0.01	0.01	0.01	0.01	0.01	0.01
12	0.02	0.02	0.02	0.02	0.01	0.01
14	0.03	0.04	0.04	0.03	0.03	0.02
16	0.04	0.07	0.07	0.06	0.05	0.04
18	0.07	0.10	0.11	0.09	0.08	0.07
20	0.11	0.14	0.16	0.14	0.12	0.11
22	0.16	0.20	0.23	0.21	0.18	0.17
24	0.23	0.27	0.31	0.29	0.26	0.24
26	0.33	0.37	0.42	0.40	0.36	0.34
28	0.45	0.49	0.55	0.53	0.50	0.47
30	0.61	0.65	0.70	0.70	0.66	0.63
32	0.81	0.84	0.89	0.89	0.86	0.83
34	1.06	1.08	1.11	1.11	1.09	1.08
36	1.38	1.38	1.38	1.38	1.38	1.38
38	1.75	1.73	1.69	1.68	1.70	1.73
40	2.21	2.16	2.06	2.03	2.08	2.14
42	2.76	2.67	2.49	2.43	2.51	2.61
44	3.41	3.27	2.99	2.88	3.00	3.16
46	4.18	3.98	3.58	3.40	3.55	3.79
48	5.08	4.80	4.25	3.98	4.17	4.49

1 kip = 1000 lb.

axles. The equivalence factors also tend to increase with decreasing terminal PSI level.

17.48 The flexible sections using wedges of different roadbase materials (gravel, crushed stone, wet-mix, bituminous stone, and cement-bound stone, Table 17.3) were 160 ft long and were divided for the purpose of analysis into sub-sections 40 ft long over which the thickness of base was assumed to be constant at the average value for that length. The results could not be analysed statistically because of the small amount of data available. A comparison was made of the materials in terms of equivalent roadbase thickness, for the same surfacing and sub-base. Figure 17.18 shows results for sections with a 3-in surfacing and 4-in sub-base. The conclusion from these data is that 1 in of crushed stone roadbase gave a performance equivalent to about 0.6 in of cemented roadbase and about 0.4 in of bituminous roadbase. The experimental sections with the gravel roadbase failed very early, and no useful equivalence values could be obtained for the material.

Thickness combinations used for concrete experiment

17.49 The axle loads used on the concrete pavements were identical with those used on the flexible sections since both types of construction were on the same loops. The axle loads together with the combinations of slab thickness and base thickness used are shown in Table 17.5.

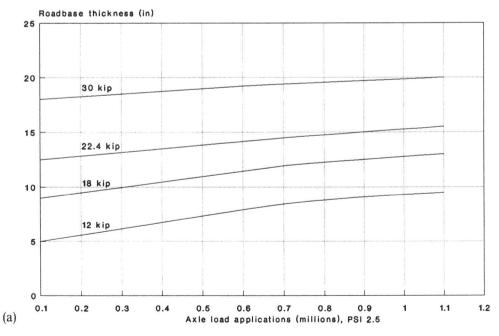

(a)

Figure 17.18 AASHO road test: effect of type of roadbase on performance: (a) crushed-stone roadbase

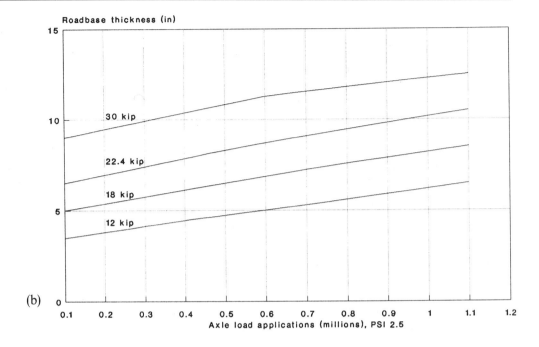

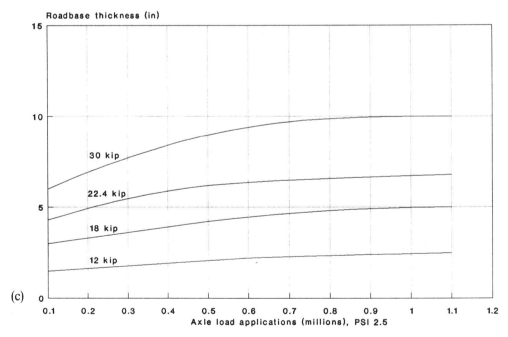

Figure 17.18–*contd*–AASHO roadtest: effect of type of roadbase on performance: (b) cement roadbase; (c) bituminous roadbase

Table 17.5 Axle loads and pavements used in the concrete experiment

	Loop 2		Loop 3		Loop 4		Loop 5		Loop 6	
	Lane 1	Lane 2	Lane 1	Lane 2	Lane 1	Lane 2	Lane 1	Lane 2	Lane 1	Lane 2
Axle load, lb	2000	6000	12000	24000	18000	32000	22400	40000	30000	48000
	S*	S	S	T*	S	T	S	T	S	T
Sub-base, in	0, 3, and 6		3, 6, and 9		3, 6, and 9		3, 6, and 9		3, 6, and 9	
Slab thickness (unreinforced), in	$2\frac{1}{2}$, $3\frac{1}{2}$, and 5		$3\frac{1}{2}$, 5, $6\frac{1}{2}$, and 8		5, $6\frac{1}{2}$, 8, and $9\frac{1}{2}$		$6\frac{1}{2}$, 8, $9\frac{1}{2}$, and 11		8, $9\frac{1}{2}$, 11, and $12\frac{1}{2}$	
Slab thickness (reinforced), in	$2\frac{1}{2}$, $3\frac{1}{2}$, and 5		$3\frac{1}{2}$, 5, $6\frac{1}{2}$, and 8		5, $6\frac{1}{2}$, 8, and $9\frac{1}{2}$		$6\frac{1}{2}$, 8, $9\frac{1}{2}$, and 11		8, $9\frac{1}{2}$, 11, and $12\frac{1}{2}$	

*S = carried on single axles; T = carried on tandem axles.

The experiment was again fully factorial, giving 20 sections in each lane for loop 2 (with duplicates) and more than 28 sections in the other loops. Reinforced sections were 240 ft long with contraction joints at 40 ft spacing. Unreinforced sections were 120 ft long with contraction joints at 15 ft intervals. All joints were dowelled.

17.50 The sub-base was identical with the sub-base used in the flexible sections (see Fig. 17.8). The mix design for the concrete was 6 bags/yd^3 with a maximum water content of 5 gal. per bag. The ratio of sand to total aggregate was 1:3. The average 28-day flexural and compressive strengths of the concrete were 725 and 4450 lbf/in^2 (5 and 30.5 MN/m^2) respectively.

For the reinforced sections the weight of reinforcement ranged from 21–81 lb/100 ft^2 for the thickness range 2.5–12.5 in for the slabs and was approximately proportional to the thickness. All longitudinal and transverse joints were dowelled irrespective of whether the sections were reinforced or not.

Evaluation of the performance of the concrete sections

17.51 The present serviceability index was measured at 14-day intervals using the equation already discussed and curves relating PSI and the number of applications were obtained for each section. No weighting factor for the seasonal effect was applied to the curves obtained in the case of the concrete pavements. The model used for representing the results statistically was of a form similar to that discussed for the flexible sections, but the constants and coefficients were different. The model equation was

$$PSI = 4.5 - 3\left(\frac{W}{\rho}\right)^{\beta} \tag{17.9}$$

where β and ρ are given by the equations

$$\beta = 1 + \frac{3.63(L_1 + L_2)^{5.20}}{(D_2 + 1)^{8.46} \cdot L_2^{3.52}} \tag{17.10}$$

and

$$\rho = \frac{10^{5.85}(D_2 + 1)^{7.35} \cdot L_2^{3.28}}{(L_1 + L_2)^{4.62}}$$
(17.11)

It will be noted that the thickness of sub-base and degree of reinforcement do not appear in these equations, since they were found not to be significant variables in determining performance. In Eq. (17.10) and (17.11), D_2 is the thickness of slab and L_1 and L_2 are the same load factors as were defined in connection with the flexible sections. By combining Eqs (17.9), (17.10), and (17.11), the slab thickness can be related to the number of applications of the axle load for any level of terminal PSI. As for the flexible pavement experiment, the results are presented as families of curves related to specific values of PSI. The curves for terminal PSI levels of 2.5 and 1.5 are shown in Fig. 17.19. Largely because of the range of variables used in the test, extensive extrapolation based on Eq. (17.9) is involved in producing these curves as indicated on the diagrams.

17.52   The conclusion that reinforcement had no influence on the performance of the concrete pavements is not surprising in view of the relatively short bay lengths used for the reinforced sections (40 ft). That sub-base thickness had no significant influence is rather more surprising in view of the liability of the thinner concrete pavements to pumping at the AASHO site. This suggests that the sub-base and subgrade materials may have been equally liable to pumping.

17.53   Equations (17.9), (17.10) and (17.11) can be used to obtain axle-load equivalence factors for different thickness of concrete and different levels of PSI. Such factors for a slab thickness of 9 in and PSI value of 2.5 are given in Table 17.6. These refer to loads carried on single axles. As with flexible pavements, the thickness of concrete and the other variables have a small effect on the equivalence factors, but in view of the extrapolation involved in the concrete pavement analysis it is suggested that the equivalance factors given in Table 17.6 should be used for all concrete pavements.

17.54   Comparison between Tables 17.4 and 17.6 shows that the equivalence factors for flexible and concrete pavements deduced from the AASHO road test are very similar, and, bearing in mind the extrapolation involved in their development, the use of slightly different factors for the two forms of pavement is hardly justified. The mean values for loads on single axles given in Table 8.20 (see Para. 8.43) are recommended for normal use.

Comparison between the results from the AASHO and WASHO road tests for flexible pavements

17.55   Comparison between Figs 17.8 and 17.14 shows that the sub-base and crushed stone roadbase materials used in the WASHO and AASHO road tests were very similar. The surfacings too were the same and it is therefore relevant to make some comparison between the performance of the flexible sections at the two sites. This cannot be done directly because of the different performance criteria used.

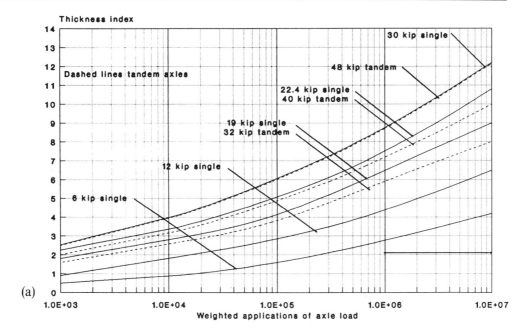

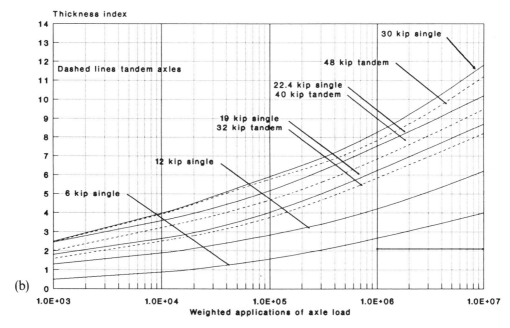

Figure 17.19 AASHO road test relationship between pavement thickness and number of load applications for (a) PSI 2.5 (concrete) and (b) PSI 1.5 (concrete)

Table 17.6   Axle-load equivalence factors for concrete pavements

Gross axle load, kips*	Equivalence factor
2	0.0002
4	0.002
6	0.01
8	0.03
10	0.08
12	0.18
14	0.34
16	0.60
18	1.00
20	1.57
22	2.34
24	3.36
26	4.67
28	6.29
30	8.28

*1 kip = 1000 lb.

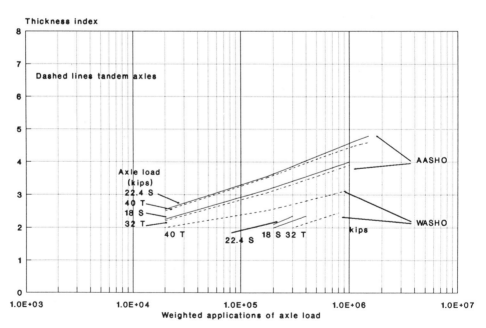

Figure 17.20 Comparison between AASHO and WASHO test results for flexible pavements—PSI 2.5

However, using the relationship between permanent deformation and PSI shown in Fig 17.13 it is possible from Fig. 17.9 to obtain for the WASHO test approximate relationships between pavement thickness and load applications for terminal PSI levels in excess of 2. Such relationships are shown in Fig. 17.20 together with the corresponding curves from the AASHO road test. A terminal PSI value of 2.5 was adopted. In developing the curves for the WASHO test the AASHO formula was used to calculate the thickness indices.

17.56   The relative positions of the curves corresponding to the different axle loads is similar for both tests but the performance of the WASHO pavements was clearly much superior to similar pavements in the AASHO test. This probably reflects the higher initial strength of the WASHO subgrade (16 per cent compared with 4 per cent for the AASHO test).

Relevance of the AASHO and WASHO road tests to pavement design in Britain

Flexible pavements

17.57   The materials used for the crushed stone roadbase of the WASHO and AASHO road tests did not conform to the British grading specification for wet-mix roadbase material (see Fig. 17.15). More important, the asphaltic concrete wearing course material had very different properties from the hot rolled asphalt normally used for major roads in Britain. These differences alone would limit seriously the direct application of the results of the American tests to British roads.

17.58   The major effect which freezing of the soil had on the performance of both road tests also needs careful consideration. In Britain the relatively small depth of frost penetration permits the economic use of sufficiently thick sub-bases to prevent frost action in subgrades. In large areas of northern American this is not feasible and designs must accommodate subgrade freezing such as occurred in the two road tests. This is undoubtedly a major reason why pavements with crushed-stone roadbases appear to perform better in Britain than would be expected from the evidence of the WASHO and AASHO tests (see Chapter 18).

Concrete

17.59   The performance of concrete pavements is less dependent on subgrade strength, and it would be expected therefore that the results of the AASHO road test would be more applicable to British conditions, and this has been found to be the case (see Chapter 18). However, the average strength of the concrete used in the American test was significantly lower than the requirements of the current British specification for pavement-quality concrete and this, together with the use of a sub-base not liable to pumping, probably explains why British pavements appear to perform rather better than the results of the AASHO road tests would indicate.

Axle load equivalence factors

17.60   The absolute performance of the AASHO road rest pavements expressed in axle load applications to give a specified terminal PSI level was clearly influenced by the thickness of the pavement layers and the strength of the subgrade. However, the relative performance of identical pavements when subjected to different axle loads was not seriously influenced by the thickness of the pavement. There seems therefore no reason why the axle-load equivalence factors developed from the road test should not apply to British or any other environmental conditions. However, it must be remembered that the AASHO road experiment was not fully factorial in the sense that all the axle loads were not used on all the pavement thicknesses, but the traffic loading was to some extent matched to the pavement strength. Also, the maximum axle load was about 10 tonnes. Therefore, it would be dangerous to assume that the fourth-power damaging law necessarily applies to thin overloaded pavements or to very heavy axle loads outside normal road practice.[8]

References

1. Boulnois, H. P.: *Modern Roads*, Edward Arnold, London, 1919.
2. Woodrow, J. H. and J. Y. Welborn: Development of asphalt tests and specifications in the United States, *Pub. Rds., Wash.*, **39**(1), 7–15, 1975.
3. Department of Scientific and Industrial Research: *Report of the Road Research Board with the Report of the Director of Road Research for the Year Ended 31st March, 1936*, HMSO, London, 1937.
4. Thrower, E. N., N. W. Lister, and J. F. Potter: Experimental and theoretical studies of pavement behaviour under vehicular loading in relation to elastic theory, *Proc. 3rd Int. Conf. on the Structural Design of Asphalt Pavements, London, 1972*, vol. 1, 1972 University of Michigan, Ann Arbor, pp. 521–35, 1972.
5. Van Vuuren, D. J.: Pavement performance in the S12 road experiment, an AASHO satellite test road in South Africa. *Proc. 3rd Int. Conf. on the Structural Design of Asphalt Pavements, London, 1972*, vol. 1, University of Michigan, Ann Arbor, pp. 938–45, 1972.
6. Highway Research Board: *The AASHO Road Test, Report 5: Pavement Research*, Special Report 61E, National Academy of Sciences, National Research Council, Publication 954, Washington, D.C., 1962.
7. Liddle, W. J.: Application of AASHO Road Test results to the design of flexible pavement structures, *Proc. Int. Conf. on the Structural Design of Asphalt Pavements, Ann Arbor, Michigan, 1962*, University of Michigan, Ann Arbor, pp. 42–51, 1962.
8. Van Vuuren, D. J.: Prepared discussion of the paper by Brown and Pell, *Proc. 3rd Int. Conf. on the Structural Design of Asphalt Pavements, London, 1972*, vol. 2, University of Michigan, Ann Arbor, p. 172, 1972.

18. Performance studies of experimental sections incorporated in in-service highways in the United Kingdom

Introduction

18.1　The approach adopted in the United Kingdom to the development of pavement design standards has been rather different from that followed in the USA. A decision was made as early as 1930 in Britain to build experimental sections within the normal road system. The intention was to make performance assessments at regular intervals and to inject the early conclusions, with a measure of caution, into normal road construction procedures.

18.2　Since the early thirties a very large number of experiments on in-service roads have been carried out. Most of the early flexible experiments were concerned with deformation and reduction of skid resistance associated solely with the properties of bituminous mixtures. The very early large experiments were concerned with concrete pavements, which were slowly being introduced into major road construction.

18.3　In this chapter a selection only of the larger experiments concerned with the structural design of flexible and concrete pavements are reviewed. The intention is to indicate how the current design standards in the UK have been developed.

Flexible pavement studies

18.4　Table 18.1 gives details of seven experiments briefly discussed in this chapter. The locations, the factors studied, the subgrade conditions, and details of the traffic are summarized. At most of the sites, a recording weighbridge is set into the road surface at the beginning of the experimental length, so that the cumulative number of standard axles carried can be obtained.

18.5　The Transport and Road Research Laboratory has been responsible for

Table 18.1 Details of major full-scale pavement design experiments using flexible construction

Year of construction	Location	Main variables (numbered) and construction details	Subgrade type and strength	Initial traffic* (commercial vehicles/ day)	Growth rate of commercial traffic (% per annum)	Damaging effect of commercial traffic (standard axles/100 commercial axles)
1949	A1 (16 km north of Boroughbridge), North Yorkshire	1. Type of roadbase—dry stone, hand pitching, tarmacadam 2. Thickness of roadbase—200–430 mm 3. Type of wearing course—bitumen macadam, rolled asphalt **Surfacing**—100 mm thick **Sub-base**—None	Silty sand CBR 10%	1000	4	13
1956	A1 East Retford Bypass, Nottinghamshire	1. Type of roadbase—wet-mix, dry stone using different aggregate types and gradings in both cases **Surfacing**—Coated macadam—90 mm thick **Roadbase**—200 mm thick **Sub-base**—Colliery shale—200 mm thick	Well-graded gravel CBR 20%	80	9	15 (northbound)
1957	A1 Alconbury Hill, Cambridgeshire	1. Type and thickness of surfacing—asphalt, bitumen macadam—38–100 mm thick 2. Type and thickness of roadbase—wet-mix, soil-cement, lean concrete, tarmacadam, rolled asphalt—75–230 mm thick 3. Thickness of sand sub-base—100–350 mm	Silty clay (average) LL 57% (average) PL 21% CBR 4%	1400	5	25

Year	Location	Details	Soil	Traffic		
1963	A30 Nately Scures (3 km west of Hook), Hampshire	1. Type and thickness of roadbase—wet-mix, lean concrete, dense-coated macadam, rolled asphalt—80–300 mm thick 2. Type of basecourse over coated macadam roadbases **Sub-base**—Gravel—150 mm thick	Silty clay LL 60% PL 21% CBR 3.5%	1500	5	35
1963	A40 Wheatley Bypass (12 km east of Oxford)	1. Grading and strength of cemented roadbase materials—200 mm thick 2. Grading and binder content of bituminous roadbase materials—200 mm thick **Surfacing**—Asphalt—100 mm thick **Sub-base**—Gravel—150 mm thick	Silty clay LL 57% PL 20% CBR 5.5%	850–1 300†	3	20–35† (eastbound) 25–30† (westbound)
1964	A1 Alconbury Bypass, Cambridgeshire	1. Thickness of certain of the cemented and bituminous roadbase materials used in the Wheatley Bypass experiment (see above) in the range 150–250 mm 2. Type and thickness of surfacing—rolled asphalt, bitumen macadam—100–200 mm thick **Sub-base**—Gravel—150 or 300 mm thick	Silty clay (average) LL 51% (average) PL 20% CBR 5%	1 300–2 200†	3	25 (northbound) 45–55† (southbound)
1965	A1 Conington, Cambridgeshire	1. Type of basecourse under asphalt wearing course (total thickness 100 mm), on wet-mix roadbase 200 mm thick 2. Type of bituminous roadbase 150 mm thick under rolled asphalt surfacing 100 mm thick **Basecourse and roadbase**—Crushed rock, various gravel aggregates **Sub-base**—Gravel—150 mm thick	Silty clay LL 50% PL 20% CBR 4%	2 400	3	50

*Traffic on each carriageway on dual-carriageway roads, or in each direction on single carriageway roads.

†Depends on location along site and position of side roads.

331

carrying out the soil survey, for preparing the specification for the work, and for carrying out the necessary testing work during construction. The start of each section is marked by a numbered road stud set in the road verge, and at three or five points, depending on the length of the section, transverse rows of levelling studs are sunk into the road surface at intervals of 300 mm across the full width of the carriageway. The studs have a circular recess in which the levelling staff is located. This enables the transverse profile and the total movement from the initial level to be recorded. Routine levelling was carried out at least twice yearly and transverse deformation profiles of the type shown in Fig. 4.1 were prepared. Performance was assessed primarily from the deformation caused by traffic in the left-hand wheel path.

18.6   Twice yearly, measurements of transient deflection are made using the deflection (Benkelman) beam. Again, these measurements are made at marked points in the nearside lane wheel-tracks at three or five points along each experimental section. In some of the larger experiments, gauges built into the road structure are used to measure stresses in the subgrade and in the pavement layers.

The Boroughbridge experiment (1946)[1]

18.7   In 1946 the traditional form of rural road construction in England was either handpitched stone or dry crushed stone under a 100-mm two-course bituminous surfacing. The Road Research Laboratory had done sufficient research into multilayer elastic theory to feel that bound bases would provide an economic alternative. This experiment compared the performance of hand-pitched, dry stone and stone bases bound with tar under composite surfacings consisting of a tarmacadam basecourse under alternative rolled asphalt and bitumen macadam wearing courses. The layout of the experimental sections is shown in Fig. 18.1.

18.8   The hand-pitched sections deformed very quickly. This form of construction requires the use of a temporary wearing course, which is replaced or over-laid once traffic compaction is completed and it is unsuitable for modern heavily-trafficked roads. The deformation of the other sections under traffic is shown in Figs 18.2 and 18.3, and the lives of the sections in cumulative standard axles (based on a failure

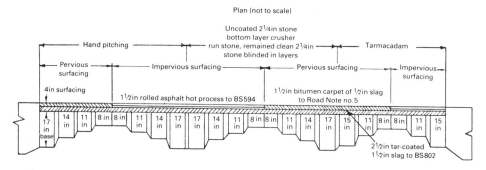

Figure 18.1   Layout of the experimental sections at Boroughbridge

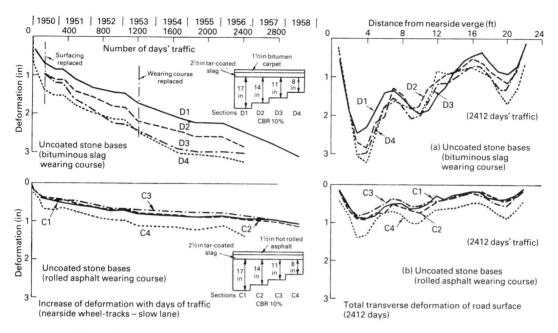

Figure 18.2 Comparisons of deformations for sections surfaced with bituminous-slag and rolled asphalt wearing courses—uncoated stone bases

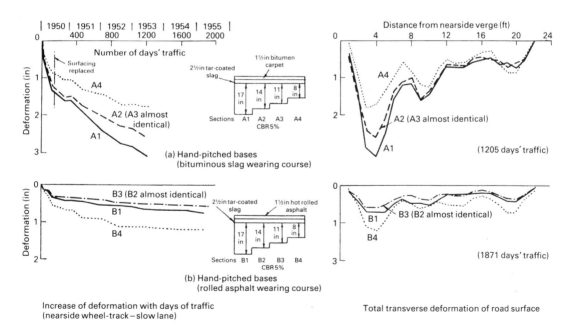

Figure 18.3 Comparison of deformations for sections surfaced with bitminous-slag and rolled-asphalt wearing courses—tar-coated stone bases

Table 18.2 Lives of sections incorporated in the Boroughbridge pavement design experiment

Section No.	Life millions of standard axles
9	1.5
10	1.5
11	1.2
12	0.4
13	Less than 0.1
14	Less than 0.1
15	Less than 0.1
16	0.1
17	1.1
18	0.5
19	0.2
20	Greater than 3*
21	Greater than 3*
22	Greater than 3*

*Corresponds to a 10-year life–the period of the observations.

criterion of 25 mm of deformation in the left-hand wheel tracks) are listed in Table 18.2. The results show the following:

1. The marked superiority of rolled asphalt as a surfacing material, compared with open-textured bitumen macadam. This was attributed to the greater stiffness of rolled asphalt, and its complete impermeability to water.
2. The equally marked superiority of the tar-coated stone base compared with the unbound crushed-stone base.
3. The influence of base thickness is not apparent under the rolled-asphalt wearing course, indicating that the thinnest of the bases performed adequately on the strong subgrade. Under the weaker bitumen macadam wearing course the influence of base thickness was clear and even the greatest thickness of tar-coated base was not adequate for a long life.

The sections other than those with tar-coated bases under the rolled asphalt wearing course were replaced after 10 years. So far as is known, the remaining sections with the tar-coated bases are still functioning under a thin overlay.

The East Retford experiment (1956)[2]

18.9 This experiment was designed to examine the importance of aggregate grading in roadbase performance. In all, 19 sections were laid with different crushed rock base materials all 200 mm thick. The sub-base was colliery shale 200 mm thick laid on a granular embankment. Because the foundation was strong, a relatively weak surfacing was adopted to accentuate differences of performance due to the different base materials and gradings. A description of each of the base materials, with its grading, is given in Table 18.3. The surfacing used consisted of a basecourse of open-textured bitumen macadam 70 mm thick, and a wearing course of close-textured bitumen macadam 20 mm thick. Twelve of the materials consisted of a coarse aggregate blinded by fines. Five bases were wet-mix materials and the remaining two were crusher-run materials. The grading envelopes embracing all the dry stone and wet-mix materials are shown in Fig. 18.4. The gradings of the crusher-run bases were within the wet-mix envelope.

18.10   The sections were in use for 9–12 years. The number of millions of standard axles (msa) carried by each, before overlaying, is shown in Table 18.3. Based on deformation, the average life of the dry-stone sections was 1.2 msa and that of the wet-mix sections 1.4 msa. There was no evidence to suggest that there was a significant difference between the performance of any of the crushed stones used. However, the crushed slag appeared to be rather better than any of the crushed rock materials. The wet-mix process has the considerable advantage that the material can be machine-laid, and this leads to an improved riding quality. Dry stone bases are now little used in the UK.

The Alconbury Hill experiment (1957)—flexible pavements[3,4]

18.11   Both flexible and concrete sections were laid at this site. The concrete length is considered in the later discussion dealing with concrete experiments. The flexible length was divided into 33 sections. The main purpose of the experiment was to determine the performance of wet-mix, open-textured tarmacadam, lean concrete, rolled asphalt, and sand-cement bases laid to a range of thicknesses between 75 and 230 mm under two coarse asphalt surfacings 38–100 mm thick. A few duplicate sections with a two-course bitumen macadam surfacing 100 mm thick were also included. The thickness of the sub-base varied along each section as shown in the layout diagram (Fig. 18.5). A relatively weak sand sub-base of CBR 14 per cent was used to accentuate differences in the performance of the various bases. The soil was medium to heavy clay of CBR 4 per cent.

18.12   At the time the experiment was constructed in 1957 the road was one of the more heavily trafficked industrial trunk roads in Britain, with an average damaging effect per commercial vehicle of about 0.9 standard axles. On modern industrial motorways the current figure is between 2 and 3. The performance of the sections (based on the deformation of the left-hand lane) is shown in Figs 18.6–18.11 and summarized in Table 18.4. The sections using the five roadbase materials have been grouped together in the table for easy comparison. Observations at the site were discontinued after about 15 years and most of the sections have now been overlaid, as part of a general upgrading of this length of the trunk road. The lives of the sections still in satisfactory condition at that time have been obtained by extrapolation of the deformation–standard axle plots which were developed for all of the sections.

Table 18.3 Details of unbound roadbases laid in the East Retford experiment and their performance

Section number	Material	Total percentage passing BS sieve size														Dry density of roadbase, kg/m³	Life of section in millions of standard axles
		50 mm	37.5 mm	28 mm	20 mm	14 mm	10 mm	6.3 mm	5 mm	2.36 mm	1.18 mm	600 µm	300 µm	150 µm	75 µm		
1	57 mm single-size hard limestone and dust—one 200-mm layer	89	63	29	25	24	23	23	22	18	16	12	8	6	5	2240	0.9
2	57 mm single-size hard limestone and dust—two 100-mm layers	94	66	34	32	39	29	29	28	25	21	16	11	8	6	2370	0.9
3	38 mm graded, mixed, and wetted hard limestone—two 100-mm layers	100	100	89	78	69	56	29	25	24	19	16	14	12	10	2420	1.4
4	38 mm graded, mixed, and wetted hard limestone—one 200-mm layer	100	100	89	78	69	56	29	25	24	19	16	14	12	10	2420	1.5
5	57 mm crusher-run hard limestone—two 100-mm layers	198	89	76	66	52	45	35	31	24	17	13	10	8	7	2260	1.4
6	76–100 mm hard limestone and dust—one 200-mm layer	48	33	30	29	28	28	27	27	24	17	12	9	7	5	2320	1.5
7	38 mm crusher-run hard limestone—two 100-mm layers	100	99	78	63	52	45	36	31	24	17	12	9	7	5	2230	1.4
8	38 mm quartzite gravel and limestone dust—two 100-mm layers	100	97	68	36	31	30	29	29	22	16	12	9	6	4	2350	1.4
9	57 mm basalt and dust—two 100-mm layers	100	81	38	32	31	30	29	27	22	14	9	6	4	3	2450	1.5
10	38 mm graded, mixed, and wetted Breccia—100-mm layers	100	100	88	73	60	50	42	37	29	21	17	15	13	11	2390	1.3
11	57 mm burnt colliery shale and dust—two 100-mm layers	99	94	65	54	44	38	31	27	21	18	14	8	5	3	2050	1.0
12	64 mm quartzite and dust—two 100-mm layers	89	58	40	34	31	30	28	23	18	14	11	8	5	3	2310	1.2
13	38 mm graded, mixed and wetted granite—two 100-mm layers	100	100	90	80	57	50	34	24	25	22	18	14	11	9	2290	1.3
14	57 mm granite and dust—two 100-mm layers	100	81	32	28	26	25	24	24	22	16	12	8	5	3	2310	1.2
15	57 mm steel slag and dust—two 100-mm layers	99	53	37	35	33	33	30	27	19	14	9	4	3	1	2260	1.3
16	57 mm soft limestone and dust—two 100-mm layers	99	86	48	37	29	25	21	18	15	12	10	9	7	4	2000	0.9
17	50 mm Breccia and dust—two 100-mm layers	100	85	44	36	32	31	30	29	21	15	10	7	4	2	2400	1.1
18	38 mm graded, mixed, and wetted blast-furnace slag—two 100-mm layers	100	100	87	72	65	54	41	35	22	17	12	10	7	5	2210	2.2
19	57 mm blast-furnace slag and dust—two 100-mm layers	98	74	43	40	37	36	35	33	16	11	8	6	4	3	2190	1.3

336

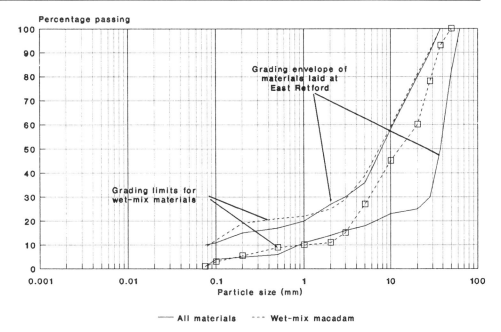

Figure 18.4   East Retford Experiment: grading envelope of all the unbound base materials used

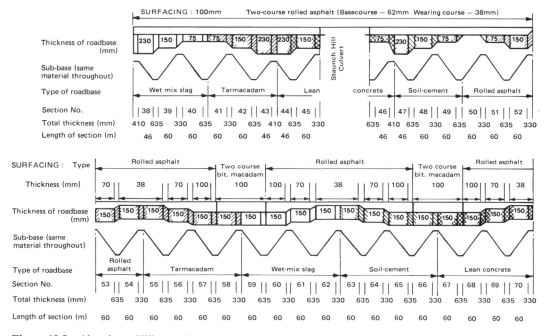

Figure 18.5   Alconbury Hill experiment: layout of flexible pavement sections

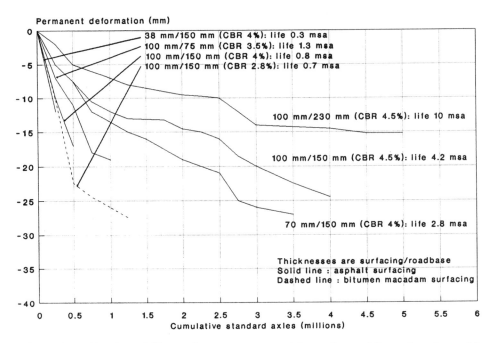

Figure 18.6 Alconbury Hill experiment: permanent deformation and lives of sections with wet-mix bases

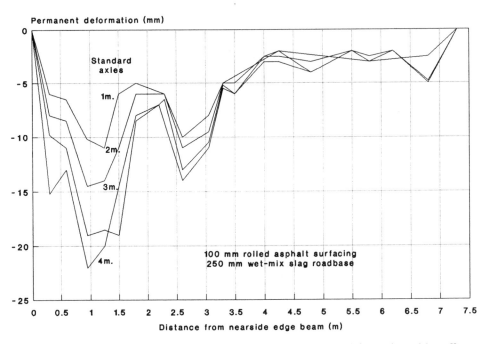

Figure 18.7 Alconbury Hill experiment: development of transverse deformation with traffic—wet-mix bases

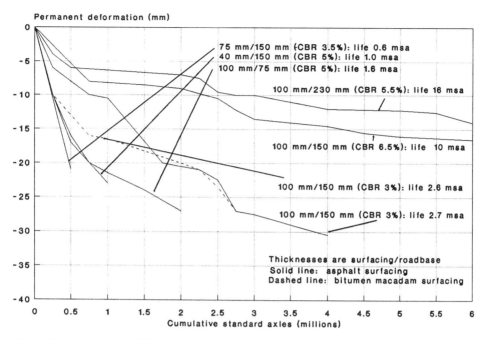

Figure 18.8 Alconbury Hill experiment: permanent deformation and lives of sections with lean concrete bases

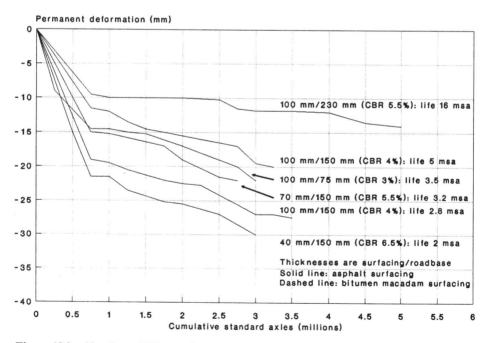

Figure 18.9 Alconbury Hill experiment: permanent deformation and lives of sections with tarmacadam bases

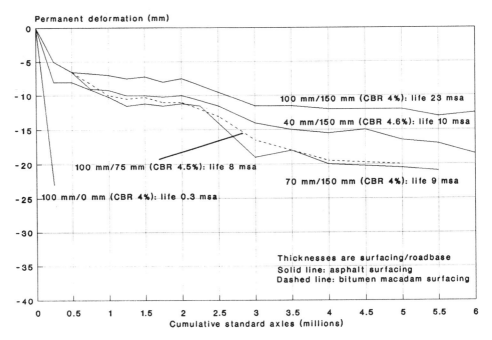

Figure 18.10 Alconbury Hill experiment: permanent deformation and lives of sections with rolled asphalt bases

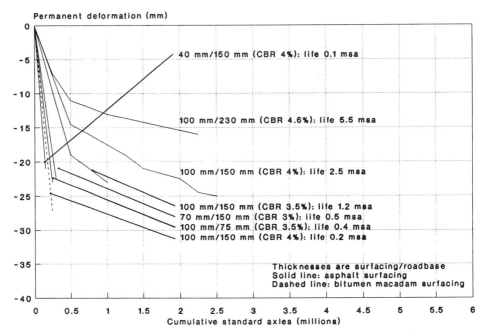

Figure 18.11 Alconbury Hill experiment: permanent deformation and lives of sections with soil cement bases

Table 18.4   Performance of sections in the Alconbury Hill experiment, A1 trunk road

Section No.	Surfacing	Base thickness, mm	Subgrade CBR, %	Life in million standard axles
Sections with wet-mix roadbases				
38	100-mm RA*	230	4.5	8
39	100-mm RA	150	4.5	4.2
60	100-mm RA	150	4	0.7
40	100-mm RA	75	3.5	1.3
61	70-mm RA	150	4	2.8
62	40-mm RA	150	4	0.3
59	100-mm CM*	150	4	0.8
Sections with lean concrete bases				
44	100-mm RA	230	5.5	16
45	100-mm RA	150	6.5	10
68	100-mm RA	150	3	2.7
46	100-mm RA	75	5	1.6
69	70-mm RA	150	5	0.6
70	40-mm RA	150	5	1
67	100-mm CM	150	3	2.6
Sections with tarmacadam bases				
43	100-mm RA	230	4	14
42	100-mm RA	150	4	5
41	100-mm RA	75	5	3.5
56	70-mm RA	150	5.5	3.2
55	40-mm RA	150	5.5	2
58	100-mm CM	150	4	2.5
Sections with rolled asphalt bases				
52	100-mm RA	150	4	23
51	100-mm RA	75	4.5	8
53	70-mm RA	150	4	9
54	40-mm RA	150	4	10
Sections with soil-cement bases				
47	100-mm RA	230	5	5
48	100-mm RA	150	4	2.5
65	100-mm RA	150	3.5	1.2
49	100-mm RA	75	3.5	0.4
64	70-mm RA	150	3.5	0.5
63	40-mm RA	150	4	0.1
66	100-mm CM	150	4	0.2

*RA = rolled asphalt; CM = coated macadam (surface-dressed).

18.13   Dealing first with those sections with wet-mix stone bases, only one section had a life in excess of 5 million standard axles. This was the one with the thickest roadbase (230 mm). The other sections behaved logically except for the replicate section with a 150-mm base under a 100-mm asphalt surfacing. The short life of this section was found to be due to a local drainage failure.

18.14   The lean concrete bases had a 28-day compressive strength of 18 N/mm².

Again the performance of the sections is logical with the life for the section with the thickest base (230 mm) being 16 million standard axles.

18.15   The soil cement bases were made with a sand aggregate, plant-mixed with cement to give a 28-day crushing strength of about 2 N/mm^2. The performance of these sections was poor with only the two thickest lasting for more than 2 years. It was concluded that this material was not suitable for use in heavily trafficked pavements. The sections with the rolled asphalt and tarmacadam bases gave the best and most consistent performance, with the rolled asphalt giving a longer life than the tarmacadam. The experiment was instrumental in establishing the present wide use of bituminous-bound bases in the UK.

18.16   The rolled-asphalt surfacing gave a performance much superior to that of the more open-textured bitumen macadam surfacing on those sections where a direct comparison could be made. Another lesson learned from these early experiments was that although the use of a weak sub-base or weaker surfacing enables road bases to be assessed in order of their performance fairly quickly, the results do not necessarily indicate the true life of the materials when the latter are used in conjunction with a good quality sub-base and a dense surfacing. In the later experiments a substantial granular sub-base was used.

The Nately Scures experiment (1963)[5]

18.17   This experiment consisted of 21 sections using the materials shown in Fig. 18.12. The CBR value of the subgrade varied along the site between 3.5 and 7 per cent. The object was to compare the performance of the base materials then in general use, on a road carrying medium heavy traffic. In 1972 the route was bypassed by the newly constructed M3 motorway and the commercial traffic virtually disappeared. By that time the experiment had carried about 4 million standard axles.

18.18   The sections with wet-mix bases began to show deformation and cracking during the first few years of the experiment and sections 2 and 3 had to be overlaid in 1968. Sections 15 and 16 failed within 3 years by deformation and cracking, owing

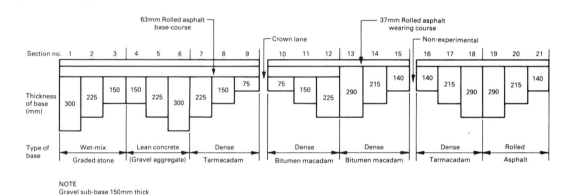

NOTE
Gravel sub-base 150mm thick

Figure 18.12   Nately Scures experiment: layout and description of the experimental sections

partly to their underdesign and the absence of a basecourse to the surfacing, but also to a rather poorly compacted area of foundation. The comparison sections with a basecourse are still in service, although they are deformed and show some cracking. Section 21, which joined the old existing road, deteriorated owing mainly to foundation settlement and was reconstructed after 5 years. The performance of the sections is summarized in Table 18.5. For sections still in service the life in standard axles has been estimated by plotting and extrapolating the relationships between the deformation measured in the wheel tracks and the cumulative traffic in msa.

Table 18.5   Performance of sections in the Nately Scures experiment, A30 trunk road

Section No.	Surfacing	Base thickness, mm	Life in million standard axles	Present condition (1988)
Sections with wet-mix roadbases				
1	100-mm RA*	300	4.5	Deformed and cracked
2	100-mm RA	225	3	Overlaid
3	100-mm RA	150	2	Overlaid
Sections with lean concrete bases				
4	100-mm RA	150	20	Satisfactory
5	100-mm RA	225	>20	Satisfactory
6	100-mm RA	300	>20	Satisfactory
Sections with dense tarmacadam bases				
7	100-mm RA	225	>20	Satisfactory
8	100-mm RA	150	>20	Satisfactory
9	100-mm RA	75	4	Cracked
16	37-mm RA	140	2.5	Reconstructed
17	37-mm RA	215	>20	Satisfactory
18	37-mm RA	290	>20	Satisfactory
Sections with dense bitumen macadam bases				
10	100-mm RA	75	5	Deformed and cracked
11	100-mm RA	150	>20	Satisfactory
12	100-mm RA	225	>20	Satisfactory
13	37-mm RA	290	>20	Satisfactory
14	37-mm RA	215	15	Satisfactory
15	37-mm RA	140	2.5	Reconstructed
Sections with rolled asphalt roadbases				
19	37-mm RA	290	>20	Satisfactory
20	37-mm RA	215	>20	Satisfactory
21	37-mm RA	140	2	Reconstructed because of local foundation slip

*RA = rolled asphalt.

18.19   This experiment indicated clearly that there is a critical combination of base and surfacing thickness for a given traffic condition, below which failure will occur rapidly, but above which a further increase in thickness produces little apparent change in performance.

The Alconbury and Wheatley Bypass experiments (1964)[6,7]

18.20   These two large experiments were designed to be complementary. They were each laid on both carriageways of newly constructed bypasses using two-lane dual-carriageway layouts (see Figs 18.13 and 18.14). At Wheatley a wide range of bituminous-bound and cement-bound roadbases were laid to a constant thickness of 200 mm under a 100 mm asphalt surfacing and on a granular sub-base 150 mm thick. The variables were cement content and bitumen content in the two types of base. At Alconbury Bypass a selection of the base materials used at Wheatley were incorporated in sections in which the thickness of the base and the surfacing was varied. The performance has been under observation for more than 20 years.

18.21   Based on present UK specifications, three grading zones were selected for bituminous materials and four for cemented bases. These grading zones are shown in Figs 18.15 and 18.16. The sections were distributed along the two carriageways at each site. Both roads were more heavily trafficked on the London-bound carriageway. However, the axle load spectrum in each carriageway was determined by a permanent weighbridge and the number of cumulative standard axles applied to each section during the current life of about 25 years is known.

18.22   The section numbers and the materials used for the bases in the sections are shown in Figs 18.17 and 18.18. The surfacing throughout at Wheatley Bypass was 100 mm of rolled asphalt, and the sub-base was well compacted gravel 150 mm thick. The subgrade was a boulder clay of CBR 4–5 per cent. For each aggregate grading, and using both crushed rock and gravel aggregates, cemented bases with 28-day compressive strengths of 3.8, 7.6, and 15.2 N/mm^2 were laid. The cement contents used were determined from prior laboratory testing. For sections with bituminous binder, for each grading zone and aggregate type, three binder contents of 2.5, 3.5, and 5.0 per cent bitumen or 2.5, 3.5, and 5.5 per cent tar, were used. A few additional sections with slag aggregate were also included, together with some sections with no binder, laid as dry-stone or wet-mix bases.

18.23   After Wheatley Bypass had been opened to traffic for about a year the line of the carriageway carrying sections 1–8 was altered to meet a further road improvement contract to the east. These sections were then lost. However, some of them are duplicated in sections 31–33.

18.24   At the Alconbury Bypass site, sections constructed to the middle crushing strength (7.6 N/mm^2) used at Wheatley Bypass in the case of the cemented bases, and to the middle binder content (3.5 per cent) for bitumen-bound and tar-bound sections, were laid under a 100-mm asphalt surfacing with a constant 150-mm granular sub-base as used at Wheatley. In the second half of the experiment, bases

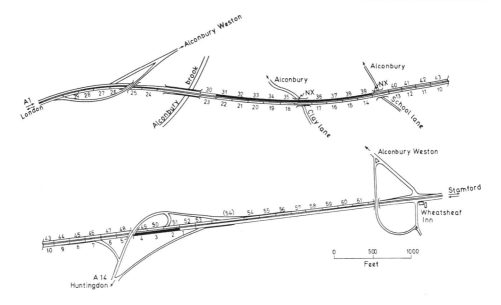

Figure 18.13   Alconbury Bypass experiment: layout of sections

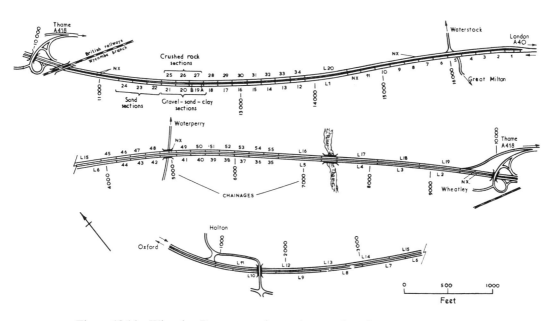

Figure 18.14   Wheatley Bypass experiment: layout of sections

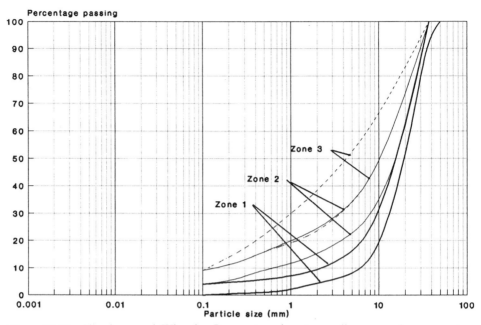

Figure 18.15 Alconbury and Wheatley Bypass experiments: grading zones for aggregates used in bituminous bases

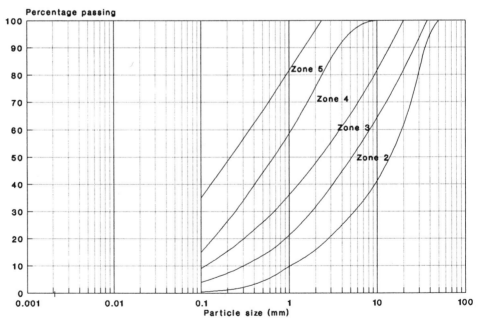

Figure 18.16 Alconbury and Wheatley Bypass experiments: grading zones for aggregates used in cemented bases

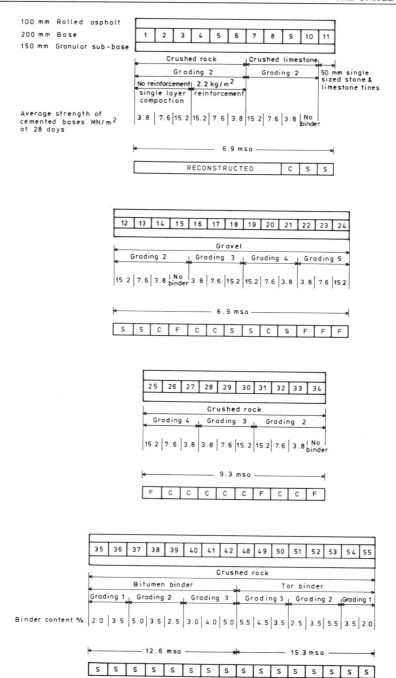

Figure 18.17 Wheatley Bypass: experimental sections and condition after 22 years. The condition of the sections was assessed in 1987: S = satisfactory; C = critical; and, F = failed

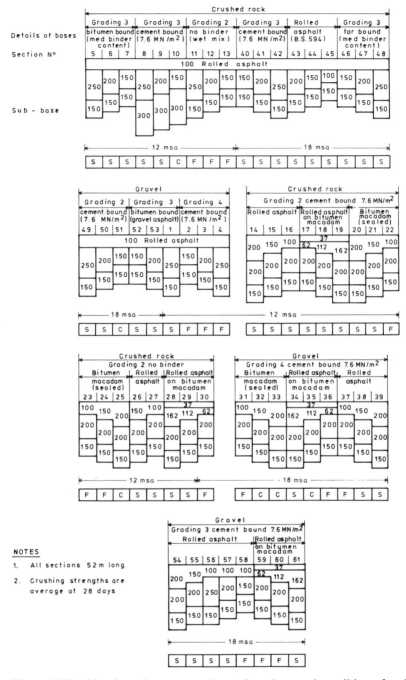

Figure 18.18 Alconbury Bypass: experimental sections and condition after 22 years. The condition of the sections was assessed in 1987: S = satisfactory; C = critical; and F = failed

to the same thickness as used at Wheatley were used in conjunction with surfacings of different types and thicknesses as shown in Fig. 18.18. Again, the condition of the sections late in 1987 is shown on the figure. The subgrade at Alconbury Bypass was also a boulder clay of CBR 4–5 per cent.

18.25   Detailed levelling at the site was discontinued after approximately 18 years and since straight-edge surveys have been made. The results of such a survey made in 1987 are included on Figs 18.17 and 18.18. Sections classed as satisfactory showed deformation under a 2-m straight-edge of 5 mm or less and no significant cracking. Those with a deformation up to 15 mm were classed as critical. Sections classed as failed had either been replaced already or were severely deformed and patched. The numbers of standard axles carried at that time are shown on Figs 18.17 and 18.18.

18.26   The following conclusions relating to materials can be drawn from the Wheatley Bypass experiment:

1. All the sections with wet-mix or dry-stone bases (11, 15, 44, and 34) had failed before the road had carried 7 msa.
2. All the sections with bitumen-bound and tar-bound bases were still carrying traffic after 23 years or 12–15 msa. The performance of these sections did not vary significantly with the binder content used, or with the grading zone and type of the aggregate.
3. The grading of the aggregate had a more marked effect on the performance of the cemented bases, as follows:
   (a) The sections with bases of grading 5 gravel aggregate (22–24) had all failed by 7 msa, irrespective of the 28-day compressive strength.
   (b) The sections with bases made with grading 4 crushed-rock aggregate (25–27) had failed or become critical by the time 9.3 msa had been carried, irrespective of their 28-day compressive strength. Of the corresponding sections made with gravel aggregate (19–21), the weakest and strongest remained satisfactory after 7 msa, but the intermediate strength section had become critical.
   (c) The sections made with grading 3 crushed-rock aggregate (28–30) were all critical by 9 msa. Of those with the same grading using gravel aggregate, the strongest (18) was satisfactory after 7 msa, but the two with lower strength (16 and 17) had become critical.
4. Of the sections with bases of grading 2 crushed rock the strongest (31) had failed after 9.3 msa, and the two lower-strength sections (32 and 33) had become critical. The corresponding sections made with gravel aggregate were satisfactory for the two higher-strength sections (12 and 13) but critical for the lowest strength (14) after 7 msa.
5. There can be little doubt that by the time the sections with cemented bases have been subjected to the 15.3 msa which the sections with bituminous bases have already accepted, they will all have failed or be in a critical condition.

18.27   The following further conclusions can be drawn from the Alconbury

Bypass experiment:

1. All but one of the sections with wet-mix bases under 100 mm of asphalt (11–13 and 27) failed before the traffic reached 12 msa, even when the base thickness was increased to 250 mm. Increasing the thickness of asphalt surfacing to 150 mm (26) gave a satisfactory performance at 12 msa. The substitution of sealed-bitumen macadam surfacing for rolled asphalt (23–25) produced early failure even when the thickness of surfacing was increased to 200 mm (25). A composite rolled-asphalt–bitumen macadam surfacing of thicknesses 150 mm (29) and 200 mm thickness (28) gave a life greater than 12 msa.

2. All the sections with 200-mm bases under 100-mm of rolled asphalt (5–7, 43–48, 52, 53, and 1) were still satisfactory after 12–18 msa. This confirms the conclusion from Wheatley Bypass, for rather heavier traffic. Furthermore, sections with a base thickness of only 150 mm under 100 mm of asphalt (7 and 46) had lives of 7–18 msa, and the single section with a 100-mm asphalt base (45) also survived 18 msa. The sections with tar-bound and bitumen-bound bases have performed equally well.

3. The sections with cemented bases using gravel aggregate to grading 4, under a 100-mm asphalt surfacing (2–4 and 37), had failed in all three thicknesses at 12 msa. Increasing the thickness of asphalt surfacing to 150 and 200 mm (38 and 39) extended the life beyond 18 msa. A composite asphalt–bitumen macadam surfacing 150 mm thick (35) produced a critical condition at 18 msa and increasing this composite surfacing thickness to 200 mm (34) extended the life beyond 18 msa.

4. The sections with cemented bases using gravel aggregate to grading 3 under a 100-mm asphalt surfacing survived 18 msa in thicknesses of 200 and 250 mm (56 and 57) but failed earlier with a thickness of 150 mm (58).

5. The sections with cemented bases of crushed rock to grading 2, 200 mm thick (14–19 and 50), all survived 12 msa under the three thicknesses of asphalt used, as did the three associated sections with composite asphalt and bitumen macadam surfacings 150 and 200 mm thick. However, the section of base thickness 150 mm (51) was critical after 18 msa. Of the three sections 200 mm thick under the sealed bitumen macadam surfacing (20–22), those under 150 and 200 mm thicknesses survived 12 msa, but that under only 100 mm (22) was critical at that stage. For a high-modulus cemented material there is clearly a fairly well-defined thickness limit for the base, determined by the traffic and a similarly well-defined minimum limit for the surfacing thickness. However, the latter is not sensitive to the type of bituminous materials used.

18.28   These two experiments give long-term confirmation of the superiority of bituminous bases over cemented or unbound bases when used under a normal-thickness asphalt surfacing. This conclusion does not mean that there is no place for cemented materials in flexible pavement construction. However, it is essential that structural design procedures should be applied to any composite design to guard against cracking and degregation under traffic. Such a safe design can then be compared with a fully flexible design on a cost basis.

18.29   When the Wheatley Bypass experiment was being constructed it was thought that the leanest of the bitumen-bound and tar-bound bases would have a short life under the heavy traffic carried by the road. However, the binder content has to date had no significant effect on the performance.

The Conington Lodge Experiment 1969[8]

18.30   This is the most heavily trafficked of all the full-scale pavement design experiments. Figure 18.19 shows the layout of the sections. The purpose was primarily to compare the performance of bituminous surfacings and base materials made with different types of gravel aggregate with those of similar materials made with the more usual crushed rock aggregates. The first part (sections 3–13) compares with performance of dense coated macadam basecourse made with gravel aggregates with that of crushed rock materials, all laid on a roadbase of wet-mix macadam. The second part (sections 15–26) compares the performance of dense-coated macadam road bases made with gravel aggregates under a predominantly two-course rolled asphalt surfacing made with crushed rock aggregate. A few additional sections (27–30) use a dense tarmacadam basecourse made with crushed rock aggregate in place of the rolled asphalt basecourse, and there are two control sections (1 and 2) with thicker wet-mix and lean concrete bases.

18.31   The performances of the sections in terms of msa carried before failure are shown in Tables 18.6 to 18.8. The failure condition is based on deformation and patching. Where a section has not reached the failure condition, the life is estimated from the rate of deformation and degree of cracking.

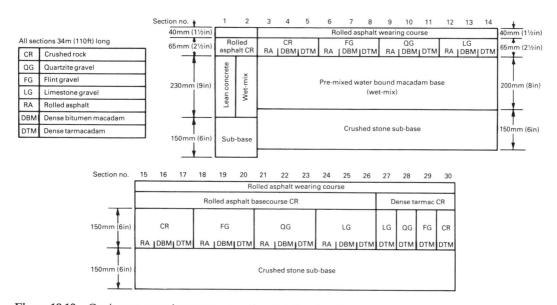

Figure 18.19   Conington experiment: construction details of sections

18.32   The conclusions from the basecourse part of the experiment (sections 3–14; Table 18.7) are:

1. The performances of the sections with basecourses of rolled asphalt (3, 6, 9, and 12) show that the life is reduced significantly where limestone aggregate is used, but otherwise the other gravels give an equal performance to crushed rock.
2. The rolled asphalt made with crushed rock (2) gives a marginally better performance in terms of life than the dense bitumen macadam (DBM) material made with crushed rock (4), and a significantly better performance than the dense

Table 18.6   Performance of all sections in the Conington experiment

Section No.	Basecourse material*	Roadbase material*	Estimated life, msa
1	RA/CR	LC	200
2	RA/CR	WM	24
3	RA/CR	WM	27
4	DBM/CR	WM	20
5	DTR/CR	WM	16
6	RA/FG	WM	27
7	DBM/FG	WM	25
8	DTM/FG	WM	27
9	RA/QG	WM	27
10	DBM/QG	WM	20
11	DTM/QG	WM	6.5
12	RA/LG	WM	10
13	DBM/LG	WM	12
14	DTM/LG	WM	13
15	RA/CR	RA/CR	50
16	RA/CR	DBM/CR	100
17	RA/CR	DTM/CR	100
18	RA/CR	RA/FG	200
19	RA/CR	DBM/FG	40
20	RA/CR	DTM/FG	80
21	RA/CR	RA/QG	25
22	RA/CR	DBM/QG	11
23	RA/CR	DTM/QG	23
24	RA/CR	RA/LG	40
25	RA/CR	DBM/LG	35
26	RA/CR	DTM/LG	11
27	DTM/CR	DTM/LG	25
28	DTM/CR	DTM/QG	150
29	DTM/CR	DTM/FG	200
30	DTM/CR	DTM/CR	120

Note: All sections have a RA/CR wearing course 40 mm thick.

*CR = crushed rock; DBM = dense bitumen macadam; DTM = dense tarmacadam; FG = flint gravel; LG = limestone gravel; RA = rolled asphalt; QG = quartzite gravel; WM = wet-mix.

Table 18.7 Conington experiment: summary of lives of sections with wet-mix bases in relation to the basecourse material

Section	Basecourse material*	Estimated life, msa	Mean life, msa
3	RA/CR	27	
6	RA/FG	27	
9	RA/QG	27	23
12	RA/LG	10	
3	RA/CR	27	
4	DBM/CR	20	21
5	DTM/CR	16	
6	RA/FG	27	
7	DBN/FG	25	26
8	DTM/FG	27	
9	RA/QG	27	
10	DBM/QG	20	18
11	DTM/QG	6.5	
12	RA/LG	10	
13	DBM/LG	12	12
14	DTM/LG	13	

Note: All sections have a RA/CR wearing course.
*For key to abbreviations see footnote to Table 18.6.

tarmacadam (DTM) material made with crushed rock (5).

3. When flint gravel is used there is little difference in the performances of rolled asphalt, DBM, and DTM (6, 7, and 8).

4. With quartzite gravel, DBM (10) gives a performance inferior to rolled asphalt (9) and DTM (11) gives a performance much inferior to rolled asphalt.

5. With limestone gravel (12, 13, and 14) the performance of all three mixes is poor in relation to the other aggregates.

18.33   The conclusions from the roadbase part of the experiment (15–30; Table 18.8) are:

1. The sections with crushed rock (15–17) and with flint gravel (18–20) have performed very similarly, whether mixed as rolled asphalt, as DMB or as DTM.

2. The performance when the aggregate is quartzite gravel (22–23) or limestone gravel (24–26) is significantly inferior.

3. When DTM was used as the roadbase binder under a DTM basecourse made with crushed-rock aggregate, the performance with the gravel aggregate (other than limestone gravel) was excellent.

4. When the basecourse of the surfacing is changed to DTM made with crushed-rock aggregate over roadbase made with DTM (27–30) the base material with limestone gravel gave a comparatively poor performance.

Table 18.8 **Conington experiment: summary of lives of sections with bitumen and tarbound roadbase materials**

Section	Basecourse material*	Roadbase material	Estimated life, msa	Mean life, msa
15	RA/CR	RA/CR	70	
16	RA/CR	DBM/CR	100	90
17	RA/CR	DTM/CR	100	
18	RA/CR	RA/FG	200	
19	RA/CR	DBM/FG	40	107
20	RA/CR	DTM/FG	80	
21	RA/CR	RA/QG	25	
22	RA/CR	DBM/QG	11	20
23	RA/CR	DTM/QG	23	
24	RA/CR	RA/LG	40	
25	RA/CR	DBM/LG	35	29
26	RA/CR	DTM/LG	11	
30	DTM/CR	DTM/CR	120	
29	DTM/CR	DTM/FG	200	157
28	DTM/CR	DTM/QG	150	
27	DTM/CR	DTM/LG	25	

Note: All sections have a RA/CR wearing course.
*For key to abbreviations see footnote to Table 18.6.

18.34   The overall conclusion from the experiment is that flint gravel and crushed rock aggregate give a similar performance when used in basecourse or roadbase. Quartzite gravel gives a somewhat inferior performance, particularly in road bases, and limestone gravel gives a much inferior performance both as basecourse and roadbase.

Review of the performance of the flexible pavements incorporated in the road experiments

18.35   The performance of the experimental flexible pavement sections in relation to the recommendations for pavement thickness made in the 1970 edition of Road Note 29 (*A Guide to the Structural Design of Pavements for New Roads*—see Chapter 19) is shown in Fig. 18.20 for pavements with unbound bases, in Fig. 18.21 for pavements with lean concrete bases, and in Fig. 18.22 for pavements with bituminous bases. Each figure shows the performance in terms of standard axles carried for the various combinations of surfacing and base used in the experiments.

18.36   Considering first the data for unbound bases, (Fig. 18.10), below 10 msa the thicknesses of surfacing, base, and sub-base required by the Road Note are supported by the experimental evidence. Between 10 msa and 100 msa, the thickness

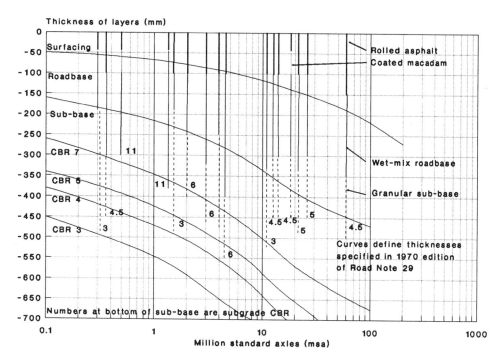

Figure 18.20 Performance of experimental sections with unbound roadbases

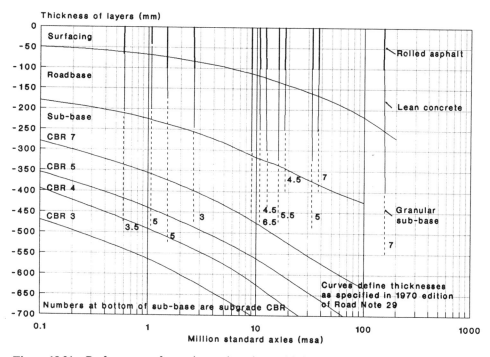

Figure 18.21 Performance of experimental sections with lean concrete bases

355

Table 18.9 Details of major full-scale pavement design experiments using concrete construction

Year of construction	Location	Main objectives and construction details	Subgrade type	Initial traffic (commercial vehicles/day)	Growth rate of commercial traffic (% per annum)	Damaging effect of commercial traffic (standard axles/100 commercial axles)
1930	A316 Great Chertsey Road, Middx.	To obtain information on the design of joints and load transfer devices. **Slab thickness**—230 mm (reinforced). **Compressive strength**—(28 days) 21.4 MN/m². **Sub-base**—Clinker—75 mm thick. **Slab length***—6.1 m	Silty clay and gravel	500	4	20 (average)
1933	A309 Hampton Court Way, Surrey	As above, but slab length increased to 9.1 m	Deep gravel fill	300 [estimated]	4	15 (average)
1946	A6097 at Oxton, Notts.	To study the effect on performance of: 1. Thickness of slab (100–200 mm) 2. Thickness of sand–cement sub-base (50–150 mm). **Compressive strength**—37 MN/m². **Slab length***—4.5 m (unreinforced) 9.0 m (reinforced)	Sandy gravel	200	10 (average)	25
1948	B379 Longford to Stanwell road, Middx.	To study: 1. Performance of unreinforced concrete slabs 2. Effect of spacing of expansion joints in unreinforced concrete pavement on joint movements. **Slab thickness**—200 mm. **Compressive strength**—39 MN/m². **Slab length***—4.6 m. **Sub-base**—None	Gravel embankment	500	4	20
1955	A48 Llangyfelach, Glams.	To study the influence of strength of the concrete on the performance of a reinforced concrete pavement. **Slab thickness**—200 mm. **Slab length***—37 m. **Reinforcement**—3.5 kg/m². **Sub-base**—Clinker—150 mm thick	Gravel	450	5	25

356

Year	Location	Description	Sub-grade			
1957	A1 Alconbury Hill, Cambs.	To study the effect on performance of: 1. Slab thickness for reinforced and unreinforced slabs 2. Strength of concrete 3. Weight of reinforcement when one slab length was used 4. Thickness and type of sub-base **Slab thickness**—125–200 mm **Slab length***—4.5 m (unreinforced) 37 m (reinforced) **Compressive strength**—(28 days) 44 MN/m² and 66 MN/m² **Sub-base**—Gravel and lean concrete 76 mm and 230 mm thick	Silty clay	1400	5	25
1961	A46 Winthorpe (3 km east of Newark), Notts.	To study the effect on performance of pre-stressing thin concrete slabs **Slab thickness**—125 mm and 178 mm **Compressive strength**—(28 days) 48 MN/m² **Sub-base**—Lean concrete—100 mm thick	Imported granular material	500	4	20
1962	A1 Grantham Bypass, Lincs.	To study the effect on performance of: 1. Type and weight of reinforcement in relation to slab length (including continuously reinforced concrete) 2. Using a sliding layer between the concrete slabs and the sub-base **Slab thickness**—230 mm, increased to 254 mm on embankments **Compressive strength**—(28 days) 38 MN/m² Sub-base—Lean concrete—75 mm thick	Various— ranging from silty clay to limestone brash	1200	5	30
1966	A1 Tuxford Bypass, Notts.	To study the compressive stresses generated in concrete slabs constructed without expansion joints **Slab thickness**—230 mm **Compressive strength**—(28 days) 30 MN/m² **Sub-base**—Lean concrete—125 mm thick on crushed rock—100 mm thick	Silty clay	1500	0	30

*Length between contraction joints.

357

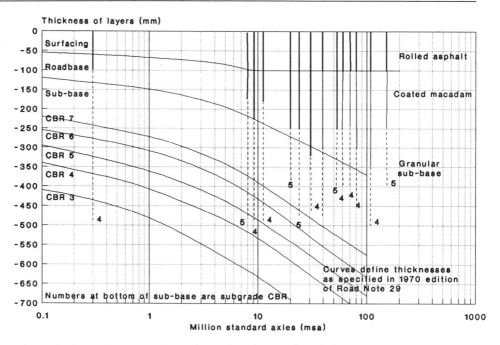

Figure 18.22 Performance of experimental sections with asphalt or coated macadam bases

of surfacing required by the Road Note appears rather excessive, as does also the thickness of sub-base on weak subgrades. However, it must be remembered that the experimental evidence has been extrapolated above 30 msa, and it would appear unwise to make any reductions in the Road Note requirements at this stage.

18.37 For pavements with strong lean concrete bases (28-day compressive strength $>20 \text{ N/mm}^2$; Fig. 18.21) the latest evidence suggests that above 10 msa the thickness requirements for surfacing, base, and sub-base given in Road Note are rather excessive. However, when the Road Note was written the main problem with lean concrete bases was the tendency for cracks in the lean concrete (often due to poor quality control) to be reflected through the surfacing. For this reason a conscious decision was made to control cracking by increasing the thickness of both the surfacing and the base. Although this may appear from the experimental evidence not to be justified, the standard of workmanship on normal road contracts may not be reflected in experimental work and for this reason it is not proposed here that any change should be made to the present Road Note requirements.

18.38 The evidence, particularly from the Wheatley Bypass experiment, is that the weaker cemented bases are not suitable for pavements designed to carry more than 10 msa and the present restrictions imposed in the Road Note appear to be justified by the later evidence.

18.39 If we now consider pavements with bituminous bases (Fig. 18.22), the recommendations given in Road Note 29 for base and surfacing thicknesses appear to be justified by the later evidence up to 100 msa. However, a measure of extrapolation is again involved in the experimental evidence between 30 and 100 msa. The important conclusion from the new evidence obtained from the Wheatley and Alconbury Bypass experiments is that lower-quality road bases than those specified in the Department of Transport specification can be used without affecting the performance of the pavement. This could result in a significant saving in the cost of bituminous bases. The experiment at Conington Lodge has shown that basecourses and road bases made with flint gravel perform as well as similar materials made with crushed rock. When quartzitic gravel is used the performance is rather inferior to flint gravel. Limestone gravel mixtures give a much inferior performance, both as basecourses and as road bases.

Concrete pavement studies

18.40   Table 18.9 gives details of the more important experimental roads constructed in the UK using concrete pavements. The first two roads, now more than 50 years old, were early experiments financed by central government funds. They were designed and supervised by the Experimental Branch of the then Ministry of Transport. The other experiments are more recent and these have been designed and supervised wholly or partly by the TRRL.

The Great Chertsey Road and Hampton Court Way experiments[9]

18.41   The thickness design and concrete compressive strength used for these early experimental roads were based on the current American practice at the time. Despite the relatively short bays used, the slabs were reinforced at the top and bottom, using mats made up on site from 6- and 8-mm bars, to give a total weight of reinforcement of 3.2 kg/m². In the thirties a major problem with concrete pavements in the US was faulting at the joints due to differential settlement and spalling. The main purpose of these two experiments was to establish the best method of load transfer across the joints, and six types of joint, as shown in Fig. 18.23, were adopted in both the experiments.

18.42   The relative deflection as a 6000-kg axle load passed over each joint was measured by a dial gauge assembly fixed to one side of the joint and recording on the other side. Measurements of this type have been made at regular intervals at each of the two sites. Table 18.10 shows the movements recorded at night-time in June 1952 and during the day in July 1968. These measurements were recorded on the Great Chertsey Road. The figures shown are the means for 10 joints of each type. From the riding quality point of view the joints appeared equally good for the first 10 years. In the longer term it is clear from Table 18.10 that the butt joints gave the worst performance and the dowelled joints the best. The sleeper-supported butt joints were particulary poor, owing to problems of settlement of the sleepers. By 1968 considerable permanent settlement was present at all the sleeper joints, owing mainly to rotation of the sleepers. At this stage the dynamic deflection of this type of joint was less than at the unsupported butt joints. The tongue-and-groove joints were providing indifferent load transfer by 1968, although they were effective for the first

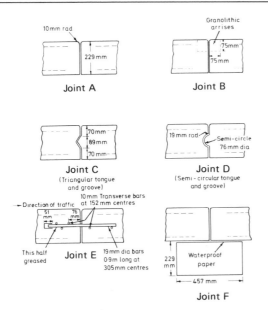

Figure 18.23 Great Chertsey Road and Hampton Court Way experiments: types of joints used

Table 18.10 Vertical deflections observed on six types of joint used in the Great Chertsey Road, June 1952 and July 1968

Joint type (see Fig. 18.23)	Average total deflection observed, μm	
	June 1952	July 1968
A	145	284
B	185	279
C	46	198
D	5	107
E	3	25
F	572	96

20 years after construction. After 40 years some necking due to corrosion was observed in the 19-mm dowel bars, but this was not at all serious. The joint maintenance was no more thorough than for normal concrete roads. The results from the Hampton Court Way experiment gave the same order of performance for the various types of joint, but the magnitude of the deflections and the permanent deformation was less for all the joints, owing to the deep gravel subgrade at that site.

18.43 Despite the relatively low compressive strength of the concrete used at both sites (21.4 N/mm² at 28 days) there has been very little cracking in the 230-mm slabs. At the Great Chertsey Road site, 6 of the 150 slabs have full-length longitudinal cracks at mid-width and this is attributed to the almost square slab dimensions. At Hampton Court Way, where the number of slabs is much greater (approximately 500), there is even less cracking, owing probably to the greater length–width ratio of the slabs. The absence of cracking could also be related to the fact that both of these 'new' roads included a bridge over the River Thames. In each case the paving was completed well in advance of the bridge works, so that the concrete was about 1 year old when trafficking commenced. Reference to Chapter 15 (Table 15.4) shows that during this period the modulus of rupture of concrete made with gravel aggregate would have increased by about 20 per cent with respect to the 28-day value. The material at an age of 1 year would be behaving similarly to concrete having a crushing strength of 30 N/mm^2 at 28 days.

18.44   Both of these experiments are still carrying increasing commercial traffic. The Great Chertsey Road was given an asphalt overlay in 1970 to improve the riding quality. Hampton Court Way has been progressively overlaid with a thin asphalt wearing course, starting in 1983. Most of the length is now covered. This work was carried out to restore adequate skid resistance; the riding quality has remained excellent. It has been estimated that the traffic carried by the Chertsey Road to date is equivalent to about 17 msa, and by Hampton Court Way 10 msa.

The Oxton experiment[10]

18.45   This was the earliest experiment in which the relationship between traffic and slab thickness was investigated for both reinforced and unreinforced concrete. The experiment was sited on an industrial main road carrying moderately heavy commercial traffic. The concrete had an average compressive strength of 37 N/mm^2 at 28 days, and the thicknesses used ranged from 75 mm to 200 mm. For the reinforced slabs, which were 9 m long, a weight of reinforcement of 4.1 kg/m^2 was used. The unreinforced slabs were 4.5 m long. The layout of the experiment, showing the combinations of slab and sub-base thickness used, is shown in Fig. 18.24. The subgrade at the site was a sandy gravel of CBR value in excess of 15 per cent. The sub-base was a cement stabilized sand of average 28-day crushing strength 1.5 N/mm^2.

18.46   The performance of the sections was assessed in terms of the amount of cracking. Since they were sited on a dual-carriageway road, the nearside slabs carried 80–90 per cent of the commercial axles and were therefore most liable to cracking. The performance was judged on the degree of cracking of the nearside slabs only. For these moderately thick slabs the cracking is almost entirely confined to the nearside slabs, showing that it was almost entirely traffic-generated (see Fig. 18.25). Figure 18.26 shows the crack length per 100 mm of left-hand lane measured at intervals up to an age of 15 years. Using the definition of failure of 250 m of cracking per 100 m of left-hand lane discussed in Chapter 4, the lives of the various sections can be derived in years. From traffic observations made on the road, these lives can be expressed in terms of cumulative standard alxes. This has been done in Table 18.11.

18.47   For the thinner sections (less than 175 mm) there was a significant advantage in terms of life using reinforcement. However, this advantage decreased

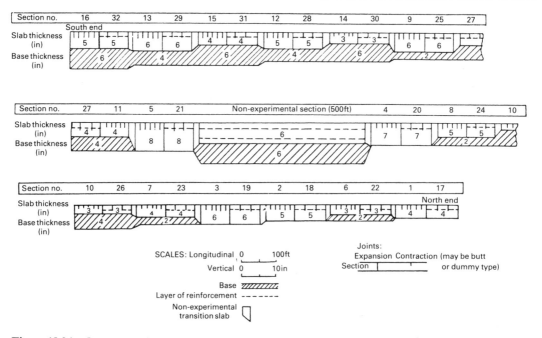

Figure 18.24 Oxton experiment: construction details

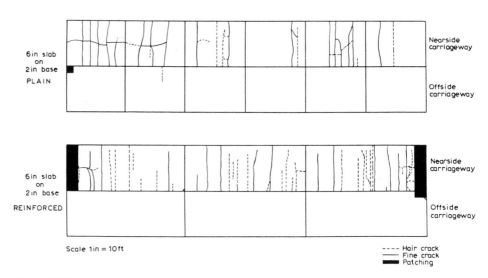

Figure 18.25 Oxton experiment: crack patterns in reinforced and unreinforced slabs after 15 years' traffic

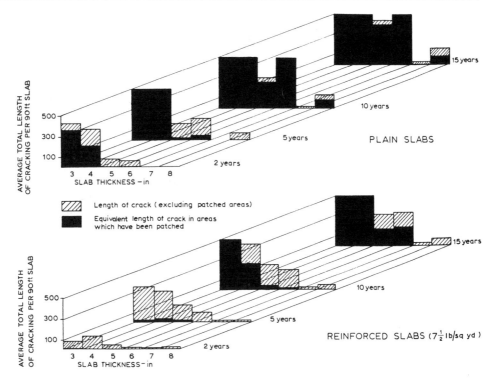

Figure 18.26   Oxton experiment: performance of unreinforced and reinforced concrete slabs

Table 18.11   Oxton experiment: lives of experimental sections

Slab thickness, mm	Life	
	Years	msa
75U*	1.3	0.2
75R*	7	1
100U	1.5	0.3
100R	5	0.5
125U	8	1.3
125R	11	1.7
150U	9	1.4
150R	13	2.2
200U	36	12
200R	50	26

*U = unreinforced; R = reinforced.

for greater slab thicknesses. For the traffic carried by this experiment there also appeared to be no advantage in increasing the slab thickness above 175 mm. In fact the 175 mm slabs appeared to behave rather better than the 200 mm slabs. This may reflect small differences in the quality of the concrete as laid (the slabs were hand-laid). For the relatively strong subgrade at this site the presence and the thickness of the sub-base had no significant influence on the performance. The relative performance of the pavements at this site with respect to other experiments is considered later.

The Alconbury Hill experiment[11]

18.48   The concrete pavements at this site were a short distance to the south of the flexible experiment already discussed. The traffic over the two sets of experimental pavements was identical. The pavements are on the northbound carriageway of a dual carriageway layout. The axle load spectrum is monitored by a weighbridge set in the pavement surface.

18.49   The design of the experiment is complementary to that at Oxton discussed above. Because the traffic is much heavier the minimum thickness of concrete used is 125 mm and the maximum 275 mm. The layout of the sections is shown in Fig. 18.27. It will be noted that the two strengths of concrete were used. For the main part of the experiment the average measured 28-day strength was 44.1 N/m^2, but seven sections were repeated using high-strength concrete of average 28-day crushing strength 66.1 N/mm^2. The lower-strength concrete used a gravel aggregate and the higher-strength one used crushed rock. Most of the 35 sections were reinforced but seven were unreinforced. Full details of the slab thickness and their lengths are given in Fig. 18.27 together with details of the reinforcement, the dowel bars, and the types and thicknesses of sub-base used. The subgrade at this site is boulder clay of CBR value 4.5 per cent.

18.50   As with the Oxton experiment, crack surveys were made at regular intervals during the first 20 years of service. The results in terms of the total crack length per 100 m of left-hand lane for the sections having the lower-strength concrete and a 75-mm granular sub-base are given in Fig. 18.28. Four widths of cracking have been recorded as indicated in the figure. Figure 18.29 shows the influence of base type and thickness on cracking for the lower-strength concrete and Fig. 18.30 compares the performance of the higher-strength concrete sections with the performance of equivalent sections using the lower strength.

18.51   The long period of observation of the Alconbury Hill experiment gave the Transport and Road Research Laboratory the opportunity to review the failure criterion of 250 m of total cracking per 100 m of left-hand lane, developed from the Oxton experiment. It was found that some sections, particularly the unreinforced ones, had to be reconstructed before that degree of cracking had been reached, whereas other sections with heavy reinforcement continued to be serviceable after the 250-m level of total cracking had developed. It was decided to adopt a modified failure criterion based only on the length of wide cracking. The failure criterion adopted was 20 m of wide cracking per 100 m of left-hand lane. This criterion has

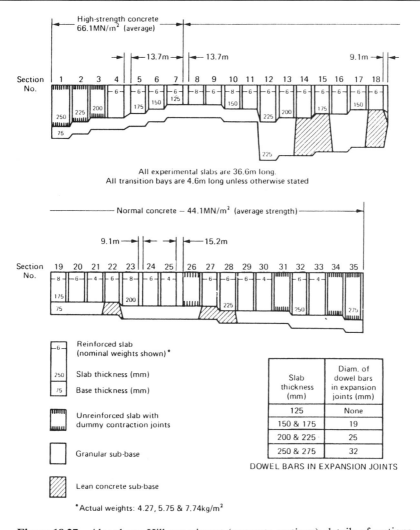

Figure 18.27 Alconbury Hill experiment (concrete sections): details of sections

been adopted in assessing the performance of the concrete pavements at Alconbury Hill. Table 18.12 shows the lives in years and in terms of standard axles carried for all 35 sections included in the experiment. These lives were derived from Figs 18.28–18.30 except for sections 1, 2, and 3. These sections had no cracking at all after 20 years and they therefore do not appear in the figures.

18.52   Analysis of the results of the Alconbury Hill experiment is best centred round the sections reinforced with 5.75 kg/m² steel and the lower-strength concrete. Figure 18.31 shows the relationship between slab thickness and life for all the sections using this weight of reinforcement which had 75–225 mm thicknesses of granular sub-base. The conclusion is that increasing the thickness of sub-base from

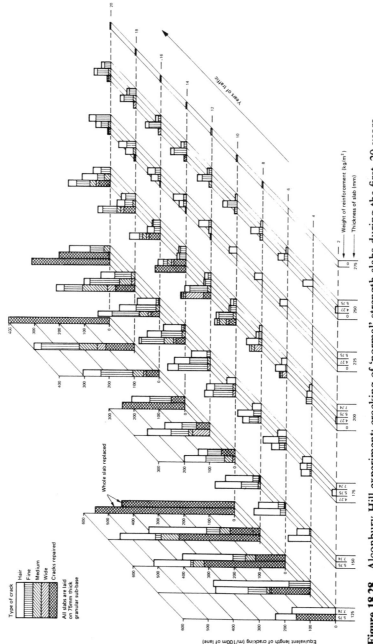

Figure 18.28 Alconbury Hill experiment: cracking of 'normal'-strength slabs during the first 20 years

366

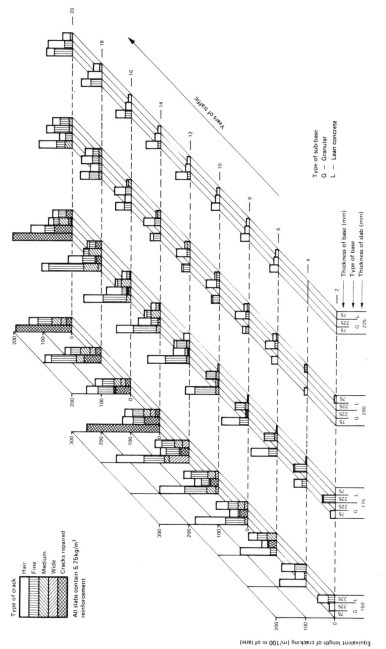

Figure 18.29 Alconbury Hill experiment: influence of type and thickness of sub-base on cracking of reinforced slabs

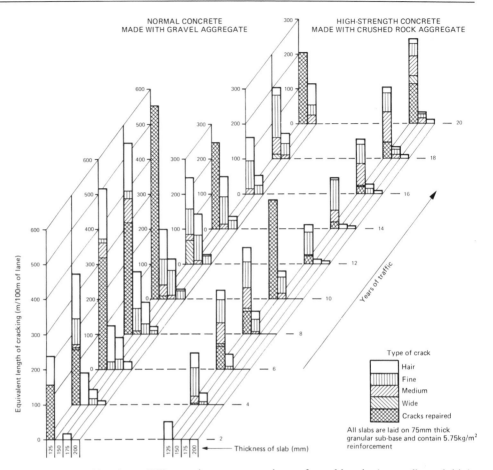

Figure 18.30 Alconbury Hill experiment: comparison of cracking in 'normal'- and high-strength concrete slabs

75 to 225 mm had no significant influence on the pavement life. However, a thick sub-base may have advantages in relation to drainage and construction convenience.

18.53   The relationship shown in Fig. 18.31 is reproduced in Fig. 18.32. Isolated results relating to the 75-mm and 225-mm lean concrete sub-base have been superimposed on the diagram. The lean concrete used had a 28-day compressive strength of 19 N/mm^2, i.e., less than half that of the slab. There is evidence that for the thinner slabs (less than 200 mm) the lean concrete improved the performance. For the 150-mm slabs the 225-mm lean concrete sub-base approximately doubled the life of the pavement with respect to a similar pavement with a granular sub-base. For 175-mm slabs the corresponding increase in life was about 50 per cent. The 75-mm thickness of lean concrete also had no signficant influence on the pavement life for slab thicknesses greater than 200 mm. The one observation made on thinner

Table 18.12   Alconbury Hill experiment: lives of concrete sections

Section No.	Concrete strength, N/mm²	Slab thickness, mm	Reinforce- ment weight, kg/m²	Sub-base		Life	
				Type	Thickness, mm	Years	msa
1	66.1	250	None	G*	75	40+ †	40+
2	66.1	225	None	G	75	40+	40+
3	66.1	200	None	G	75	40+	40+
4	66.1	200	5.75	G	75	40+	40+
5	66.1	175	5.75	G	75	30	27
6	66.1	150	5.75	G	75	17	10
7	66.1	125	5.75	G	75	5	2.5
8	44.1	125	7.74	G	75	5	2.5
9	44.1	125	5.75	G	75	1	0.4
10	44.1	150	7.74	G	75	9	4.9
11	44.1	150	5.75	G	225	11	6.1
12	44.1	225	5.75	G	225	40+	40+
13	44.1	200	5.75	G	225	30	28
14	44.1	200	5.75	LC*	225	27	23
15	44.1	175	5.75	LC	225	22	16
16	44.1	175	5.75	G	225	18	11
17	44.1	150	5.75	G	225	8	4.5
18	44.1	150	5.75	LC	225	12	7
19	44.1	175	7.74	G	75	18	11
20	44.1	175	5.75	G	75	17	10
21	44.1	175	4.27	G	75	13	7.3
22	44.1	175	5.75	LC	75	30	28
23	44.1	200	7.74	G	75	30	28
24	44.1	200	5.75	G	75	23	18
25	44.1	200	4.27	G	75	13	7
26	44.1	200	None	G	75	8	4.3
27	44.1	200	5.75	LC	75	30	28
28	44.1	225	5.75	LC	75	40+	40+
29	44.1	225	5.75	G	75	35	35
30	44.1	225	4.27	G	75	30	28
31	44.1	225	None	G	75	24	18
32	44.1	250	5.75	G	75	30	27
33	44.1	250	4.27	G	75	30	27
34	44.1	250	None	G	75	25	20
35	44.1	275	None	G	75	40+	40+

*G = gravel; LC = lean concrete.
†40+ = probably between 40 and 100.

pavements suggests an effect greater than occurs with the 225-mm thickness of lean concrete sub-base. It seems that there was no bond between the slab and the sub-base and that the latter was cracked either before or during the laying of the concrete.

18.54   Figure 18.33 shows a well-defined relationship between the 28-day com-pressive strength of the concrete and the life of the pavement. For 125-mm slabs the

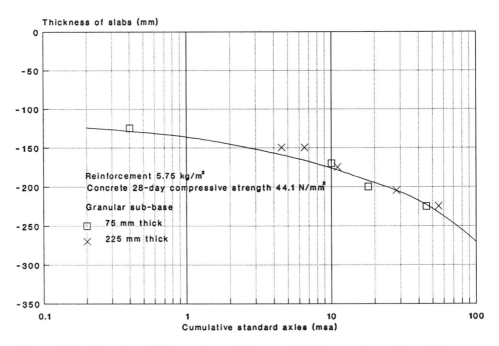

Figure 18.31 Alconbury Hill experiment: influence of thickness of granular sub-base on pavement life

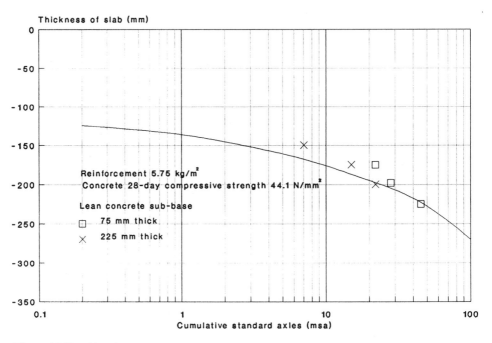

Figure 18.32 Alconbury Hill experiment: influence of sub-base type on pavement life

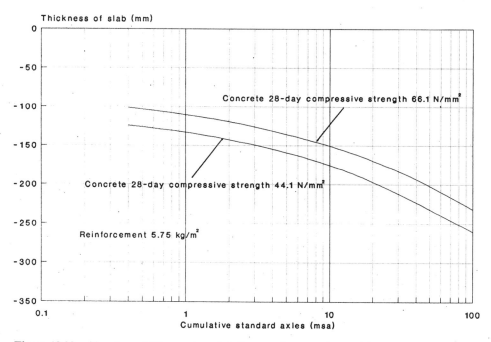

Figure 18.33 Alconbury Hill experiment: influence of concrete strength on pavement life

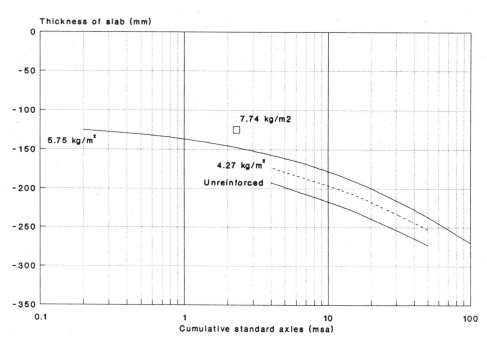

Figure 18.34 Alconbury Hill experiment: influence of weight of reinforcement on pavement life

life is increased by a factor of six when the higher-strength concrete is used. For slab thickness of 150 and 200 mm the corresponding ratios are three and two. As is discussed in Para. 15.15, this is due not solely to the higher compressive strength of the concrete, since the modulus of rupture is greater for concretes made with crushed rock aggregate than for gravel concrete having the same compressive strength.

18.55   Figure 18.34 shows the influence of reinforcement on life for the lengths of slab used in the Alconbury Hill experiment (4.6 m between dummy joints for the unreinforced slabs and 37 m for the reinforced slabs). Increasing the weight of reinforcement from 5.75 kg/m² to 7.74 kg/m² increased the life of the slabs thinner than 250 mm but had little effect on thicker slabs. Decreasing the weight of reinforcement from 5.75 kg/m² to 4.27 kg/m² decreased the life by about 40 per cent. For thicknesses of 200–300 mm the unreinforced slabs needed to be 50 mm thicker than slabs reinforced with 5.75 kg/m² reinforcement to give the same life, and about 25 mm thicker than slabs reinforced with 4.27 kg/m² steel.

The Llangyfelach experiment[12]

18.56   This experiment was designed and constructed 2 years before the Alconbury Hill one. The proposals were comprehensive and were intended to give long-term information on the relative importance of compressive and flexural strength in the performance of concrete slabs. Seven different concrete mixes, A–G, and slabs made from these mixes were distributed along the half-mile length used for the experiment, as shown in Fig. 18.35. Mixes A–C used gravel aggregate and mixes D–G crushed

To Morriston ──────▶

Slab no.	10	9	8	7	6	5	4	3	2	1
Mix	A	E	B	E	B	G	A	F	C	D
Slab no.	30	29	28	27	26	25	24	23	22	21
Mix	C	D	A	F	A	E	C	E	B	G

Slab no.	20	19	18	17	16	15	14	13	12	11
Mix	F	C	F	B	E	G	A	D	C	D
Slab no.	40	39	38	37	36	35	34	33	32	31
Mix	D	B	E	A	D	F	C	F	B	G

◀────── To Penilergaer

	Mix	Proportions by weight		Mix	Proportions by weight
Thames Valley gravel aggregate	A	1:9.2/0.69	North Wales porphyry aggregate	D	1:8.7/0.66
	B	1:7.2/0.55		E	1:7.6/0.58
	C	1:4.0/0.4		F	1:6.7/0.54
				G	1:4.5/0.45

Figure 18.35   Llangyfelach experiment: details of experimental concrete mixes used

porphyry. The mix proportions are shown in the figure. The concrete was of constant thickness 200 mm. The slabs were 37 m long and 4.6 m wide, and they were all reinforced with a weight of 3.5 kg/m².

18.57   The mixes as laid gave the 28-day compressive and flexural strengths given in Table 18.13. For each slab 14 beams (50.8 × 10.2 × 10.2 cm) were cast at the time of laying; 6 were tested at 28 days and 2 each at 3 months and 1, 2, and 5 years. The tests were for flexural strength and for compressive strength using the equivalent-cube method. The results of the means of these tests are shown in Table 18.13. The relationships between 28-day compressive and flexural strength for the mixes are shown in Fig. 18.36.

18.58   The site made available for this experiment, through the ready co-operation of the then Glamorgan County Council, was not heavily trafficked. In 1955 it carried only about 500 commerical vehicles per day in each direction. Figure 18.37 shows the latest results published by the TRRL. They relate to the first 12 years, by which time the road had carried a little over 2 msa. The weakest gravel mix shows the greatest degree of cracking, but the strongest gravel mix shows a lesser tendency to cracking than the strongest crushed stone mix. The latter has a marginally greater flexural strength and a significantly greater compressive strength. It will obviously be many years before positive conclusions can be drawn under this comparatively light traffic.

18.59   Unfortunately in the UK it has long been difficult for pavement engineers to gain access to heavily trafficked roads for experimental work. In particular, pavement performance studies on industrial motorways have not been permitted by the Department of Transport on the grounds of possible interruption of traffic. Many of these roads are now carrying 3–4 msa per year, and trials on roads carrying less than that amount of traffic in 20 years are becoming less and less relevant. On the motorway system of Britain interruption of traffic flow for repair work is now endemic. How far this could have been avoided by earlier experimental work must remain a matter for conjecture. In the United States, each state has its own Highway Research Division attached to the Highways Department and experimentation appears less stifled.

Table 18.13   Compressive and flexural test results for mixes laid at Llangyfelach

	Average strength, N/mm²									
	Flexural					Compressive				
Mix	28-day	3-month	1-year	2-year	5-year	28-day	3-month	1-year	2-year	5-year
A	2.8	3.2	3.8	4.1	4.7	27	34	40	43	45
B	3.5	4.3	4.6	4.9	5.6	39	50	57	58	62
C	4.5	4.9	5.2	5.7	6.1	55	66	69	73	71
D	3.3	3.8	4.4	4.7	4.6	29	37	44	46	49
E	3.9	4.8	5.0	5.0	5.1	37	48	54	57	57
F	4.6	5.1	5.5	5.6	5.4	45	56	65	68	67
G	5.4	5.9	6.0	6.2	6.5	57	69	78	81	79

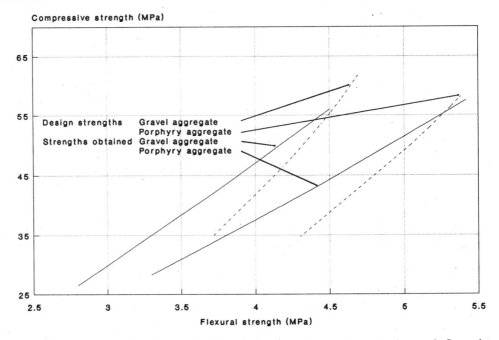

Figure 18.36 Llangyfelach experiment: relationship between compressive and flexural strengths of mixes at 28 days

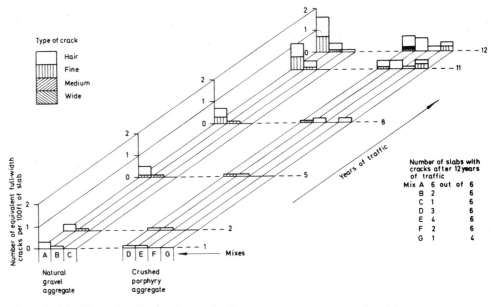

Figure 18.37 Llangyfelach experiment: development of transverse cracks with age

The Longford–Stanwell road (A3044)[13]

18.60   The construction of London Airport (Heathrow) closed a number of minor north–south roads in the area. The Longford–Stanwell road constructed round the western perimeter of the airport was a replacement giving access to Staines and Kingston. It was initially lightly trafficked, but with the opening of the M4 and M3 motorways the traffic has increased markedly. In 1980 a second carriageway was constructed. In the first 20 years, the estimated cumulative traffic in each direction was 4.3 msa. At the time of construction the site was chosen as suitable for a concrete pavement experiment designed to investigate the frequency necessary for expansion joints in an unreinforced concrete road.

18.61   The length of road available was divided into 24 sections of length between 36.6 m and 690 m, each with contraction joints at 4.6-m intervals. There were thus 7 contraction joints in the shortest section and 45 in the longest. The layout of the sections is shown in Fig. 18.38. The road was constructed on deep gravel fill and no dowel bars were used at any of the joints. The pavement was of uniform thickness of 200 mm, and the average 28-day compressive strength was 39.2 N/mm². The construction work was carried out during the summer months. The performance of the sections has been assessed by crack surveys at regular intervals. A number of

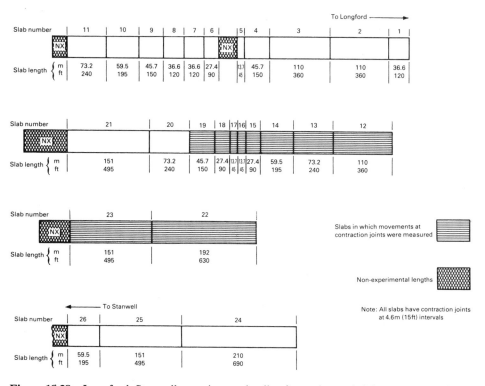

Figure 18.38   Longford–Stanwell experiment: details of experimental slabs

sections, as indicated in Fig 18.38 were used to study seasonal movements at the contraction and expansion joints.

18.62   The experimental sections contained a total of 854 slabs (between contraction joints). Of these only 16 had cracked during the first 20 years and in 3 of these the cracks had developed from the corners of gulley inlets. The distribution of the cracks with respect to the section lengths is shown in Table 18.14. This small amount of cracking started in the fifteenth year of the life of the experiment and coincided with the increase of traffic due to the completion of the M3 and M4 motorways. The number of lane-width cracks related to the age of the road is shown in Fig. 18.39. There is no evidence that the length of the sections, between expansion joints, had any effect on the distribution of cracking.

18.63   Comparison with the cracking of the 200-m unreinforced sections at Alconbury Hill (Fig. 18.28) shows that at 4 msa the amount of cracking at Alconbury was greater, despite the fact that the 28-day strength of the concrete was marginally higher. This could be due to the stronger foundation at the Longford site, but it is more likely to be attributable to the relatively slow build-up of traffic at that site, permitting the development of a higher modulus of rupture before the traffic loading increased.

18.64   Joint movements were measured using the equipment shown in Fig. 18.40. All slabs involved were drilled soon after construction to take the brass inset gauge points located at approximately 150 mm from the joint. The precalibrated joint-width gauge was used to measure both permanent and diurnal changes of the joint width. Figure 18.41 shows for one expansion joint the measurements made over the

Table 18.14   The distribution of transverse cracks in the slabs of various lengths

Expansion joint m (ft) → Years of traffic	13.7 (45)		27.4 36.6 45.7 59.5 73.2 (90 120 150 195 240)		110 (360)	151 (495)		192 (630)		210 (690)		Totals		
Traffic lane →	S/B	N/B	S/B*	N/B*	S/B*	S/B	N/B	S/B	N/B	S/B	N/B	S/B	N/B	Both
15				1		1	1					1	2	3
16		2		1		1	2				1	1	6	7
17		2		1		1	2	1			2	2	7	9
18		2	1	1		1	2	1		1	2	4	7	11
19	1	2	1	1	1	1	2	1		1	2	6	7	13
20	1	2	1	1	2	1	3	1	1	1	2	7	9	16

*1. Where cracks in one traffic lane only are listed there were no cracks in the other lane.

  2. The numbers of cracks are totals in the three slabs of each length (except for the single 192-m and 210-m slabs).

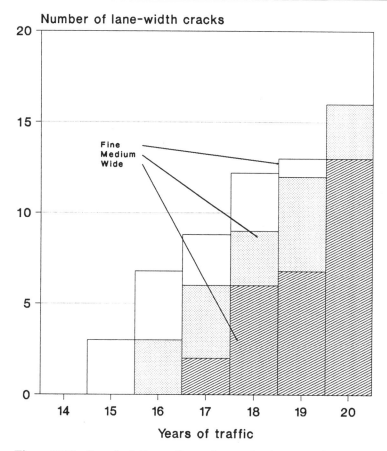

Figure 18.39   Longford–Stanwell experiment: development of transverse cracks with age

7-year period from winter 1949 to winter 1956, which—at 5 °C—show a permanent joint closure of nearly 9 mm. The cumulative opening of contraction joints in sections 15, 19, 13, and 22 are shown in Fig. 18.42.

18.65   Figure 18.43 shows the reversible movements at each joint in the sections 12–23, and Fig. 18.44 gives the permanent changes of width after 7 years. It has been calculated that the expansion joints will close fully in 34 years from the date of construction and this will lead to compression at the contraction joints. Given the strength which the concrete will then have, it is unlikely that erosion at the joints will occur. In the UK in recent years there has been a move towards the omission of expansion joints in reinforced pavements laid in the spring and summer months. Under these circumstances the Longford–Stanwell experiment would indicate a much more rapid buildup of compressive stress with a greater risk of failures. There have in fact been several potentially very dangerous blowups on concrete motorways

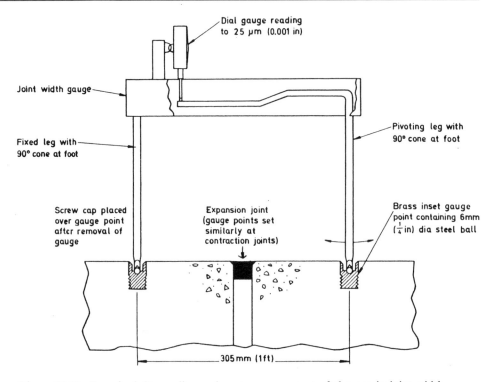

Figure 18.40   Longford–Stanwell experiment: measurement of changes in joint width

in abnormally hot weather, and the practice of omitting expansion joints is not recommended.

The Grantham Bypass Experiment[14]

18.66   This was not a structural design experiment of the type constructed at Alconbury Hill, under the supervision of the TRRL. Certain constructional variations were written into the contract, but the work was carried out to normal construction and supervision standards. The thickness design was based on the recommendations of UK Road Note 19, which was subsequently replaced by Road Note 29 in 1970. For the observed traffic flow and growth rate, the design thickness of the concrete was 230 mm, and the average 28-day compressive strength of the concrete was 37 N/mm². The sub-base consisted of 75 mm of lean concrete and the subgrade was predominantly a lias clay with a local area of limestone brash. The cumulative total of standard axles during the 6 years of the performance study was 9 msa.

18.67   There were three main objectives, as follows:

1. to establish a relationship between slab length, weight of reinforcement, and degree of cracking for reinforced concrete pavements;

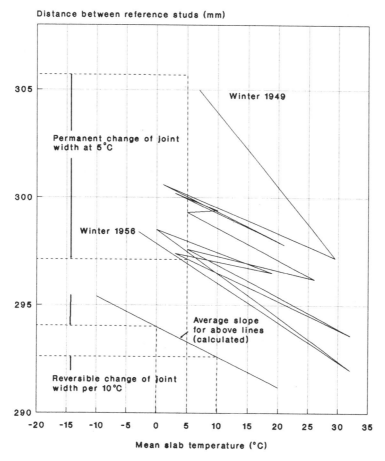

Figure 18.41 Longford–Stanwell experiment: record of movement at an expansion joint

2. to compare the performance of pavements reinforced with (a) hard-drawn and (b) mild-steel reinforcement of the same weight;

3. to compare the performance of pavements reinforced with (a) hard-drawn and (b) ribbed-wire reinforcement of the same weight.

A subsidiary objective was to investigate the performance of several continuously reinforced sections.

18.68   The relationship between cracking and weight of reinforcement established for four weights of round, hard-drawn steel fabrics after 6 years is shown in Fig. 18.45. The two curves shown separate (1) uncracked concrete and concrete with acceptable hair and fine cracking, and (2) concrete with hair and fine cracks and concrete with unacceptable medium and wide cracks. The left-hand curve is currently adopted in Road Note 29.

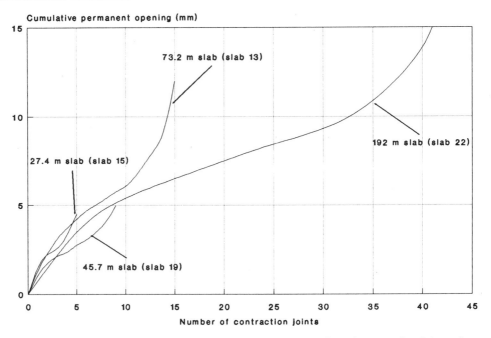

Figure 18.42   Longford–Stanwell experiment: permanent opening of contraction joints after 7 years

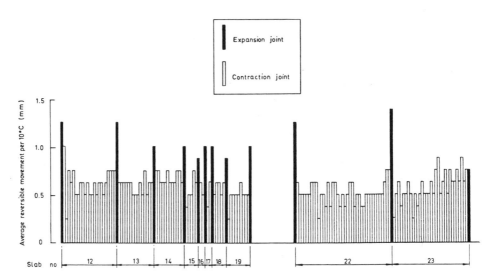

Figure 18.43   Longford–Stanwell experiment: reversible movement of joints in the first 7 years

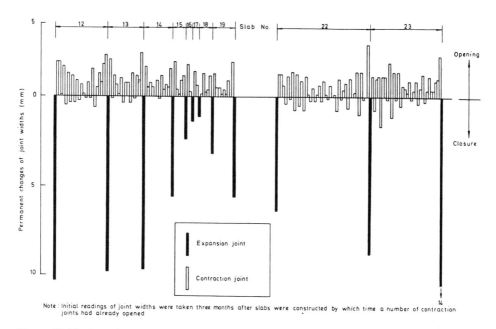

Figure 18.44 Longford–Stanwell experiment: permanent changes in the widths of joints after 7 years

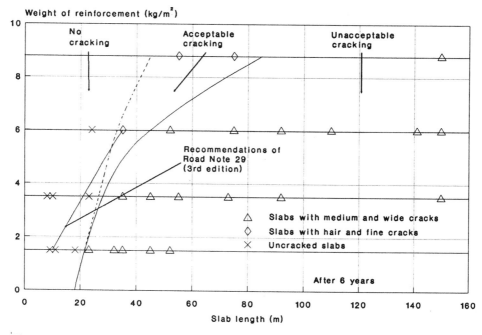

Figure 18.45 Grantham Bypass experiment: cracking in slabs reinforced with plain round, hard-drawn steel wire fabric

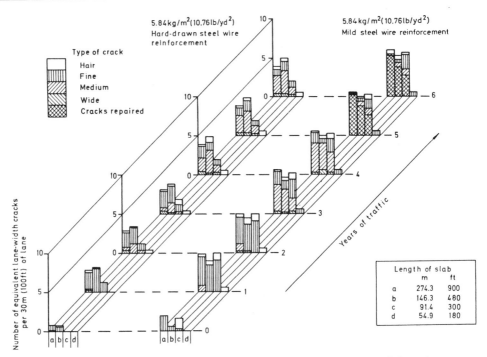

Figure 18.46 Grantham Bypass experiment: development of cracking in reinforced concrete slabs: comparison of hard-drawn steel and mild steel wire fabrics

18.69   Figure 18.46 compares the performance of 5.84 kg/m² hard-drawn steel wire reinforcement with the same weight of mild-steel wire reinforcement for slabs between 54.9 m and 274 m long. The performance of the hard-drawn steel is clearly much superior to mild steel, particularly for the longer slabs. For this weight of reinforcement, Fig. 18.45 indicates a maximum length of slab of 44 m, which is less than the condition 'd' of Fig. 18.46. For this length of slab the difference in performance of the two types of reinforcement over the 6-year period is small and both types would probably give a long life.

18.70   Figure 18.47 compares the performance of 3.56-kg/m² hard-drawn and ribbed-wire reinforcements. There appears to be a rather better performance from the hard-drawn material than the ribbed-wire reinforcement, but the difference is less marked for slabs of the length appropriate from Fig. 18.45. When the weight of reinforcement is reduced from 5.84 kg/m² to 3.51 kg/m², Fig. 18.48 shows a rather better performance from the ribbed-wire reinforcement. For the slab length appropriate to Fig. 18.33, both materials showed no cracking after 6 years.

18.71   The continuously reinforced sections of the Grantham Bypass occupied some 7 km of carriageway. Two weights of reinforcement, 5.84 kg/m² and 8.87 kg/m², were used. Pretraffic cracking increased markedly with the mean slab temperature at the time of placement. The first wide cracks appeared at, or close to,

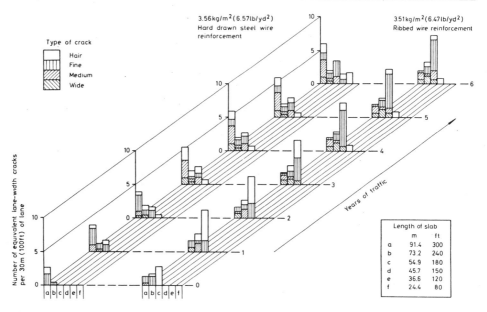

Figure 18.47   Grantham Bypass experiment: development of cracking in reinforced concrete slabs: comparison of lighter hard-drawn steel and ribbed wire fabrics

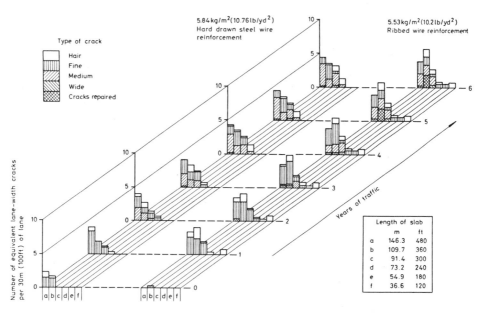

Figure 18.48   Grantham Bypass experiment: development of cracking in reinforced concrete slabs: comparison of heavier hard-drawn steel and ribbed wire fabrics

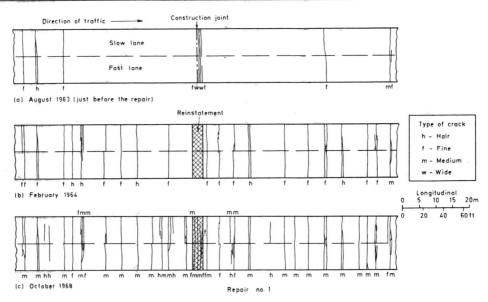

Figure 18.49 Grantham Bypass experiment: incidence of cracking in a continuously reinforced slab following repairs of wide cracks: 1219-m-long slab with 8.87-kg/m² hard-drawn steel wire reinforcement

construction joints, as shown in Fig. 18.49. This may have been due to weak reinforcement bonds at these points or to delays in construction. After repair, further wide cracks tended to develop in the same areas over a period of 1–3 years. There was little difference in performance between the sections with the lighter and heavier reinforcement. This suggests that the weights used were insufficient.

18.72   The main lesson learned from these experiments with continuously reinforced concrete was the importance of adequate preparation, and the development of constructional skills beyond those required for jointed reinforced and unreinforced concrete. In 1974 a study group was set up by the Department of the Environment and the TRRL to examine the possible future for this form of construction in the UK when compared with normal concrete or flexible construction. The conclusion was that it was unlikely to be economic except perhaps in congested urban situations, where a very long, maintenance-free life was required. Unfortunately, these are the conditions where a sufficiently long site is unlikely to be available and where excavations through the pavement are likely to be most frequent. Since 1975 trial lengths of motorway have been laid using continuously reinforced concrete, but it is too early to assess their performance. Some concrete overlays using this principle have also been constructed.

The prestressed concrete experiment at Winthorpe[15]

18.73   Cracking of concrete pavements is induced by a combination of tensile stresses arising from temperature changes and traffic loading. If a compressive stress is applied to the concrete by a prestressing procedure, the tensile stresses developed in the above manner can be wholly or partly neutralized. It follows that thin slabs which would normally be liable to cracking might be used successfully in a prestressed situation. The procedure would of course be economically viable only if the saving in concrete thickness and subsequent maintenance costs was signficiantly greater than the additional cost generated by the prestressing method adopted.

18.74   Various experimental prestressed concrete pavements have been laid, particularly in France and Belgium, using either prestressing wires in the slabs or external jacking between abutments. The latter form of prestressing was adopted in an experimental road constructed at Winthorpe in Nottinghamshire in 1961. The prestressed pavement was laid on one carriageway of a dual-carriageway road, in a situation where all the traffic could be conveniently transferred to the other carriageway during prestressing operations.

18.75   Prestressed slabs 125 and 175 mm thick (without reinforcement except in the immediate vicinity of prestressing joints) were laid, each of approximately 300 m in length between abutments. The latter consisted of heavily reinforced slabs anchored to the supporting soil by vertical walls of depth approximately 2 m. Each abutment was some 70 m long. The slabs were provided with dowelled prestressing joints faced with channel-section steel, at a distance of 85 m from each abutment. A similar stress-measurement joint was installed in each section adjacent to one abutment. Flat jacks were permanently installed in the latter joints, so that the compressive stress could be monitored at any time.

18.76   Prestressing was carried out by piston jacks, each of 125 mm diameter, and placed approximately 150 mm apart. These jacks were placed and removed in blocks of four. When the required degree of prestress had been achieved the blocks of four jacks were removed singly and replaced by adjustable spacers, the stress being gradually transferred to the spacers from the jacks in this manner. After all the jacks were removed the joint was filled with concrete. This procedure obviated the need for the complicated pipework necessary for a permanently installed jacking system and allowed a more economic use of the jacks. The need to break out the blocking, and to replace the jacks whenever an adjustment to the prestress level was necessary, made stress changes a laborious and somewhat hazardous procedure.

18.77   The prestressed slabs were provided with a lean concrete sub-base and they were laid on a sliding layer consisting of two sheets of polythene separated by a slip additive. Control slabs of normal reinforced concrete of thickness range 125–200 mm were laid on the same carriageway so that the performance of the prestressed slabs could be assessed in terms of an equivalent thickness of conventional concrete.

18.78   Setting the level of prestress was complicated by the effects of temperature and creep. The prestress–temperature ratio was found to be approximately $450\,kN/m^2$ per °C. The minimum prestress at -10 °C was designed to be $700\,kN/m^2$, which meant that at 10 °C the prestress level needed to be set at about $9\,MN/m^2$ (allowing $1.4\,MN/m^2$ to overcome the subgrade restraint). With such a level of prestress, considerable creep occured in the concrete and during the 5 years that the pavements were under observation the slab 125 mm thick decreased in length by about 230 mm. To allow for the effect of creep it was necessary to restress the slabs annually, generally in the late autumn. The general pattern of the stress records showed an increase in maximum stress level in the spring followed by a small decrease during the summer months, reflecting creep, and a much more rapid decrease in the autumn arising from the combined effects of creep and decreasing temperature. Figure 18.50 shows such records for the 125 mm slab after the initial prestressing in March 1963. The recurring problem was to set the prestress in the autumn at a level which would ensure adequate residual prestress the following autumn without the danger of a bucking failure in the early summer. The level chosen depended to some extent on the weather at the time of prestressing, and allowance had to be made for the coldest conditions likely to prevail at the time of the next annual prestress. If during the year the gauges indicated a dangerous buildup of compressive stress it was necessary to close the carriageway. (On the basis of early experience a compressive stress of 20 MN/m^2 was regarded as the dangerous level in the later stages of the experiment.)

18.79   Early in July 1968 there was an abnormally sudden increase in temperature at the site and the mean slab temperature on 8 July rose to a maximum of 35°C. When the maximum compressive stress reached 24MN/m^2, the major blowup of the 125 mm slab shown in Fig. 18.51 occurred. No damage was sustained by the 175-mm

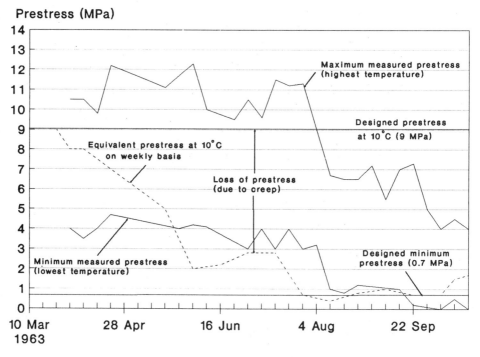

Figure 18.50 Winthorpe prestressed concrete experiment: variation of prestress in 125-mm slab

Figure 18.51   Blow-up of 125-mm pre-stressed concrete pavement at Winthorpe, 1968

slab, but this was subsequently destressed and the experiment as a whole terminated. This damaged length of the 125-mm slab was cut out and replaced and both experimental slabs were overlaid with 100 mm of asphalt.

18.80   For prestressed concrete pavements to be economically viable the cost saving in concrete, reinforcement, and joint assemblies must exceed the cost of providing and maintaining a 'safe' level of prestress. The latter would need to be automatically controlled. The experience gained from the Winthorpe experiment suggests that for normal road pavements there is little chance that prestressed concrete could ever be economic. For slabs intended to carry abnormally heavy loads the situation might be different. The 125- and 175-mm slabs constructed at Winthorpe using normal reinforced concrete did not show any significant cracking during the period of the experiment and no assessment could be made of the potential saving in concrete thickness. However, since it would not be practicable to prestress slabs thinner than 125 mm, the savings on thickness would be small except for very heavily trafficked roads.

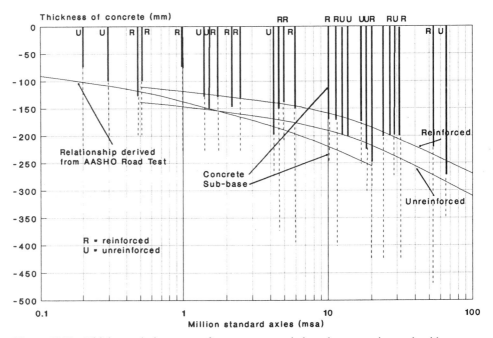

Figure 18.52 Thickness design curves for concrete roads based on experimental evidence

Thickness design for concrete pavements based on experimental evidence

18.81   Figure 18.52 shows the thickness design requirements for concrete pavements based on the evidence from the full-scale road experiments. The curves relate to 'normal' strength concrete with a 28-day compressive strength of 35–45 N/mm². There is a clearly defined need for a greater thickness for unreinforced concrete, the difference being about 25 mm irrespective of the cumulative traffic. The figure also includes the relationship between thickness and standard axles deduced from the results of the AASHO road test.[16]

References

1. Lee, A. R. and D. Croney: British full-scale design experiments. *Proc. 1st Int. Conf. on the Structural Design of Asphalt Pavements, Ann Arbor, 1962*, University of Michigan, Ann Arbor, 1962.
2. Grainger, G. D.: The performance of granular base materials under traffic. *Roads and Road Constrn*, **43** (512), 243–7, 1965.
3. Croney, D. and J. A. Loe: Full-scale pavement design experiment on A1 at Alconbury Hill, *Proc. Instn Civ. Engrs*, **30** (Feb.), 225–70, 1965.

4. Thompson, P. D., D. Croney, and E. W. H. Currer: The Alconbury Hill experiment and its relation to flexible pavement design, *Proc. 3rd Int. Conf. on the Structural Design of Asphalt Pavements, London, 1972*, University of Michigan, Ann Arbor, 1972.

5. Salt, G. F.: Recent full-scale pavement design experiments in Britain, *Proc. 2nd Int. Conf. on the Structural Design of Asphalt Pavements, Ann Arbor, Michigan, 1967*, University of Michigan, Ann Arbor, 1967.

6. *Road Research 1963*: Annual Report of the Road Research Laboratory pp. 87–90, HMSO, London, 1964.

7. *Road Research 1964*: Annual Report of the Road Research Laboratory pp. 92–95, HMSO, London, 1965.

8. *Road Research 1967:* Annual Report of the Road Research Laboratory, p. 104, HMSO, London, 1968.

9. Gregory, J. M.: *An Experimental Concrete Road 38 Years Old: Condition and Performance of Sections of A316, Great Chertsey Road*, Transport and Road Research Laboratory Report LR317, TRRL, Crowthorne, 1972.

10. Loe, J. A.: The performance during the first 5 years of the experimental concrete road at Oxton, Nottinghamshire, *Proc. Instn Civ. Engrs*, **4** (1), 137–66, Part II, 1955.

11. Nowak, J. R.: *The Concrete Pavement Design Experiment on Trunk Road A1 at Alconbury Hill: Twenty Year Performance*, Transport and Road Research Laboratory Report LR887, TRRL, Crowthorne, 1979.

12. Nowak, J. R.: *Influence of Strength on the Performance of Concrete Slabs. Report on the Performance after 12 years of the Experimental Road at Llangyfelach*, Road Research Laboratory Report LR199, TRRL, Crowthorne, 1968.

13. Nowak, J. R. and J. Gaunt: *The Full-scale Unreinforced Concrete Experiment on Longford–Stanwell Road, B 379. Performance during the first 20 years*, Road Research Laboratory Report LR349, TRRL, Crowthorne, 1970.

14. Nowak, J. R.: *The Full-scale Reinforced Concrete Experiment on the Grantham Bypass. Performance During the First Six Years*, Road Research Laboratory Report LR345, TRRL, Crowthorne, 1970.

15. Kidd, R. A. and J. P. Stott.: The construction of an experimental prestressed concrete road at Winthorpe, Nottinghamshire, *Proc. Instn Civ. Engrs*, **36**, 473–98, 1967.

16. Highway Research Board: The AASHO Road Test, Report 5: Pavement Research, Special Report 61E, National Academy of Science, National Research Council, Publication 954, Washington, D.C., 1962.

19. Current design procedures for flexible and concrete pavements in the United Kingdom

Introduction

19.1   Current design standards for flexible and concrete pavements in the UK are based on Road Note 29, one of a series of monographs on highway design and construction matters produced by the TRRL during the last 40 years. The Road Note is entitled *A Guide to the Structural Design of Pavements for New Roads*. The first edition was published in 1960, followed by a second edition in 1965, and a third in 1970.[1] Since then a number of changes have been made affecting the document by Department of Transport memoranda and by two recent reports issued by the TRRL.[2,3] In this chapter the various changes are brought together for the convenience of engineers and comments on the changes are provided.

19.2   The various factors involved in formulating a design suitable for a particular situation are (1) present commercial traffic, (2) growth rate of commercial traffic, (3) design life required, (4) conversion of traffic to equivalent standard axles to be carried during the design life, and (5) a series of relationships between sub-base thickness, base thickness, and surfacing thickness and cumulative standard axles for flexible construction, and similar relationships between sub-base thickness, slab thickness, and weight of reinforcement for concrete pavements.

Traffic

19.3   The 1970 edition of Road Note 29 included a series of charts of the type shown in Fig. 19.1, each relating to a different growth rate of commercial traffic between 2 and 6 per cent. They were constructed using the assumption that 80 per cent of the commercial traffic would be carried by the left-hand or slow traffic lane. Figure 8.9 shows that this would apply to carriageways carrying about 4000 commercial vehicles per day. In Appendix B of LR1132 these charts have been replaced by the following formula:

$$T_n = 365F_0 \frac{(1+r)^n - 1}{r} P \tag{19.1}$$

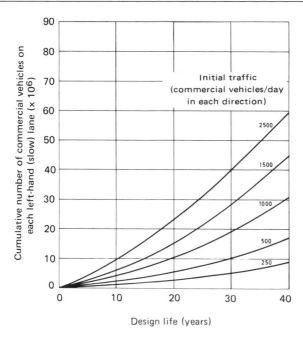

Figure 19.1 Relation between the cumulative number of commercial vehicles carried by each slow lane and design life-growth rate 4 per cent per annum

where T_n = the total number of commercial vehicles using the slow lane over the design life, n

F_0 = the initial flow in commercial vehicles per day

r = the growth rate expressed as a percentage

P = the proportion of the commercial vehicles in the slow traffic lane

Strictly, P will be changing as the traffic increases (see Fig. 8.9), but an average figure representing the mid-life should be sufficient.

Equation (19.1) gives the same total flow as the charts in Road Note 29 so that either approach can be used where the value of P is close to 0.8.

19.4   The total number of commercial vehicles to be carried by the slow lanes during the design life, was converted to cumulative standard axles by multiplying factors given in Table 2 of the Road Note. These factors were modified by the Department of Transport in 1978[4] and further modified by the TRRL in 1979.[5] These changes were made necessary by the normal development of road transport together with the increase in oil prices which occurred in the seventies and changes in the Construction and Use Regulations.[6] These factors were reflected in the returns from the TRRL weighbridges. On the basis of this information, the numbers of standard axles per commercial vehicle were increased considerably above the 1970 values as shown in Table 19.1.

19.5   To avoid the rather illogical steps in Table 19.1 the TRRL has developed an equation to relate the vehicle damaging factor to the commercial traffic flow. It gives an estimate of the vehicle damage factor D for any mid-term year t based on

**Table 19.1   Vehicle damage factors recommended
for the design of new roads**

Category of road (commercial vehicles per day in one direction)	Standard axles per commercial vehicle	
	Road Note 29, (1970)	1979
> 2 000	1.08	2.9
1 000–2 000	1.08	2.25
250–1 000	0.72	1.25
< 250	0.45	0.75

the 24-hour flow of commercial vehicles for that year F; the base year is 1945, so that the year 1984 corresponds to $t = 39$. The equation is

$$D = \frac{0.35}{0.93^t + 0.082} - \frac{0.26}{0.92^t + 0.082} \cdot \frac{1.0}{3.9^{(F/1550)}} \tag{19.2}$$

As an example, the equation generates vehicle damage factors which vary with time and daily flow of commercial vehicles, as shown in Table 19.2.

19.6   Table 19.2 shows that extrapolation from the evidence available in 1984 indicates that by the year 2030 the *average* damaging effect of commercial vehicles will be about four standard axles per vehicle. If the eventual EC agreement on vehicle and axle loading allows either 11-t axle loads or 44-t gross vehicle weights the maximum damaging effect of commercial vehicles will rise to between five and seven standard axles. It is unlikely therefore that the *average* will rise to four, although this is not impossible in the case of some industrial motorways.

Table 19.2   Vehicle damage factors

Year	Daily flow of commercial vehicles, AADF*			
	250	1 000	2 000	4 000
1985	0.78	1.64	2.17	2.49
1990	0.93	1.89	2.49	2.84
1995	1.18	2.12	2.76	3.14
2000	1.22	2.31	3.00	3.40
2005	1.34	2.47	3.18	3.60
2010	1.43	2.60	3.33	3.76

*Average annual daily flow.

Thickness of flexible pavement layers

Sub-base thickness

19.7   The 1970 edition of Road Note 29 defined the thickness and type of sub-base in relation to the CBR value of the soil and the cumulative traffic in standard axles. The relevant requirements for all types of flexible construction are shown in Fig. 19.2 reproduced from Road Note 29. The thicknesses are largely based on the early experience gained from the full-scale road experiments described in Chapter 18. However, in drawing up these thickness standards consideration was also given to the ability of the sub-base/subgrade layers to carry construction traffic, particularly during the laying of the base. For this reason, thicknesses were increased above those shown to be necessary by structural requirements. In Figs 18.20, 18.21, and 18.22 the sub-base thickness requirements of Fig. 19.2 have been superimposed on the experimental results and the measure of the overdesign intended to protect the subgrade during construction can be seen. This latest examination of the performance of the full-scale experiments does not indicate that any change of sub-base thickness is required. As is discussed in Chapter 11, the concept of introducing a capping layer between low-CBR-value earthworks and the sub-base has been introduced recently by the Department of Transport in the UK. The onus of finding a suitable material of CBR in the region of 10 per cent is thus passed to the contractor. This is a common cause of dispute and whether any money or resources are saved is doubtful.

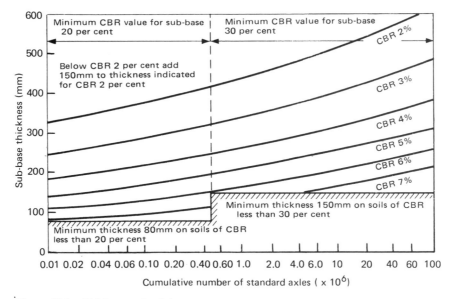

Figure 19.2   Thickness of sub-base

Pavements with bituminous roadbases

19.8   Bituminous materials are now widely used for roadbases in Europe and the USA. They are generally more costly than unbound and cemented bases, and overdesign should be avoided, particularly because with this form of construction overlaying is simple if allowed for in the initial design. Figure 18.22 has shown the performance of bituminous surfacing–base combinations used in the British full-scale pavement design experiments discussed in Chapter 18. A variety of coated macadam bases have been used including rolled asphalt, dense coated macadam, and the lean bitumen and tar-coated materials included in the Alconbury and Wheatley Bypass experiments. The thicknesses of surfacing and dense coated macadam bases recommended in the 1970 edition of Road Note 29 are included in Fig. 18.22. These thicknesses were based on the results then available from the full-scale road experiments.

19.9   The later evidence does not appear to justify any significant changes to the thicknesses recommended in Road Note 29. It does appear that when rolled asphalt is used as the base material some reduction in thickness (with respect to coated macadam) can be made, as was permitted in the 1970 edition of the Road Note. However, it is not now recommended that substantial thicknesses of rolled asphalt bases should be used on economic grounds. There does not appear to be any significant difference between the performance of dense coated macadam and the leaner bituminous bases adopted in the Alconbury and Wheatley Bypass experiments. This is an area where significant savings could be made.

19.10   Figure 19.3 compares the latest British recommendations relating to the total surfacing and base thicknesses for pavements with rolled asphalt surfacings and coated macadam bases given in Transport and Road Research Laboratory Report LR1132[2] with the Road Note 29 (1970) recommendations. It will be seen that the total thickness of base and surfacing has been increased by about 40 mm. The reason for this is not clear, since the latest recommendations are understood to be based on the full-scale experiments. For traffic in excess of 10 msa, some extrapolation is inevitable. In compiling Fig. 18.22 this extrapolation has been based on the development of rutting and cracking. The extrapolation adopted in LR1132 was based partly on rutting but in addition future lives were estimated from deflection measurements. This procedure has very recently been shown to underestimate the lives of adequately designed pavements by a factor which may be as high as 3 or 4. This would have the effect of increasing the apparent thickness required. At 100 msa, where extrapolation is greatest, there may be a case for a small increase in thickness, but in the middle range > 20 msa, which covers most trunk roads, an increase of thickness of 40 mm seems excessive, and will inevitably make fully flexible pavements less competitive.

Pavements with lean concrete roadbases

19.11   As with the bituminous bases considered above, Fig. 18.21 shows the performance of full-scale experiments using lean concrete and various types of cemented bases. The thicknesses of surfacing and base recommended in Road Note

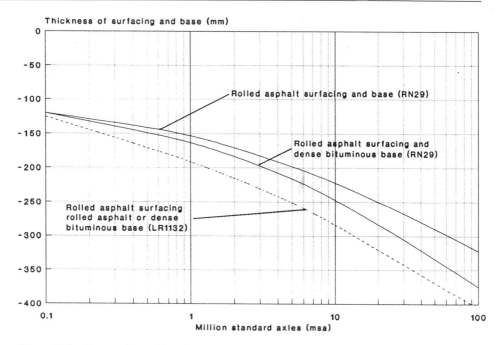

Figure 19.3 Comparison of Road Note 29 (1970) with TRRL Report LR1132 (1984)—asphalt surfacing and bituminous base

29 (1970) are also included in the figure. The later information does not suggest that any modification to the 1970 recommendations is necessary. Figure 19.4 compares the Road Note 29 thicknesses with the amended recommendations in Report LR1132. For traffic >20 msa the thickness of surfacing has been increased to 200 mm, presumably to contain reflected cracking from the base. This seems a reasonable precaution. Above 6 msa the thickness of the base has also been increased by as much as 60 mm. This may again be associated with the method of extrapolation used. The reason for the small decrease in base thickness below 6 msa is not obvious.

Pavements with unbound roadbases

19.12   Figure 18.20 shows the performance of full-scale experiments using unbound roadbases. With this type of base material, the similar strengths of the base material and the sub-base make it difficult to define the thickness necessary for the base. However, it does not appear that the later information now available requires changes to the recommendations of Road Note 29 (1970). Figure 19.5 shows that Report LR1132 recommends an increase in the thicknesses of both surfacing and base. In effect it has also limited this form of construction to traffic below 20 msa. The latter seems a wise precaution. In practice, the use of this form of construction for roads intended to carry more than 10 msa is not advisable. The experimental

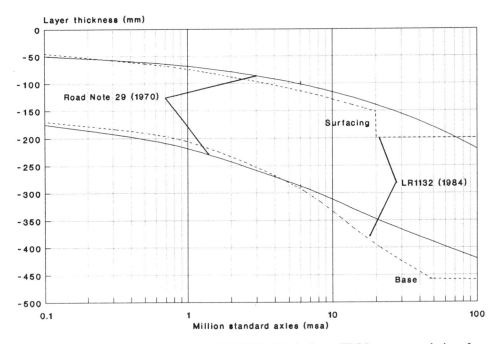

Figure 19.4 Comparison of Road Note 29 (1970) with the latest TRRL recommendations for pavements with lean concrete bases

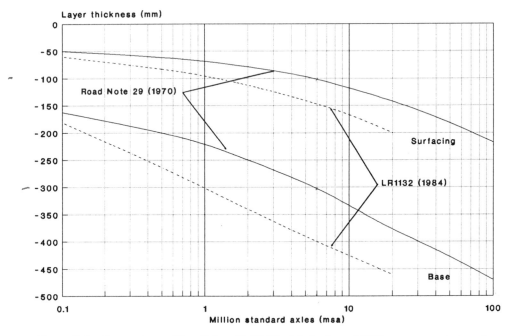

Figure 19.5 Comparison of Road Note 29 (1970) with the latest TRRL recommendations for pavements with crushed stone bases

evidence does not appear to justify the large increases in base and surfacing thickness, in a form of construction very suited to overlaying when necessary.

Concrete pavements

Slab thickness

19.13   Figure 18.51 shows the minimum slab thickness derived from British full-scale road experiments using concrete construction, related to cumulative standard axles. In Fig. 19.6 these minimum slab thicknesses are compared with the recommendations given in Road Note 29 (1970). When the Road Note was drafted, a conscious decision was made to place a lower limit on thickness of concrete roads, largely because of the difficulty of laying thin slabs without an undue risk of early thermal and traffic cracking. A small difference was made in the thickness of reinforced and unreinforced slabs for lightly trafficked roads. The latest evidence shows that the Road Note recommendations are safe except perhaps for very heavy traffic conditions, where the number of cumulative standard axles to be carried exceeds 50 msa.

19.14   The Road Note 29 recommendations have been recently reviewed in Transport and Road Research Laboratory Report RR87.[3] Based on experimental evidence, thickness curves for reinforced and unreinforced concrete pavements are

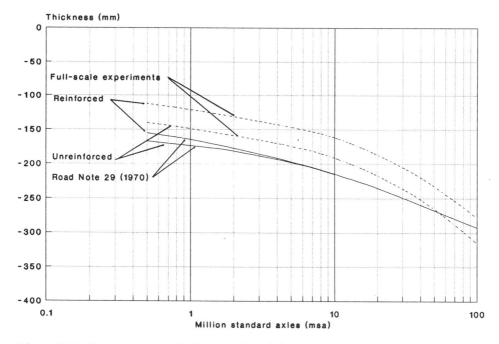

Figure 19.6   Comparison of slab thickness from full-scale experiments with the recommendations of Road Note 29

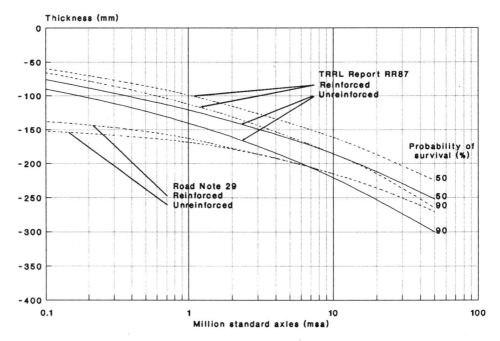

Figure 19.7 Comparison of slab thickness from TRRL Report RR87 (1987) with the recommendations of Road Note 29 (1970)

given, each with a 'probability of survival rate' of 50 and 90 per cent. These curves are reproduced in Fig. 19.7. The curves which correspond to a survival probability of 50 per cent correspond closely, for both reinforced and unreinforced concrete, with those shown in Fig. 19.6. The low survival rate compared with the evidence in Fig. 18.52 may arise from the use of different methods of failure prediction. Comparison with the recommendations of Road Note 29 indicates a considerable reduction of thickness for pavements designed to carry less than 5 msa. For the reason given in Para. 19.13 the reduction of concrete thickness below 125 mm is not recommended for public roads.

19.15   The latest evidence does suggest that there could be a greater thickness differential (about 30 mm) between designs for reinforced and unreinforced concrete pavements.

Slab length, weight of reinforcement, and the use of dowel bars

19.16   The slab length between contraction joints is determined largely by the weight of reinforcement used, which in turn is determined by the cumulative traffic to be adopted in the design. Figure 19.8 shows the relationship adopted in Road Note 29 (1970) between cumulative standard axles and the weight of reinforcement; the weights of typical long-mesh reinforcement mats available in the UK are shown in the figure. Figure 19.9 shows the relationship between the weight of reinforcement

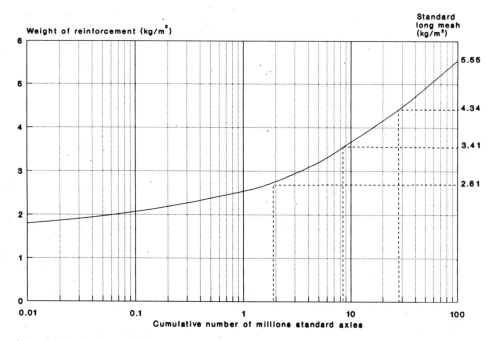

Figure 19.8 Relationship between cumulative standard axles and the weight of reinforcement

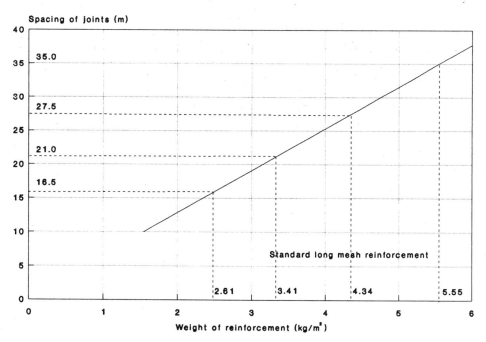

Figure 19.9 Relationship between the spacing of joints and the weight of reinforcement

399

and the spacing of joints recommended in Road Note 29. In the case of reinforced concrete pavements every third joint should be an expansion joint, and the rest contraction joints. For unreinforced concrete pavements the spacing of the joints adopted is 5 m, with expansion joints at 60-m intervals for slabs >200 mm thick and 40 m for thinner slabs. The Road Note permits the omission of expansion joints in pavements constructed during the summer months, but there is now evidence that this can lead to expansion failures in abnormally hot weather. In all concrete construction, tied longitudinal joints are provided so that the slabs are no more than 4.5 m wide.

19.17   All joints in slabs thicker than 150 mm are recommended to be provided with sliding dowel bars in accordance with Table 19.3. The Road Note also contains details concerning joint sealing.

Sub-base for concrete pavements

19.18   Road Note 29 (1970) classified subgrades for concrete roads as weak, normal, and very stable, and thicknesses of Type 1 sub-base for each class of subgrade were defined as shown in Table 19.4.

This requirement was unsatisfactory particularly with regard to normal subgrades, where the 80 mm of Type 1 sub-base was often inadequate to permit the passage of

Table 19.3   Dimensions of dowel bars for expansion and contraction joints

Slab thickness, mm	Expansion joints		Contraction joints	
	Diameter, mm	Length, mm	Diameter, mm	Length, mm
150–180*	20	550	12	400
190–230	25	650	20	500
240 and over	32	750	25	600

*Dowel bars are not recommended for slabs thinner than 150 mm.

Table 19.4   Classification of subgrades for concrete roads and minimum thickness of sub-base recommended (1970)

Type of subgrade	Definition	Minimum thickness of sub-base required, mm
Weak	All subgrades of CBR value 2% or less	150
Normal	Subgrades other than those defined by the other categories	80
Very stable	All subgrades of CBR value 15% or more This category includes undisturbed foundations of old roads	0

construction traffic. It was also insufficient to contain 'mud pumping', i.e., the slurrying of fines in the subgrade at joints and cracks. In 1978 the Department of Transport introduced into its specification the concept of capping layers already referred to in Para. 19.7. The requirement for concrete pavements was that a sub-base of Type 1 material 130 mm thick should be used for all subgrades and traffic levels. Where the subgrade had a CBR value of 2 per cent or less a capping layer having a CBR value of 7 per cent or more is additionally required. It is not clear whether this is intended to be a laboratory or *in situ* CBR value. Such a material would in general be hard for the contractor to find, outside the Type 2 sub-base grading limits.

Design of hard shoulders

19.19   Hard shoulders are an important feature of motorways and some trunk roads. They are provided to accommodate temporarily disabled vehicles. Observations suggest that a heavy commercial vehicle in stopping traverses 100–200 m of shoulder and that each length of shoulder will be traversed by not more than 150 disabled commercial vehicles per year. In view of the light intensity of the commercial traffic and the absence of a need for a high-quality riding surface, early motorways in Britain were provided with granular shoulders, surfaced in some cases

Table 19.5   Commercial vehicle flows recommended for the design of estate roads

Type of road	Estimated traffic flow commercial vehicles per day in each direction	Estimated damaging effect of commercial vehicles (st. axles/veh.)
1. Culs-de-sac and minor residential roads	10	0.45
2. Through roads carrying up to 25 PSVs* per day in each direction	75	0.7
3. Ditto carrying 25–30 PSVs per day in each direction	175	1.0
4. Main shopping centre of large development carrying delivery trucks and more than 50 PSVs per day in each direction	350	1.5

*Public service vehicles

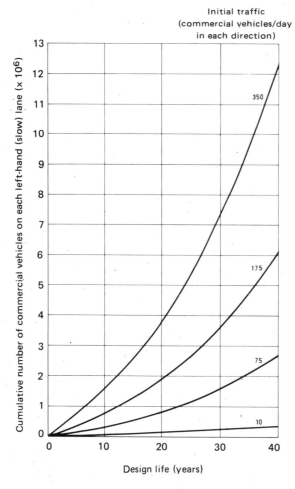

Figure 19.10 Roads in residential areas: relation between the cumulative number of commercial vehicles carried by each slow lane and design life

with a humus-rich stone-sand-soil layer intended to encourage the growth of grass. Such shoulders soon proved inadequate to support heavy vehicles, particularly in winter and in situations where jacking was necessary.

19.20   It has also been found necessary from time to time to divert slow-lane traffic onto the shoulder while carriageway maintenance and repairs are carried out. This has dictated a minimum width of shoulder of about 3.5 m and required a riding quality similar to that of the carriageway. Even with such use, the structural design of the shoulder will seldom need to accommodate more than 1 million standard axles during the life of the road. However, other considerations affect the design of the shoulder. The Type 1 sub-base provided under the carriageway is intended to act as a drainage, as well as a structural layer and to be effective it must be continued under the shoulder to connect with the side drainage system. Further, it is now normal practice to carry the carriageway surfacing across the shoulder for both concrete and flexible pavements, separation being defined by a continuous white line with red reflecting studs. These factors require a substantial thickness of sub-base under the shoulder but permit a reduction in the thickness of the other layers. Where there is a probability that carriageway widening may be necessary there is a case for constructing the shoulder to carriageway standards.

Design of housing estate and similar roads

19.21   Traffic census data are generally not available for residential estate roads. However, the Transport and Road Research Laboratory has made limited surveys in several such estate complexes. The results, in terms of commercial traffic, are summarized in Table 19.5. Information on the damaging effect of the commercial vehicles is based on the types of vehicles using the different categories of road. The information given in Table 19.5 can be used in conjunction with Fig. 19.10 to derive the cumulative number of standard axles to be used in the design.

References

1. Transport and Road Research Laboratory: *A Guide to the Structural Design of Pavements for New Roads*, Department of the Environment, Road Note 29, 3rd edn, HMSO, London, 1970.
2. Powell, W. D., J. F. Potter, H. C. Mayhew, and M. E. Nunn: *The Structural Design of Bituminous Roads*, Transport and Road Research Laboratory, Report LR1132, TRRL, Crowthorne, 1984.
3. Mayhew, H. C. and H. M. Harding: *Thickness Design of Concrete Roads*, Transport and Road Research Laboratory, Report RR87, TRRL, Crowthorne, 1987.
4. Department of Transport: *Road Pavement Design*, Technical Memorandum No. H6/78, HMSO, London, 1978.
5. Currer, E. W. H. and M. G. D. O'Connor: *Commercial traffic: its estimated damaging effect, 1945–2005*, Transport and Road Research Laboratory Report 910, TRRL, Crowthorne, 1979.
6. Department of Transport: *The Motor Vehicle (Construction and Use) Regulations*, Statutory Instrument No. 24, HMSO, London.

20. Current design procedures for flexible and concrete pavements in the USA

Introduction

20.1   Unlike European countries, the United States of America includes a very wide range of climatic and geological conditions ranging from the permafrost regions of Alaska to the semitropical environment of Florida and Southern California. Each state has its own Highway and Traffic Engineering Departments responsible for developing design and maintenance procedures suited to its own environmental and traffic conditions. Many of the States, notably California, Michigan, and Illinois, have however made major contributions to the world-wide understanding of road pavement design, construction, and rehabilitation.

20.2   Founded in 1914, the AASHO (see Para. 1.13) has played a major part in coordinating research and field studies for the benefit of all the participating states. This information is disseminated mainly through regular meetings and through publications such as *Standard Specifications for Transportation Materials and Methods of Sampling and Testing*. This is revised annually and is issued in two parts, the first of which deals with specifications and the second with materials. The ASTM also covers road and paving materials in Volume 04.03, which is also revised annually.

20.3   Particularly relevant to this chapter is the AASHTO *Guide for Design of Pavement Structures* (1986),[1] which is discussed below. Also relevant to flexible pavement design and construction are the publications of the Asphalt Institute, particularly Manual MS-1, entitled *Thickness Design—Asphalt Pavements for Highways and Streets*.[2] The Portland Cement Association has produced a similar document, *Thickness Design for Concrete Highway and Street Pavements*.[3] These three publications are discussed in this chapter.

The AASHTO *Guide for Design of Pavement Structures*

20.4   The concepts used in this guide are those developed in connection with the AASHO road test, the results from which were published in 1962.[4] In Britain and most other European countries the failure condition of flexible pavements is defined in what can be broadly classified as engineering terms such as deformation and cracking. For concrete pavements the criterion is cracking and differential movement at cracks and joints. In the AASHO road test described in Chapter 17, failure was subjectively defined in terms of the quality of the ride experienced by the 'average' road user, defined as the present serviceability rating (PSR), and interpreted by a panel of road users using a scale of 1–5 as defined in Fig. 17.11. It was the responsibility of the road engineer to interpret quantitatively the PSR in terms of the various factors such as deformation, cracking, patching, and surface regularity. The value so interpreted is defined as the present serviceability index (PSI), and its relationship with engineering terms has been defined in Eqns (17.1) and (17.3), in relation respectively to flexible and concrete pavements.

Flexible pavements

20.5   The basic design equation used in the *Guide* for flexible pavements is as follows:

$$\log W_{18} = Z_R S_0 + 9.36 \log (SN + 1) - 0.20$$

$$+ \frac{\log \dfrac{\Delta PSI}{4.2 - 1.5}}{0.40 + \dfrac{1094}{(SN + 1)^{5.19}}}$$

$$+ 2.32 \log M_R - 8.07 \tag{20.1}$$

where W_{18} = the predicted number of 18-kip equivalent single-axle load applications

Z_R = the standard normal deviate

S_0 = the combined standard error of the traffic prediction and performance prediction

ΔPSI = the difference between the initial design serviceability index, p_0, and the design terminal serviceability index, p_t

M_R = the resilient modulus (psi)

SN is equal to the structural number indicative of the total pavement thickness required:

$$SN = a_1 D_1 + a_2 D_2 m_2 + a_3 D_3 m_3$$

where a_i = ith layer coefficient

D_i = ith layer thickness (inches)

m_i = ith layer drainage coefficient

20.6   The values of the reliability factors Z_R and S_0 depend on the validity of the traffic and materials data used as input to the equation. Values of Z_R proposed for general use where a detailed analysis of such data is not made are given in Table 20.1. Where the variance of proposed future traffic is not to be considered in detail the value of S_0 for flexible pavements is taken between 0.4 and 0.5.

Table 20.1 Standard normal deviate (Z_R) values corresponding to selected levels of reliability

Reliability, R (%)	Standard normal deviate, Z_R
50	−0.000
60	−0.253
70	−0.524
75	−0.674
80	−0.841
85	−1.037
90	−1.282
91	−1.340
92	−1.405
93	−1.476
94	−1.555
95	−1.645
96	−1.751
97	−1.881
98	−2.054
99	−2.327
99.9	−3.090
99.99	−3.750

20.7   The concept of the structural number, SN, as defined in Para. 20.5, was developed from the AASHO road test, in which various combinations of surfacing thickness D_1 (asphaltic concrete) were used in conjunction with base thickness D_2 (wet-mix stone, bitumen-coated aggregate, or cement-coated aggregate) and thickness D_3 of sub-base (sandy gravel). It was concluded that if the coefficients a_1, a_2, and a_3 were correctly chosen, the structural number derived from any combination of surfacing, base, and sub-base thicknesses would provide the same performance. A series of charts are provided, reproduced here as Figs 20.1 to 20.5, from which the values of a_1, a_2, and a_3 can be obtained from applicable tests such as elastic modulus, Marshall stability, CBR, R-value, and the results of triaxial and unconfined compression tests. There is in these charts useful implied equivalence relationships between the various test results. The values of m_2 and m_3, in the structural number equation depend on the drainage conditions which apply to the unbound materials, and the extent to which these conditions change seasonally. Where the surfacing is impermeable, and side drains are provided to keep the water table below sub-base level, the values of m_2 and m_3 in the base and sub-base respectively will be between 1.0 and 1.4. However, where the water table during the annual weather cycle rises to a level where the unbound materials saturate, the value may fall to about 0.4.

20.8   In the AASHTO method of flexible pavement design the PSI value of a new pavement is assumed to be 4.2 and that of a failed pavement 1.5. The term

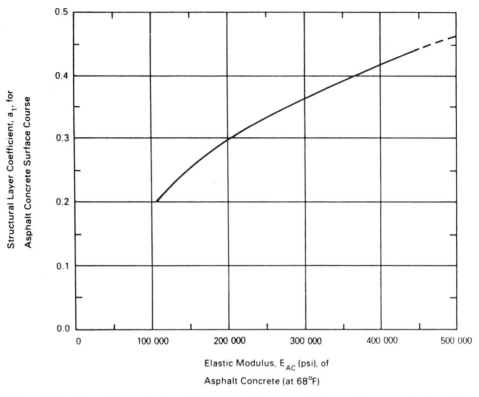

Figure 20.1   Chart for estimating the structural layer coefficient of dense-graded asphalt concrete based on the elastic (resilient) modulus

$\Delta PSI/(4.2 - 1.5)$ therefore represents the point in the life-span corresponding to W_{18} applications of a standard (18 000-lb or 8.2-t) axle.

20.9   The value used for the foundation modulus M_R needs careful consideration. In the USA frost penetration can be considerable, particularly in the northern states. As a consequence the foundation modulus is subject to a large increase above the average value during the winter, followed by a fall below the average value during the thaw. For this reason a procedure for obtaining an average value is described as part of the AASHTO design procedure. Where this effect is small, the average value of M_R can be obtained from the average CBR value of the subgrade in the manner discussed in Chapter 10.

Application of the AASHTO design procedure for flexible pavements to UK experimental roads
20.10   In Chapter 19 the performance of British full-scale pavement design experiments has been analysed in terms of the number of standard axles carried. The predicted performance of two sections of the Alconbury Hill experiment using the AASHTO design procedure is compared in Fig. 20.6 with the actual performance

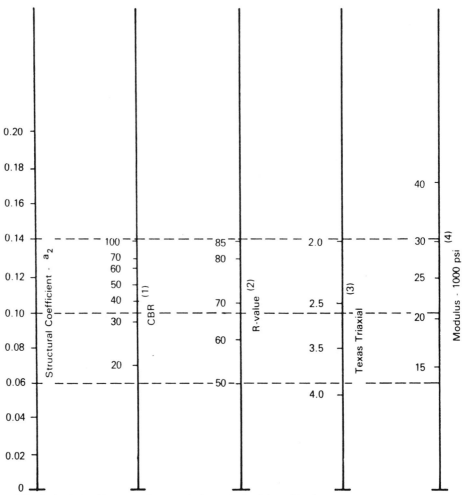

(1) Scale derived by averaging correlations obtained from Illinois.
(2) Scale derived by averaging correlations obtained from California, New Mexico and Wyoming.
(3) Scale derived by averaging correlations obtained from Texas.
(4) Scale derived on NCHRP project

Figure 20.2 Variation in the granular base layer coefficient, a_2, with various base strength parameters

determined in relation to rutting and cracking. The sections chosen for the analysis are 61 and 52 (see Fig. 18.5). The failure condition chosen is 20 mm of rutting accompanied by some cracking in the wheel paths. This equates to a PSI value of 2.0 using the data given in reference 4.

20.11   The constitution of the pavements in terms of materials and layer thickness are shown in the upper part of the figure. Below are the inputs to the AASHTO

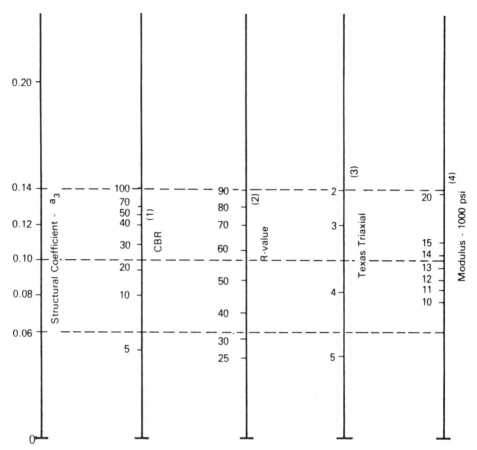

(1) Scale derived from correlations from Illinois.

(2) Scale derived from correlations obtained from The Asphalt Institute, California, New Mexico and Wyoming.

(3) Scale derived from correlations obtained from Texas.

(4) Scale derived on NCHRP project

Figure 20.3 Variation in the granular sub-base layer coefficient, a_3, with various sub-base strength parameters

equation, Eq. (20.1), together with the resulting estimated lives in standard axles. The observed lives are shown for comparison. In the case of section 52, the pavement has not failed to date and an estimated life of PSI 2.0 is given based on the rate of deformation and cracking.

20.12   The agreement between the calculated and observed lives for section 52 is good, bearing in mind that the observed life had to be extrapolated. The agreement is poor in the case of section 61. Clearly, differences in the failure conditions cannot

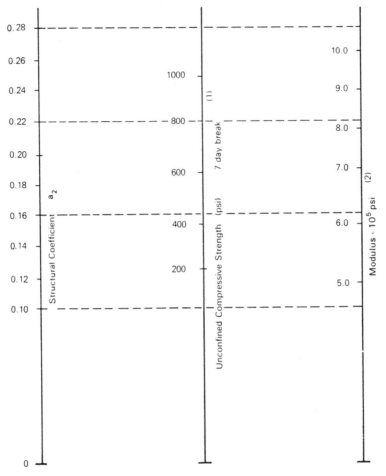

(1)   Scale derived by averaging correlations from Illinois. Louisiana and Texas.
(2)   Scale derived on NCHRP project

Figure 20.4   Variation in *a* for cement-treated bases with the base strength parameter

explain this since the middle term of Eq (20.1) is very close to zero for terminal PSI values of 2.5–1.5. The explanation must lie in the coefficient a_2 used for the unbound base material. The material actually used for the base was crushed and graded blastfurnace slag. This material has a mild cementing action. If as a result of this the value of a_2 rose from 0.14 to 0.2 then the predicted life would have risen close to the observed value of 2 million standard axles.

Concrete pavements
20.13   The AASHTO equation for the design of concrete pavements is as follows:

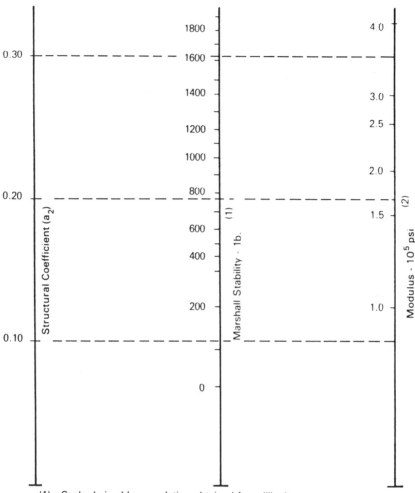

(1)   Scale derived by correlation obtained from Illinois.

(2)   Scale derived on NCHRP project

Figure 20.5   Variation in a_2 for bituminous-treated bases with the base strength parameter

$$\log W_{18} = Z_R S_0 + 7.35 \log(D+1) - 0.06 + \frac{\log \dfrac{\Delta PSI}{4.5 - 1.5}}{1 + \dfrac{1.624 \times 10^7}{(D+1)^{8.46}}}$$

$$+ (4.22 - 0.32 p_t) \log \frac{S_c' C_d (D^{0.75} - 1.132)}{215.63 \, J \left(D^{0.75} - \dfrac{18.42}{(E_c/k)^{0.25}} \right)} \tag{20.2}$$

where W_{18} = the predicted number of 18-kip equivalent single-axle load applications

Z_R = the standard normal deviate

S_0 = the combined standard error of the traffic prediction and performance prediction

D = the thickness (inches) of the pavement slab

ΔPSI = the difference between the initial design serviceability index, p_0, and the design terminal serviceability index, p_t

S_c' = the modulus of rupture (lbf/in^2) for Portland cement concrete used on a specific project

J = the load transfer coefficient used to adjust for load transfer characteristics of a specific design

C_d = the drainage coefficient

E_c = the modulus of elasticity (lbf/in^2) for Portland cement concrete

k = the modulus of subgrade reaction (lbf/in^3)

20.14 Equation (20.2) is clearly of the same form as Eq. (20.1) for flexible pavements. Again, the middle term will be close to zero for pavements approaching the terminal condition. The terms J and C_d are deduced from Tables 20.2 and 20.3, and the value of k is obtained from Fig. 20.7 and the elastic moduli of the sub-base and subgrade. The values of E_c and S_c must be obtained from tests carried out on the concrete being used.

Table 20.2 Recommended load transfer coefficient for various pavement types and design conditions

Shoulder	Asphalt		Tied PCC	
Load transfer devices	Yes	No	Yes	No
Pavement type				
Plain-jointed and jointed reinforced	3.2	3.8–4.4	2.5–3.4	3.6–4.2
CRCP	2.9–3.2	n.a.	2.3–2.9	n.a.

Table 20.3 Recommended values of drainage coefficient, C_d, for rigid pavement design

Quality of drainage	Percentage of time pavement structure is exposed to moisture levels approaching saturation			
	<1%	1–5%	6–25%	>25%
Excellent	1.25–1.20	1.20–1.15	1.15–1.10	1.10
Good	1.20–1.15	1.15–1.10	1.10–1.00	1.00
Fair	1.15–1.10	1.10–1.00	1.00–0.90	0.90
Poor	1.10–1.00	1.00–0.90	0.90–0.80	0.80
Very poor	1.00–0.90	0.90–0.80	0.80–0.70	0.70

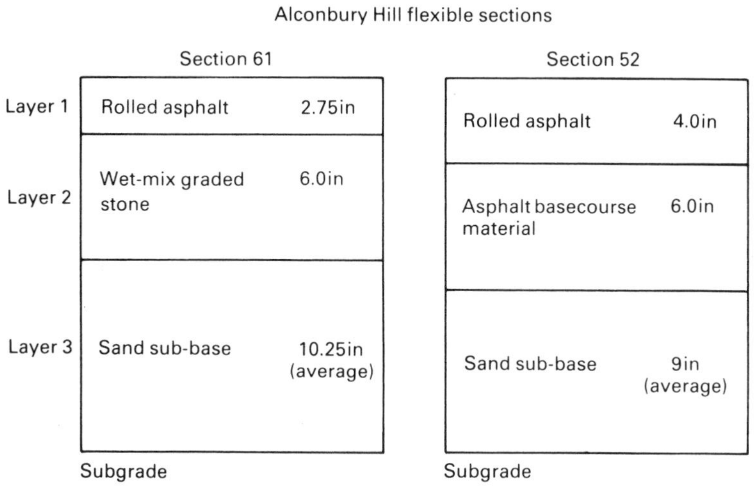

Alconbury Hill flexible sections

	Section 61		Section 52	
Layer 1	Rolled asphalt	2.75in	Rolled asphalt	4.0in
Layer 2	Wet-mix graded stone	6.0in	Asphalt basecourse material	6.0in
Layer 3	Sand sub-base	10.25in (average)	Sand sub-base	9in (average)
	Subgrade		Subgrade	

Layer 1

E	$4.6 \times 10^3\,\mathrm{N/mm^2}$ (20° C)	$4.6 \times 10^3\,\mathrm{N/mm^2}$ (20 °C)
	$(660 \times 10^3\,\mathrm{lb/in^2})$	$(660 \times 10^3\,\mathrm{lb/in^2})$
a_1 (Fig. 20.1)	0.55	0.55
$a_1 D_1$	1.51	2.20

Layer 2

E	$200\,\mathrm{N/mm^2}$	$2 \times 10^3\,\mathrm{N/mm^2}$ (20 °C)
	$(29\,000\,\mathrm{lb/in^2})$	$(290 \times 10^3\,\mathrm{lb/in^2})$
a_2	0.14 (Fig. 20.2)	0.35 (Fig. 20.1)
m_2	1.2	n/a
$a_2 D_2 m_2$	1.01	2.10

Layer 3
CBR 20 per cent

a_3 (Fig. 20.3)	0.095	0.095
m_3	0.8	0.8
$a_3 D_3 m_3$	0.78	0.70
SN	3.3	5.0

Applicable to both sections

Z_R (80% reliability—Table 20.1)		-0.841
S_0		0.45
$\triangle$PSI		2.2
Log $\triangle$PSI/2.7		-0.09
M_R	(35 N/mm^2)	$5.1 \times 10^3\,\mathrm{lb/in^2}$

Pavement life deduced using the AASHTO design method

log W_{18}	5.8	7.7
W_{18}	600 000	13 million

Observed life

W_{18}	2 million	10.5 million (estimated)

Figure 20.6 Comparison between the lives estimated using the AASHTO design procedure and the observed lives of flexible pavements

Application of the AASHTO design procedure for concrete pavements to
UK experimental roads

20.15   As for the flexible pavement design procedure, a comparison has been made between predicted and actual lives for concrete sections included in the Alconbury Hill experiment. The sections selected are both reinforced and of the same thickness of 175 mm (6.9 in). The difference is that one section (section 20) is made with concrete of strength 44 N/mm^2 at 28 days, and the other (section 5) has a 28-day compressive strength of 66 N/mm^2. The layout of the sections is shown in Fig. 18.27.

20.16   The values used for the material properties in Eq. (20.2) are shown in Fig. 20.8, expressed in imperial units. The figure also shows the pavement lives deduced using the AASHTO procedure compared with the observed lives (see Table 18.12). The observed lives are more than five times those indicated by the AASHTO procedure, although the ratio of the lives for the two sections is much the same for the predicted and actual lives. A probable explanation for this marked difference in performance is that at the AASHTO test site (which provided the evidence for the AASHTO design procedure) heave due to frost and subgrade volume changes may have been a more important factor than cracking in determining the serviceability index.

General

20.17   The AASHTO guide is a very comprehensive document and it has been possible here to produce only a very brief summary of its contents. In particular it includes nomographs which permit designs to be prepared quickly. Engineers proposing to use the method are strongly advised to consult the full document. In the United Kingdom copies of this and the other US publications referred to in this and other chapters can be obtained through Technical Standards Services Ltd, at Hitchin, Hertfordshire.

The Asphalt Institute design procedure for flexible pavements

20.18   The Asphalt Institute Manual[2] relates the thickness and constitution of flexible pavements to the traffic to be carried during the design life, expressed as cumulative standard axles. The end of the design life is defined as the onset of the period when an overlay is required to seal the surface and restore the riding quality.

20.19   The traffic considered includes all commercial vehicles with the exception of all small vans and panel trucks. For use when the detailed constitution of the traffic is unknown, a table is provided giving the percentages of two-, three-, four-, and five-axle trucks likely to be found on different classes of highway in the United States. Information is also given concerning the distribution of commercial vehicles between the different lanes on single and dual carriageways. A growth rate table is provided to give cumulative totals of traffic for periods up to 35 years, for growth rates of 0–10 per cent per annum. The procedure for calculating cumulative standard axles is therefore very similar to that adopted in the UK Road Note 29.[5] The main

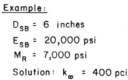

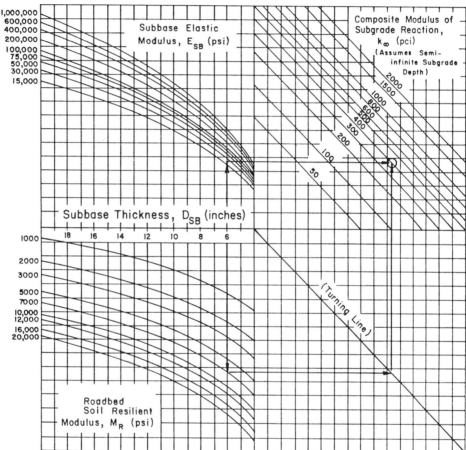

Figure 20.7 Chart for estimating the composite modulus of subgrade reaction, k_∞, assuming a semi-infinite subgrade depth. (For practical purposes, a semi-infinite depth is considered to be greater than 10 feet below the surface of the subgrade)

difference is that in Britain tandem axles are treated as two separate axles, each carrying half the total load on the tandem unit. The Asphalt Institute uses the equivalence values developed by Liddle from the AASHTO road test data,[6] which rate dual axles as being rather less damaging.

20.20   The thickness design charts included in the document are based on three- and four-layer elastic analyses. The three-layer solutions are for what is termed full-depth asphalt construction and the four-layer solution for the case where emulsified asphalt is used beneath the asphaltic concrete wearing course. Three types of emulsified asphalt mix are specified as follows:

Type I   made with processed graded crushed aggregate;
Type II   made with clean crusher-run or pit-run materials;
Type III made with as-dug sands or silty sands.

20.21   A total of 10 design charts are provided, which relate subgrade resilient modulus M_r with the cumulative number of standard axles to be carried during the design period. These design charts are for full-depth asphaltic concrete, for the three types of emulsified asphalt, and for six thicknesses of untreated aggregate base–sub-base layer. Where emulsified asphalt is used, the design includes a minimum thickness of asphaltic concrete wearing course of 50–130 mm depending on the design traffic.

20.22   There are several aspects of this design procedure likely to confuse British and European engineers. The term 'Full-depth asphaltic concrete' would generally be interpreted in Europe as a pavement of hot-mixed bituminous material laid directly on the subgrade. The design charts cater for soil resilient modulus values down to 20 MPa or CBR value 1.9 per cent. Under UK climatic conditions bituminous laying plant could not operate on such a foundation and material would have to be spread by hand, with little chance of adequate compaction. The Manual does state the following:

> Improved subgrade is normally not required in the design and construction of a full-depth asphalt pavement structure. It should be considered only when a subgrade that will not support construction equipment is encountered. In such cases it is used as a working platform for the construction of the pavement courses and does not affect the design thickness of the pavement structure.

This may be the case in the USA but British experience is that a foundation of CBR not less than 20 per cent is necessary to permit satisfactory performance of bituminous pavers and their supply trucks. For this reason a granular sub-base of at least 200 mm thickness is used and this material is normally tipped and spread by grader.

20.23   Emulsified asphalt could presumably be laid by hand in a similar manner or processed in place, but this would be regarded as impractical in the wet climate of Britain and much of Europe, and engineers would prefer to lay any bituminous material on a properly designed sub-base.

20.24   Table 20.4 compares the different forms of construction discussed in the Manual when applied to a pavement designed to carry 10 msa. The CBR of the subgrade is assumed to be 5 per cent. For comparison, the AASHTO and UK designs for the same traffic and soil conditions are included. The terminal PSI condition assumed for the AASHTO design is 2.0. The implication for the Asphalt Institute design is that beneath an asphaltic concrete wearing course the emulsified asphalt material performs, as a base, nearly as well as normal asphaltic concrete

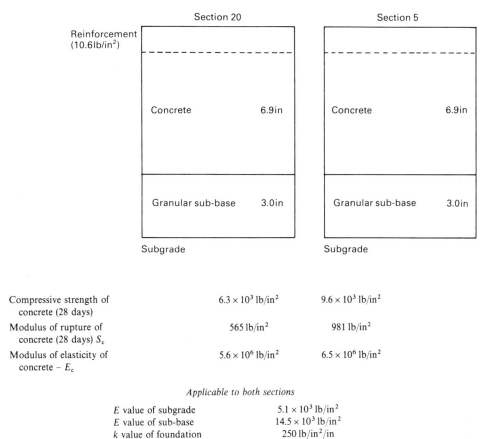

Alconbury Hill concrete sections

	Section 20	Section 5

Reinforcement (10.6 lb/in²)

Concrete	6.9 in	Concrete	6.9 in
Granular sub-base	3.0 in	Granular sub-base	3.0 in

Subgrade   Subgrade

Compressive strength of concrete (28 days)	6.3×10^3 lb/in²	9.6×10^3 lb/in²
Modulus of rupture of concrete (28 days) S_c	565 lb/in²	981 lb/in²
Modulus of elasticity of concrete – E_c	5.6×10^6 lb/in²	6.5×10^6 lb/in²

Applicable to both sections

E value of subgrade	5.1×10^3 lb/in²
E value of sub-base	14.5×10^3 lb/in²
k value of foundation (from Fig. 20.7)	250 lb/in²/in
C_d (from Table 20.3)	0.95
J (from Table 20.2)	3.2
Z_R	-0.841
S_0	0.45
$\triangle$PSI	2.5
s	4.5

Pavement life deduced using the AASHTO design method

$\log_{10} W_{18}$	6.322	6.65
W_{18}	2 million	5 million

Observed life

W_{18}	10 million	27 million

Figure 20.8 Comparison between the lives estimated using the AASHTO design procedure and the observed lives of flexible pavements

basecourse (or binder course) material. This is in line with the UK research finding that lean bituminous bases perform as well as rich ones under a rolled asphalt surfacing. The table also shows that the provision of a 100-mm crushed aggregate base/sub-base layer allows the thickness of the Type II emulsified asphalt upper base to be reduced by about 80 mm, but further increases in the thickness of the crushed aggregate permit much smaller reductions in the thickness of the Type II material.

20.25   Comparison with the AASHTO and UK designs for the same traffic and foundation conditions indicates that the UK thickness requirements for the base thickness is about 10 per cent less than the Asphalt Institute design and AASHTO thickness is about 17 per cent greater.

Thickness Design for Concrete Highway and Street Pavements[3]

20.26   This document has been produced on behalf of the Portland Cement Association (PCA) in the United States. It follows the general approach adopted in Chapter 22 of considering the response of the pavement to the highest axle loads in the traffic spectrum. This is in contrast to the AASHTO procedure of using equivalent standard axle loads, which can be misleading when the traffic spectrum includes abnormally heavy axle loads. Therefore it would be expected that the PCA would be more reliable for situations where heavy handling equipment, such as front and side-lift trucks, is to be used, e.g., dock terminal areas.

20.27   However, the document attempts to cover a very wide variety of design aspects such as erosion, load transfer, and shoulder design, by a series of nomographs and tables, the background to which is far from clearly stated. The reader has to take a great deal on trust, sometimes without adequate definition of the terms used. This makes it difficult to comment upon it in detail.

20.28   With regard to traffic, the document differentiates between single, tandem, and tridem axles. This is a complication unlikely to be of much importance in thickness design. It is probably an intake from the AASHO road test. In practice, dynamic weighbridges do not differentiate accurately between single and multiple axles, and this is not generally a factor covered by visual traffic surveys. From limited observations one can attempt to provide 'average' contents of multiple axles in the commercial traffic flow, but the accuracy is likely to be low in the present situation where the use of multiple axles is changing in response to legislation on maximum vehicle weights. This is the current situation in Europe. In practice, little error is introduced into design thickness calculations if multiple axles are treated as two or three single axles carrying one-half or one-third of the total axle assembly load.

References

1. American Association of State Highway and Transportation Officials: *Guide for Design of Pavement Structures*, ASSHTO, Washington, D.C., 1986.
2. *Thickness Design—Asphalt Pavements for Highways and Streets*, Asphalt Institute Manual Series No. 1 (MS-1), Asphalt Institute, College Park, Maryland, 1984.

Table 20.4 Comparison of flexible pavement designs based on the Asphalt Institute, the AASHTO and the UK design procedures, assuming a design traffic 10 million standard axles and a CBR of subgrade 5 per cent

Thickness, mm

| | Asphalt Institute designs | | | | | | AASHTO design | UK design |
| | Full-depth asphaltic concrete (Design Chart VI-1) | Emulsified asphalt base | | Pavements with untreated aggregate base of thickness, mm | | | | |
		Type I	Type II	100	200	300		
Surfacing	50	50	100	100	100	100	100	100*
Bituminous base and/or basecourse	308	310	316	235†	215†	205†	246‡	182
Untreated aggregate base/sub-base	0	0	0	100	200	300	250	250

*Rolled asphalt.
†Emulsified asphalt Type II.
‡Asphalt-treated base.

3. *Thickness Design for Concrete Highway and Street Pavements*, The Portland Cement Association, Skokie, Illinois, 1984.
4. Highway Research Board: *The AASHO Road Test, Report 5: Pavement Research*, Special Report 61E, National Academy of Sciences, National Research Council, Publication 945, Washington, D.C., 1962.
5. Road Research Laboratory: *A Guide to the Structural Design of Pavements for New Roads*, Department of the Environment, Road Note 29, 3rd Edn, HMSO, London, 1970.
6. Liddle, W. J.: Application of AASHO Road Test results to the design of flexible pavement structures, *Proc. Int. Conf. on the Structural Design of Asphalt Pavements, Ann Arbor, Michigan, 1962*, University of Michigan, Ann Arbor, pp. 42–51, 1962.

PART FIVE Analytical Design Procedures Based on Elastic Theory

21. The structural design of flexible pavements

Introduction

21.1   The methods of pavement design which have evolved world-wide since the Second World War have largely been derived empirically from the results of full-scale experiments and the detailed study of the performance of in-service roads. Since the 'forties there has also been a sustained interest in the development of more fundamental structural procedures which attempt to relate the stresses and strains caused by traffic loading in pavement materials with the performance of those materials under repetitive loading.

21.2   Despite concentrated efforts in such centres as the University of California, the TRRL and the University of Nottingham and by many similar organizations, no fully satisfactory, comprehensive alternative to the empirical approach has yet been found for the design of flexible pavements. As is discussed in Chapter 22, the position is rather different for concrete pavements, largely because concrete, although a complex material chemically, has physical properties which are easier to study and quantify than is the case with materials bound with bitumen and tar.

21.3   The limitations of the structural approach do not mean that it ceases to be a valuable tool in assessing pavement life. Full-scale experiments on a sufficiently large scale and carried out at sites embracing a range of traffic and subgrade conditions are costly and slow. The theoretical method, appropriately calibrated by comparison with the lives of experimental pavements, allows a much better understanding of the manner in which flexible pavements perform, and the role played by the different layer thicknesses. The full-scale approach is of necessity limited by the axle loading of road vehicles, and only by rather risky extrapolation can it be extended to the design of industrial pavements intended for very heavy wheel loads, which are becoming important in relation to port terminals and to other heavy industrial complexes. The same limitations of empirical methods also apply to the design of pavements under abnormal temperature conditions. A structural analysis should form part of any pavement failure investigation.

21.4   The structural method of design has two main objectives:

1. to produce deflection spectra for the axle loading distribution and in particular for the 6350-kg axle loading used in Deflection Beam and Deflectograph surveys;
2. to compute stresses and strains in the pavement materials under the full range of

axle loads and temperature conditions and hence, from fatigue and permanent deformation data, to determine the potential mode of failure and the potential life.

21.5   A modern highway pavement designed for a life of 20 years or more will, during its life, carry a cumulative total in excess of 50 million commercial axles. Using a maximum deformation of 25 mm to define failure (see Chapter 4), it follows that the average permanent deformation caused by each application of a loaded wheel is less than 10^{-6} mm. It follows that stresses, strains, and deflections under a loaded wheel can be estimated with sufficient accuracy by elastic theory.

21.6   The material parameters required for predicting:

1. the surface deflection,
2. the stresses and strains in each layer, and
3. the fatigue life and permanent deformation

are summarized in Chapters 10–14 for the soil foundation, unbound granular materials, cement-bound sub-bases, and bases and bituminous bases and surfacings.

21.7   As bituminous materials are the most expensive element of a flexible pavement, much research effort has been concentrated on them. There is no doubt that as part of the failure process bituminous surfacings crack. The origin of this cracking is not clear. It is generally assumed that it originates at the underside of the bituminous material as a consequence of fatigue and fairly quickly spreads upwards to the surface. In a brittle material like concrete this is clearly a likely mechanism, but with a viscoelastic material like a bituminous mixture compressive stress in the upper part of the material might be expected to delay or even heal cracks as they become apparent. There is evidence from many cores taken in bituminous materials by the TRRL that cracks in the surface material often extend only to a depth of 10–15 mm, suggesting that in some cases cracking originates from the surface and may be due to thermal changes. A recent reanalysis of deflection measurements, referred to in Chapter 29, has shown clearly that the stiffness of bituminous materials increases progressively over a period of at least 5 years. This information has been incorporated into the figures of Chapter 14 (Figs 14.23 and 14.24) which present effective moduli for use in structural analyses and as a result good predictions of early- and late-life deflections of flexible pavements can now be made. It would be expected that there would be similar effects on the fatigue relationships. Unfortunately, correspondingly detailed information on fatigue data is not currently available and this may be a source of inaccuracy in the prediction of pavement life.

21.8   As part of the deflection studies referred to in Chapter 29 it was found that there was a significant phase lag in the response of bituminous materials to diurnal temperature changes. The effect of this lag was such that the modulus of the bituminous material was most satisfactorily modelled by taking the mean 24-hour temperature of the bituminous material. It is thus adequate in almost all cases to use the monthly average air temperature to determine the percentage of axle loads in each 10-°C temperature interval and to consider the deformation and fatigue properties for each of these intervals.

21.9   Chapter 8 presents typical axle load spectra. In most cases, when a prediction is required of pavement life, stresses and strains must be predicted for each of the axle loading bands (bands are usually taken in 2-tonne intervals, as shown in Fig. 8.13). Chapter 8 also gives details of typical axle configurations and details of tyre pressures and contact areas.

Principles of structural analysis of pavements

21.10   It appears that Lord Kelvin in 1848 was the first to calculate the displacements which occur when a force is applied to an elastic half-space, i.e., to the surface of a homogeneous material infinite in area and depth.[1] In 1868 the French mathematician and engineer Boussinesq gave his attention to the same subject and developed expressions for the stresses and displacements under a point load.[2] The stresses which arise when an area is loaded are readily obtained by elastic summation. In 1943 Burmister extended the analysis to two layers infinite in the horizontal direction. As early as 1945 Burmister had extended his theoretical treatment to three layers[3] and six years later Acum and Fox[4] published the first axial solutions for this more complicated case. Westergaard in 1926 took a different approach, more applicable to concrete pavements, in which the pavement was modelled as a slab supported on springs representing the soil.[5] All these methods were useful in demonstrating to the engineer the method of behaviour of the pavement and the relative importance of the various layers. They were not sufficiently detailed or flexible to be developed into an accurate design method. This was changed by the advent of the computer and the development of the finite element method pioneered by Clough[6] and Zienkiewicz[7] in the middle sixties.

The finite element method

21.11   The versatility of the method allows the modelling of any number of layers which may have variations in structural properties with area and depth subjected to complex non-uniform loading patterns.

21.12   The principle of the method is that the region of interest, i.e., the pavement and subgrade is discretized or divided into a number of elements. At the top centre of the region of interest is a single loaded wheel. The elements extend horizontally and vertically from the wheel to include all the area within the influence of the wheel. The analysis of a pavement is almost invariably axisymmetric and the loading is assumed to be applied by a single wheel. The elements are annular in shape and need only be described in two dimensions on one side of the axis of symmetry. The interrelationship between multiple wheels and axles is readily considered by summation. The elements interconnect at nodes. The early element types were triangular in section with three nodes. These could model only a constant stress within the element and hence large numbers of elements were required to give accurate modelling. Increasingly more sophisticated element types have been introduced. A particularly stable and successful element is the eight-noded isoparametric element with reduced integration rule. The section through the pavement is divided into quadrilaterals (the majority of which are rectangles). Most pavement problems are satisfactorily modelled by 150–200 of these eight-noded elements. For a typical wheel loading it is adequate to extend the mesh to a radius of the order of 3.5 m and to a depth of 2.5 m. The boundaries of the mesh are vertical and horizontal and are assumed to be supported by rollers. The wheel loading is applied as a pressure acting on a circular area of the upper surface.

21.13   The output from the finite-element program consists of the following:

1. displacements at each node;
2. strain tensor and principal strains and directions at a number of points within each element;
3. stress tensor and principal stresses and directions at the same points as the strains.

21.14   From the geometry of a single element and its material properties a single matrix is readily developed which relates the load on each node of the element to the displacement of all the nodes of the element. This stiffness matrix for each element can then be assembled into a global stiffness matrix which relates the load at each node in the problem area to the displacement of all the nodes. The displacement of each node subject to boundary conditions is known and can be input to the equations. The global matrix can then be inverted using conventional matrix algebra and the result is the calculated displacement of each node in the area of interest under the input loading. From the stiffness matrix of each separate element the strains and stresses within the element are directly calculated at any point.

21.15   The stiffness matrix of a single element is most easily generated by the mutiplication of two separate matrices. The first, the strain matrix, relates the strains in the element to the displacements of the nodes and the second the elasticity matrix which relates the stresses in the element to the strains. In its simplest, most widely used form, all the terms in this elasticity matrix are functions of the modulus of elasticity and the Poisson ratio. The method is sufficiently flexible for it to be straightforward to include more complex relationships if the actual data are available (rarely the case). It is also easy to consider thermal effects, creep, etc. The finite-element method is routinely used for the analysis of a large number of geotechnical problems. In the latter it is often necessary to model the non-linear behaviour of soils at large strains, including shear strength cutoff. To model this correctly the program is usually run incrementally, the load being applied in stages and the stress and strain output from one stage being the input to the next stage. Although programs which include these features are readily available, the practising pavement engineer will be adequately served by a robust linear elastic program using a stable element type.

21.16   Each element may be ascribed individual material properties. The different pavement layers and even variations of stiffness within a single layer are readily accommodated.

Deflection Beam and Deflectograph deflection measurement

21.17   Chapter 29 describes the two most common methods of pavement deflection measurement, i.e., the Deflection Beam and the Deflectograph. Figure 29.2 shows the principal dimensions of the Deflection Beam. The two-axle truck used for deflection measurements should have a rear-axle load of 6350 kg (14 000 lb) equally divided between the twin-wheel assemblies at each end of the axle. The recommended tyre size is 7.50 × 20 or 8.25 × 20. The inflation pressure should be 590 kPa. The arrangement can be satisfactorily modelled by assuming a loaded radius of 92.5 mm for each wheel and a separation of 285 mm between the centres of the twin-wheels. The appropriate spacing for the Deflectograph is 335 mm.

21.18   In the USA the dimensions of the Benkelman Beam are similar to those used in the UK but the axle load is 8200 kg (18 000 lb). The tyres are dual 279 × 572 mm 12-ply, inflated to 483 kPa (AASHTO Designation T256-77 (1986)).

21.19   The program output tables and plots show the deflection dishes appropriate to both these wheel spacings when the dual wheel loading is carrying 3175 kg. The maximum deflection indicated by the dish is not in fact measured either by the Deflection Beam or the Deflectograph because in both cases the beam supports are influenced to some extent by the deflection dish being measured. This is particularly the case with the Deflectograph because of the relatively short beams. An advantage of using a finite element method is that the beam support movements and the influence of all the wheels can be relatively easily modelled to provide corrections to the observed deflections.

21.20   If we refer to Figure 29.1, the deflection at the centre of the dish is first calculated by doubling the deflection predicted due to a single wheel with loading 1588 kg at a distance of 142 mm from the centre of the wheel. This represents the absolute maximum deflection as the shoe passes between the twin wheels. When the shoe is in this position, which is 2.74 m from the twin feet, the latter experience a smaller deflection, S. When the wheels are in the initial position the wheel is 1.30 m from the shoe and 1.44 m from the twin feet; the shoe then has an initial deflection, D. Lister[8] determined that the reading of the dial gauge would be smaller than the maximum absolute deflection by an amount d_2, where

$$d_2 = 1.4S - 0.5D$$

21.21   Similar explicit calculations of support movement can be made for the Deflectograph but it is still normal practice to express measured Deflectograph deflections as equivalent Deflection Beam deflections using a correlation figure such as that shown in Chapter 29 (Fig. 29.22). AASHTO Designation T256-77 (1986) has similar curves to convert Dynaflect and Road Rater deflections.

The application of the finite-element method to flexible pavement design

21.22   The use of the finite element approach in the solution of pavement design problems is best illustrated by the analysis of some existing pavements which have been in service for some time and which have known construction and for which the constitution and intensity of the traffic is available. For this purpose three types of pavement construction which have been incorporated into a number of experimental sections from the TRRL's programme of full-scale experiments have been considered. These include lean concrete, rolled asphalt, and wet-mix road bases. The sections considered have been taken from the following experiments:

Conington Lodge on trunk road A1;
Alconbury Bypass on trunk road A1;
Wheatley Bypass on trunk road A40;
Nately Scures on trunk road A30.

These full-scale experiments have been described in detail in Chapter 18.

21.23   The axle load distribution of the commercial vehicles using Alconbury Bypass, Wheatley Bypass, and Nately Scures (prior to 1972) is sufficiently similar to be represented by the axle load spectrum shown in Table 21.1. The damaging effect of this traffic over the past 20 years has corresponded to approximately 30 standard axles per 100 commercial axles. The axle load distribution at the Conington Lodge experiment is more damaging. The axle load spectrum is also included in Table 21.1. At this site the damaging effect per 100 commercial axles is approximately 60 standard axles.

21.24   The average numbers of commercial axles per year using the left-hand lanes at the four sites, based on a period of 10–15 years are as follows:

Conington	2.14 million
Alconbury Bypass	1.4 million
Wheatley Bypass	1.2 million
Nately Scures	1.6 million (1964–72)

Table 21.1   Axle load spectra at experiment road sites

Axle load, t	Conington Lodge, %	Alconbury Bypass, Wheatley Bypass, and Nately Scures
0–2	9	22
2–4	25	45
4–6	35	18
6–8	16	8
8–10	8	5
10–12	5	2
12–14	2	0.42
14–16	0.42	0.07
16–18	0.07	0.042

Table 21.2 Asphalt temperature distribution

Temperature band, °C	Percentage of year
0–5	25
5–10	16
10–15	17
15–20	17
20–25	25

21.25   Table 21.2 shows the percentage of the year for which the mean 24-hour temperature of asphalt surfacings falls between temperature bands covering the range 0–25 °C (see Tables 9.4–9.7).

The structural design of pavements with bituminous roadbases

21.26   The experiments referred to in Para. 21.22 above include a number of sections with 100-mm asphalt surfacings on 150-mm dense bitumen macadam and rolled asphalt roadbases. The sections are laid on 150-mm granular sub-bases and the subgrade CBR is close to 5 per cent. It is proposed here to follow through in detail the structural design process for a section with a rolled-asphalt roadbase 150 mm thick using the axle load distribution appropriate to Conington. The conclusions from similar analyses of pavements with lean concrete and wet-mix bases will also be based mainly on that axle load distribution.

21.27   The computer program is first used to analyse the maximum tensile strains induced in the asphalt for a wide range of temperature and axle load conditions. Because of the stiffening of the asphalt with time, it is necessary to differentiate between early-life and late-life strains. The elastic moduli used to cater for temperature and ageing are shown in Table 21.3. These are derived from Fig. 14.23.

21.28   Figures 21.1 and 21.2 show the maximum tensile strain–axle load–temperature relations for the 100-mm asphalt surfacing on 150-mm asphalt road base for the early- and late-life conditions. From the traffic and temperature data given in Paras 21.22–21.24, Table 21.4 has been constructed to show the annual numbers of axles corresponding to six axle-load and five temperature categories at the Conington Lodge site.

21.29   Using Figs 21.1 and 21.2 and Table 21.4, Table 21.5 has been prepared to show the maximum tensile strain developed in the asphalt for each load band and each temperature band. Both the early- and late-life conditions are considered. Using the fatigue data for rolled asphalt given in Fig. 14.29, each strain value in Table 21.5 is related to the number of applications of that strain to cause fatigue failure. The proportion of the fatigue life absorbed during the year by that strain level is recorded. These proportions are summed for the early and late life years. The table shows that during the early life period 0.15 of the fatigue life will be absorbed in one year. At the lower rate applicable to the late-life years, 0.016 of the fatigue life will be absorbed per year.

Table 21.3   Asphalt modulus values used in analyses

Temperature band, °C	Vehicle speed	Asphalt age	Modulus, GPa
0–5	Normal traffic	Early life	10
		Late life	12
5–10	Normal traffic	Early life	6.5
		Late life	10
10–15	Normal traffic	Early life	5.5
		Late life	8
15–20	Normal traffic	Early life	2.2
		Late life	6.5
20–25	Normal traffic	Early life	1.8
		Late life	5
10	Deflection beam	Early life	4.5
		Late life	6
20	Deflection beam	Early life	1.8
		Late life	3.5
30	Deflection beam	Early life	0.45
		Late life	1.4

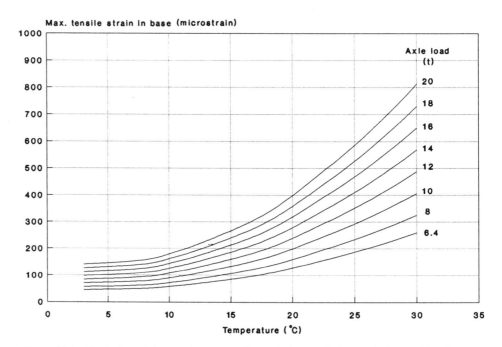

Figure 21.1   Variation of the maximum tensile strain in a rolled asphalt base with axle load and temperature: 250-mm rolled asphalt, early life

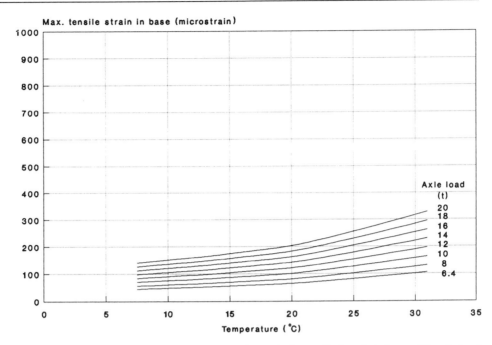

Figure 21.2 Variation of the maximum tensile strain in a rolled asphalt base with axle load and temperature: 250-mm rolled asphalt, late life

Table 21.4   Numbers of axle loads per year in various axle load and temperature ranges—Conington Lodge

	Number of axle loads per year in temperature bands, °C				
Axle load category, t	0–5	5–10	10–15	15–20	20–25
6–8	86 000	55 000	58 000	58 000	86 000
8–10	43 000	27 000	29 000	29 000	43 000
10–12	27 000	17 000	18 000	18 000	27 000
12–14	11 000	6 700	7 200	7 200	11 000
14–16	2 200	1 400	1 500	1 500	2 200
16–18	380	240	255	255	380

21.30   The early life was assumed applicable to the first year and the late life condition after 10 years. On this assumption a curve was constructed relating the fraction of the fatigue life absorbed each year. Using this curve, Table 21.6 sets out the predicted fraction of life for each year. In the first 10 years 59 per cent of the life is absorbed and the total life predicted is 35 years.

21.31   To date the relevant sections at the Conington Lodge experiment have had a life of 18–19 years and they are still in good condition. The life of the four sections,

Table 21.5 Strain levels and fatigue life in relation to axle loading and temperature in the Conington experiment

Temperature, °C	Early life			Late life		
	Strain, microstrain	Fatigue life, millions of applications	Fraction of fatigue life	Strain, microstrain	Fatigue life, millions of applications	Fraction of fatigue life
6–8-t axle						
0–5	40	200	0.0004	40	200	0.0004
5–10	60	70	0.0008	50	140	0.0004
10–15	70	60	0.0009	60	100	0.0006
15–20	100	30	0.002	70	110	0.0005
20–25	180	4	0.02	80	110	0.0008
8–10-t axle			Total 0.0241			Total 0.0027
0–5	50	70	0.0006	50	70	0.0005
5–10	65	50	0.0006	65	50	0.0005
10–15	90	22	0.0013	75	56	0.0005
15–20	160	4.5	0.0065	80	70	0.0004
20–25	230	1.5	0.0285	100	50	0.0009
10–12-t axle			Total 0.0375			Total 0.0028
0–5	65	25	0.0011	65	25	0.001
5-10	75	27	0.0007	75	27	0.0006
10–15	130	4.5	0.0004	90	20	0.0009
15–20	180	2.7	0.0067	110	14	0.001
20–25	270	0.9	0.0297	130	20	0.001
12–14-t axle			Total 0.0386			Total 0.0045
0–5	90	8	0.0013	90	8	0.001
5–10	100	8	0.0009	100	8	0.0008
10–15	155	2.5	0.0029	110	8	0.0009
15–20	225	1.1	0.0066	120	10	0.0007
20–25	310	0.5	0.021	150	10	0.001
14–16-t axle			Total 0.0327			Total 0.0044
0–5	98	5	0.0004	98	5	0.0004
5–10	106	5	0.0003	106	6.5	0.0002
10–15	170	1.5	0.001	125	6	0.0002
15–20	260	0.6	0.0025	155	5.5	0.0003
20–25	360	0.3	0.0075	170	5	0.0004
16–18-t axle			Total 0.0117			Total 0.0015
0–5	115	3	0.0001	102	4.5	0.0000
5–10	134	2	0.0001	123	2.5	0.0001
10–15	190	2.2	0.0001	137	4	0.0000
15–20	276	0.3	0.0009	161	4	0.0001
20–25	415	0.15	0.0025	193	4	0.0003
			Total 0.0037			Total 0.0005
Totals for all axles			0.1483			0.0164

Table 21.6 Sections with 150-mm rolled asphalt base—fraction of life absorbed each year—Conington Lodge

Year	Fraction of life absorbed
1	0.15
2	0.10
3	0.075
4	0.06
5	0.05
6	0.04
7	0.035
8	0.03
9	0.025
10	0.020
11	0.016

15, 18, 21, and 24, estimated from the present deformation, ranges from 25 to 200 msa with a mean of 80 msa (see Table 18.6). The mean number of equivalent standard axles per commercial vehicle for the site over the years 1971–85 for this experiment is 1.80. Therefore the estimated experiment life would be about 44 years, and there is reasonable agreement with the structural analysis.

21.32   Two important conclusions can be drawn from Table 21.5, as follows:

1. With a bituminous roadbase, the axles carrying less than 6 t contribute little to the structural damage of the pavement.
2. The amount and damaging effect of the traffic in the early life of such a pavement has a major influence on the life. If a pavement with a bituminous road base survives the first 5 years without serious damage then it is likely to have a long life.

21.33   The only other experimental section directly comparable with those at Conington Lodge, considered above, is section 44 at Alconbury Bypass. This is still in excellent condition after carrying traffic for 22 years. However, the traffic at this site is rather less damaging than that at Conington, although both experiments are on trunk road A1. Rather thicker bases at Nately Scures had an estimated life of more than 20 years, prior to the opening of the M3 motorway (see Table 18.5).

21.34   The computer program was also used to predict the late-life deflection measured by the Deflection Beam for a pavement consisting of 250 mm of rolled asphalt on a 150-mm granular sub-base, using the modulus values used in the structural analysis referred to above. The predicted deflection–temperature relationship is shown in Figs 21.3 and 21.4 (for early- and late-life conditions) compared with the measured relationships on a number of relevant experimental pavements. There is some scatter due partly to the different conditions of the pavements and the different amounts of traffic they have carried. There were also differences in the

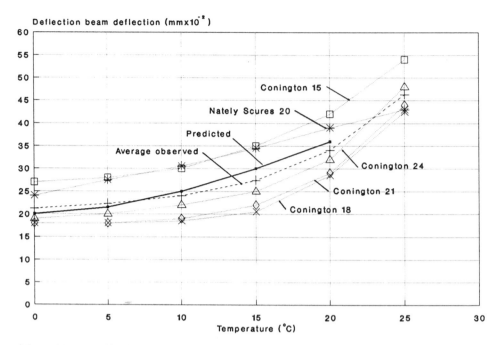

Figure 21.3 Predicted and observed deflections for sections with 250-mm total rolled asphalt on a 150-mm granular sub-base: early life

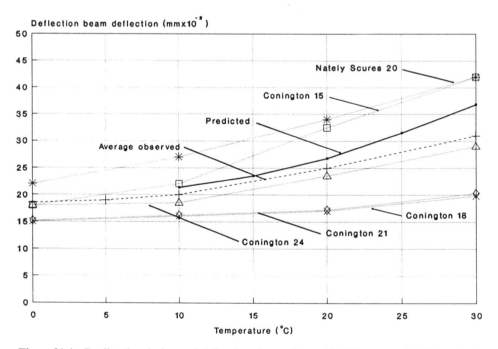

Figure 21.4 Predicted and observed deflections for sections with 250-mm total rolled asphalt on a 150-mm granular sub-base: late life

composition of the asphalts. However, the mean curve is very similar to the computed relationship. A comparison of Fig. 21.3 with Fig. 21.4 shows the substantial differences between early- and late-life deflections.

21.35 A similar exercise was carried out for sections with a 150-mm dense bitumen macadam (DBM) base under 100-mm rolled asphalt surfacing. In this case, during the early life period 0.30 of the fatigue life will be absorbed in one year. At the lower rate applicable to the late-life years 0.033 of the fatigue life will be absorbed per year. The predicted life for these sections is 10 years. The relevant sections at Conington Lodge with this construction have an estimated life from the currently observed permanent deformation of between 11 and 100 msa with a mean of 47 msa. The implication is that the fatigue curves for DBM shown in Fig. 14.29 are probably overconservative.

The structural design of pavements with wet-mix roadbases

21.36 An asphalt surfacing laid on a wet-mix or unbound stone roadbase is generally assumed to fail as a result of fatigue cracking in the surfacing. It should be possible, if this assumption is correct, to regard the construction as a thin asphalt pavement laid on an unbound material of properties superior to those of a normal sub-base. Therefore, it should be feasible to analyse such a pavement in exactly the same way as is followed in the previous section of this chapter, dealing with flexible pavements with an asphalt roadbase.

21.37 As an example of the procedure the analyses below refer to a 100-mm asphalt surfacing laid on a wet-mix base 230 mm thick over a granular sub-base 150 mm thick. Such analyses will model three sections included in the Conington Lodge experiment, sections 3, 6, and 9 (see Chapter 18). Because it is known that the subgrade under these sections was strengthened at the time of construction by rolling in granular material, two values of modulus have been assumed for the subgrade. These are 45 and 60 MPa. A value of modulus of 150 MPa was assumed for the wet-mix material, but as in the case of the sub-base under the thick asphalt pavement this value was adjusted by the computer program to ensure that unacceptable tensile strains were not developed in the unbound materials.

21.38 The early- and late-life strain-temperature-axle load relations are shown in Figs 21.5–21.8. The conclusions from these analyses are shown in Tables 21.7 and 21.8. The implication is that over the weaker subgrade the traffic at Conington Lodge should have caused failure, using the early-life condition, in 2 to 3 months. For the stronger subgrade the life would have been approximately doubled. In fact, the performance was very different, as is shown in Table 21.9. Certain other sections included in the experiment using the same thickness of surfacing and base did fail earlier by cracking, but these used other than asphalt basecourses. However, the life of no section was less than 10 years.

21.39 The conclusion must be that the structural approach cannot be applied in this relatively simple manner to pavements with unbound bases and thin surfacings. The reason may well be that a thin asphalt surfacing is capable of accommodating deformation by creep and that any tendency to crack at lower temperatures is controlled by the more viscous properties at higher temperatures.

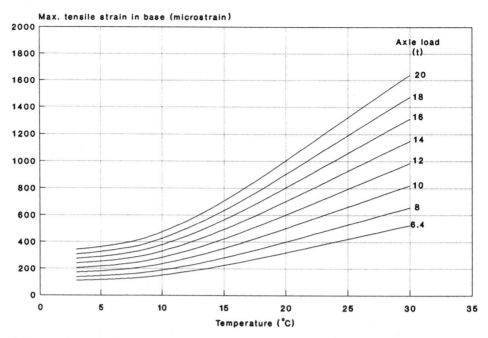

Figure 21.5 Maximum tensile strain in 100-mm rolled asphalt surfacing with 230-mm wet-mix base, 150-mm granular sub-base, subgrade modulus 45 MPa: early life

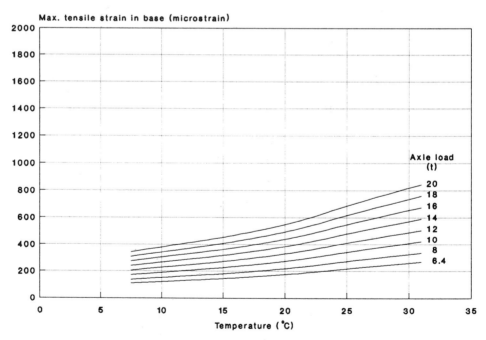

Figure 21.6 Maximum tensile stress in 100-mm rolled asphalt surfacing with 230-mm wet-mix base, 150-mm granular sub-base, subgrade modulus 45 MPa: late life

436

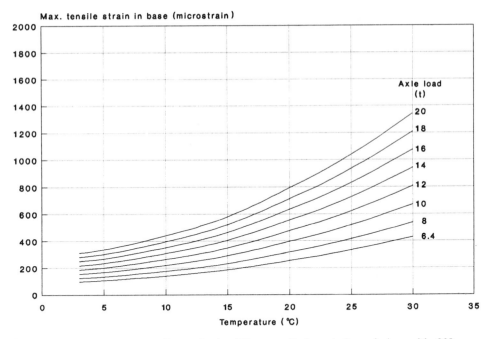

Figure 21.7 Maximum tensile strain in 100-mm rolled asphalt surfacing with 230-mm wet-mix base, 150-mm granular sub-base, subgrade modulus 60 MPa: early life

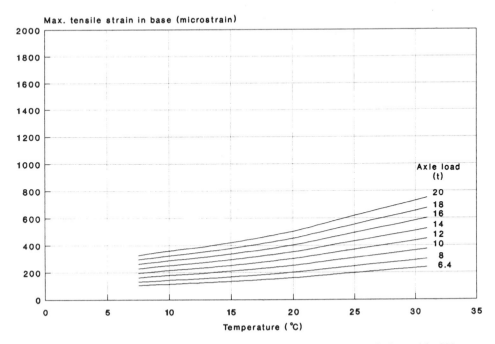

Figure 21.8 Maximum tensile strain in 100-mm rolled asphalt surfacing with 230-mm wet-mix base, 150-mm granular sub-base, subgrade modulus 60 MPa: late life

Table 21.7   Maximum strain levels in relation to axle loading, temperature, and fatigue life at Conington Lodge*

Temperature, °C	Early life			Late life		
	Calculated strain microstrain	Fatigue life	Fraction of fatigue life	Calculated strain, microstrain	Fatigue life	Fraction of fatigue life
6–8 tonne axle load						
0–5	110	2.5×10^6	0.03	100	4.6×10^6	0.02
5–10	160	9×10^5	0.06	110	6.5×10^6	0.008
10–15	220	5×10^5	0.12	150	3.3×10^6	0.02
15–20	320	2.5×10^5	0.12	180	2×10^6	0.03
20–25	410	1×10^5	0.86	220	1.6×10^6	0.05
18–10 tonne axle load						
0–5	140	1.3×10^6	0.03	130	1.8×10^6	0.02
5–10	200	5×10^5	0.05	150	1.5×10^6	0.02
10–15	290	2.2×10^5	0.13	170	1.3×10^6	0.02
15–20	390	1×10^5	0.29	230	1×10^6	0.03
20–25	510	8×10^4	0.54	270	8×10^5	0.05
10–12 tonne axle load						
0–5	150	8×10^5	0.03	160	8×10^5	0.03
5–10	240	2.5×10^5	0.07	190	6×10^5	0.03
10–15	350	1×10^5	0.18	240	5×10^5	0.04
15–20	460	6×10^4	0.30	270	5×10^5	0.04
20–25	650	3×10^4	0.90	350	4×10^5	0.07
12–14 tonne axle load						
0–5	200	3×10^5	0.04	190	2×10^5	0.06
5–10	270	2×10^5	0.03	240	4×10^5	0.02
10–15	400	6×10^4	0.12	270	2.6×10^5	0.03
15–20	560	3×10^4	0.24	330	2×10^5	0.04
20–25	750	1.4×10^4	0.78	380	2×10^5	0.06
14–16 tonne axle load						
0–5	230	1.4×10^5	0.02	200	2×10^5	0.01
5–10	330	8×10^4	0.02	250	2×10^5	0.007
10–15	450	2.5×10^4	0.06	330	1.8×10^5	0.008
15–20	650	1.6×10^4	0.09	370	1.6×10^5	0.009
20–25	870	1×10^4	0.22	460	8×10^4	0.03
Totals for all axle loads and temperatures		5.33				0.76

Subgrade modulus = 45 MPa

*Pavement structure: 100-mm asphalt surfacing, 230-mm wet-mix, 150-mm sub-base.

21.40   The computer program was again used to derive temperature–deflection relations for the two sub-base modulus cases considered in the structural analysis of the sections with wet-mix bases. The predicted curves for the subgrades of modulus 45 MPa and 60 MPa are compared with experimental curves for similar experimental sections in Fig. 21.9. The relationship for sections from the Conington experiment fall below the predicted and other experimental curves. This may reflect a rather

Table 21.8   Maximum strain levels in relation to axle loading, temperature and fatigue life at Conington Lodge*

Temperature, °C	Early life			Late life		
	Calculated strain, microstrain	Fatigue life	Fraction of fatigue life	Calculated strain, microstrain	Fatigue life	Fraction of fatigue life
6–8 tonne axle load						
0–5	100	4.5×10^6	0.02	100	4.5×10^6	0.02
5–10	140	1.8×10^6	0.03	120	2.6×10^6	0.02
10–15	190	1.2×10^6	0.05	130	6×10^6	0.01
15–20	260	5×10^5	0.1	160	4×10^6	0.01
20–25	340	3×10^5	0.3	200	2.4×10^6	0.04
8–10 tonne axle load						
0–5	110	2×10^6	0.02	130	1.8×10^6	0.02
5–10	170	1.2×10^6	0.02	150	1.7×10^6	0.02
10–15	240	3×10^5	0.01	180	1.2×10^6	0.02
15–20	340	2×10^5	0.15	200	1.7×10^6	0.02
20–25	420	1.4×10^5	0.31	260	1×10^6	0.04
10–12 tonne axle load						
0–5	160	4×10^5	0.07	150	7×10^5	0.04
5–10	210	2.5×10^5	0.07	180	8×10^5	0.02
10–15	300	2×10^5	0.09	210	5.5×10^5	0.03
15–20	400	1×10^5	0.20	260	4.8×10^5	0.04
20–25	520	5.5×10^4	0.50	300	8×10^5	0.03
12–14 tonne axle load						
0–5	200	3.2×10^5	0.03	180	4×10^5	0.03
5–10	250	2.2×10^5	0.03	220	3.6×10^5	0.02
10–15	330	1.4×10^5	0.05	260	3×10^5	0.02
15–20	460	6.5×10^4	0.17	300	3.5×10^5	0.02
20–25	620	3×10^4	0.40	360	3×10^5	0.04
14–16 tonne axle load						
0–5	240	1.4×10^5	0.02	200	3.2×10^5	0.006
5–10	310	8×10^4	0.02	250	2.1×10^5	0.007
10–15	410	5×10^4	0.03	300	2×10^5	0.008
15–20	550	4.5×10^4	0.03	350	6.5×10^5	0.002
20–25	700	1.8×10^4	0.12	430	6.5×10^4	0.03
Totals for all axle loads and temperatures		2.84				0.563

Subgrade modulus = 60-MPa

*Pavement structure: 100-mm asphalt surfacing, 230-mm wet-mix base, 150-mm sub-base.

stiffer foundation at the Conington site or it may be influenced by the wide variety of aggregates used in the basecourse of the surfacing at that site.

The structural design of flexible pavements with lean concrete bases

21.41   In a pavement with an asphalt surfacing and a lean concrete base, the design criterion is the maximum tensile stress developed by traffic in the underside of the

Table 21.9   Performance of sections 3, 6, and 9 in the Conington Lodge experiment

Section no.	Condition in mid-1975	Condition in 1984	Life, years
3	10-mm deformation in wheel-tracks. No cracking.	18-mm deformation. No cracking.	21
6	12-mm deformation. No cracking	20-mm deformation. No cracking.	19
9	12-mm deformation. No cracking	20-mm deformation. No cracking.	19

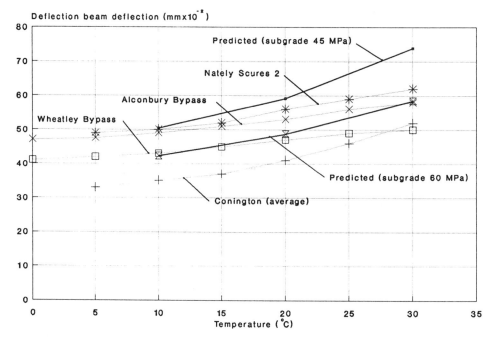

Figure 21.9   Predicted and observed deflection beam deflection for sections with 100 mm of rolled asphalt on 230 mm of wet-mix: late life

lean concrete. An asphalt surfacing reduces the stress in the lean concrete only marginally, and the influence of temperature fluctuations in the asphalt is small, and it is permissible therefore to carry out a structural analysis using a constant temperature of 20 °C in the asphalt. The cases selected here for analysis are those of a 100-mm asphalt surfacing on a 150- and a 200-mm thickness of lean concrete. A granular sub-base 150 mm thick is assumed. The structural properties adopted for the asphalt, the sub-base, and the subgrade are the same as those used in the previous analysis of pavements with asphalt bases. Three 28-day target compressive strengths are assumed for the lean concrete. These are shown in Table 21.10 and the associated moduli of rupture in Table 21.11. The computed stresses in the lean concrete are shown in Table 21.12.

Table 21.10 Structural properties assumed for the lean concrete

28-day compressive strength, MPa		Modulus of rupture, MPa	Elastic modulus, GPa
Target	Field		
7.5	6.4	1.26	18
10	8.5	1.50	23
14	11.9	1.91	27

Table 21.11 Relationship between field compressive strength of lean concrete and the modulus of rupture

Field compressive strength (28 days), MPa	Modulus of rupture, MPa			
	28 days	3 month	1 year	5 year
6.4	1.26	1.43	1.57	1.80
8.5	1.50	1.75	1.94	2.09
11.9	1.91	2.13	2.31	2.40

21.42 For the three strengths of lean concrete considered in Tables 21.10 and 21.11, Figs 21.10–21.12 show fatigue curves from which the probable lives of pavements with lean concrete bases can be evaluated.

21.43 The computed maximum tensile stresses induced in the lean concrete by axle loads between 6 and 18 tonnes are given in Table 21.12, together with the number of repetitions of each axle load which would be imposed by the axle load distribution and number of commercial axles at the Conington Lodge site. The numbers of axle loads are in periods of 3 months, 1 year, and 5 years. The table also gives the stress induced by a 'standard' 8.16-tonne axle.

21.44 Inspection of Table 21.12 in conjunction with Figs 21.10–21.12 shows that the 150-mm thickness of lean concrete would fail as a result of most of the axle bands considered. The 200-mm thickness at the highest of the three strengths would accept the 14–18-tonne axles without failure and would accept easily the other axle loads. The life of the 200-mm pavement would be controlled by the 16–18 tonne axle to about 25 years. In designing a pavement for the traffic at Conington Lodge it would therefore be prudent to use the highest strength lean concrete and to increase the thickness from 200 mm to about 230 mm. Fracturing of the lean concrete base under tensile stresses does not imply instantaneous failure. Heavily fractured lean concrete will behave as a rather inferior form of wet-mix and hence the life expectancy may still be substantial.

21.45 Figures 21.13 and 21.14 show measured deflections for a number of experimental sections with 150- and 230-mm lean concrete bases of different strengths. As would be expected, the deflections are small but the computed values model the measured values quite well. A comparison of observed and predicted deflection is useful in determining the state of the lean concrete base. At section 1,

Table 21.12   Computed maximum tensile stress in lean concrete roadbases of thickness 150 and 200-mm under 100-mm of rolled asphalt

Axle load range, t	Field compressive strength (28-day), MPa	Computed max. tensile stress (MPa)		No. of repetitions of axle load in		
		150 mm	200 mm	3 m	1 yr	5 yr
6–8	6.4	0.94	0.68	8.6×10^4	3.4×10^5	1.7×10^6
	8.5	0.95	0.73			
	11.9	0.99	0.77			
8–10	6.4	1.21	0.88	4.3×10^4	1.7×10^5	8.6×10^5
	8.5	1.27	0.93			
	11.9	1.32	0.99			
10–12	6.4	1.48	1.07	2.7×10^4	1.1×10^5	5.5×10^5
	8.5	1.55	1.25			
	11.9	1.62	1.21			
12–14	6.4	1.75	1.27	1.1×10^4	4.3×10^4	2.2×10^5
	8.5	1.83	1.35			
	11.9	1.91	1.43			
14–16	6.4	2.02	1.47	2.2×10^3	8.8×10^3	4.4×10^4
	8.5	2.11	1.56			
	11.9	2.21	1.65			
16–18	6.4	2.29	1.65	3.8×10^2	1.5×10^3	7.5×10^3
	8.5	2.39	1.77			
	11.9	2.50	1.87			
Standard 8.16-t axle	6.4	1.10	0.80			
	8.5	1.15	0.85			
	11.9	1.20	0.90			

Conington Lodge, with 230-mm base thickness, there is very close agreement between the predicted and observed deflection and there has been relatively little change of deflection with time. This would indicate that the base is still largely unfractured. Section 4, Nately Scures, with a 150-mm lean concrete base, had a deflection before it was overlaid more than double the predicted value, indicating that it was heavily fractured almost immediately after trafficking.

21.46   A 230-mm strong lean concrete base under a 100-mm asphalt surfacing laid at the Conington site in 1968 is still in excellent condition after 20 years and its present life expectancy is about 30 years under the present traffic. At Nately Scures a 150-mm lean concrete base laid under a 100-mm asphalt surfacing had, after 5 years' traffic (2.4 msa), extensive cracking and was overlaid. The section with a 200-mm base showed no sign of distress at the time of opening of the M3 motorway (which took most of the traffic off the experimental sections). This evidence gives considerable confidence in the use of the structural approach to the design of lean concrete bases.

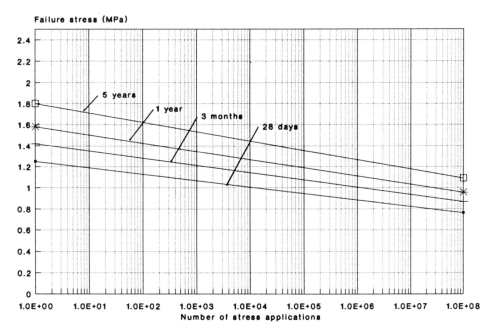

Figure 21.10 Fatigue relationship for cement-bound base materials with 7.5-MPa 28-day compressive strength

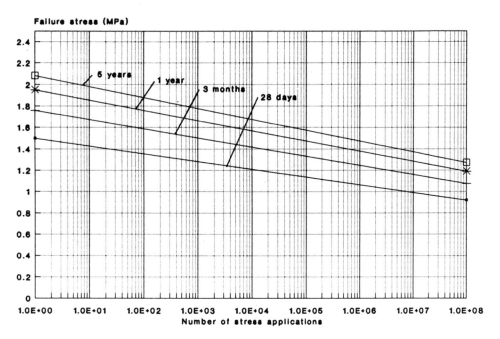

Figure 21.11 Fatigue relationship for cement-bound base materials with 10-MPa 28-day compressive strength

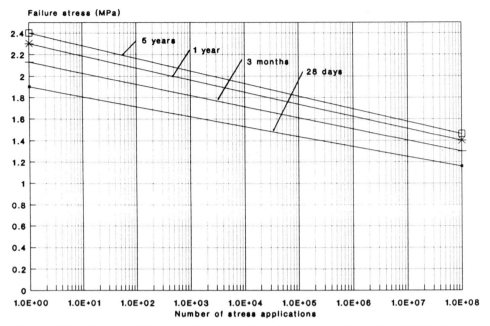

Figure 21.12 Fatigue relationship for cement-bound base materials with 14-MPa 28-day compressive strength

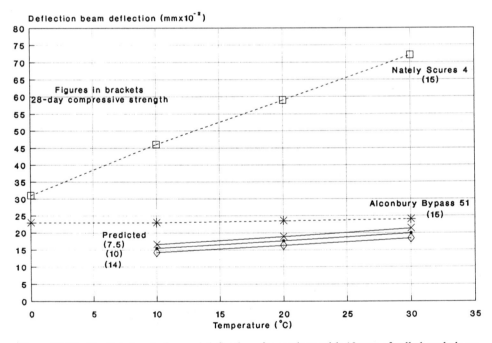

Figure 21.13 Predicted and observed deflections for sections with 10 mm of rolled asphalt on a 150-mm lean-concrete base

444

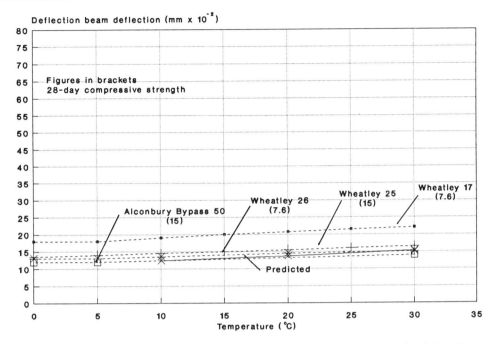

Figure 21.14 Predicted and observed deflections for sections with 100 mm of rolled asphalt on 200-mm lean-concrete base

21.47 The use of the structural approach in conjunction with the damaging effect of standard axles is sometimes proposed. This can give highly misleading conclusions. Table 21.12 shows that 150 mm of the weakest lean concrete used at Conington would be capable of sustaining 7×10^7 standard axles. At the Conington site the number of standard axles per year is about 1.28 million. This would suggest a life of more than 50 years for the thinnest and weakest lean concrete laid at the site.

References

1. Thomson, W.: Note on the integration of the equations of equilibrium of an elastic solid, *Cambridge and Dublin Mathematical Journal*, 1848.
2. Boussinesq, V. J.: *Application des potentiels a l'étude de l'équilibre et du mouvement des solides élastiques avec les notes étendues sur divers points de physique, mathématique et d'analyse*, Gauthier-Villais, Paris, 1885.
3. Burmister, D. M.: The theory of stresses and displacement in layered systems and applications to the design of airport runways, *Proc. Highw. Res. Bd, Wash.*, **23**, 126–44, 1943.
4. Acum, W. E. A. and L. Fox: Computation of load stresses in a three-layer elastic system, *Geotechnique, London*, **2** (4), 293–300, 1951.
5. Westergaard, H. M.: Stresses in concrete pavements computed by theoretical analysis, *Pub Rds, Washington*, **7** (2), 25–35, 1926.

6. Clough, R. W.: The finite element method in structural mechanics, *Stress Analysis*, Wiley, London, 1965.
7. Zienkiewicz, O. C.: *The Finite Element Method in Structural and Continuum Mechanics*, McGraw-Hill, London, 1967.
8. Lister, N. W.: *A Deflection Beam for Investigating the Behaviour of Pavements Under Load*, Road Research Laboratory Research Note RN/3842/NWL (unpublished), RRL, Crowthorne, 1960.

22. The analytical design of concrete pavements

Introduction

22.1   The finite-element program used to compute the stresses in the various layers of a flexible pavement can also be applied to concrete pavements. The stress which primarily determines whether or not a concrete slab will crack is the maximum tensile stress which develops in the underside of the concrete. Because of the very considerable difference in the elastic properties of the concrete on the one hand and of the sub-base and subgrade on the other, the latter two elements of the pavement have less influence than is the case with flexible pavements.

22.2   Since concrete is less able to deform in response to temperature changes than is bitumen, thermal stresses have to be taken into account as well as traffic stresses in analysing the behaviour of concrete pavements. This matter is considered first below.

Thermal stresses in concrete

22.3   Temperature stresses in concrete slabs can be conveniently divided into three categories as follows:

1.   end-restraint compressive stress;
2.   foundation restraint compressive and tensile stress;
3.   partially or completely restrained warping stresses.

These are considered separately below.

End-restraint compressive stress

22.4   If a slab is located between rigid abutments without space for expansion, an increase of temperature above the temperature at the time of placing will induce an internal compressive stress. If the coefficient of linear expansion of the concrete is a and the rise of temperature is t then the strain induced in the concrete will be at and the compressive stress induced in the concrete is given by:

$$\sigma_{es} = Eat \qquad (22.1)$$

where E is the elastic modulus of the concrete.

Table 22.1 Influence of aggregate type on the coefficient of thermal expansion of concrete

Aggregate (geological group)	Coefficient of thermal expansion (per °C $\times 10^{-6}$)	
	Range	Mean
Chert	11.4–12.2	11.8
Quartzite	11.7–14.6	13.2
Quartz	9.0–13.2	11.1
Sandstone	9.2–13.3	11.3
Marble	4.1– 7.4	5.8
Siliceous limestone	8.1–11.0	9.6
Granite	8.1–10.3	9.2
Basalt	7.9–10.4	9.2
Limestone	4.3–10.3	7.3
Gravel	9.0–13.7	11.4
	Mean	10.0

Shacklock[1] has given a useful summary of the coefficients of linear expansion of concretes made with difference aggregates and this is reproduced in Table 22.1.

22.5   The placing of pavement concrete is not permitted when the temperature is likely to fall below 3 °C and this can therefore be taken as the lowest temperature at the time of construction. For the southern and central climatic zones considered in Chapter 9 the maximum temperature at the mid-depth of a concrete slab is likely to be 29 °C. Therefore it follows that the maximum temperature range which a slab will experience is about 26 °C. From Eq. (22.1), for a concrete of coefficient of linear expansion 10×10^{-6} per °C and Young's modulus 35 000 N/mm²,

$$\sigma_{es} = 35\,000 \times 10^{-5} \times 29$$
$$= 10.15 \text{ MN/m}^2$$

This represents the largest compressive stress likely to be generated by thermal expansion in a restrained slab and it is small in comparison with the minimum compressive strength required of 43 N/mm² at 28 days (see Para. 15.14). It follows that compression failures are very unlikely to occur in restrained slabs, unless the concrete in the immediate vicinity of joints has been badly compacted or otherwise disturbed by the formation of the joints. Under such circumstances the restraint stress can give rise to spalling round the joints. However, end-restraint stresses can give rise to buckling or blowup-type failures in extreme temperature conditions, and for this reason it is usual practice in Britain to require expansion joints to be included in all concrete pavements constructed between 22 October and 20 April. For pavements constructed in the summer months, i.e., outside this period the increase of temperature between the time of laying and the hottest part of the year is unlikely to exceed 10 °C and the compressive stress generated will be less than 3.5 N/mm². Experience in Britain and America indicates that there is no risk of buckling with such a level of stress.

22.6 In reinforced concrete pavements the widely spaced joints can open up sufficiently to trap road grit, and thermal closure of the joint can then lead to stress concentration sufficient to cause spalling. This is less likely to occur with plain concrete pavements where the more frequent joints lead to correspondingly smaller joint movements. If joint grooves and arrises are well formed and properly compacted then the risk of damage from spalling is small.

Foundation restraint stress

22.7 The opening and closing of joints in a concrete road entails sliding between the slabs and their foundation (sub-base or subgrade), or in extreme cases shearing within the foundation itself. The friction between the slab and its foundation will thus generate in a slab not subject to end-restraint, a compressive or tensile stress depending on whether the slab is increasing or decreasing in temperature. The stress resulting from foundation restraint will be a maximum at the midpoint.

22.8 The magnitude of the foundation restraint stress depends on the force necessary to cause sliding between the concrete and its foundation and the displacement necessary to initiate such sliding. This has been examined in some detail by Sparkes and Stott;[2,3] both studied the force necessary to move horizontal concrete slabs supported by different foundation materials, and the relationship between force and displacement. The results they obtained are summarized in Fig. 22.1.

22.9 There is a large difference between the values obtained by Sparkes using a clinker foundation and those of Stott using various other foundations. In each case the slab was cast on the foundation under test to simulate practical conditions and essentially the same procedure of moving the slabs by jacks was adopted. It is possible that the clinker used by Sparkes may have exhibited a slight pozzolanic effect which increased the bond between the waterproof paper and the foundation. On the other hand Stott was consciously trying to reduce the restraint force in his tests and the surface finish which he obtained on the foundation may have been to a closer tolerance than that used by Sparkes. In the absence of other information it would seem reasonable to adopt a value of restraint which is the average of Sparkes's value and the mean of the values obtained by Stott. The relationship shown by the broken line on Fig. 22.1 is recommended. Clearly the type and smoothness of the foundation has some effect on the restraint stress, but it is impossible to quantify on this evidence. Both Sparkes and Stott used slabs 150 mm thick for their tests. The restraint stress will increase with increasing weight and hence thickness of slab. Stott made some tests on surcharged slabs and showed that the foundation restraint stress was approximately proportional to the thickness of slab and this enables restraint stresses to be calculated for thickness other than the 150 mm to which Fig. 22.1 applies.

22.10 The stress due to foundation restraint can be calculated as follows using

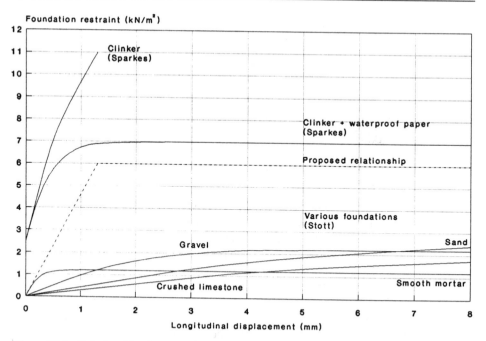

Figure 22.1   Relationships between foundation force and slab displacement (150-mm slabs)

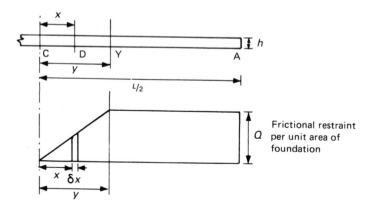

Figure 22.2   Relationship between subgrade restraint force and slab displacement (150-mm slabs)

the method originally developed in *Concrete Roads*.[4] Figure 22.2 shows in elevation one-half of a concrete slab of length *L*, C being the mid-point and A one extremity. On expansion or contraction, all points between C and A will tend to move away from or towards C, thereby generating the foundation restraint stress. There will be one point Y at which the movement will be just sufficient to mobilize the maximum restraint force, *Q*, which will apply to the length between Y and A. Between C and

Y the movement will be smaller and only part of the maximum restraint force will be mobilized, as indicated on Fig. 22.2. The actual proportion generated at any point can be deduced from the thermal displacement using Fig. 22.1.

22.11   The force acting on unit width of the slab to the right of point D, Fig. 22.2, is given by

$$\sum Q = Q\left(\frac{L}{2}-y\right)+Q\left(\frac{1+x/y}{2}\right)(y-x) \tag{22.2}$$

If we consider the equilibrium of the length of slab between C and Y then the element of slab δx shown on Fig. 22.2 will be subject to a foundation restraint force $(x/y)/Q\,\delta x$. The elastic extension or contraction of length CD as a result of the restraint force acting on δx will be

$$\frac{Q}{Eh}\cdot\frac{x^2}{y}\,\delta x$$

and for the length CY the change in length due to foundation restraint will be

$$\frac{Q}{Ehy}\int_0^y x^2\,dx$$

i.e.

$$\frac{Q}{Eh}\cdot\frac{y^2}{3}$$

The change in length of CY due to restraint acting over the length YA will be

$$\frac{Q}{Eh}y\left(\frac{L}{2}-y\right)$$

The total change of length of CY due to foundation restraint over the length CA will thus be

$$\frac{Q}{Eh}y\left(\frac{L}{2}-y\right)+\frac{Q}{Eh}\frac{y^2}{3} \quad\text{or}\quad \frac{Q}{Eh}\left(\frac{Ly}{2}-\tfrac{2}{3}y\right)$$

If the slab is subjected to a uniform temperature change θ, and the coefficient of linear expansion is a, then the unrestrained length change in CY would be $ya\theta$ and the restrained length change, Δ, over the length CY will be given by

$$\Delta = ya\theta - \frac{Q}{Eh}y\left(\frac{L}{2}-\tfrac{2}{3}y\right) \tag{22.3}$$

Equation (22.3) used in conjunction with Fig. 22.1 enables the value of y to be calculated. This is then used in Eq. (22.2) to deduce the restraint force acting over length DA, and hence the foundation restraint stress acting over the cross-section of the slab at D. The maximum stress will be generated at the centre of the slab, where

$x=0$, and where

$$\sum Q = Q\left(\frac{L-y}{2}\right)$$

If the foundation restraint stress, σ_{fr}, is assumed to act uniformly over the cross-section of the slab,

$$\sigma_{fr} = \sum \frac{Q}{h} \tag{22.4}$$

Near the ends of the slab the eccentricity of loading will result in a marked non-uniformity of stress with depth, but Wallace has shown that the assumption of uniformity is valid except in the end metre of the slab.[5]

22.12   The values of σ_{fr} deduced from Eqs (22.2), (22.3), and (22.4) using Fig. 22.1 in conjunction with a value of slab thickness, h, of 150 mm will apply to all thicknesses of slab if it is assumed that the value of Q is proportional to h. Using values of $E = 35\,000\,\text{N/mm}^2$ and $a = 10^{-6}/°\text{C}$, which are representative of normal-strength pavement concrete, Fig. 22.3 shows relationships between foundation restraint stress, slab length, and temperature change, which, using the assumption above, will apply to slabs of any thickness.

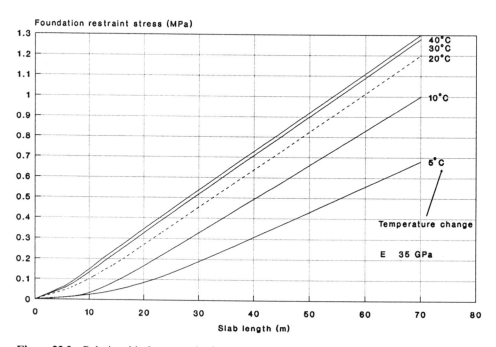

Figure 22.3   Relationship between the foundation restraint stress at the centre of a slab and slab length

Thermal warping stress

22.13   If at a given instant the measured temperature of a concrete slab decreases with depth then the greater thermal expansion at the surface will tend to produce warping such that the central area is higher than the edges. Similarly, if the temperature increases with depth then the slab will tend to warp upwards at the edges. If the temperature change with the depth is linear then bending in an unrestrained slab will be symmetrical about the mid-depth of the concrete and no internal stress will be developed by the bending process. If vertical movement of the slab is restrained, as it will be in practice by the self-weight of the concrete, then restrained warping stresses will be created in the slab. If the temperature at a given instant decreases with depth then the horizontal stress in the surface will be compressive and the horizontal stress in the bottom of the slab will be tensile. Westergaard[6] showed that if the top face of a slab had a temperature $t/2°$ greater than that at the mid-depth, and the bottom face had a temperature $t/2°$ less than the mid-depth, then the restrained tensile warping stress in the undersurface of the slab would be given by

$$\sigma_{rw} = \frac{Eat}{2(1-v)} \tag{22.5}$$

where v is the Poisson ratio and the other symbols have the previous definitions.

It follows from Eq. (22.5) that the restrained warping stress defined in this way is independent of the dimensions of the slab.

22.14   Reference to Table 9.9 shows that at certain times of day the temperature gradient is approximately linear with depth. At 16.00 h on 17 July 1969 the temperature difference between the top and bottom faces of the 254-mm concrete slabs referred to in the table was 4.4 °C. Assuming that $E = 35000 \text{ N/mm}^2$, $a = 10 \times 10^{-6}/°\text{C}$, and $v = 0.14$, σ_{rw} deduced from Eq. (22.5) will be approximately 0.9 N/mm^2.

22.15   However, the variation of temperature with depth in a concrete slab is not normally linear, as is shown by Table 9.9. When the surface of the concrete has its maximum or minimum daily temperatures, the temperature difference between the surface and the mid-depth may be more than double the difference between the mid-depth and the underface. As a result, internal stresses are set up by the bending process and these tend to increase the restrained warping stress at the top of the slab and decrease it at the underface.

22.16   Thomlinson has made a detailed analysis of the warping stress in concrete slabs taking into account the effects of internal stress.[7] To generalize the treatment, he assumed that the surface of the slab was subject to a sinusoidal variation of temperature such that the temperature at any instant was given by

$$\theta = \theta_0 \sin \frac{2\pi}{T} t \tag{22.6}$$

where $\theta_0 =$ the amplitude of the temperature variation (difference between maximum temperature and mean temperature)

$\theta =$ the temperature at time t after the start of the temperature cycle (generally when the surface is at its mean temperature)

$T =$ the length of the time cycle (i.e., for diurnal variations, 24 hours)

Using the well-known thermal diffusion equations, Thomlinson calculated the temperature distribution with depth at any instant, assuming that the thermal diffusivities of the concrete and its foundation were equal. Normal elastic theory was then used to calculate the amplitude and phase of the internal stress variation in the top and bottom of the concrete for various slab thicknesses. The amplitude of the restrained warping stress was similarly calculated and hence the amplitude and phase of the combined internal stress and restrained warping stress.

22.17   If a value of 0.009 CGS units is used for the thermal diffusivity of moist concrete then Thomlinson's method for calculating the thermal gradients in concrete slabs agrees quite closely with measured values such as those shown in Table 9.9 and therefore the method can be used with confidence to calculate daily and annual variations of warping stress. Thomlinson quoted the stress amplitudes in terms of coefficients to be multiplied by $Ea\theta_0/(1-v)$. Coefficients for slabs in the thickness range 200–300 mm are given in Table 22.2.

22.18   Figure 22.4 shows the variation of combined internal and restrained warping stress with time of day for a 250-mm slab subjected to a surface temperature amplitude of 7 °C. This corresponds to the summer period when the temperature amplitude is likely to be greatest (see Table 9.9). The maximum tensile stress occurs in the top of the slab in the early hours of the morning. A smaller maximum tensile stress occurs in the bottom of the slab in the early afternoon. The values of E, a, and v used are shown on the figure and they are those previously used in Para. 22.14. In the early summer, days may occur when the temperature amplitude in the surface of

Table 22.2   Amplitude of combined internal and restrained warping stresses for concrete slabs of various thicknesses

Slab thickness, mm	Coefficient of combined internal and restrained warping stress*	
	Top of slab	Bottom of slab
200	0.59	0.38
250	0.68	0.38
300	0.73	0.38

*To be multiplied by $\dfrac{Ea\theta_0}{(1-v)}$ to give actual amplitude of stress.

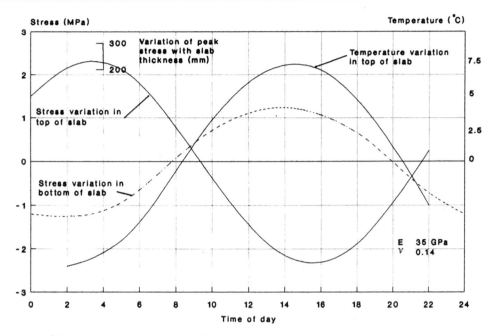

Figure 22.4 Variation of combined internal and restrained warping stress with time of day

the concrete is as great as 10 °C. On such days the stress amplitudes will be larger in proportion to the temperature amplitude. The stress amplitude in the top of the slab is slightly affected by slab thickness as indicated on Fig. 22.4, but the stress amplitude at the bottom of the slab is not significantly affected by the thickness.

22.19   Thomlinson's method can also be used to calculate the warping stresses due to the annual temperature cycle and these can be compounded with the effects of the daily cycle. However, the temperature gradients associated with the annual cycle are small and the warping stresses they induce can generally be neglected.

Combination of warping, foundation restraint, and traffic-induced stress

22.20   A reinforced concrete slab designed in the UK to Road Note 29[8] will normally have a maximum length between sliding joints of about 30 m. For such a slab constructed in the summer months the maximum temperature drop at the mid-depth in the following winter will, from Table 9.8, be about 20 °C. From Fig. 22.3 the maximum tensile foundation restraint stress generated in the winter would be approximately 0.4 N/mm². In short unreinforced slabs of length about 5 m, Fig. 22.3 shows that the foundation restraint stress would be negligible.

22.21   Table 9.9 shows that in the summer in the UK the amplitude of the temperature fluctuation in the top of the slab is about 5 °C and from Fig. 22.4 it can be concluded that the asssociated maximum tensile warping stress will be about

0.8 N/mm^2. This will occur in the afternoon with an average value of about 0.4 N/mm^2 between 08.00 and 20.00.

22.22   It is not difficult, given the information in Chapter 8 relating to the traffic distribution on major roads during the 24-hour period, together with deductions from Figs 22.3 and 22.4, to compute combined traffic and thermal stresses on a daily and seasonal basis during the life of a concrete road. However, a 'safe' procedure in the UK would be to add 0.8 N/mm^2 to traffic stresses to cover the influence of thermal stresses for both reinforced and unreinforced pavements. Throughout the life of the road this would significantly overestimate the combined stress and provide a factor of safety. For more extreme climates this procedure would need re-examination based on Figs 22.3 and 22.4.

Design criterion for concrete pavements

22.23   If at any time during the life of a concrete pavement the tensile stress in the underside of the concrete, due to the combined effects of traffic and temperature, exceeds the modulus of rupture at that time then cracking may be initiated. It has been seen in Chapter 15 that the modulus of rupture is related to the compressive strength, and as a consequence it increases with the age of concrete over a period of about 5 years. The relation between modulus of rupture and compressive strength depends also to some extent on the aggregate used in the concrete. Values of modulus of rupture for concretes of compressive strength between 10 and 60 N/mm^2 made with gravel and crushed rock aggregates have been shown in Table 15.4.

22.24   Taking as an example a concrete with 28-day compressive strength 20 N/mm^2 made with gravel aggregate, Fig. 22.5 shows fatigue lines corresponding to ages of from 28 days to 5 years. In accordance with Para. 15.18, the fatigue strength at 10^5 applications is taken as 0.8 times the modulus of rupture at 28 days. Were stress applications applied so quickly that no significant gain of strength occurred then the behaviour of the concrete would be represented by a single fatigue line. However, in practice a road pavement is designed for a long life and during the first 5 years a considerable change of strength will occur, as shown in Fig. 15.1. As a consequence of the increase in the modulus of rupture, the rupture envelope representing the behaviour of the concrete will cross the fatigue lines representing different ages in the manner shown in Fig. 22.5. For a rate of five applications per day the rupture envelope is represented by the path ABCDEFG on the figure, and the material will then fatigue on approximately the 5-year fatigue line. The 'safe' stress is represented by the point B and the life in terms of number of stress applications applied at that rate will correspond to the point G. As the rate of application of stress is increased the life in terms of number of applications is increased, although it is decreased in terms of time.

22.25   The procedure shown in Fig. 22.5 has been applied to all the concretes considered in Table 15.4 and the results are summarized in Table 22.3. The maximum 'safe' stress for rates of loading of 5, 50, and 500 applications per day are shown.

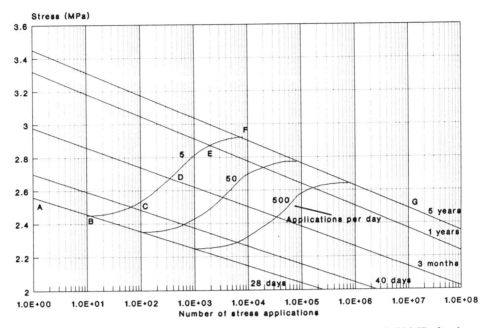

Figure 22.5 Rupture envelopes for concrete of 28-day compressive strength 20 MPa for three rates of loading

Computation of traffic stress

22.26   The finite-element computer program already discussed in connection with flexible pavement design was used to compute the maximum tensile stress generated by axle loads in the range 6–20 tonnes in concrete pavements of thickness 160–360 mm. The elastic properties assumed for the concrete are shown in Table 22.4. Two strengths of subgrade, CBR 2 and 5 per cent, are considered. In accordance with the discussion in Chapter 15, a constant value of elastic modulus was assumed for the concrete, irrespective of its compressive strength. The computed traffic generated stresses are shown in Table 22.5. To these stresses a further tensile stress of 0.8 must be added in accordance with Para. 22.22 to obtain the maximum combined tensile stress due to traffic and temperature. This has been done in Fig. 22.6. This enables the 'safe' stress to be read off for any thickness of slab and any axle load. As would be expected, the CBR of the subgrade has a relatively small influence on the tensile stress in the concrete.

22.27   The maximum safe levels of tensile stress given in Table 22.3 for each of the three rates of loading can be applied in Fig. 22.6 to obtain the relations between the thickness, axle load, and 28-day compressive strength. This has been done in Figs 22.7, 22.8, and 22.9 for the three rates of loading of 5, 50, and 500 applications per day. These three figures apply only to concrete made with gravel aggregate. From

Table 22.3 Maximum acceptable tensile stress for various rates of loading and various strengths of concrete made with gravel and crushed rock aggregates, together with fatigue lives

28-day compressive strength of concrete [N/mm²]	Number of stress applications per day	Maximum acceptable tensile stress [N/mm²]		Life for maximum acceptable stress applications [number of applications]	
		Gravel aggregate	Crushed rock	Gravel aggregate	Crushed rock aggregate
10	5	1.68	1.70	1.5×10^7	3.2×10^8
	50	1.61	1.65	8.5×10^7	2.5×10^9
	500	1.53	1.58	4.0×10^8	4.6×10^9
20	5	2.45	2.82	1.8×10^7	3.3×10^8
	50	2.35	2.68	1.0×10^8	8.2×10^8
	500	2.25	2.57	6.2×10^8	2.4×10^9
30	5	3.05	3.75	5.2×10^6	1.6×10^8
	50	2.94	3.58	2.5×10^7	5.0×10^8
	500	2.80	3.43	1.6×10^8	3.4×10^9
40	5	3.59	4.57	1.1×10^6	2.7×10^7
	50	3.43	4.38	8.0×10^6	1.3×10^8
	500	3.25	4.20	5.5×10^7	7.0×10^8
50	5	4.05	5.35	2.7×10^5	2.6×10^6
	50	3.89	5.12	1.9×10^6	1.6×10^7
	500	3.72	4.90	1.2×10^7	8.2×10^7
60	5	4.45	6.08	4.5×10^4	4.0×10^5
	50	4.25	5.75	4.4×10^5	2.2×10^6
	500	4.07	5.58	3.4×10^6	1.3×10^7

Table 22.4   Elastic properties of the pavement materials

Pavement layer	Modulus of elasticity E (MN/m^2)	Poissons ratio
Concrete slab	40 000	0.15
Granular sub-base	Maximum 300	0.40
Subgrade:		
CBR 2%	10	0.40
CBR 5%	30	0.40

Table 22.5   Computed tensile stress caused by various axle loads in concrete slabs of various thickness

Slab thickness, mm	CBR of subgrade, %	Maximum tensile stresses in concrete (MN/m^2) for axle loads shown (tonnes)							
		6	8	10	12	14	16	18	20
140	2	1.53	1.93	2.49	2.98	3.56	4.04	4.65	5.30
	5	1.39	1.72	2.31	2.71	3.23	3.83	4.30	4.82
160	2	1.29	1.62	2.08	2.46	2.92	3.32	3.80	4.30
	5	1.16	1.47	1.93	2.25	2.67	3.11	3.52	3.94
180	2	1.06	1.41	1.77	2.11	2.46	2.82	3.16	3.54
	5	0.97	1.29	1.62	1.94	2.25	2.59	2.90	3.24
200	2	0.87	1.16	1.46	1.74	2.03	2.33	2.62	2.92
	5	0.82	1.09	1.37	1.63	1.90	2.18	2.48	2.74
220	2	0.74	0.99	1.24	1.48	1.72	1.98	2.22	2.48
	5	0.70	0.93	1.17	1.39	1.62	1.86	2.08	2.34
240	2	0.65	0.86	1.08	1.29	1.50	1.72	1.94	2.16
	5	0.61	0.81	1.01	1.21	1.40	1.62	1.82	2.02
260	2	0.57	0.75	0.94	1.13	1.31	1.51	1.70	1.88
	5	0.53	0.70	0.88	1.06	1.23	1.41	1.58	1.76
280	2	0.50	0.66	0.83	0.99	1.15	1.33	1.48	1.66
	5	0.45	0.60	0.76	0.90	1.05	1.21	1.40	1.54
300	2	0.44	0.59	0.74	0.88	1.02	1.18	1.32	1.48
	5	0.40	0.53	0.67	0.80	0.93	1.07	1.20	1.34
320	2	0.39	0.52	0.65	0.78	0.90	1.04	1.16	1.30
	5	0.35	0.47	0.59	0.70	0.82	0.94	1.06	1.18
340	2	0.35	0.47	0.59	0.70	0.82	0.94	1.06	1.18
	5	0.32	0.43	0.53	0.64	0.74	0.86	0.96	1.08
360	2	0.31	0.42	0.52	0.62	0.73	0.83	0.94	1.04
	5	0.29	0.39	0.49	0.58	0.68	0.78	0.88	0.98

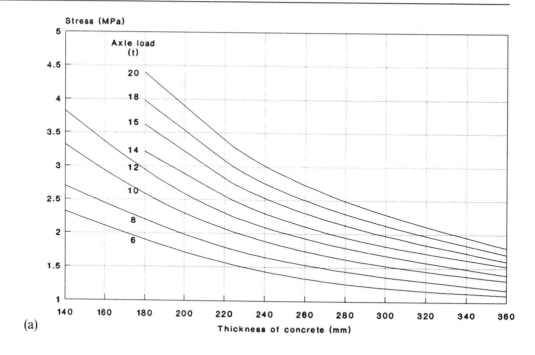

(a)

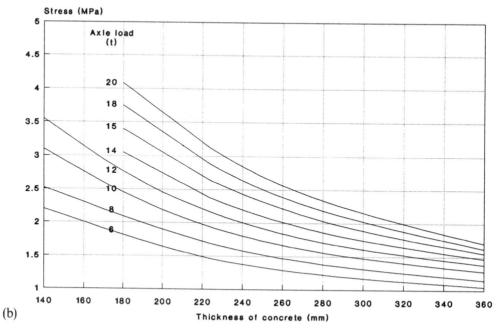

(b)

Figure 22.6 Relation between slab thickness and combined traffic/thermal stress for various axle loads: (a) CBR 2 per cent; (b) CBR 5 per cent

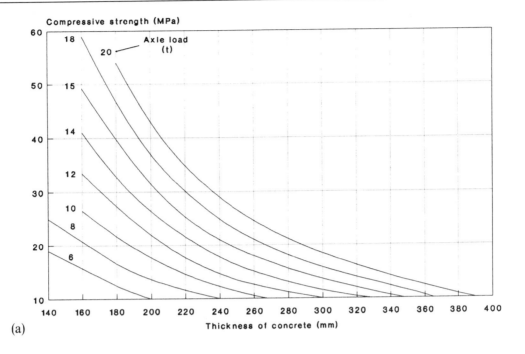

(a)

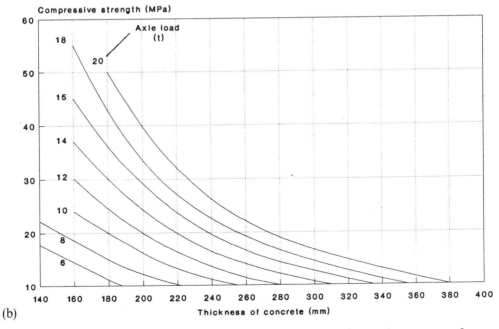

(b)

Figure 22.7 Relation between compressive strength and thickness of concrete at 5 applications per day: (a) CBR 2 per cent; (b) CBR 5 per cent

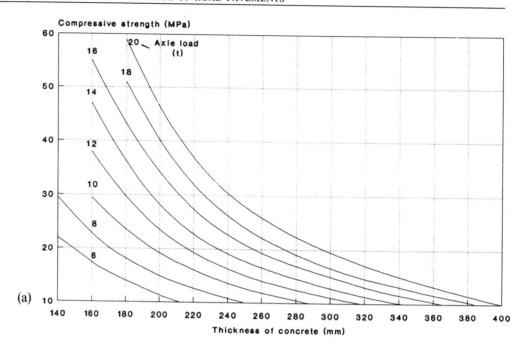

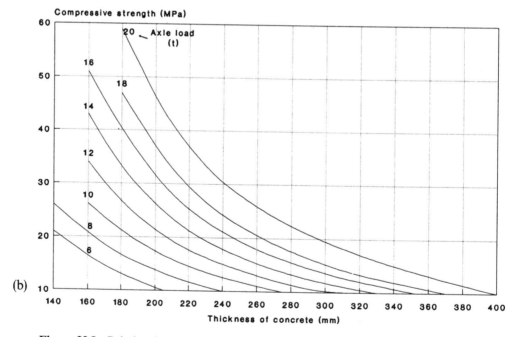

Figure 22.8 Relation between compressive strength and thickness of concrete at 50 applications per day (a) CBR 2 per cent; (b) CBR 5 per cent

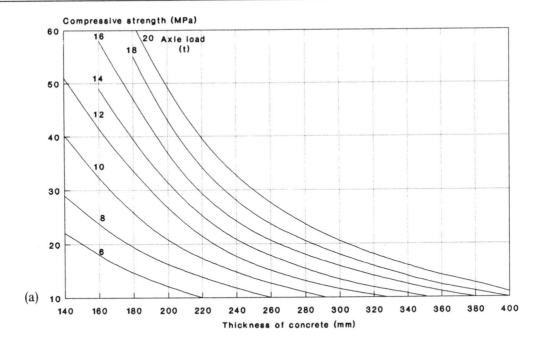

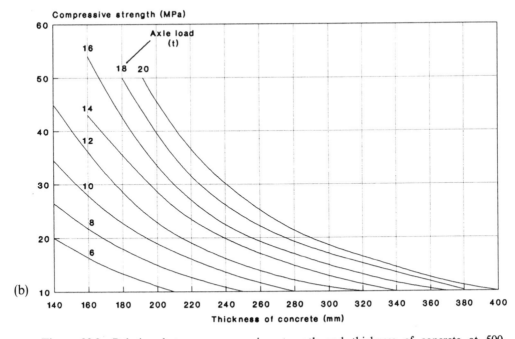

Figure 22.9 Relation between compressive strength and thickness of concrete at 500 applications per day: (a) CBR 2 per cent; (b) CBR 5 per cent

the safe stresses given in Table 22.3 for concretes of the same compressive strength made with crushed-rock aggregate a companion set of curves can be developed.

Application of the structural design approach to concrete road pavements

22.28   The design procedure described in this chapter is based on the maximum axle load the pavement is likely to carry. A check should be carried out to verify that the design so obtained will be capable of carrying the appropriate number of other axle loads to be carried during the design life without the danger of fatigue failure. An example is used below to illustrate the procedure in detail.

22.29   The Alconbury Hill pavement design experiment on trunk road A1 is suitable for analysis since the performance over a period of 20 years has been documented.[9] The experiment is described in detail in Chapter 18. Concrete sections of various thicknesses were incorporated in the experiment and concrete made with gravel aggregate and crushed rock aggregate were used, the strengths at 28 days being 44 and 66 N/mm^2 respectively. The axle load distribution, determined from a recording weighbridge, is shown in Fig. 8.13, and the total number of commercial axles which passed over the sections in 20 years was 33 million.

22.30   The number of axles of loading in the range 1–20 tonnes which passed over the experimental section during the first 20 years is shown in columns 1, 2, and 3 of Table 22.6. There are a significant number of axles carrying 20 tonnes, some of which

Table 22.6   Axle loading at the Alconbury Hill Experimental road, Trunk Road A1

(1) Axle load [tonnes]	(2) Percentage	(3) Number of axles in 20 years	(4) Stress level, N/mm^2	(5) Fatigue life applications (40 N/mm^2 gravel aggregate)
1–2	34.75	11.5×10^7		
2–3	21.11	7.0×10^6		
3–4	16.08	5.3×10^6		
4–5	7.40	2.4×10^6		
5–6	6.17	2.0×10^6	1.6	$> 10^{12}$
6–7	4.57	1.5×10^6		
7–8	3.21	1.06×10^6	1.8	$> 10^{12}$
8–9	2.68	8.84×10^5		
9–10	1.42	4.68×10^5	2.2	$> 10^{12}$
10–11	1.34	4.42×10^5		
11–12	0.54	1.78×10^5	2.45	$> 10^{10}$
12–13	0.39	1.28×10^5		
13–14	0.13	4.29×10^4	2.7	$> 10^9$
14–15	0.11	3.63×10^4		
15–16	0.11	3.63×10^4	2.95	$> 10^9$
16–17	0.03	9.9×10^3		
17–18	0.007	2.3×10^3	3.25	10^8
18–19	0.016	5.2×10^3		
19–20	0.032	1.0×10^4	3.5	3×10^6

will be associated with heavy indivisible loads. The design must cater for these, although the number is only 1–2 per day. Reference to Figs 22.7 and 22.8 shows that the thickness requirements for 5 and 50 stress applications per day are very similar and there is likely to be very little difference between the requirements for 2 and 5 applications per day. The design for this road would therefore be based on Fig. 22.7 for the sections of gravel aggregate. This approach gives the following design thicknesses for a 20-tonne maximum axle load on concrete pavements laid on a foundation of CBR 5 per cent

Aggregate	28-day compressive strength
Gravel	40 N/mm², 200 mm
Gravel	60 N/mm², 172 mm
Crushed rock	46 N/mm², 165 mm
Crushed rock	60 N/mm², 135 mm

22.31   Reference to Table 18.12 shows that the lower-strength concrete made with gravel aggregate of thickness 200 mm gave a life in excess of 20 years, while that with a thickness of 175 mm had a life of 16–18 years. The same table shows that 175 mm of the higher-strength concrete had a life in excess of 20 years while a thickness of 150 mm had a life of about 16 years. These results show close agreement between the theoretical and observed performance. With the high-strength crushed rock concrete the actual life was a little less than the theoretical life and this may well reflect the difficulty of compacting this material *in situ*.

22.32   In applying the structural approach it is advisable to check that the combined loading due to the axle loads less than the maximum used in the design will not lead to earlier fatigue failure. To provide this confirmation, Table 22.6 has been extended to show the maximum combined loading and thermal stress levels due to axle loads of between 6 and 18 tonnes. These stress levels are deduced from Fig. 22.6 for a 200-mm pavement. Figure 22.10 shows the 5-year fatigue relationships for concrete made with gravel aggregates. For such relationships the proportion of the fatigue life absorbed by each axle load can be estimated. The fatigue lives are shown in column 5 of Table 22.6. Inspection shows that less than five per cent of the fatigue life would be absorbed by axle loads less than the maximum used in the design.

Structural design and the concept of standard axles

22.33   In recent years some research workers have used structural design procedures to design pavements on the basis of repetitions of standard axles. This is inadmissible in the case of concrete pavements. Reverting to the Alconbury Hill experiment referred to above, the concrete pavements at that site have carried 9.43×10^6 standard axles in 20 years, or about 1290 per day. Following the procedure discussed in this chapter, for a concrete made with a gravel aggregate of 28-day strength 40 N/mm², the maximum tensile stress which the concrete would

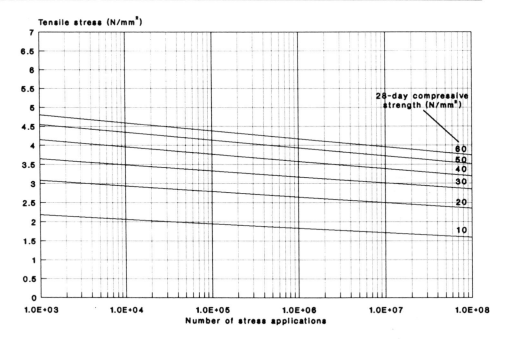

Figure 22.10 Five-year fatigue relationships for concretes of 28-day compressive strength 10–60 N/mm²

accept without cracking is 3.2 N/mm² for this rate of loading. Figure 22.6 shows that for this level of combined traffic and thermal stress, the thickness of concrete required would be about 105 mm. Figure 22.10 indicates that fatigue failure at this stress level would occur at about 10^8 applications, i.e., after a life much in excess of 20 years. However, the experimental evidence (Fig. 18.31) shows that a pavement of this thickness would have lasted less than 2 years. The conclusion is that concrete pavements must be designed for the maximum axle loads they are likely to carry.

22.34 This does not mean that standard axles should not be used, as in Road Note 29, to quantify traffic. The constituents of the traffic in terms of axle loading is inevitably taken into account when designs are based solely on experimental evidence from in-service roads.

22.35 The structural approach to the design of concrete roads highlights the critical influence of all the factors, namely axle loading, thickness and concrete strength, in formulating designs.

References

1. Shacklock, B. W.: *Concrete Constituents and Mix Proportions*, Cement and Concrete Association, London, 1974.
2. Sparkes, F. N.: Stresses in concrete road slabs, *Struc. Engr*, **17** (2) 98–116, 1939.

3. Stott, J. P.: Tests on materials for use in sliding layers under concrete road slabs, *Civ. Engng, London*, **56** (663), 1297, 1299, 1301; (664), 1466–8 (665), 1603–5, 1961.
4. Road Research Laboratory: *Concrete roads—design and construction*, HMSO, 1955.
5. Wallace, K. B.: Subgrade restraint stresses in concrete roads, *Roads and Road Construction*, **46** (505), 303–4, 1968.
6. Westergaard, H. M.: Analysis of stresses in concrete roads caused by variations of temperature, *Publ. Rds, Wash.*, **8** (3), 54–60, 1927.
7. Thomlinson, J.: Temperature variations and consequent stresses produced by daily and seasonal temperature cycles in concrete slabs, *Conc. Constr. Engng*, **35** (6), 298–307; (7), 352–60, 1940.
8. Transport and Road Research Laboratory: *A Guide to the Structural Design of Pavements for New Roads*, Department of the Environment Road Note 29, 3rd edn, HMSO, London, 1970.
9. Nowak, J. R.: *The Concrete Pavement Design Experiment on Trunk Road A1 at Alconbury Hill: Twenty Years' Performance*, Transport and Road Research Laboratory Report LR887, TRRL, Crowthorne, 1979.

PART SIX Design of Specialized Roads and Pavements

23. The design of heavily loaded industrial pavements

Introduction

23.1   The last 40 years have seen a revolution in the handling of heavy goods, particularly in port areas. The almost random packing of miscellaneous commodities in the holds of fleets of small ships has given way to the use of standard containers, which are lifted from large purpose-built container ships in a fraction of the time taken by dockers dealing with mixed cargoes. ISO containers are limited by convention to a maximum gross loaded weight of 20.3 tonnes for the shorter 6-m type and 30.5 t for the larger 12-m type. Weights of the empty boxes are approximately 2.5 and 4 t for the two sizes. Where the larger containers are to be transported by road the gross weight is of necessity limited to 18–20 t to conform with the current Construction and Use Regulations.[1]

23.2   A container ship is expected to be in port for only 2–3 days and effective handling dictates that the location and stacking both of imported and exported boxes must be controlled in the most efficient manner and computer control is necessary, so that the port manager knows the exact location of any box at any time. The transfer of containers between ship and quay is normally effected by a railed crane. However, a variety of plant may be used to move, stack, and retrieve containers which may be stacked up to five high in the transit areas.

23.3   The plant available for site movements includes the following:

1. rubber-tyred gantry cranes with clusters of four wheels on each of four legs;
2. straddle carriers with three or four wheels spaced on each side.
3. front-lift trucks with dual wheel assemblies on the front axle and single wheels on the rear axle.

23.4   *Rubber-tyred gantry cranes*   These have the ability to move containers sideways over distances of 15–20 m. They are therefore very robust with a tare weight of 90–100 t, and a maximum wheel load when carrying a loaded container of about 16 t.

Straddle carriers   These lift containers to the required height for stacking. Although they cannot move boxes sideways while stationary, they are highly mobile

471

and can place containers accurately. They have a tare weight of about 45 t and a maximum wheel load when fully loaded of 12–14 t.

Front-lift trucks   These are made in various sizes. For container handling there are two main groups, with lifting capacities of 12 t for the smaller group and 30–35 t for the larger machines. The smaller type are used mainly for handling empty containers. The load on the front axle of the smaller type when fully loaded is likely to be about 30 t, i.e., 8 t per wheel. For the larger machines the front axle load can be 70–80 t or 20 t per wheel.

23.5   Irrespective of the method of handling, the layout of a container terminal incorporates 'roadways' running at right angles to the quay. The arrangement of the stacking blocks depends on the handling plant. Straddle carriers require a spacing of about 1 m between the standing boxes to allow movement of the side frames. With gantry cranes the boxes can be packed more closely with rather larger gaps at intervals to allow passage for the crane legs. Front-lift trucks will pack the boxes close together, but to allow access the boxes need to be only two deep between access roadways. Each type of plant requires a different width of roadway for easy operation.

Design approach for heavily loaded industrial pavements

23.6   An engineer commissioned to design pavements for a container depot or similar facility must become fully aware of the intended function of the installation and how it is to be operated, and on submitting the design should make clear all the assumptions which have been made. Stacking areas need to be marked out and numbered so that plant operators can locate a particular container with the minimum of delay. This tends to establish a layout in which the heavily trafficked roadways become permanent. In such a situation the design could use a variable thickness with the roadways thicker than the stacking areas. However, the client should be made fully aware of the limitations imposed by such an arrangement. In practice, clients generally prefer uniform construction.

23.7   Flexible pavements using bituminous or unbound bases are not recommended for pavements designed to accept very heavy wheel loads. To avoid unacceptable deformation and wheel-tracking the bituminous material would need very careful design and the addition of expensive additives throughout the full depth. Concrete pavements or bituminous surfacings on a strong lean concrete base generally provide the best solution. In the case of the lean concrete base, the surfacing can be of precast concrete or ceramic blocks if preferred.

23.8   It is fairly common for hauliers to reduce space charges at dockside terminals by constructing small depots outside the dock area. These are used as a storage area for empty containers or as a staging point for the distribution of loaded containers. In designing such a facility the engineer responsible must make it quite clear for which items of plant the pavement is designed.

Examples of structural design applied to industrial pavements

23.9   The following examples refer to actual designs for heavily loaded pavements prepared during the past 10–15 years.

Lean concrete construction for straddle carrier use

23.10   The design relates to a site operated by straddle carriers of maximum static wheel load 10.5 t. These machines in turning tend to transfer load from the wheels on one side to those on the other. In braking the transfer is from the wheels at the back to those in the front. In addition, as with a normal road, unevenness of the surface tends to increase the maximum static wheel load. These effects produce a combined dynamic factor which may be in the range 1.2–1.6. However, it is unlikely in practice to exceed 1.3 when the vehicle is safely driven and the riding quality of the roadways is acceptable.

23.11   The pavement was designed to have a two course rolled asphalt surfacing, with a high-stone-content wearing course for increased stability. The total thickness of the asphalt selected was 100 mm. The base was of lean concrete to the Department of Transport specification, with a 28-day compressive strength of 10 N/mm². The deep sand foundation had an *in situ* CBR value of 15 per cent. The finite element computer program described in Chapter 21 was used to compute the maximum tensile stress induced in the bottom of the lean concrete base by the passage of wheel loads of 7.5 to 10.5 t with dynamic effects of 1.0–1.6. The thicknesses of lean concrete included in the analysis were in the range 200–350 mm. The results are summarized in Table 23.1, and beneath the table are shown the elastic properties ascribed to the various materials. A check was made to show that the stress generated by each wheel was not significantly augmented by that due to the adjacent wheels.

23.12   Figure 23.1 shows fatigue lines corresponding to ages of 28 days and 5 years for lean concrete of compressive strength 9 N/mm² at 28 days. These curves were derived using the equation shown in Para. 15.15. The value of 9 N/mm² for the crushing strength was chosen as more nearly representing the actual strength of the base as laid rather than the 10 N/mm² required for fully compacted cubes.

23.13   Table 23.1 shows that for all the wheel loads considered the lean concrete base would fail by cracking if laid with a thickness of 200 mm. Assuming a dynamic factor of 1.3, a thickness of 250 mm would fail for all the wheel loads. Increasing the thickness to 300 mm would result in failure owing only to the 9.5 and 10.5 t wheel loads, in conjunction with a dynamic factor of 1.3. The 350-mm thickness would be safe for all the wheel loads and all the dynamic factors. For the reasons given in Chapter 22, fatigue failure would then occur on the 5-year fatigue line, and it is clear from Fig. 23.1 that the thickness of 350 mm would accept about 10^8 applications of the 10.5-t wheel load, and would have a much greater fatigue life for the smaller wheel loads. Since rather less than 1 per cent of the wheel loads were expected to be in the 10–11-t load bracket, it was clear that if the pavement was correctly constructed it should have a life well in excess of 100 years.

Table 23.1 Maximum tensile stress at the bottom of the lean concrete (N/mm^2) for various wheel loads and dynamic factors

Static wheel load, t	7.5				8.5				9.5				10.5			
Dynamic factor	1.0	1.2	1.4	1.6	1.0	1.2	1.4	1.6	1.0	1.2	1.4	1.6	1.0	1.2	1.4	1.6
Thickness of lean concrete base (mm)																
200	1.58	1.90	2.21	2.53	1.80	2.16	2.52	2.88	2.18	2.62	3.05	3.49	2.53	3.04	3.54	4.05
250	1.24	1.49	1.74	1.98	1.40	1.68	1.96	2.24	1.56	1.87	2.18	2.50	1.73	2.08	2.42	2.77
300	0.91	1.09	1.27	1.46	1.03	1.24	1.44	1.68	1.15	1.38	1.61	1.84	1.27	1.52	1.78	2.03
350	0.68	0.82	0.95	1.09	0.77	0.92	1.08	1.23	0.86	1.03	1.20	1.40	0.95	1.14	1.33	1.52

Elastic properties of the materials:

Rolled asphalt $E = 2.5 \times 10^3 \, N/mm^2$ [20°C] Poissons ratio 0.4

Lean concrete $E = 34 \times 10^3 \, N/mm^2$ Poissons ratio 0.15

Sand foundation $E = 150 \, N/mm^2$

Tyre pressure $1 N/mm^2$

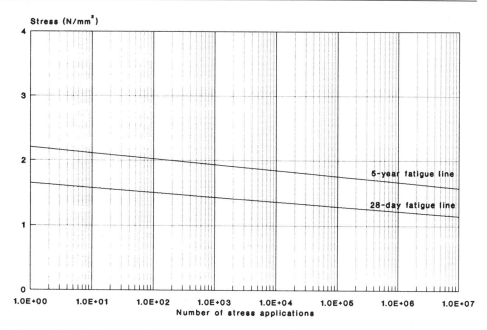

Figure 23.1 Fatigue relationships for lean concrete base material with 28-day compressive strength 9 N/mm² (gravel)

Concrete pavement suitable for the temporary storage of empty container boxes

23.14   This is an example of a yard designed to be operated by Hyster 250 or similar front-lift trucks loading empty container boxes onto and off articulated trucks. The design was for a 200-mm concrete slab laid on a 150-mm crushed-stone sub-base placed on a 150-mm capping layer on a soil of CBR 6 per cent. The concrete was to comply with the Department of Transport specification (minimum crushing strength 28 N/mm² at 28 days). Lifting a 12-m box, the load on the front axle was calculated to be 18 t with a rear axle load of 2.5 t. The maximum load on each front dual wheel assembly was thus 9 t.

23.15   The maximum tensile stress in the bottom of the slab due to the load was computed for a wheel load of 4.5 t. The spacing of the dual wheels was approximately 540 mm between the centres of the contact areas, and the stresses were compounded in the manner shown in Fig. 23.2. The spacing between the two dual-wheel assemblies was too large to give any stress interaction. In accordance with Paras 22.21 and 22.22, a maximum tensile warping stress of 0.8 N/mm² was added to the computed load stress of 1.8 N/mm² taken from Fig. 23.2, to give a possible total tensile stress of 2.6 N/mm². The 28-day compressive strength of the concrete of 29 N/mm² corresponded to a modulus of rupture of 3.1 N/mm². The design therefore allowed for a substantial dynamic component of load. As the modulus of rupture increased with age the design would become safer, with no danger of fatigue failure.

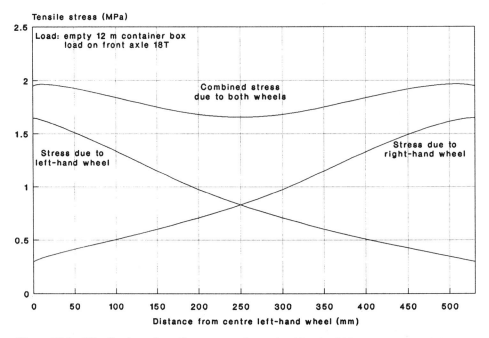

Figure 23.2 Distribution of tensile stress at the underside of a 200-mm concrete slab—dual front wheel Hyster Challenger

Concrete pavement to accommodate large front-lift trucks operating with full containers

23.16   A similar calculation was made for one of the larger front-lift trucks carrying a loaded 12-m container. The calculated front axle load was 55 t, with 9 t on the rear axle. In this case the 27.5-t load on each dual-wheel assembly generated a maximum tensile loading stress midway between the two contact areas of the dual tyres. This stress was calculated for three thicknesses of concrete as shown in Table 23.2. The stresses were also calculated for the unloaded machine.

For the loaded truck the total tensile stress including the warping stress would be

Table 23.2 Tensile stress developed in the underside of concrete slabs of various thicknesses by a large front lift truck (N/mm^2)

| Thickness of concrete, mm | Lancer Henley 68 truck | |
	Fully loaded	Unloaded
200	5.10	2.70
300	2.76	1.45
350	2.11	1.14

2.91 for the 350-mm slab. With the modulus of rupture of 3.1 N/mm² there would be only a small reserve in the design to allow for dynamic loading.

Dock pavement using a cement-stabilized base, mixed *in situ*, with a concrete block surfacing

23.17   In this case the pavement was to be used primarily by rubber tyred gantry cranes with a cluster of four wheels on each of the four legs. The maximum load on each leg was to be 16 t (including a dynamic factor of 1.2). The configuration of the wheel clusters is shown inset in Fig. 23.4. In this example two variables were considered. These were the crushing strength of the stabilized material and the required thickness. A considerable depth of sandy gravel had been imported to provide the foundation and the upper part of this material was to be stabilized *in situ*. In accordance with the discussion in Chapter 16, an elastic modulus of 45 MPa was adopted for the concrete blocks and their sand foundation, of total thickness of 150 mm. The same modulus was assumed for the sandy-gravel foundation. The elastic modulus of the base is considered in Fig. 23.3. The dynamic modulus in relation to the compressive strength is taken from Fig. 13.6 and the deduced static value from Fig. 13.4. In accordance with the recommendation in Para. 13.20, the mean value was adopted in the structural analysis.

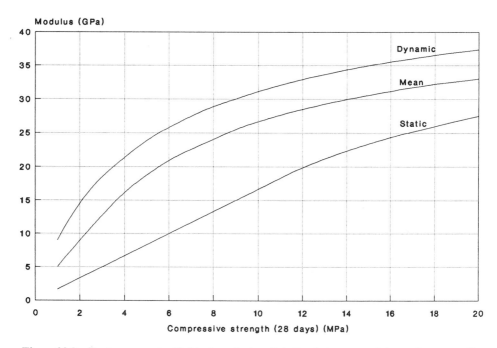

Figure 23.3   Port pavement with block surfacing. Relation between modulus and compressive strength of lean concrete

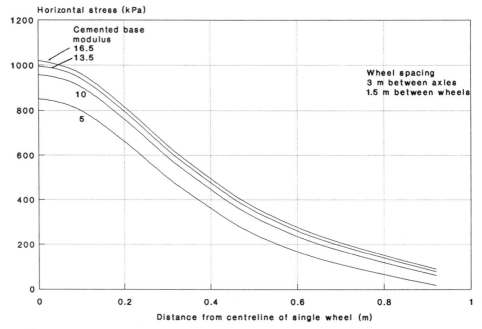

Figure 23.4 Port pavement with block surfacing. Tensile stress in underside of base 400 mm thick

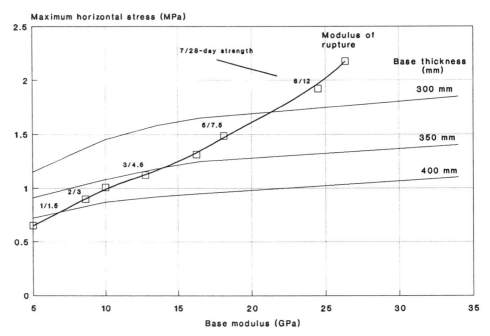

Figure 23.5 Port pavement with block surfacing. Tensile stress in underside of base related to base modulus and thickness

23.18   The radius of loading adopted was deduced from the tyre size, the maximum wheel load, and the tyre pressure applicable to the machine, and the finite-element program was used to deduce the stress distribution beneath the centre of the tyre contact area. Figure 23.4 shows the maximum tensile stress both on and off the axis of loading, corresponding to four strengths of cemented material defined in terms of their modulus of elasticity. It was clear that there was no significant interaction of stress between the four wheels of each cluster. Figure 23.4 refers to a base thickness of 400 mm; similar families of curves were computed for base thicknesses of 300 and 350 mm. This permitted the maximum tensile stress developed to be related to the modulus of elasticity of the base as shown in Fig. 23.5.

23.19   By using Fig. 23.3 and Eq. (15.1) in Para. 15.15, the variation of modulus of rupture with base modulus of elasticity can be superimposed on Fig. 23.5, and the moduli of elasticity necessary to prevent rapid failure can be determined from the points of interception between the stress curves and the modulus of rupture. Compressive strengths can be added to the rupture curve, again by using Fig. 23.3. The fatigue situation can then be investigated, as in the first example considered above. In using this approach it must be remembered that with mix-in-place stabilization the actual strength obtained in the base may be considerably lower than the equivalent cube strength, and the preliminary trial should be carried out to investigate the efficiency of mixing throughout the full depth of the stabilized layer.

Reference

1. Department of Transport: *The Motor Vehicle (Construction and Use) Regulations*, Statutory Instrument No. 24, HMSO, London.

24. Soil trafficability and design of haul roads

Introduction

24.1   A contractor preparing to tender for a contract involving significant earthworks must decide which types of plant will be able to operate on the soils at the site and particularly the speeds at which they will be able to operate. This decision must be made from the information given in the site investigation report and from a desk study of the climatic conditions which apply to the site. When large volumes of soil have to be transferred from one location on the site to another, or from a borrow pit to the site, the extent to which the haul route will need to be strengthened by the addition of a compacted stone topping must also be decided. Although good haul roads may appear to represent an unnecessary expense, they have a major influence in reducing journey times and minimizing plant down-time. This chapter discusses these two important aspects of earthmoving.

Trafficability of soil by construction plant

24.2   The information given here in relation to the trafficability of soil by construction plant is taken from the published work of A. W. Parsons and his team at the Transport and Road Research Laboratory in the UK.[1,2] It is based on site studies made at 18 motorway and 7 trunk road construction sites in Britain over the years 1973–1978. The plant considered ranges from small, medium, and large scrapers of struck capacity 11–25 m^3 and small, medium, and large dump trucks of struck capacity 8–22 m^3. Details of the plant studied are given in Table 24.1 and Table 24.2 shows the soil types on which each piece of plant operated and the prevailing gradients.

24.3   In the field studies, the strength of the soil was expressed in terms of the moisture condition value (MCV), which has been discussed in Chapters 10 and 11. The MCV of a soil which defines the engineering properties *at the field moisture content* can be derived from the liquid and plastic limit values and the field moisture content, w, using the following equations

$$w = a - b \times \text{MCV} \tag{24.1}$$

For soils of PI less than 20, $b = 0.075 \cdot \text{PI} + 0.253$

$$a = \text{LL} - 0.175 \cdot \text{PI} + 2.8 \tag{24.2}$$

480

Table 24.1 Main details of the earthmoving machines observed in the study

Type of machine	Struck capacity, m³	Nominal mass of machine loaded (empty), Mg	Nominal power available, kW	Normal tyre size(s), inches	Number of wheels × number of driven wheels
Small, twin-engined scraper	11	45 (24)	214	29.5 × 25	4 × 4
Small, twin-engined scraper	11	54 (32)	336	29.5 × 29 29.5 × 35	4 × 4
Small, single-engined scraper	11	43 (27)	187	26.5 × 29	4 × 2
Medium, twin-engined scraper	16–18	78 (43)	450–530	33.5 × 33 33.25 × 35	4 × 4
Medium, single-engined scraper	16	73 (39)	310	29.5 × 35 33.25 × 35	4 × 2
Large, twin-engined scraper	25	110 (63)	700	37.5 × 39	4 × 4
Large, single-engined scraper	21	99 (53)	410	33.5 × 39 37.5 × 39	4 × 2
Towed scraper	9–14	30–38 (11–13) (Scraper)	200–240 (Tractor)	16.0 × 21 23.5 × 25 Front 18.0 × 25 29.5 × 29 Rear (scraper)	4 (Scraper)
Small dump truck (rigid chassis)	8	24–27 (10–11)	170–200	10.0 × 20 11.0 × 20 12.0 × 20	6(4 paired) × 4
Small dump truck (articulated chassis)	8–12	29–44 (13–19)	125–170	16.0 × 24 18.0 × 25 20.5 × 25 23.5 × 25	6 × 4 6 × 6 4 × 4
Medium dump truck	17	59 (27)	300	18.0 × 33	4(2 paired) × 2
Large dump truck	22	74 (33)	360	18.0 × 25 Front 21.0 × 35 Rear	4(2 paired) × 2

$$\text{For soils of PI greater or equal to 20, } b = 0.030 \cdot \text{PI} + 0.421$$
$$a = \text{LL} - 0.67 \cdot \text{PI} + 4.6 \qquad (24.3)$$

where w = the natural moisture content
  PI = the plasticity index
  LL = the liquid limit

In field studies the MCV is measured directly using the equipment described in Chapter 10.

Table 24.2   Main characteristics of construction sites where studies were made

Type of machine	Number of sites where observations contributed useful data	Range of gradients of haul road (in direction of travel of loaded machines), %	Main geological strata encountered
Small, twin-engined scraper (214 kW)	4	−2.9 to +1.0	Alluvium; Bagshot Sands; Boulder clay; London Clay; Lower Sandstone; Reading Beds; Sand and gravel.
Small, twin-engined scraper (336 kW)	3	−5.3 to +1.7	Boulder clay; London Clay and Claygate Beds; Reading and Thanet Beds; Sand and gravel; Valley gravel.
Small, single-engined scraper	1	−0.6	Valley deposits.
Medium, twin-engined scraper	9	−4.3 to +1.7	Bagshot Sands, Boulder clay; Etruria Marl; Gault Clay; London Clay and Claygate Beds; Productive Coal Measures; Reading Beds; Sand and gravel, Valley gravel.
Medium, single-engined scraper	5	−2.0 to +0.8	Boulder clay; Claygate Beds; Gault Clay; London Clay; Sand and gravel; Valley deposits; Valley gravel.
Large, twin-engined scraper	None	—	—
Large, single-engined scraper	1	−0.8 to +0.1	Boulder clay; Chalk Marl; Gault Clay; River gravel.
Towed scraper	5	−4.6 to +2.9	Boulder clay; Gault Clay; Kimmeridge Clay; Lower Old Red Sandstone; Shale (Millstone Grit and Culm Measures).
Small dump truck (rigid chassis)	6	−3.0 to −0.1	Bagshot Sands; Boulder clay; Clay with flints; Gault Clay; London Clay; Reading Beds; Red Marl; Red Sandstone; Shale (Lower Lias).
Small dump truck (articulated chassis)	4	−4.6 + 1.8	Bagshot Sands; Boulder clay; Chalk Marl; Gault Clay; London Clay; Lower Old Red Sandstone; Reading Beds.
Medium dump truck	4	−3.0 to +0.1	Boulder clay; Bunter Sandstone; Chalk Marl; Clay with flints; Gault Clay.
Large dump truck	1	−0.5	Boulder clay; Chalk Marl; Gault Clay.

24.4   As part of the investigations referred to above routine measurements of MCV were related to the ability of the various pieces of plant (1) just to move and (2) to move at a constant velocity, V. Empirical relations for these two cases were developed and these are represented by the Eqs (24.4) and (24.5) below. The minimum MCV to permit movement is given by

$$MCV = 15.8 - 0.738N - 0.399T - 0.001\,84P + 0.113M \qquad (24.4)$$

where N = the number of driven wheels

T^* = mean tyre width in inches

P = the maximum available engine power in kW

M = the total loaded mass of machine in t

The MCV to permit movement of the plant at a speed V (km/h) is given by

$$\text{MCV}_{(V)} = 15.8 - 0.35V + (0.054V - 0.783)N + (0.031V - 0.399)T - \\ (0.000\,84V + 0.001\,84)P + (0.113 - 0.003\,V)M \qquad (24.5)$$

where $\text{MCV}_{(V)}$ is the moisture condition value of the soil necessary to achieve a velocity of V in km/h and N, T and P are as given above.

24.5   For operations in the cut-and-fill areas a value of V in the region of 2–10 km/h would be appropriate but over the haul roads V would be expected to be well above 20 km/h. Eqs (24.6), (24.7), and (24.8) refer to speeds of 2, 10, and 20 km/h:

$$\text{MCV}_{(2)} = 15.1 - 0.675N - 0.337T - 0.00352P + 0.107M \qquad (24.6)$$

$$\text{MCV}_{(10)} = 12.3 - 0.243N - 0.089T - 0.0102P + 0.083M \qquad (24.7)$$

$$\text{MCV}_{(20)} = 8.8 - 0.297N - 0.221T - 0.0186P + 0.053M \qquad (24.8)$$

24.6   The MCV values appropriate to the various items of plant included in the field observations are summarized in Table 24.3, for the plant in the loaded and empty conditions. The figures on the right-hand side of the table are obtained directly from Eq. (24.4) and those on the left by extrapolation to zero velocity using Eqs (24.6)–(24.8).

24.7   For most plant, changing the speed from 2 km/h to above 20 km/h will more than double the required MCV of the soil and the probability is therefore that the natural soil will not be adequate for use as a haul road, and it will be necessary to strengthen it with a compacted stone topping. The second half of this chapter deals with the design of haul roads.

Design of haul roads

24.8   In haul roads, the strength of the natural soil is supplemented by a thickness of compacted graded stone, the strength of which will be little influenced by changes of moisture content. The haul road can thus be regarded as a simple, two-layer pavement in which the heaviest wheel loads imposed by plant will not cause unacceptable shear deformation in the foundation.

24.9   The structural design procedure described in Chapter 21 has been applied to haul roads of this type on soils with a wide range of shear strength and using maximum wheel loads in the range 5000 kg to 12 000 kg. The design curves developed in this manner are shown in Fig. 24.1(a), (b), and (c). Because the tyre pressure affects the radius of the loaded area it has been necessary to show for each

*Tyre dimensions are normally expressed in inches. The mean width of all the tyres on the plant is used. For twinned wheels the combined tyre width is used in calculating the mean.

Table 24.3 Summary of minimum MCVs for effective operation of the machines studied

Type of machine	Minimum MCV by extrapolation of speed of travel/ MCV relation		Minimum MCV from loss of productivity/ MCV relation	Calculated minimum MCV using Eq. (24.1)	
	Loaded	Empty	Loaded	Loaded	Empty
Small, twin-engined scraper (214 kW)	7	1.5	—	5.5	3
Small, twin-engined scraper (336 kW)	—[1]	—[1]	—	6.5	4
Small, single-engined scraper	—	—	—	8	6.5
Medium, twin-engined scraper	7	3.5	7	7	3
Medium, single-engined scraper	8	5	9	8.5	5
Large, twin-engined scraper	—	—	—	9	3.5
Large, single-engined scraper	9.5	—[2]	—	9.5	4.5
Towed scraper	—	—	—	—	—
Small dump truck (rigid chassis)	8.5	4.5	—	7.5	6
Small dump truck (articulated chassis)	6.5	6	—	7.5	5
Medium dump truck	—[3]	6.5	10	9.5	6
Large dump truck	—	—	—	10	5.5

Notes

1. The results for the 336 kW machines were not used for analysis as they were obtained for a relatively small range of MCVs with an associated low accuracy in the slope of the relation obtained between speed of travel and MCV.
2. The experimental result for the empty machines was omitted from the analysis in this case as it was so little different from that for the loaded machine and clearly was anomalous in comparison with the result for the empty medium single-engined scraper.
3. This value was omitted from the analysis as the discrepancy between the result of extrapolation of the speed/MCV relation and the productivity loss/MCV relation gave rise to doubts regarding the accuracy of the former result. The result calculated confirms the productivity loss/MCV relation.

maximum wheel load condition a range of curves relating to different tyre pressures. The shear strength axes of Fig. 24.1(a)–(c) can be converted to an MCV scale if desired using the data given in Fig. 10.17.

24.10 It should be appreciated that haul roads of this type will be subject to some deformation under repeated passes of the plant, and it may be necessary to apply a heavy roller from time to time during the earthmoving operations.

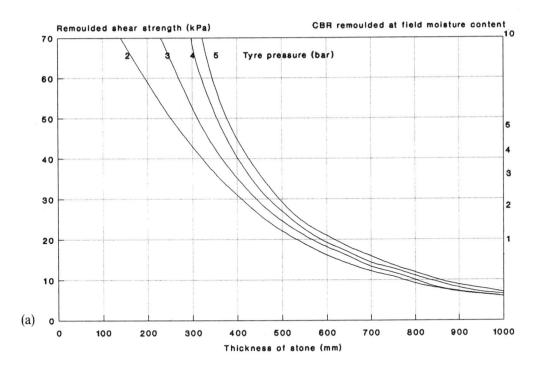

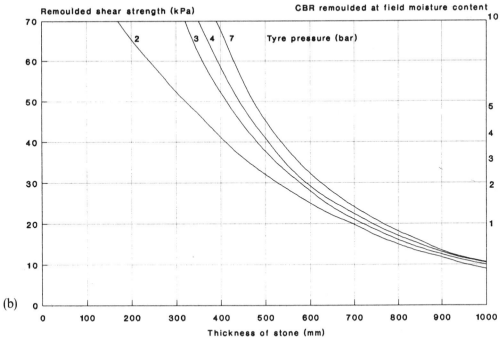

Figure 24.1 Design of haul road thickness: (a) 5000-kg maximum wheel load; (b) 9000-kg maximum wheel load

485

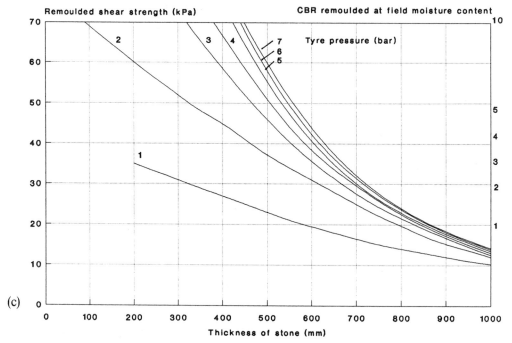

Figure 24.1—*contd*—(c) 12 000 kg maximum wheel load

References

1. Parsons, A. W. and P. Darley: *The effect of soil conditions on the operation of earthmoving plant*, Transport and Road Research Laboratory Report LR1034, TRRL, Crowthorne, 1982.
2. Parsons, A. W. and A. F. Toombs: *Pilot-scale Studies of the Trafficability of Soil by Earthmoving Vehicles*, Transport and Road Research Laboratory Research Report 130, TRRL, Crowthorne, 1988.

25. Roads over bridge decks

Introduction

25.1   The need for grade separation on modern highways has increased markedly the number of bridge structures and the question arises as to what changes are necessary in the normal pavement construction when a bridge is encountered.

25.2   When the bridge is of concrete construction and has a concrete deck, if the approach road is in concrete it is possible to carry the normal road slabs over the bridge, provided the usual provision for expansion is made. However, it is normal in Britain to use flexible construction over the bridge and on the approaches even where the road is otherwise in concrete construction. The reason for this is to allow subsidence at the bridge abutments to be corrected, which is more easily done where the pavement is flexible.

25.3   Over major river crossings it is common practice throughout the world to use light, orthotropic steel decks fabricated with 11- or 12-mm steel plates. Over such a structure the only form of pavement the design will permit is a relatively thin bituminous surfacing.

25.4   Whatever type of bridge is used, it is now regarded as essential that a waterproof membrane should be placed between the surfacing and the deck to protect the steel or concrete below from de-icing salts in solution applied to the road surface. The bridge surfacing thus has two components, the running surfacing and the waterproof layer.

Water-proofing systems

25.5   During the last 20 years numerous proprietary materials have been produced and marketed specifically for this purpose and engineers have found it very difficult to make an intelligent choice between them. In the middle eighties the TRRL began a very comprehensive field trial to assess a large number of these materials and a recent report published after three years' work gives an invaluable record of their performance.[1] Much of the information given here is taken from that report, but engineers are strongly advised to read the complete report itself before making any decision.

25.6   The systems available consist either of sheet materials or of liquid coatings bonded to the deck surface to form a waterproof membrane. The materials of both types, used in the TRRL trials, are shown in Figs 25.1 and 25.2.

25.7   The materials were generally laid under the supervision of the suppliers on

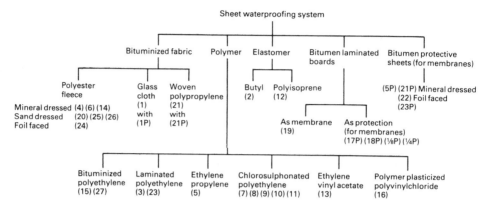

Note: Numbers in brackets refer to bay numbers in the trial

Figure 25.1   Sheet waterproofing systems used in trials

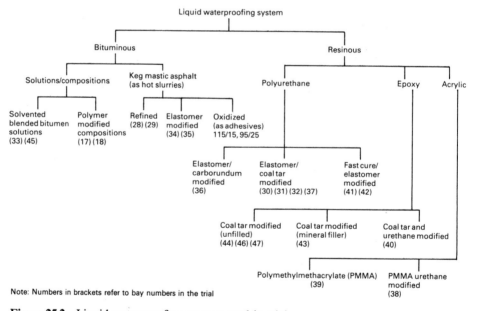

Note: Numbers in brackets refer to bay numbers in the trial

Figure 25.2   Liquid waterproofing systems used in trials

a concrete slab of size 24 × 6 m, divided into 48 equal-numbered bays. (The numbers shown in Figs 25.1 and 25.2 refer to these bays.)

Table 25.1 shows the primers and bonding materials used for the membrane applications and Table 25.2 shows the primers used for the liquid applications. (A more detailed description of the materials is given in Appendix A of reference 1.)

25.8   As an important part of the investigation, after the various waterproofing materials had been applied alternative surfacings of hot rolled asphalt basecourse

Table 25.1 Summary of sheet membrane application

Bay No	Membrane	Primer	Bonding medium	Method of application	Laid thickness (mm)
1	Bit. glasscloth*	Latex	Latex	Membrane laid on to adhesive coated concrete	1.9
2	Butyl elastomer felt laminated	Bit./solvent	Ox-bit. 95/25 (250 °C)	Pour and roll	3.9
3	Polyethylene Polymer	None	Self bit. based	Laid on to concrete	1.9
4	Bit. polyester fleece mineral dressed	Bit./solvent	Ox-bit. 115/15 (295 °C)	Pour and roll	5.2
5	Ethylene propylene polymer,†	Bit./solvent	115/15 (295 °C)	Pour and roll	3.6
6	Bit. polyester fleece mineral dressed	Bit./solvent	Modified bit.	Torch on	4.4
7	Chlorosulphonated polyethylene polymer	Bit./solvent	Ox-bit. 115/15 (295 °C)	Pour and roll	3.8
8	Chlorosulphonated polyethylene polymer	Bit./solvent	115/15 (255 °C)	Pour and roll	3.1
9	Chlorosulphonated polyethylene polymer	Bit./solvent	115/15 (255 °C)	Pour and roll	2.7
10	Chlorosulphonated polyethylene polymer	Bit./solvent	115/15 (255 °C)	Pour and roll	2.2
11	Chlorosulphonated polyethylene polymer	Bit./solvent	115/15 (255 °C)	Pour and roll	1.7
12	Polyisoprene elastomer	Latex	Latex	Membrane adhesive coated then laid on to concrete	1.9
13	Ethylene vinyl acetate polymer	Bit./solvent	Ox-bit. 95/25 (230 °C)	Pour and roll	1.6
14	Bit. polyester fleece mineral dressed	Bit./solvent	Ox-bit. 95/25 (195 °C)	Pour and roll	4.7
15	Bit. polyethylene polymer	Bit./solvent	Ox-bit. 115/15 (250 °C)	Pour and roll	3.9
16	Plasticized polyvinyl chloride polymer	Bit./solvent	Ox-bit. 95/25 (260 °C)	Pour and roll	2.0
18	(See Table 25.2)				
19	Bit. laminated board	Bit./solvent	Self bit. based	Laid on to concrete	5.0
20	Bit. polyester fleece	Bit./solvent	Self bit. based	Laid on to concrete	3.3
21	Bit. woven polypropylene*	Bit./solvent	Self bit. based	Laid on to concrete	1.8
22	Bit. aluminium foil	Bit./solvent	Self bit. based	Laid on to concrete	1.2
23	Laminated polyethylene polymer	Bit./solvent	Self bit. based	Laid on to concrete	1.5
24	Bit. polyester fleece Aluminium foil faced	Bit./solvent	Ox-bit. 95/25 (230 °C)	Pour and roll	4.9
25	Bit. polyester fleece. Sand dressed	Bit./solvent	95/25 (230 °C)	Pour and roll	4.3
26	Bit. polyester fleece. Sand dressed	Bit./solvent	95/25 (230 °C)	Pour and roll	2.2
27	Bit. polyethylene polymer	Bit./solvent	Self bit. both faces	Laid on to concrete	2.2

For detailed description of each membrane see Appendix A of reference 1
*Normally protected by bitumen laminated boards
†Normally protected by mineral dressed protective sheet
Bit.—Bitumen or bituminized
Ox-bit.—Oxidized bitumen—(   ). Temperature of bitumen

material and of a sand asphalt carpet (the basecourse asphalt with the coarse aggregate omitted) were laid in the normal manner. Saw cuts were then made through the surfacings down to the concrete deck so that individual squares of the surfacing could be lifted where necessary to study the appearance and waterproofing properties of the membrane following the rolling of the surfacing.

25.9   The results of the tests are summarized in Tables 25.3 and 25.4. These show

Table 25.2   Summary of liquid membrane application

Bay No	Membrane	Primer	Method of application	Laid thickness, mm
17	Polymer modified* bit. 2 part	None	1 coat slurried on to concrete	10.6[A]
18	Polymer modified* bit. 2 part	None	1 coat slurried on to concrete	6.3[B]
28	Mastic asphalt	Bit/solvent	1 coat hot slurried on to concrete	24.4
29	Mastic asphalt	None	1 coat hot slurried on to concrete	20.7
30	Elastomer/coal tar modified polyurethane 2 part	Moisture cure polyurethane	1 coat trowelled on to concrete	0.7
31	Elastomer/coal tar modified polyurethane 2 part	Moist/chem cure polyurethane	1 coat spray applied to concrete	0.6
32	Elastomer/coal tar modified polyurethane 1 part	Polymeric emulsion	1 coat applied by paint roller	0.5
33	Blended bit.-in-solvent	None	1 coat applied by paint roller	0.4
34	Elastomer modified mastic asphalt	None	1 coat hot slurried on to concrete	11.9
35	Elastomer modified mastic asphalt	None	1 coat hot slurried on to concrete	11.9
36	Carborundum modified polyurethane 2 part	Moisture cure polyurethane	1 coat applied by paint roller	0.3
37	Elastomer/coal tar modified polyurethane 2 part	Water based epoxy emulsion	1 coat applied by paint brush	1.0
38	Urethane modified polymethyl-methacrylate acrylic 2 part	Acrylic	2 coats spray applied	2.2
39	Polymethylmethacrylate acrylic 2 part	Acrylic	2 coats spray applied	3.0
40	Urethane and coal tar mod epoxy with polyester fleece	Epoxy emulsion	2 coats squeegee applied	8.7
41	Rapid cure elastomer modified polyurethane 2 part	Chemical cure polyurethane	2 coats applied by paint brush	2.2
42	Rapid cure elastomer modified polyurethane 2 part	Chemical cure epoxy	1 coat spray applied to concrete	2.7
43	Elastomer/coal tar modified filled epoxy 2 part	Epoxy	1 coat squeegee applied to concrete	6.2
44	Elastomer/coal tar modified epoxy 2 part	None	2 coats applied by paint brush	0.8
45	Blended bit.-in-solvent	None	2 coats applied by yard brush	1.5
46	Elastomer/coal tar modified epoxy 2 part	None	2 coats applied by yard brush	1.2
47	Elastomer/coal tar modified epoxy 2 part	None	1 coat squeegee applied to concrete	0.6

For detailed description of each membrane see Appendix A of Reference 1
*Normally protected by bitumen laminated boards
A—Thickness included 6 mm thick protection board as part of system
B—Thickness included 3 mm thick protection board as part of system
Bit.—Bitumen

Table 25.3 Performance of membranes: Sheet systems

Bay no.	Membrane	Resistance to damage		Bond		
		Unprotected	Protected (Sand Carpet)	Concrete 3 years	Sand carpet	Base course
1	Bituminized glass cloth	●	●	●	●	○
2*	Butyl elastomer felt laminated	●	○	●	●	○
3	Laminated polyethylene polymer	●	★	●	○	○
4*	Bituminized Polyester Fleece—mineral dressed	●	○	●	★	○
5*	Ethylene propylene polymer	●	○	●	★	○
6*	Bituminized polyester fleece—mineral dressed	★	○	●	●	○
7*	Chlorosulphonated polyethlene polymer	●	○	●	●	○
8*	Chlorosulphonated polyethlene polymer	★	○	●	★	★
9	Chlorosulphonated polyethlene polymer	●	○	●	★	★
10	Chlorosulphonated polyethlene polymer	●	○	●	★	★
11	Chlorosulphonated polyethlene polymer	●	○	●	●	★
12	Polyisoprene elastomer	○	○	●	●	●
13*	Ethylene vinyl acetate polymer	●	○	●	●	●
14*	Bituminized polyester fleece—mineral dressed	★	○	●	○	○
15	Bituminized polyethylene polymer	●	○	●	○	○
16	Plasticized polyvinylchloride polymer	★	○	★	●	●
17*	Laminated bitumen board/polymer modified bitumen	●	○	★	★	○
18*	Laminated bitumen board/polymer modified bitumen	●	○	★	★	○
19*	Bitumen laminated board	●	○	★	★	○
20	Bituminized polyester fleece	●	○	★	○	○
21*	Bituminized woven polyproplene	●	○	★	○	○
22	Bituminized aluminium foil	●	●	●	○	○
23	Laminated polyethylene polymer	●	★	★	★	○
24*	Bituminized polyester fleece—aluminium foil faced	★	○	●	○	○
25	Bituminized polyester fleece—sand dressed	★	○	●	○	○
26	Bituminized polyester fleece—sand dressed	★	○	●	○	○
27	Bituminized polyethylene polymer	●	●	●	●	○

● Poor; ★ Moderate; ○ Good
* Systems with a Road and Bridges Certificate

Table 25.4   Performance of membranes: Liquid systems

Bay no.	Membrane	thick mm	Resistance to damage		Bond		
			Unprotected	Protected	Concrete 3 years	Sand carpet	Base course
28	Mastic asphalt (primed)	(24.4)	●	★	○	○	○
29	Mastic asphalt (unprimed)	(20.7)	●	★	●	○	○
30	Elastomer coal tar modified polyurethane	(0.7)	●	●	○	○	○
31	Elastomer coal tar modified polyurethane	(0.6)	●	●	○	●	●
32	Elastomer coal tar modified polyurethane	(0.5)	●	★	○	●	●
33	Blended bitumens-in-solvent	(0.4)	●	●	★	○	○
34	Elastomer modified mastic asphalt	(11.9)	★	★	●	○	○
35	Elastomer modified mastic asphalt	(11.9)	★	★	●	○	○
36	Carborundum modified polyurethane	(0.3)	●	●	●	●	●
37	Elastomer coal tar modified polyurethane	(1.0)	●	○	○	●	●
38	Urethane modified acrylic	(2.2)	○	○	○	★	★
39*	Polymethylmethacrylate acrylic	(3.0)	○	○	○	★²	★²
40*	Urethane and coal tar modified reinforced epoxy	(8.7)	○	○	○	★	★
41	Rapid cure elastomer modified polyurethane	(2.2)	○	○	○	★	★
42*	Rapid cure elastomer modified polyurethane	(2.7)	○	○	○	★¹	★¹
43	Coal tar modified mineral filled epoxy	(6.2)	○	○	○	●³	●³
44	Elastomer/coal tar modified epoxy	(0.8)	●	●	○	●	★
45	Blended bit.-in-solvent	(1.5)	●	●	●	○	○
46	Elastomer/coal tar modified epoxy	(1.2)	●	●	○	★	★
47	Elastomer/coal tar modified epoxy	(0.6)	●	●	○	★	★

●Poor; ★Moderate; ○Good
*Systems with a Road and Bridges Certificate
Since ⎧ 1 Bond modified by using a resinous tack coat
the ⎨ 2 Bond modified by using a resinous tack coat and no hand dressing
trial ⎩ 3 Bond modified by reducing quantity of hand dressing

that some of the liquid membranes performed well with regard to the resistance to damage by the surfacing compaction and provided a good bond with the concrete and a moderate bond with the surfacing. Others were much less effective in these respects. The sheet materials performed reasonably well when protected with the sand asphalt but much less well when the basecourse was laid directly upon them. The bonding of the sheet materials to the concrete was generally inferior to that of the liquid membranes.

The surfacing of orthotropic bridge decks

25.10   The surfacing of steel orthotropic bridge decks is much more difficult than that of concrete bridges. The deflection of steel decks under heavy wheels loads is considerable, owing to the comparatively thin steel used. This imposes requirements on the part of the surfacing materials which they are not able to meet over long periods. At present, the designs for such surfacings are a compromise between lightness and fatigue properties and lives much in excess of 10 years are difficult to achieve.

25.11   Prior to the construction of the River Severn bridge in the United Kingdom, the TRRL built two of the proposed sections into the slow lane of a heavily trafficked trunk road.[2] The panels were supported on transverse beams, as in the bridge, and the soil beneath was excavated to provide an underground laboratory with access to the underside of the steel panels (see Fig. 25.3). There were

Figure 25.3   The access pit under panel PII

two main purposes, (1) to study the integrity of the steel construction and welding and (2) to examine the performance of surfacings. Elastic deflections were also measured, and Fig. 25.4 shows the deflection dish for a 3175-kg wheel load passing over the gap between two longitudinal stiffeners. This wheel load was chosen because it is the one normally used in pavement deflection studies (see Chapter 29). The deflection measured on the bridge panel is about three times that expected on a typical motorway pavement.

25.12   The eight surfacings laid on the two panels are shown in Fig. 25.5. Those on panel PI were laid in the laboratory before the panel was positioned in the road.

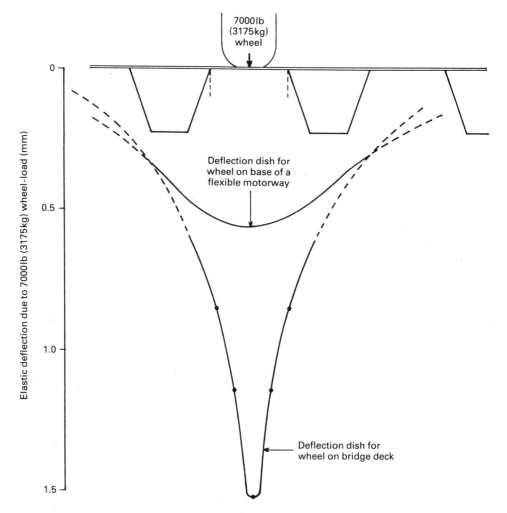

Figure 25.4 Comparison between the deflection of an orthotropic steel bridge deck and the deflection of a typical heavily trafficked road base, prior to surfacing (3175-kg wheel load)

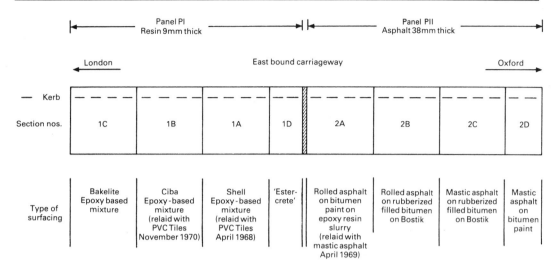

Figure 25.5 Surfacings used on the bridge deck panels

The other surfacings were laid *in situ*. The pretreatment of the surface of the plates consisted of a zinc spray followed by one coat of etch primer. The experimental sections were opened to traffic in November 1963 and the experiment was discontinued in January 1973. All the materials on panel PI were laid to a thickness of 9 mm and on panel PII to a thickness of 38 mm. The performance is summarized in Table 25.5.

Table 25.5 Summary of the surfacing trial

Section	Type of surfacing	Summary of performance
PANEL PI		
1A	SHELL epoxy-based mixture	After extensive cracking and loss of adhesion the original surfacing was replaced to the same formulation in October 1964. This second trial was replaced with PVC tiles in April 1968.
1B	CIBA epoxy-based mixture	Replaced with PVC tiles in November 1970 after cracking and loss of adhesion.
1C	BAKELITE epoxy-based mixture	Some cracking but no loss of adhesion.
1D	ESTERCRETE Polyester resin cement mixture	Extensive cracking in the first year of the trial, but no further deterioration.
PANEL PII		
2A	} Rolled Asphalt	Cracking and deformation within two years. Replaced
2B	} BS 594: 1961	with mastic asphalt in April 1969.
2C	} Mastic Asphalt	
2D	} BS 1447: 1962	In very good condition throughout the trial.

25.13   The mastic asphalt to BS 1447 gave the best overall performance. Only the bakelite epoxy-based mixture and the Estercrete polyester resin–cement mixture survived with some cracking. The rolled asphalt and the other epoxy mixtures had a comparatively short life. This trial confirmed that mastic asphalt was the best surfacing for British conditions and for this type of bridge. It appears that the epoxy based materials did not perform as well as they did in the concrete deck trials referred to above, owing no doubt to the increased flexibility of the foundation.

Report of B. L. Phillips

25.14   Prior to the surfacing of the Lower Yarra Bridge in Melbourne in the late seventies, B. L. Phillips, an engineer with the then Country Roads Board of Victoria, made a tour of inspection of major steel bridges in Europe and the United States. He subsequently produced a most useful report.[3] As copies of it are unlikely to be available now, a short review is given here, with the aid of tables taken from the report.

25.15   The bridges inspected are listed in Table 25.6 together with the principal dimensions. Table 25.7 gives details of the pretreatment of the decks and the types and thickness of the surfacings used, and Table 25.8 summarizes the condition of the surfacings at the time of the inspections (1973).

Table 25.6   Bridges included in tour of inspection[3]

Bridge	Location	Type	Steel-decked section	
			Length, ft	Width, ft
Auckland Harbour*	Auckland, New Zealand	Box girder	3 597	2 × 32
Queens Way	Long Beach, California, USA	Box girder	1 200	98
San Mateo–Hayward	San Francisco, California, USA	Box girder	5 500	80
Port Mann	Vancouver, BC, Canada	Arch	1 920	54
Mission	Mission City, BC, Canada	Box Girder		
Poplar Street	St Louis, Missouri, USA	Box Girder	2 165	113
Severn	Bristol, Glouc., UK	Suspension	5 240	86
Wye	Bristol, Glouc., UK	Cable stayed	1 340	87
Firth of Forth	Edinburgh, Scotland, UK	Suspension	3 300	86
Oberkasseler	Düsseldorf, Germany	Cable stayed	2 000	120
Düsseldorf North	Düsseldorf, Germany	Cable stayed	1 560	89
Mulheim	Cologne, Germany	Suspension	2 300	$88\frac{1}{2}$
Zoo	Cologne, Germany	Box girder	1 960	108
Severin	Cologne, Germany	Cable stayed	1 486	97
Caronte	Marseilles, France	Propped box girder	984	98
West Gate	Melbourne, Vic. Australia	Cable stayed	2 800	120

*Data applies to extensions only.

Table 25.7 Details of deck treatment and of surfacing[3]

Bridge	Deck Plate Thickness	Surfacing	
		Deck treatment and surfacing constituents	Thickness
Auckland Harbour	$\frac{7}{16}$ in (11 mm)	Sand blast, zinc sprayed, etch primed. Cut-back-bitumen bond coat. $1\frac{1}{4}$ in rubberized asphalt	$1\frac{1}{4}$ in (32 mm)
Queens Way	$\frac{1}{2}$ in (12 mm)	Sand blast, 3 ml inorganic zinc paint. Bitumen extended epoxy bond coat. 2 in epoxy asphalt	2 in (50 mm)
San Mateo–Hayward	$\frac{5}{8}$ in (16 mm)	Sand blast. 5 ml inorganic zinc paint. Bitumen extended epoxy. 2 in epoxy asphalt	2 in (50 mm)
Port Mann	$\frac{7}{16}$ in (11 mm)	Sand blast, 5 ml red lead epoxy. Coal tar epoxy+chips. Emulsion tack coat. $\frac{5}{8}$ in sand asphalt, $1\frac{1}{2}$ in asphaltic concrete	2 in (50 mm)
Mission	$\frac{5}{16}$ in (8 mm)	As for Port Mann	
Poplar Street	$\frac{9}{16}$ in (14 mm)	Sand blast, 3–5 ml inorganic zinc paint, 16–20 ml coal tar epoxy+stone chips. Rubberized emulsion tack coat, $2\frac{1}{2}$ in in rubberized asphalt.	$2\frac{1}{2}$ in (64 mm)
Severn	$\frac{7}{16}$ in (11 mm)	Sand blast, zinc sprayed etch primed. Bostik 1255 bond coat, $\frac{1}{8}$ in rubber bitumen compound, $1\frac{3}{8}$ in stone filled mastic asphalt.	$1\frac{1}{2}$ in (38 mm)
Wye	$\frac{7}{16}$ in (11 mm)	As for Severn	
Firth of Forth	$\frac{1}{2}$ in (12 mm)	As for Severn	
Oberkasseler	—	Sand blast, zinc Chromate, Isotex primer, Mastix insulating layer. 6 cm Gussasphalt.	$2\frac{1}{8}$ in (54 mm)
Düsseldorf North	$\frac{9}{16}$ in (14 mm)	Anchor bars, sand blast. Okta bonding compound. $1\frac{1}{2}$ in stone filled mastic asphalt.	$1\frac{1}{2}$ in (38 mm)
Mulheim	$\frac{1}{2}$ in (12 mm)	Sand blast. Bituminous paint $\frac{3}{64}$ in thick, $\frac{5}{16}$ in mastic asphalt, $\frac{3}{4}$ in Gussasphalt, Bitumen impregnated paper, $\frac{7}{8}$ in Gussasphalt with stone chips.	2 in (50 mm)
Zoo	$\frac{1}{2}$ in (12 mm)	Sand blast, cold bituminous tack coat, 8–10 mm mastic asphalt, 3 cm asphaltic concrete, 3 cm Gussasphalt, Synopal chips rolled into surface	$2\frac{1}{8}$ in (54 mm)
Severin	$\frac{3}{8}$ in (9 mm)	Sand blast, $\frac{1}{4}$-in cold bituminous layer, 0.2 mm aluminium foil, $\frac{3}{4}$ in mastic asphalt, $1\frac{1}{8}$ in Gussasphalt, Synopal chips rolled into surface.	$2\frac{1}{2}$ in (64 mm)
Caronte	$\frac{5}{8}$ in (16 mm)	Sand blast, 3 mm Mobil plast. bond coat. 5 cm asphalt using Mobil plast. binder	2 in (50 mm)

25.16 In his overall conclusion, Phillips stated that in his consideration the optimum in economy and life could be obtained from both the structure and surfacing if the following criteria were realized:

1. the minimum deck plate thickness is $\frac{1}{2}$ in;
2. the maximum longitudinal stiffener spacing is 12 in;
3. the maximum floor beam spacing is 12 ft;

Table 25.8   Condition survey of the bridges inspected in 1973[3]

Bridge	Age at inspection, years	Traffic vol. V.p.d.	Remarks	Estimated total life, years
Auckland Harbour	4	56 100	Cracking over webs, bond failure, surface slippage	6–9
Queens Way	4	15 000	Excellent condition	15–20
San Mateo–Hayward	6	30 000	Aggregate polishing. Small amount of cracking	15
Port Mann	9	30 000	Cracking at paver joints. Wear in wheel tracks little traces of cracking	14–15
Mission	$\frac{1}{4}$	Approx. 10 000	Excellent condition	20
Poplar Street	6	80 000	Many longitudinal cracks and some lateral cracks. Maintenance needed	12–16
Severn	7	30 000	Few isolated cracks, some blisters. Poor skid resistance which has been rectified	19–20
Wye	7	30 000	Longitudinal cracks over webs (under control) otherwise as for Severn Bridge	19–20
Firth of Forth	9	24 000	Longitudinal cracking over stringers (largely under control). Surface beginning to polish	19–20
Oberkasseler	Nil	Approx. 30 000	Surfacing work not complete	
Düsseldorf North	16		Surfacing was replaced one year ago. Required because of wear in wheel tracks	15
Mulheim	22	50 000	Surfacing generally in poor condition. Out of shape with cracking evident. Should have been replaced by now.	22
Zoo	7		Abrasion in wheel tracks. Large areas failed due to water intrusion and frost neave.	12–13
Severin	14		Some longitudinal and lateral movement of surfacing. Abrasion in wheel tracks. Reasonable condition	19–20
Caronte	$1\frac{1}{4}$	Approx. 20 000	Generally excellent condition. Paving joints open.	12–15

4. the minimum pavement thickness is 2 in;
5. a resin-based bond coat is used;
6. a resin-based binder or binder with elastomer is used in asphalt surfacing;
7. aggregate exposed to traffic have a minimum polished stone value of 50.

25.17   After 20 years' experience with the Severn and Forth bridges and under the climatic conditions of the UK there is considerable confidence in the use of mastic asphalt. It seems probable that in hotter climates mastic asphalt made from a harder grade of bitumen would be equally successful. It is noted that this form of construction, using a relatively hard grade of binder in the mastic asphalt, is being used for the complex system of cable-stayed bridges forming the Honshu–Shikoku crossing in Japan.[4] The view in Britain is that surfacings on this type of bridge should not exceed 50 mm in thickness.

References

1. Price, A. R.: *A Field Trial of Waterproofing Systems for Concrete Bridge Decks*, Transport and Road Research Laboratory Research Report 185, TRRL, Crowthorne, 1989.
2. Nunn, D. E. and S. A. H. Morris: *Trials of Orthotropic Bridge Deck Panels Under Traffic Loading.* Transport and Road Research Laboratory Report LR627, TRRL, Crowthorne, 1974.
3. Phillips, B. L.: *Surfacing of Orthotropic Steel Deck Bridges*, Country Roads Board of Victoria, Australia, 1973.
4. Hiroyuki Tada and Takahiro Fukui: Surface pavement for Honshu–Shikoku Bridges, *Proc. 13th Meeting of the Australian Road Research Board*, vol. 13, part 4, 1986.

PART SEVEN Surface Characteristics of Pavements

26. The riding quality of pavements and its measurement

Introduction

26.1　In the twenties rural roads in the UK consisted of the original water-bound macadam to which liberal surface dressings of hot tar had been added. The riding quality by modern standards was extremely poor, and the situation was not helped by the tight suspension and indifferent shock absorbers of the vehicles of the period. It was at that time that attention was first given to the development of profilometers to quantify riding quality. The need for a rolling 'fixed' datum against which surface undulations could be measured was recognized early and by the thirties the multiwheeled profilometer shown in Fig. 26.1 had been developed. The

Figure 26.1　The Multi-wheeled profilometer

multiplicity of hinged bogies provided the 'fixed' datum, and profile measurements were made by a central recording wheel. This machine, which remained in service until the seventies, is discussed in Para. 26.8.

26.2   Riding quality, as interpreted by the road user, is highly subjective and therefore very difficult to quantify in engineering terms. Much the same problem also arose in the thirties when possible restrictions on the noise made by motor vehicles and motor horns came under consideration. Experienced observer panels were found to rate middle-order noises in a quite different order of nuisance on different days. With the increasing 'average' smoothness of road surfacings the problem of subjective rating has increased and there is a tendency for tyre and body noise to be confused with riding quality.

26.3   In some ways it is to be regretted that in the USA the subjective approach was used to assess serviceability in the AASHO road test. This has made it difficult, without studying the original data sheets, to separate the engineering conclusions from the impressions of road users. An implication from the work of the statisticians involved in the road test is that the change of slope variance of the surfacing with time is the major factor in determining pavement serviceability, and that the panels of observers used were able to differentiate between the effects of slope variance and, for example, integrated up-and-down movements. As a consequence, since 1962 effort has been expended in developing equipment to measure slope variance with greater precision than was possible during the road test, and in refining the relations between cracking and deformation and PSI. In the late sixties the multiwheel profilometer referred to in Para. 26.1 was used on many of the full-scale road experiments described in Chapter 18 and the profiles were analysed manually using the equivalent of a 230-mm (9-in) base line, as adopted in the Chloe profilometer used in the road test. In this way approximate correlations were obtained between PSI and the UK definitions of the 'critical' and 'failed' state of flexible and concrete pavements.

26.4   Modern roadlaying machines with sophisticated methods of level control, used in conjunction with a workable specification relating to the magnitude of acceptable surface undulations, should produce a satisfactory pavement, given an experienced contractor and proper supervision. However, the use of end-product specifications allows a certain amount of experimentation on the part of the contractor and this means that the riding quality may or may not be acceptable when the job is finished. At that stage it is difficult to make improvements.

Surface finish required for pavements in the United Kingdom

26.5   To ensure that the various layers of a pavement are of adequate thickness, relative to the specification, and to facilitate the achievement of an adequate riding quality, tolerances are set for the surface levels of the various courses by the UK Department of Transport specification (clause 701). These tolerances are shown in Table 26.1, and they are controlled by level measurements made over a grid with

Table 26.1 Tolerances in surface levels of pavement courses

Courses	
Road surfaces	± 6 mm
Basecourse	± 6 mm
Upper roadbase in pavements without basecourse	± 8 mm
Roadbase other than above	±15 mm
Sub-base under concrete pavement surface slabs laid full thickness in one operation by machines with surface compaction	±10 mm
Sub-bases other than above	+10 mm
	−30 mm

specified spacings, the levels being checked at the same locations on all the pavement courses.

26.6 To enable these checks to be made quickly and accurately, a laser-controlled levelling system is available.[1] The equipment consists of a rotating laser source capable of generating a datum plane with an effective radius up to 300 m, and a levelling staff fitted with a movable optical receiver, sensitive to laser light. The receiver travels up and down the staff until it locks onto the laser plane. Longitudinal profiles obtained in this manner on the various layers of two flexible pavements are shown in Fig. 26.2. These examples show how irregularities in the lower courses are to some extent reflected in the running surface, and emphasize the need to get the best possible profiles at each level.

26.7 In addition to the tolerances of surface levels, the Department of Transport specification also limits the number of surface irregularities of magnitudes 4 and 7 mm which are permitted in a given length of road. These requirements are shown in Table 26.2, where Category A roads are generally those which permit high speeds, such as trunk roads and motorways, and Category B roads are more minor, where the speed is unlikely to exceed 50 mile/h. On newly constructed roads compliance with Table 26.2 is normally checked by a hand-propelled travelling straight-edge of the type shown in Fig. 26.3.

Recent developments in profile measurement

26.8 The multiwheel profilometer shown in Fig. 26.1 was essentially a research tool. It was propelled by hand and its speed had to be controlled to prevent bounce of the sensor wheel and overrunning of the mechanical recorder. Although it was invaluable during the changeover period between hand and machine laying of both bituminous and concrete roads, there was never any possibility that it could be used for routine acceptance testing.

26.9 Consideration was being given in Britain to the development of more robust, if less accurate, forms of towed profilometer based on the AASHO Chloe design, when contactless sensor technology using the reflection of a pulsating laser

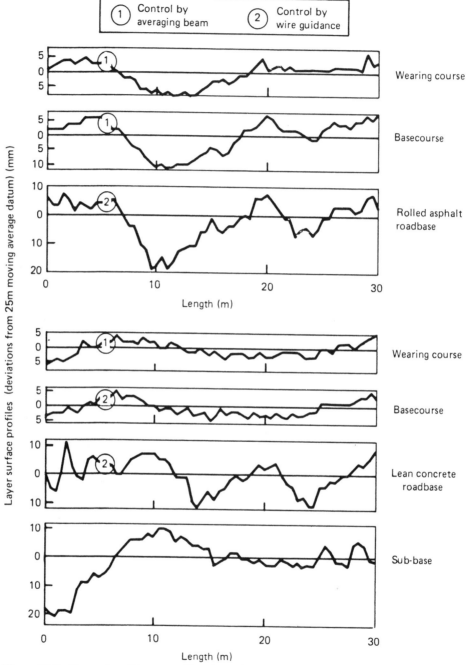

Figure 26.2 Examples of layer profiles from flexible construction obtained with different control methods (profile features longer than 25 m have been removed)

Table 26.2 Maximum permitted number of surface irregularities

Irregularity	Surfaces of carriageways, hard strips and hard shoulders				Surfaces of lay-bys, service areas all bituminous base-courses and upper roadbases in pavements without basecourses			
	4 mm		7 mm		4 mm		7 mm	
Length (m)	300	75	300	75	300	75	300	75
Category A roads	20	9	2	1	40	18	4	2
Category B roads	40	18	4	2	60	27	6	3

beam became available. In the last 15 years highly sophisticated equipment has been developed at the TRRL using this principle to measure longitudinal profile, rut depth, and the macrotexture of road surfacings. The latter application is considered in Chapter 27.

26.10   The basic design of the contactless displacement transducer is shown in Fig. 26.4.[2] A parallel beam of pulsating laser light is projected at an angle of 45° onto the surface being examined. Diffuse scattering of the laser light occurs at the point of contact on the surface, and a proportion is focused by a receiving lens onto a linear array of photodiodes to actuate one or more of the diodes. If the reflecting surface drops to position 2 or position 3 in Fig. 26.4, then the image will move across the photodiodes to give a linear relationship between the level of the surface and the activated diode. The laser source emits pulses of light of duration 2×10^{-7} seconds. It is estimated that the projection lens collects and transmits 64 per cent of the laser energy into an area on the road 0.25 mm wide by 3.8 mm long. The receiving lens focuses this area of light so that it falls on only one of the line of photodiodes over which the reflected beam sweeps. The individual photodiodes have a receiving area approximately 0.09 mm wide by 1 mm long and this determines their spacing.

26.11   The original version of the TRRL high-speed profilometer using laser sensors had a 5-m beam fabricated from three alloy tubes stiffened with cross-members as shown in Fig. 26.5. It had four sets of laser and receiver assemblies spaced along the length of the beam, which was mounted on a two-wheel unsprung axle. The end of the beam remote from the wheels was attached to the towing vehicle, which operated at speeds up to 80 km/h, and carried the associated electronic units and the computer used for the analysis of the data.

26.12   It will be appreciated that no profilometer of this type can give an accurate record of changes of road surface level in absolute terms, ranging from the texture of the surfacing to large-scale undulations associated with the ground contours. This would require accurate measurements from a horizontal plane above the highest point of the length of road under consideration. What such a profilometer can do is to give a reasonably accurate picture of the large and small undulations over a length of about 30 m. The machine does this by providing a running analysis of the surface

Figure 26.3 The rolling straightedge: (a) assembled. (b) component parts

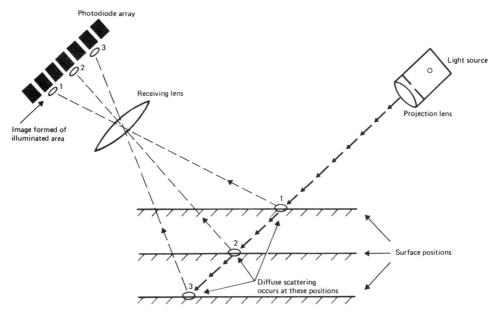

Figure 26.4   Basic contactless displacement transducer design

Figure 26.5   TRRL High-Speed Road Monitor

irregularity over lengths, of, for example, 3 and 30 m. The following six paragraphs are reproduced from reference 3, with the paragraph, figure, and equation numbers modified to accommodate the system used in this chapter.

26.13 The operation of the multisensor profilometer is based upon the three-sensor device shown schematically in Fig. 26.6. Three sensors are mounted in a straight line on a rigid beam at P, Q, and R, and measure the distances to the road surface; the sensors are equidistantly spaced at a distance δ apart. Denoting these distances by v_1, v_2, and v_3 respectively, define the quantity u_k as

$$u_k = \tfrac{1}{2}v_3 - v_2 + \tfrac{1}{2}v_1 \qquad (26.1)$$

when the front sensor, P, is at $x = k\delta$.

Since PQR is a straight line with Q as its mid-point, the height of Q above the x-axis is

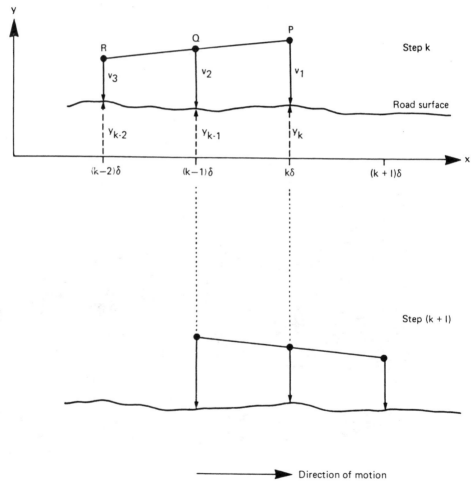

Figure 26.6 Two successive measurement positions of a three-sensor profilometer

mid-way between the heights of P and R; thus

$$v_2 + y_{k-1} = \tfrac{1}{2}[(v_3 + y_{k-2}) + (v_1 + y_k)] \qquad (26.2)$$

By combining Eqs (26.1) and (26.2), it may be shown that the profile height y_k at $x = k\delta$ is given by

$$y_k = -2u_k + 2y_{k-1} - y_{k-2} \qquad (26.3)$$

The device now moves forward in steps of δ, and successive values of u_k are found. These are, in fact, proportional to the second differences of the profile height y at intervals of δ.

26.14   At each step of the profilometer, the required value y_k may be obtained from u_k and the previous two values of y. Ideally, this recursive recovery process is perfect and the true height of the profile is found at the points δ apart where the sensors make their measurements. The recovery process is able to compensate for both the vertical motion and the pitching of the beam as it moves forward over the profile because the centre and rear sensor measurements are made at the same points as those made, on the previous step, by the front and centre sensors respectively.

26.15   In practice, three types of error occur which result in deviations, increasing with the distance travelled, between the true profile and the measured one:

1. When the recursion process is started, two initial conditions are required, corresponding to the heights of the profile at the centre and rear sensor positions. These values are usually taken as zero, but errors result unless the profilometer starts on a flat, horizontal surface. Incorrect initial conditions result in a linear deviation of the measured profile from the true one; however, for the prototype profilometer the erroneous slope is likely to be less than 1 in 50.

2. The beam carrying the sensors has to be rigid. Flexing will contribute curvature to the measured profile and a permanent deformation of the beam, unless exactly allowed for in the calculations, produces a parabolic error. For the prototype profilometer, the beam is rigid to within the resolution of the sensors.

3. As the profilometer moves forward, measurements are taken at distances nominally δ apart. Successive sensor measurements are not made at precisely the same points on the profile because of errors in step size, transverse movements of the beam, cornering, and the texture of the road surface. When cornering on a road with a crossfall, the measured vertical curvature of the road is greater than that which actually exists because the three sensors lie along a chord of the lateral curve rather than on the arc itself. To reduce the effect of the surface texture, which would be the dominant one, several sensor readings may be taken while the profilometer moves through the distance δ, and their average is then used to calculate an average profile height over this distance. Successive values are obtained at intervals of δ as before. The surface texture results in a random error in profile, the r.m.s. value of which increases with the distance travelled. For a profilometer of the type shown in Fig. 26.7(A), having the dimension δ equal to 108 mm and moving at 50 km/h, with each sensor making 2000 measurements per second, the theoretical r.m.s. 'texture error' as a function of distance is given by curve A of Fig. 26.8, where a road surface texture of 2 mm r.m.s. has been assumed. After travelling 10 m, the r.m.s. error would be 0.62 m.

26.16   This error may be reduced by increasing the spacing between the intermediate and rear sensors leading to an asymmetrical profilometer of overall length $m\delta$ as shown in Fig. 26.7(B). The step size remains equal to the spacing of the front and intermediate sensors, but the quantity u_k is now defined as

$$u_k = \frac{1}{m}v_3 - v_2 + \left(1 - \frac{1}{m}\right)v_1 \qquad (26.4)$$

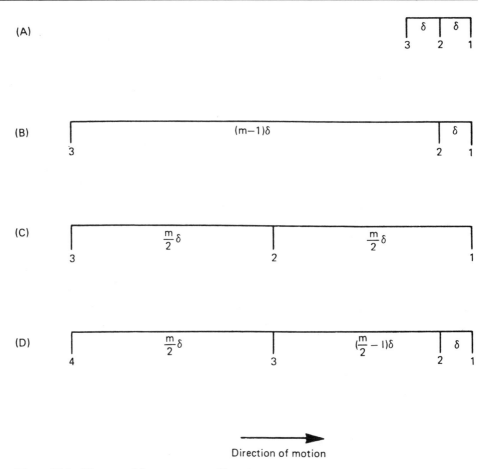

Direction of motion

Figure 26.7   Three- and four-sensor profilometers

and the recursive recovery process is given by

$$y_k = -\left(\frac{m}{m-1}\right)u_k + \left(\frac{m}{m-1}\right)y_{k-1} - \left(\frac{1}{m-1}\right)y_{k-m} \qquad (26.5)$$

The texture errors occurring with a profilometer having m equal to 40 and operating under the same conditions as before are shown in Fig. 26.8, curve B.

26.17   Consideration of a symmetrical profilometer of overall length 40δ moving in steps of 20δ with averaging over this length (see Fig. 26.7(C)), leads to curve C of Fig. 26.8 where the error is only 0.25 per cent of that for the first profilometer configuration. This improved performance is achieved at the expense of a wider spacing between the profile measurement points. A further result of the averaging process is that the effect of the finite resolution of the sensors is reduced.

26.18   It is desirable to retain the horizontal resolution of the profilometer shown in Fig. 26.7(B) while reducing the errors of those of that shown in Fig. 26.7(C). This may be done by combining a symmetrical profilometer with an asymmetrical one, both of overall

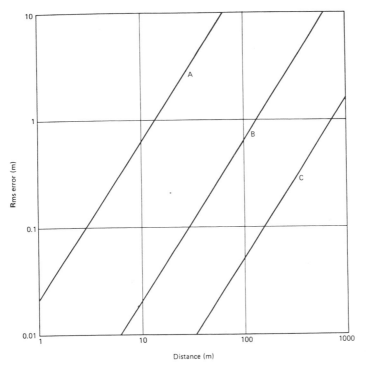

Figure 26.8 RMS error resulting from surface texture as a function of distance

length 40δ, so that the arrangement of Fig. 26.7(D) is obtained involving the use of four sensors. It is then possible to use the asymmetrical profilometer (Sensors 1, 2 and 4) to provide profile measurements at intervals of δ and to correct its drift at intervals of 20δ using the symmetrical profilometer (sensors 1, 3 and 4). The prototype profilometer shown in Fig. 26.5 was constructed to Fig. 26.7(D). In use the framework is enveloped in polyurethane foam to damp mechanical vibrations.

26.19   As part of its proving trials, tests were carried out in Turkey to examine the performance of the high-speed profilometer under hot ambient temperature conditions.[4] Figure 26.9 shows details of one of many comparisons made between surface profiles determined by direct levelling and by the profilometer. To ensure that the same path was followed using each method, the profilometer was fitted, at the rear mid-centre, with a water drip to define its path. It is clear that excellent agreement was found. The method discussed above, including all four sensors, was used in the case of the profilometer measurements.

Measurement of rut depth

26.20   On in-service roads, the high-speed profilometer can also be used to measure the depth of rutting in wheel tracks generated in the left-hand lane by heavy

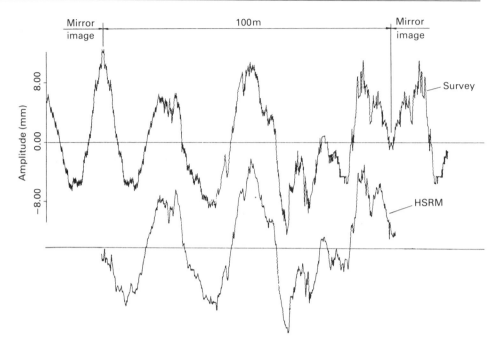

Figure 26.9 Comparison of HSRM and surveyed profiles for section 4

commercial vehicles. Observations made on trunk and principal roads have shown the centres of the two wheel paths for 70 per cent of such vehicles are separated by 1.8 m. Later versions of the high-speed profilometer have been modified to have this track width and an additional central laser assembly has been fitted a little forward of the trailer axle, as shown in Fig. 26.10[5].

26.21   It follows from Fig. 26.10 that if the distance between the rut-depth sensor

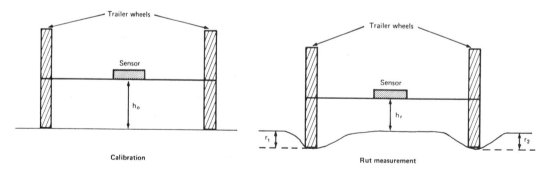

Figure 26.10 Rut-depth measurement

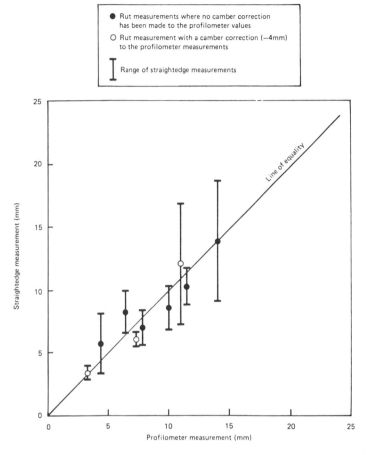

Figure 26.11 Comparison of rut depths measured by straight-edge and profilometer on roads with and without a camber

and the road surface is h_0 when there is no rutting and is h_r when the profilometer wheels are in ruts of depth r_1 and r_2, then the mean rut depth is given by $(h_0 - h_r)$ divided by 2.

26.22   Accuracy and repeatability of the measurement of rut depth in this manner does depend on the care of the operator in following the alignment of the wheel tracks. Figure 26.12 shows that with a trained operator repeatability over a considerable length of road can be obtained.

The High Speed Road Monitor

26.23   The three functions of (1) profile evaluation, (2) rut depth measurement, and (3) macrotexture determination (discussed in Chapter 27) have been integrated into

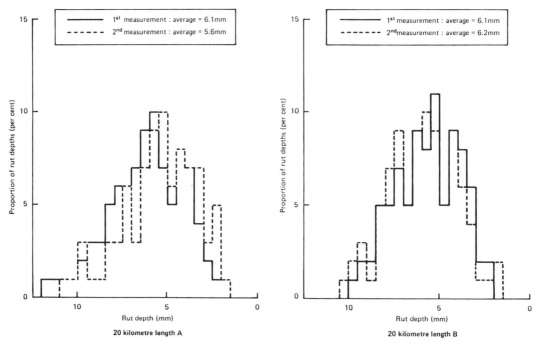

Figure 26.12   Comparison of distribution of rut depths obtained from repeat measurements on each of two 20-km lengths of motorway

a single machine called the TRRL High Speed Road Monitor.[6] This machine allows all three functions to be carried out during a single run. To permit this, the four sensors necessary to measure surface profile and macrotexture have been moved to the left-hand side of the trailer, i.e., in the nearside wheel path when the vehicle is driven normally, and the additional sensor for rut depth measurement is between the wheel-tracks where there will normally be little deformation. The layout of the sensors is shown in Fig. 26.13.

Table 26.3   Evenness/ride criteria

Moving-average length (m)	Variance levels (mm²) to give a ride that is:	
	Good/ acceptable	Poor/ very poor
3	≤ 1.0	≥ 3.0
10	≤ 4.0	> 16.0
30	≤ 55.00	≥ 150.0

The High Speed Road Monitor and riding quality

26.24   Work is currently being carried out at the TRRL to correlate rut depth and surface profile with subjective riding quality. Figure 26.14 shows histograms of rut depth and profile variance (square of standard deviation) determination; a moving average length of 3 m was used in the analysis. On the basis of this work an approximate relationship between profile variance and riding quality has been proposed,[6] (Table 26.3). This will no doubt be further refined as more evidence becomes available.

The Bump Integrator

26.25   Another relatively rapid method for assessing the irregularity of road surfaces is the Bump Integrator (BI) shown in Fig. 26.15. Originally designed in the United States, the machine has been in use in Europe for about 40 years.

26.26   The trailer, a heavy rectangular chassis, is supported on a central wheel

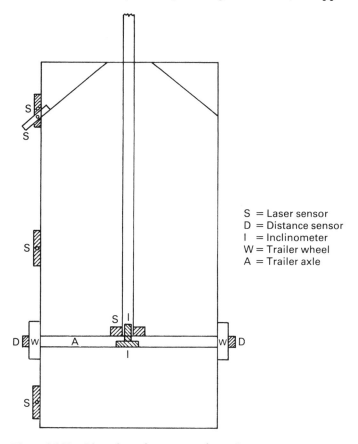

S = Laser sensor
D = Distance sensor
I = Inclinometer
W = Trailer wheel
A = Trailer axle

Figure 26.13   Plan view of sensor configuration on HRM trailer

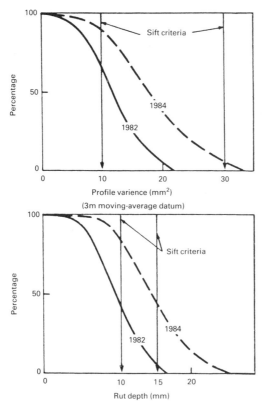

Figure 26.14   Histograms of profile and rut surveys

supported by two single-leaf springs positioned one on each side of the wheel. Two dashpot assemblies positioned between the chassis and the wheel axle provide viscous damping. In operation, the downward movement of the wheel relative to the chassis is summed by a mechanical integrator unit fitted to the chassis. The unevenness index, r, is given by the integrated vertical movements divided by the distance travelled. The integrator unit measures only in inches per mile (1 in/mile = 1.58 cm/km).

26.27   The standard speed of operation is 20 mile/h (32 km/h). However, recent research has shown[7] that higher speeds can be used if the following corrections are made:

For uneven surfaces and operating speeds 20–65 km/h and for even surfaces and operating speeds 20–32 km/h,

$$r_{32} = \sqrt{\frac{V}{32}}(r_V - 30) + 30 \text{ in/mile} \qquad (26.6)$$

for even surfaces and operating speeds 32−65 km/h

$$r_{32} = \frac{V}{32}(r_V - 30) + 30 \text{ in/mile} \tag{26.7}$$

where r_{32} is the standard value at 32 km/h and r_V and V refer to the higher speed of operation.

In practice, Eq. (26.7) would be applicable in the great majority of cases where speed corrections would be needed. For operating speeds that deviate from the standard speed by less than 10 km/h, the accuracy of estimation of the index r_{32} using Eq. (26.6) or (26.7) is within 10 per cent of the true value. The accuracy reduces to within 20 per cent for a deviation of 30 km/h; the correction procedures are applicable only within the speed range 20–65 km/h. In the practical operation of the BI, maintaining a constant speed is often difficult and the correction procedures given above then improve the flexibility of use of the machine.

26.28   A very useful correlation has been made between the variance of the road profile as determined by the High Speed Road Monitor and the Bump Integrator r-value. This is shown in Fig. 26.16.

Figure 26.15   The Bump-Integrator

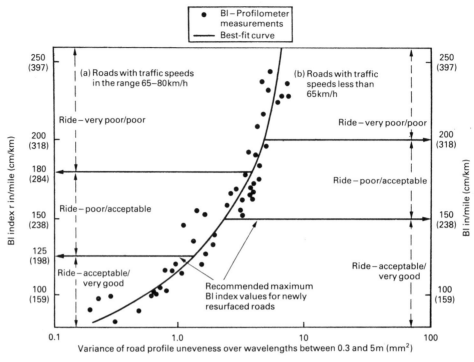

Figure 26.16 Relationship of BI index, *r*, to profile unevenness and to ride assessment on roads with different traffic speeds

References

1. McLellan, J. C.: *Pavement Thickness, Surface Evenness and Construction Practice*, Transport and Road Research Laboratory Supplementary Report 706, TRRL, Crowthorne, 1982.
2. Still, P. B. and M. A. Winnett: *Development of a Contactless Displacement Transducer*, Transport and Road Research Laboratory Report 690, TRRL, Crowthorne, 1975.
3. Dickerson, R. S. and D. G. W. Mace: *A High-speed Road Profilometer—Preliminary Description*, Transport and Road Research Laboratory Supplementary Report 182, TRRL, Crowthorne, 1976.
4. Petts, R. C.: *The TRRL High-speed Road Monitor. Evaluation of Performance in Hot Ambient Conditions in Turkey*, Transport and Road Research Laboratory Contractor's Report 3, TRRL, Crowthorne, 1984. (Prepared by Howard Humphreys and Partners.)
5. Jordan, P. G. and P. B. Still: *Measurement of Rut-depth in Road Surfaces by the TRRL Highspeed Profilometer*, Transport and Road Research Laboratory Supplementary Report 1037, TRRL, Crowthorne, 1982.
6. Jordan, P. G., B. W. Ferne, and D. R. C. Cooper: An integrated system for the evaluation of road pavements. *Proc. 6th Int. Conf. on the Structural Design of Asphalt Pavements, Ann Arbor, Michigan, 1987*, University of Michigan, Ann Arbor, 1987.
7. Jordan, P. G. and J. C. Young: *Developments in the Calibration and Use of the Bump-integrator for Ride Assessment*, Transport and Road Research Laboratory Supplementary Report 604, TRRL, Crowthorne, 1980.

27. The skid-resistance of pavements and its measurement

Introduction

27.1   Prior to the introduction of mechanically propelled transport the slipperiness of road surfaces was important only in relation to the ability of horses to retain an adequate foothold. The higher speeds of motor vehicles and the comparatively low friction between rubber tyres and the types of urban road surfaces then in use soon produced an acute skidding problem indicated by a steady increase in the number and seriousness of skidding accidents. As early as 1906 a Parliamentary Select Committee was set up in Britain to investigate the causes and control of skidding.

27.2   Since then research into the skidding problem has been two-pronged. First, it has been necessary to establish from accident statistics limits of slipperiness which can be tolerated on various types of road, bearing in mind, on the one hand, the cost of accidents, and, on the other, the increased cost of providing high-quality non-skid road surfaces. Secondly, the attributes necessary in the road surface both to obtain and retain adequate resistance to skidding have needed close study. Both these facets of the skidding problem require reliable methods of measuring the skid resistance of road surfaces.

Measurement of the slipperiness of road surfaces

27.3   The Special Advisory Committee of the Road Board (see Para. 2.11) organized long-term studies into the skidding problem nearly 70 years ago. The work was initially carried out at the National Physical Laboratory. It was early recognized that static measurements of the coefficient of friction could do no more than place road materials in an approximate order of slipperiness. The dependence of skid-resistance on vehicle speed and weather conditions necessitated standardized tests by which these factors could be investigated systematically. By the late twenties the concepts of sideway force coefficient and braking force coefficient had been introduced and machines for their measurement had been constructed.

27.4   The sideway force coefficient (SFC) was originally measured using a motorcycle combination in which the sidecar wheel could be fixed during measurements at an angle of 20° to the direction of travel, see Fig. 27.1. The force at right angles to the plane of the inclined wheel expressed as a fraction of the vertical

Figure 27.1   Motorcycle and sidecar for measuring sideway force coefficient

force acting on the wheel is defined as the sideway force coefficient (SFC). Simulta-neous measurement of the two forces enables a continuous record of SFC to be obtained. To standardize the process, a smooth tyre of standard hardness was specified and for routine testing a standard speed of 30 mile/h (48 km/h) has always been used. After the Second World War the skidding motorcycle was replaced by a series of test cars working on the same principle, in which the inclined wheel was located within the vehicle chassis, (see Fig. 27.2). With rapid advances in electronics the recording methods used have been subject to continuous improvement.

27.5   Since skidding is largely a wet-road problem, routine skid-resistance tests normally require prior wetting of the road surface by a water bowser. The SCRIM (Sideway Force Coefficient Routine Investigation Machine) equipment more recently developed at TRRL (Fig. 27.3) carries its own water supply, the road surface being wetted in advance of the test wheel. With this equipment tests can be carried out with the machine operating as part of the normal road traffic.

27.6   The braking force coefficient (BFC) was originally measured by locking the wheels of a vehicle in motion and measuring the braking torque when skidding occurred. Subsequently, various types of towed-wheel braking force machines were developed, one of which is shown in Fig. 27.4. From the measured torque, the force

Figure 27.2 Sideway force test car

Figure 27.3 The Sideway Force Coefficient Routine Investigation Machine (SCRIM)

Figure 27.4   Braking force trailer

between the tyre and the road surface is deduced and this is expressed as a fraction of the vertical load on the wheel, to give the BFC. In use, the towed wheel is locked for periods of about two seconds and then released to give a series of isolated readings rather than a continuous record. This type of machine has generally been used for high-speed testing. Because of differences in the test procedure the SFC and BFC of identical surfaces measured under the same conditions are not numerically equal. The BFC is approximately 0.8 times the SFC.

27.7   Another machine widely used to assess the slipperiness of road surfaces is the Portable Skid Resistance Tester shown in Fig. 27.5.[1] This is often referred to as the Pendulum Tester. A pad of tyre-tread rubber mounted at the end of the pendulum arm slides over the road surface on which the machine is placed. The difference in height of the centre of gravity of the slider head between the horizontal release position and the highest point of the swing after the slider has passed over the road is used to calculate the loss of energy arising from friction. The test conditions, which must be closely observed and controlled, have been chosen so that the values read off the calibrated scale of the instrument correspond to the skid resistance value (SRV) of a patterned tyre skidding at 30 mile/h (48 km/h). The test is carried out with the pavement surface wetted in a standard manner, and a number of tests spaced at 5–10 m intervals are required to give an average value.

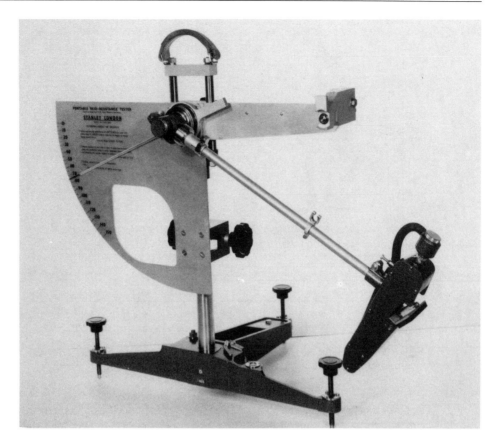

Figure 27.5   Portable Skid Resistance Tester

27.8   The Pendulum Tester assesses an area of the road surface which may not be large in relation to the coarse texture. For this and other reasons the SRV does not necessarily correlate closely with SFC or BFC measurements. However, an approximate correlation with SFC for rough-looking and medium-textured surfaces is shown in Fig. 27.6.

27.9   The principal attributes of the machine are its portability and simplicity. It is particularly useful in laboratory research aimed at the development of skid resistant surfaces and it is valuable to the road engineer for investigating potential accident sites.

The development of skid-resistance criteria for different types of road

27.10   In the fifties Giles developed skid resistance criteria for different types of road based on the detailed testing of sites from which the police had reported

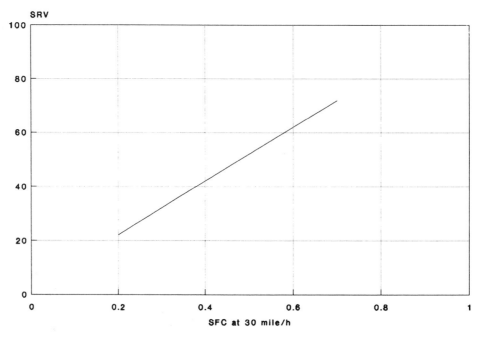

Figure 27.6 Observed correlation between SRV and SFC in 63 tests on rough-looking and medium-textured surfacing

wet-weather skidding accidents.[2] He found fairly well-established thresholds of sideway force coefficient for the different types of road, below which the possibility of skidding accidents increased markedly. These criteria were modified and to some extent simplified by Sabey in 1968.[3] Her recommendations were accepted by the Marshall Committee in 1970 as target values for skidding resistance to be used as a guide in the preparation of maintenance schedules.[4] These values and the types of road to which they apply are reproduced in Table 27.1.

27.11   The road engineer must provide pavements which will meet the requirements of Table 27.1 and which will continue to satisfy those requirements with a minimum of surface maintenance. To do this requires an understanding of the pavement factors which influence skidding.

Factors which affect the skid-resistance of road pavements

27.12   Although skidding can occur on dry roads it is a major cause of accidents only when the pavement is wet. Research into skidding has for this reason been confined largely to wet surfaces. The mechanism has been succinctly discussed by Sabey, and the following three paragraphs are reproduced from one of her publications.[3]

Table 27.1   Categories of sites and suggested target values for the sideway force coefficient proposed by the Marshall Committee

Category of site	Type of site	Sideway force coefficient Test speed km/h (mile/h)		SFC
A	Most difficult sites: (i) roundabouts (ii) bends with radius less than 150 m (500 ft) on unrestricted roads (iii) gradients of 5% (1 in 20) or steeper or longer than 100 m (330 ft) (iv) approaches to traffic signals on unrestricted roads	50	(30)	0.55
B	Average sites: (i) motorways and other high-speed roads, i.e. speeds in excess of 95 km/h (60 mile/h)	50 80	(30) (50)	0.50 0.45
	(ii) trunk and principal roads, and other roads with more than 200 vehicles per day in urban areas (sum in both directions)	50	(30)	0.50
C	Other sites: straight roads with easy gradients and curves without junctions and free from any feature such as mixed traffic especially liable to create conditions of emergency	50	(30)	0.40

27.13   The friction coefficient between two sliding surfaces can generally be expressed as the sum of two terms. The first arises from the adhesion at the points where the surfaces are in contact, and in the case of a wet road this implies that at such points of contact the lubricating layer of water on the road must have been broken through and areas of dry contact established. While drainage channels, provided by the large-scale texture of the road or by a pattern on the tyre, assist in getting rid of the main bulk of the water, the ultimate penetration of the water film can be achieved only by the presence of fine-scale sharp edges in the road, on which high pressures are built up.

27.14   The second component of friction arises if the irregularities in one surface produce appreciable deformation of the other, and at least some of the energy of deformation is irrecoverable. This deformation can occur in the presence of a lubricant, even if no actual contact between the surfaces is established.

27.15   When vehicles are travelling at speeds up to 50 km/h (30 mile/h), the fine-scale texture is the dominant factor determining the skidding resistance; the adhesion component predominates. At higher speeds, it becomes increasingly difficult to penetrate the water film in the time available. The resistance to skidding then depends largely on the deformation component of friction, and projections in the road surface must be sufficiently large and angular to deform the surface of the tyre tread, even though water may still be present on the surface. At slow speeds therefore the microtexture of the road surface or its constituents (mainly the stone), is the major factor determining the level of skidding resistance: at high speeds, its macrotexture, the size and shape of the visible asperities, is equally important.

27.16   Research into the various factors which determine the slipperiness of road surfaces has been in progress for more than 40 years. During that time the speed capability of motor vehicles has progressively increased and this capability has been increasingly utilized with the introduction of grade-separated dual-carriageway roads and motorways. Research into skidding was formerly directed mainly at the slower-speed situation relevant to urban areas, in which the bulk of skidding accidents occur. Only in the last 25 years has research been specifically directed towards improving the skid resistance of pavements at the very high speeds at which skidding accidents, although less frequent, tend to be serious in their consequences.

Research studies into the factors which influence the skid resistance of pavements

27.17   In the early thirties Bird and Scott reported systematic measurements of skid resistance made on selected roads over a period of years.[5] The motorcycle and sidecar combination shown in Fig. 27.1 was used to make the measurements of SFC. Typical results for two experimental sections on the Kingston Bypass are shown in Fig. 27.7. Section 1, with an unchipped rolled asphalt wearing course, shows an

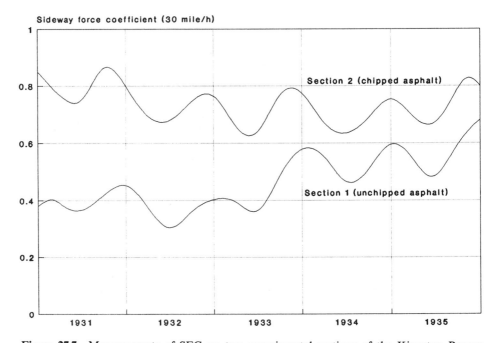

Figure 27.7 Measurements of SFC on two experimental sections of the Kingston Bypass

increase of SFC from 0.3 to 0.7 over the 5-year period, while Section 2, in which uncoated chippings were rolled into the surface, shows a corresponding decline from 0.9 to 0.8. Although at that time the processes involved in producing these changes of SFC were not fully understood, it is now clear that in the case of the unchipped asphalt it took several years (under the comparatively modest volume of heavy traffic then being carried) for the thick bituminous film to wear away to expose the microtexture of the slag aggregate. The uncoated chippings (also of slag) used in the second section had an exposed microtexture from the start of the tests and the small decline in SFC can be attributed to a modification of this microtexture by the process now known as polishing.

27.18   In standardizing the test procedure to be used in making SFC measurements, Bird and Scott repeated measurements on selected areas at various times after the commencement of rain and in this way produced idealized curves of the type shown in Fig. 27.8. They found that the magnitude of the reduction component, *d*, defined in the diagram, depended on the weather conditions immediately prior to the particular period of rain being studied. They also observed that artificial watering of the road by sprinklers consistently produced lower readings of SFC than were obtained on the same roads after prolonged rain. Because measurements after watering were generally carried out immediately after wetting, they concluded that these measurements correspond to point D in Fig. 27.8 while observations on

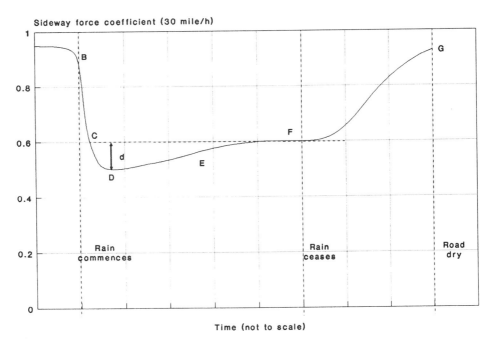

Figure 27.8   Variation of SFC from commencement of rain to road dry condition at constant speed

naturally wet roads were more likely to correspond to the condition represented by EF. Since watering appeared to reproduce the most dangerous condition relative to skidding they decided to use the method of artifical wetting for producing skidding standards.

27.19   Practical observations of the extreme slipperiness of some early road surfaces immediately after the commencement of rain resulted in the adoption of the term 'greasy' to describe this condition. This led to the erroneous conclusion that slightly wet roads were necessarily more slippery than pavements wetted to a condition at which runoff was occurring. The explanation is that the runoff of rain-water tends to remove lubricating agents left adhering to the road surface during the previous dry period. These agents probably consist of a mixture of rubber and oil deposited mainly by heavy vehicles. It is this cleansing process which accounts for the increase in SFC between the points D and F in Fig. 27.8. There is evidence that the processes of contamination, polishing, and scouring are going on continuously. In the spring and early summer when the rainfall in Britain tends to be low and evaporation rates are rising, runoff is at its lowest and deposition tends to increase. Autumnal conditions of high rainfall and decreasing evaporation favour scouring. This is probably the main reason for the apparently seasonal change in SFC in Fig. 27.7. Recent research has shown that there may be other seasonal factors affecting the microtexture of road aggregates.[6] Because of the seasonal effect it is usual to make measurements of SFC during the months May–September, and quoted figures will normally relate to this period.

27.20   The measured SFC of a wet road surface tends to decrease with increasing speed because of the time factor involved in the exclusion of water between the tyre and the pavement. This is intimately associated with both the micro- and macrotextures of the road surface and it is therefore difficult in any discussion to divorce the speed factor from textural considerations. (In practice vehicle tyres are not smooth, as in the SFC determination, and tyre tread also plays a part in determining the actual resistance to skidding between vehicle wheels and the pavement.) As would be expected, the reduction of SFC with increasing speed is greater on smooth-textured surfacings than is the case with surfaces of rougher texture. Figure 27.9 shows results reported by Giles which illustrate this effect.[2] The curves refer to two particular surfacings which gave substantially the same level of SFC at 30 mile/h (48 km/h).

27.21   It must not be inferred from Fig. 27.9 that all coarse-textured surfacings would give a lower value of SFC than smoother surfacings at speeds lower than 30 mile/h (48 km/h). Figure 27.10 shows later data reported by Sabey,[3] which relates BFC with speeds up to 80 mile/h (129 km/h). The curves illustrate the wide range of BFC values encountered in both 'rough-looking' and 'smooth-looking' surfaces. Each of the pairs of curves a and d, e and b, f and c, has approximately the same value of BFC at 30 mile/h. The divergence of the curves at higher speeds follows the trend at lower speeds indicated in Fig. 27.9. An approximate SFC scale has been added to Fig. 27.10, to permit ready comparison of the two diagrams. The textural appearances of the six surfaces referred to in Fig. 27.10 are shown in Fig. 27.11.

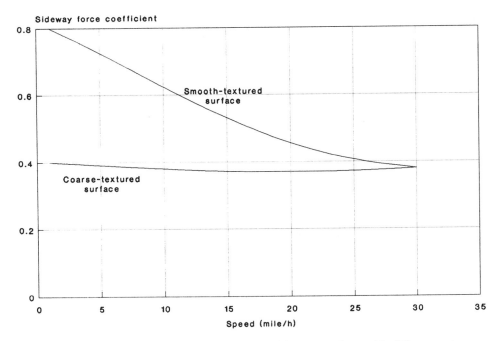

Figure 27.9 Relationships between SFC and speed for two surfaces with different textures

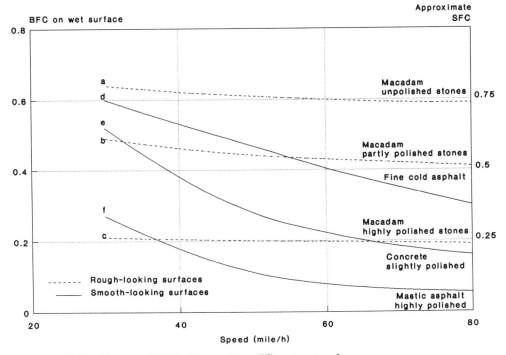

Figure 27.10 Change of BFC with speed on different wet surfaces

531

Figure 27.11   Surfaces of different textures; test results are given in Figure 27.10

The surface characteristics influencing resistance to skidding

27.22   It follows from the above discussion that if a road surface is to provide an acceptable resistance to skidding then the following conditions must exist:

1. Those areas of the surface in contact with the tyre must have a sufficiently pronounced microtexture to provide an adequate coefficient of friction.
2. The microtexture must not be readily removed by the action of traffic.
3. Between the tyre and the road there must be areas which are not in contact to facilitate the displacement of water. These areas are provided by the coarse texture on the road and by the tyre tread.
4. The coarse texture must not be readily removed by the action of traffic.

Requirements (1) and (2) are essential to all pavements; requirements (3) and (4) are particularly important on high-speed roads.

27.23   In flexible pavements the microtexture is provided mainly by the surface of the exposed aggregate or by the surface of the chippings in rolled asphalt surfacings and surface dressings. Coarse texture is provided by the spaces between the exposed aggregate or chippings. In concrete pavements the microtexture is principally associated with the sand/mortar fraction (rather than the coarse aggregate) and the coarse texture is provided by the surface brush marking or wet grooving.

27.24   To be able to meet (or attempt to meet) the SFC values shown in Table 27.1 the engineer must be able to quantify them in terms of the texture of the pavement surface. This has necessitated laboratory research into methods of measuring texture and full-scale research to relate those measurements to observed levels of SFC on the road.

Fine texture or microtexture

27.25   Fine texture of the exposed aggregate, important in the design of non-skid flexible surfaces, can be examined microscopically,[6] but for routine purposes it is generally assessed by measurements of the coefficient of friction determined by a rubber slider moving over a prepared sample of the aggregate set in a cement mortar bed.[7] The test sample is cast in a flat or cylindrical mould to ensure that the exposed surface of the aggregate conforms to a specified flat or curved profile. The determination of coefficient or friction is made with the surface of the aggregate wet, using a machine very similar to the Portable Skid Resistance Tester referred to in Paras 27.7–27.9. The sample preparation and test procedure are described in detail in BS 812:1975.[8]

27.26   Under the action of traffic certain aggregates tend to lose their fine texture quickly and are said to 'polish'. To determine the liability of aggregates to polish, an accelerated-polishing machine has been developed and this is also described in British Standard 812:1975. The machine, shown in Fig. 27.12(a), comprises a 16-in (406-mm) diameter wheel, having a periphery 2.5 in (64 mm) wide, round which curved specimens of the aggregate under test (Fig. 27.12(b)) are mounted to form the 'road' surface, which is in contact with an 8-in (203-mm) diameter pneumatic-tyred wheel, with an inflation pressure of 45 lbf/in^2 (310 kN/m^2). By means of a lever arm the tyre is pressed on to the surface of the aggregate with a normal load of 88 lb (40 kg). The specimen wheel is driven at 320 rev/min, which gives a peripheral speed of about 15 mile/h (24 km/h). The loading wheel is free to rotate on its axis. Grit or other polishing agents can be fed from a hopper on to the aggregate surface just before it passes under the loaded tyre, and water is supplied through the same chute. (It is to accommodate samples from this machine that the friction measuring device referred to in Para. 27.25 was designed to operate on curved as well as flat specimens.) The test period used is 6 hours; during the first three hours the machine is fed with No. 36 corn emery and water both at the rate of 20–35 g/min, and during the second three hours with air-floated emery powder at a rate of 2–4 g/min and water at a rate of 4–8 g/min. This method of testing was originally selected as representing the polishing effect likely to be experienced on a heavily trafficked road, but it is preferable to regard the test as a purely comparative one to be related by long-term experience to what happens on the road. The measured coefficient of friction at the end of the 6-hour period was originally defined as the polished stone

Figure 27.12 (a) Apparatus for accelerated polishing test. (b) Mould and specimen for accelerated polishing test

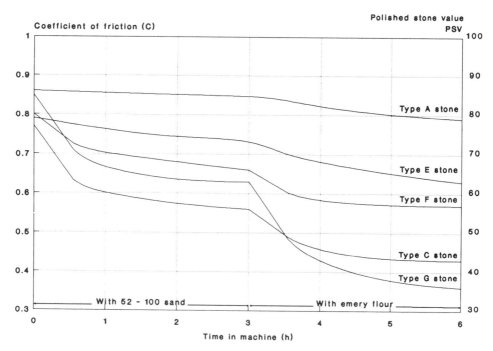

Figure 27.13   Examples of results from polished stone tests

value (PSV). Figure 27.13 shows typical variations of coefficient of friction during the test period, and indicates that different types of stone all having an initial coefficient of friction of the order 0.75–0.85 may show markedly different polishing characteristics, the PSV after the test varying between 36 and 80.

27.27   Figure 27.14 shows measured distributions of PSVs for different groups of stone tested at the TRRL. It is clear that some groups polish more readily than others, but within all the groups there is considerable variation. In addition to having a high PSV, the exposed stone must be durable. Current recommendations for Category A and B sites, as defined in Table 27.1, are given in Table 27.2.

27.28   Recent research reported by Szatkowski and Hosking shows that the mean summer values of SFC for a new road tend to fall within one year to a level which thereafter changes very little[9]. This level appears to depend on the PSV of the stone and the intensity of the commercial traffic using the lane on which the measurements are made. Typical results for rolled asphalt surfacings with precoated chippings of PSV 58–60 are shown in Fig. 27.15. It appears that the processes of contamination, polishing, and scouring referred to in Para. 27.19 may be responsible for the establishment of this 'equilibrium' SFC condition associated with the level of commercial traffic. In confirmation of this hypothesis these authors have reported a case where the daily commercial traffic decreased from 2750 to 730 vehicles per day (owing to the construction of a bypass) and the SFC increased from 0.43 to 0.58.

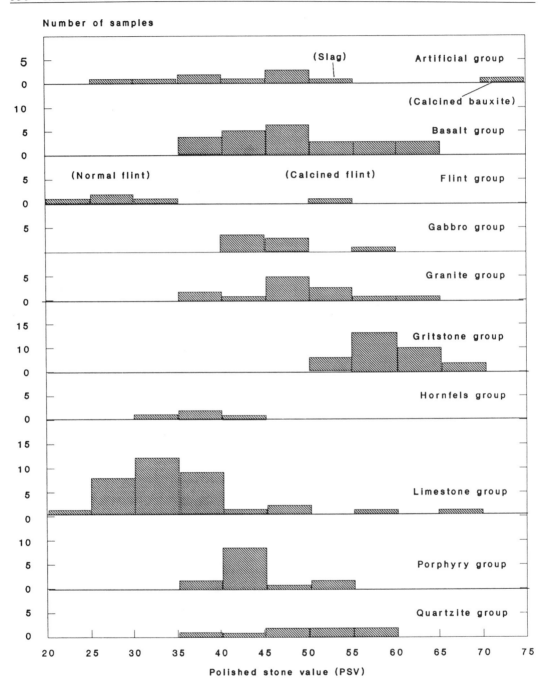

Figure 27.14 Distribution of PSVs in different groups of rock

Table 27.2   Aggregate requirements for category A and B sites

Category of site	PSV	Aggregate abrasion value (BS 812)
A	62 min	10 max
B	59 min	12 max

Note: There are currently no similar recommendations for Category C sites, but it is usually to specify a PSV value of not less than 50.

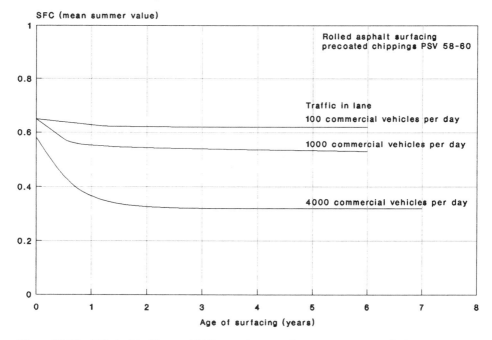

Figure 27.15   Effect of traffic on skidding resistance of motorway type surfacing

27.29   Following tests of this type on a variety of flexible pavements with stones of different PSV used in asphalt surfacings and surface dressings, Szatkowski and Hosking have proposed the relationship shown in Fig. 27.16 between SFC, PSV, and intensity of commercial traffic. This shows that for Category A and B sites carrying very heavy traffic the PSVs shown in Table 27.1 will be inadequate to ensure the required level of SFC and that PSVs as high as 70–75 will be necessary. This has led to considerable research into the properties of synthetic aggregates with high resistance to polishing.[10,11] Such aggregates incorporated in surface dressings have had a dramatic effect on urban accidents at sites such as the approaches to

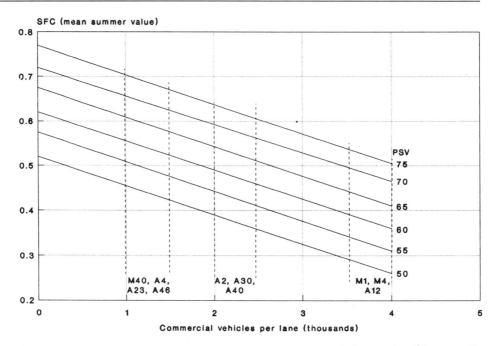

Figure 27.16 Skidding resistance achievable on bituminous surfacings under different traffic conditions

pedestrian crossings, traffic signals, and roundabouts,[12] where the relatively high cost is justified.

27.30 Although approximately half of the weight of materials constituting a concrete mix is accounted for by the coarse aggregate, its degree of exposure in the road surface is normally quite small. As a consequence, the coarse aggregate is of little importance in determining the fine texture and the resistance to skidding. Franklin and Calder have found that the PSV and aggregate abrasion value of the fine aggregate largely determines the SFC of concrete pavements at moderate speeds.[13] They studied, over a period of 4–5 years the change in skid-resistance value of concrete cores inserted in the left-hand lane wheel tracks of a motorway and a major trunk road. The concrete mixes used included coarse aggregates of PSV in the range 28–71 and fine aggregate of PSV 28–73. (Since the PSV test could not be directly applied to the small particles constituting the fine aggregate, it was assumed that the PSV of that fraction was equal to that of the rock from which it was derived.) The results of this research are summarized in Fig. 27.17. Details of the PSV and AAV of the fine aggregates used in the study are given on the figure. The values of SRV quoted are terminal values after 5 years, but the annual measurements indicated no significant reduction of SRV with time. As with flexible pavements however, the terminal value was higher for the trunk road traffic of 1600 commercial

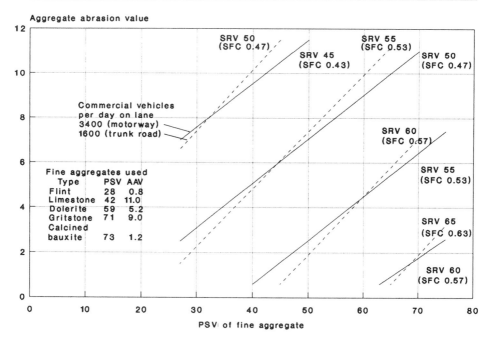

Figure 27.17 Prediction of skidding resistance valued from the properties of the fine aggregate—concrete pavements

vehicles per day on the lane studied, than on the motorway where the corresponding traffic was 3400 commercial vehicles per day.

27.31　The data given in Fig. 27.6 have been used to express SRV in terms of SFC in Fig. 27.17. It can be inferred from the figure that with certain types of fine aggregate it would be difficult to achieve and maintain the targets of SFC quoted in Table 27.1 This has been confirmed by routine measurements of SFC on modern concrete roads.

Coarse texture or macrotexture

27.32　Coarse texture is necessary to prevent a loss of resistance to skidding at high speeds. It is generally quantified in terms of the average texture depth measured by the sand patch method.[14] In this test a metal cylindrical container of diameter 19 mm and height 84 mm is filled in a controlled manner with a natural rounded sand of particle size between 150 and 300 μm. This sand is poured on to the pavement surface in a conical heap which is then spread by the circular motion of a flat wooden disc of 64 mm in diameter provided with a rubber facing. With the plane of the disc parallel with the road surface the sand is spread over an approximately circular area to fill all the depressions within that area. The mean radius of the sand-filled patch is determined with dividers and the average texture depth is obtained from the volume of sand used, divided by the area of the sand patch.

27.33   The sand patch method of assessing texture depth is not suited to the routine assessment of large lengths of highway, and this role has now been taken over by the high-speed texture meter based on the contactless depth-measuring procedure discussed in detail in Chapter 26. One of the three functions of the High Speed Road Monitor referred to in Para. 26.23 is to measure the texture depth of both flexible and concrete pavements. However, there is a separate version known as the High Speed Texture Meter (HSTM) which is much smaller and more convenient when only texture depth is under investigation.

27.34   The HSTM has only one contactless sensor, which concentrates on the depressions incorporated in the surfacing to increase the high-speed skid resistance. How this is done is shown in Fig. 27.18.[15] A rapidly pulsing semiconductor laser, producing infrared light (wavelength 906 nm) is projected on to the road surface. Light reflected from the spot so formed is focused by a receiving lens on to a linear array of 256 photodiodies. The position of the diode receiving most light gives a measure of the distance to the road surface at that instant and the depth of the texture is computed from a series of such measurements.

27.35   The sensor system moves over the road surface in a plane normal to the page in Fig. 27.18, and rays of laser light reflected from different points in the texture D_1, D_2 and D_3 are detected by appropriate diodes d_1, d_2 and d_3 in the receiving array, thus giving a measure of the depth of the points. The laser pulses at approximately 3.5 kHz and the number of the illuminated diode is transmitted to the computer on board the towing vehicle. The texture depth is computed and expressed as a root-mean-square value with averages recorded for every 10 metres travelled.

27.36   The sensor is mounted in a trailer rather than directly on the vehicle in order to isolate the sensor from any vibration from the engine and transmission. The towing vehicle carries all the equipment needed to control the texture-measuring process. The centre of the system is an Interdata 16-bit minicomputer which is connected to the various elements of the system. These are: the sensor in the trailer, a distance meter which generates pulses from a unit attached to the gearbox final

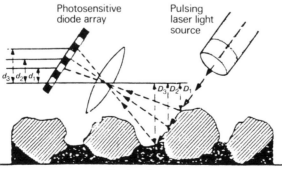

Figure 27.18 Principle of the laser-based contactless sensor for measuring texture depth

drive, a visual display unit (VDU) with keyboard, for immediate display of results, a paper-tape reader to allow rapid programming of the computer, and a control box with pushbuttons for starting and stopping texture measurements and inserting codes for location referencing.

27.37   Measurements are generally made in the left-hand wheeltrack of the carriageway and therefore the results are likely to represent the minimum texture depth for the road studied. As the wheeltracks are the parts of the road likely to be involved when vehicles are skidding, it is there that the surface texture is most relevant. Normally, test speeds are in the range 45–65 km/h, but higher speeds (up to 80 km/h) are used on motorways; however, sometimes traffic or road conditions necessitate lower speeds being used. Earlier studies with the machine showed that texture results were sensibly constant over a speed range of 15–100 km/h.

27.38   Although the trailer has a rigid suspension, slight bounce on the tyres is sometimes experienced when passing over certain types of surfaces; this is reflected in the sensor outputs being disposed along an apparently curved profile. To eliminate the effect of this motion on the readings, the sensor outputs are grouped into blocks of data. A quadratic least-squares regression technique is used to draw a curve through the data points of any one data block. The variance and standard deviation of the measured points from this curve are then calculated. The standard deviation of sensor measurements is defined as the sensor-measured texture depth (SMTD); although it is dimensionally the same as the measurement made by the sand patch method, the latter defines a mean depth of texture below a plane through the high points on the road surface. The two methods would not therefore be expected to give the same numerical results. Figure 27.19 shows the relationship between contactless sensor and sand patch measurements made as far as practicable at the same points of the road surface.[16] From this relationship it can be concluded that the ratio between the two methods of measurement is 1.7. For the time being the sand patch method is regarded as the standard.

27.39   Typical values of texture depth for new asphalt surfacings with precoated chippings lie between 1 and 2 mm. Newly laid surface dressings generally have a texture depth between 3 and 4 mm. For unchipped asphalt and asphaltic concrete pavements the texture depth may be as low as 0.2 mm. The Department of Transport specification for highway works does not give texture depth requirements for new flexible roads. Other requirements of the specification are considered to ensure an adequate initial texture depth. For concrete roads the specification calls for an initial texture depth of not less than 0.75 mm.

27.40   From studies of the SFC of flexible and concrete pavements having a range of texture depths, Salt and Szatkowski have published the information given in Table 27.3.[17] A given change of skidding resistance with speed is associated with a smaller texture depth in a concrete pavement than a flexible pavement. This probably reflects the continuous nature of the channels obtained by the brushing or grooving processes used to texture concrete.

27.41   It can be inferred from Table 27.3 that to satisfy the maximum reduction of 10 per cent in SFC between 50 and 80 km/h for motorways, which is contained

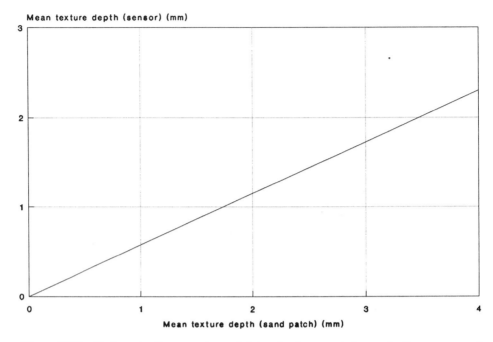

Figure 27.19 Texture depth comparison of determinations made by contactless sensor and sand patch method

Table 27.3   The effect of coarse texture on the change of skidding resistance with speed

Drop in skidding resistance with speed change from 50 to 130 km/h, %	Texture depth, mm	
	Flexible	Concrete*
0	2.0	0.8
10	1.5	0.7
20	1.0	0.5
30	0.5	0.4

*When textured predominantly transversely

in Table 27.1, a texture depth of about 0.6 mm would need to be maintained on concrete surfaces and one of 1.3 mm on flexible surfaces.

27.42   A decrease in texture depth under the action of traffic may be effected in flexible pavements by compaction during service or by the removal or embedment of chippings by traffic. On concrete surfaces wear of the brushmarks or surface grooving is responsible. Experience shows that close adherence to the specification and particularly to those parts relating to laying and rolling temperatures is essential to the production and maintenance of a satisfactory texture depth in bituminous surfaces. Comprehensive research by Weller and Maynard on existing concrete pavements, and using a wear wheel rather similar to the machine used in the PSV test, has shown that if a texture depth of 0.7 mm is to be maintained for 4–5 years on a heavily trafficked concrete road the initial texture depth will in general need to be of the order of 1.5 mm.[18] Such a texture depth is difficult to achieve by brushing and this has led to the development of alternative wet-grooving techniques. It must be appreciated that an unnecessarily heavy texture on both flexible and concrete pavements may result in unacceptable noise both inside and outside motor vehicles, and it will tend to increase tyre wear.

27.43   To obtain more information relating to the texture depth of in-service roads than could have previously been obtained using the sand patch method, the Transport and Road Research Laboratory has made a 3-year study in three counties in the UK and for four classes of road, as indicated in Table 27.4.[15] The texture depths shown are all sensor-measured and the value must therefore be multiplied by

Table 27.4   Average texture depth (SMTD) for various categories of road[15]

Road Category	Year of test	County A Length tested, km	County A SMTD (mm) mean	County A SMTD (mm) s.d.	Network County B Length tested, km	County B SMTD (mm) mean	County B SMTD (mm) s.d.	County C Length tested, km	County C SMTD (mm) mean	County C SMTD (mm) s.d.
Motorways	1982	22.1	0.71	0.25	80.4	0.67	0.17	—	—	—
	1983	32.3	0.80	0.24	83.4	0.75	0.19	78.0*	0.58	0.22
	1984	30.2	0.91	0.30	82.9	0.76	0.19	80.2*	0.58	0.22
		31.3	0.87	0.26	—	—	—	—	—	—
Class A	1982	556.7	0.77	0.30	275.8	0.67	0.26	—	—	—
	1983	546.0	0.79	0.30	277.0	0.70	0.27	637.6	0.67	0.25
	1984	560.0	0.87	0.32	272.2	0.71	0.29	630.5	0.68	0.28
		567.8	0.81	0.32	—	—	—	—	—	—
Class B	1982	75.7	0.69	0.29	80.7	0.64	0.29	—	—	—
	1983	75.2	0.70	0.28	77.7	0.65	0.28	101.8	0.63	0.23
	1984	76.3	0.74	0.28	70.1	0.66	0.35	103.8	0.63	0.27
		70.6	0.67	0.25	—	—	—	—	—	—
Unclassified	1982	26.5	0.77	0.29	4.3	0.59	0.19	—	—	—
	1983	26.7	0.68	0.25	4.2	0.47	0.14	12.4	0.66	0.22
	1984	26.4	0.71	0.24	4.3	0.44	0.12	14.8	0.66	0.22
		26.5	0.78	0.24	—	—	—	—	—	—
Concrete	1982	4.4	0.48	0.07	—	—	—	—	—	—
	1983	4.3	0.47	0.09	—	—	—	48.7	0.48	0.14
	1984	4.3	0.46	0.07	—	—	—	46.7	0.48	0.13
		4.3	0.46	0.06	—	—	—	—	—	—

*Much of the motorway tested length in county C was concrete

1.7 to make a comparison with the target values given in Paras 27.39 and 27.40. The results show that the texture depths are generally satisfactory when compared with the typical values given in Para. 27.39. The results for the three counties are surprisingly similar for the various classes of roads.

27.44   The cheapest method of restoring the coarse texture of structurally sound flexible pavements is surface dressing. Early experience with the surface dressing of smooth concrete pavements was generally disappointing. Surface grooving by closely spaced diamond saws has been increasingly used during the last 10 years to retexture concrete. Random grooving is desirable to minimize unpleasant noise effects. The cost of such grooving was originally high (several times that of surface dressing) but with improvements in the technique the process has become more competitive. Recent fullscale experiments have led to much-improved specifications for the surface dressing of concrete; some examples have performed excellently under several years of intense motorway traffic (see Chapter 30).

References

1. Giles, C. G., B. E. Sabey, and K. H. F. Cardes: *Development and Performance of the Portable Skid-resistance Tester*, Road Research Technical Paper 66, HMSO, London, 1964.
2. Giles, C. G.: *The skidding resistance of roads and the requirements of modern traffic, Proc. Instn Civ. Engrs*, **6**, 216–42, 1957; *Crushed Stone J.*, **32** (2), 8–10, 15, 1957.
3. Sabey, B. E.: The road surface and safety of vehicles. *Symposium on Vehicle and Road Design for Safety, Cranfield 3–4 July 1968*, Institution of Mechnical Engineers, London, 1968.
4. Ministry of Transport: *Report of the Committee on Highway Maintenance*, HMSO, London, 1970.
5. Bird, G. and W. J. O. Scott: *Road Surface Resistance to Skidding*, Road Research Technical Paper No. 1, HMSO, London, 1936.
6. Neville, G.: *A Study of the Mechanism of Polishing of Roadstones by Traffic*, Transport and Road Research Laboratory Report LR621, TRRL, Crowthorne, 1974.
7. Maclean, D. J. and F. A. Shergold: *The Polishing of Roadstone in Relation to Skidding of Bituminous Road Surfacings*, Road Research Technical Paper 43, HMSO, London, 1958.
8. British Standards Institution: *Method for Sampling and Testing of Mineral Aggregates, Sands and Fillers*, British Standard 812:1975, BSI, London, 1975.
9. Szatkowski, W. S. and J. R. Hosking: *The Effect of Traffic and Aggregate on the Skidding Resistance of Bituminuous Surfacings*, Transport and Road Research Laboratory Report LR504, TRRL, Crowthorne, 1972.
10. James, J. G.: *Calcined Bauxite and Other Artificial, Polish-resistant, Roadstones*, Road Research Laboratory Report LR84, RRL, Crowthorne, 1968.
11. Hosking, J. R.: *Synthetic Aggregates of High Resistance to Polishing, Part 1—Gritty Aggregates*, Road Research Laboratory Report LR350, RRL, Crowthorne, 1970.
12. Hatherly, L. W., J. H. Mahffy, and A. Tweddle: The skid-resistance of city streets and road safety, *J. Instn Highw. Engrs*, **16** (4), 3–12, 1969.
13. Franklin, R. E. and A. J. J. Calder: *The Skidding Resistance of Concrete: the Effect of Materials Under Site Conditions*, Transport and Road Research Laboratory Report LR640, TRRL, Crowthorne, 1974.
14. Weller, D. E. and D. P. Maynard: *Methods of Texturing New Concrete Road Surfaces to Provide Adequate Skidding Resistance*, Road Research Laboratory Report 290, RRL, Crowthorne, 1970.

15. Roe, P. G., L. W. Tubey, and G. West: *Surface Texture Depth Measurements on Some British Roads*, Transport and Road Research Laboratory Report RR143, TRRL, Crowthorne, 1988.

16. Cooper, D. R. C.: *Measurement of Road Surface Texture by a Contactless Sensor*, Transport and Road Research Laboratory Report LR639, TRRL, Crowthorne, 1974.

17. Salt, G. F. and W. S. Szatkowski: *A Guide to Levels of Skidding Resistance for Roads.* Transport and Road Research Laboratory Report LR510, TRRL, Crowthorne, 1973.

18. Weller, D. E. and D. P. Maynard: *The Use of an Accelerated Wear Machine to Examine the Skidding Resistance of Concrete Surfaces*, Transport and Road Research Laboratory Report LR333, TRRL, Crowthorne, 1976.

28. Antisplash surfacings

28.1 On three-lane dual-carriageway motorways in Britain, heavy trucks are permitted by law to operate at speeds up to 60 mile/h (97 km/h) on the left-hand and centre lanes. Nominally the differential between the maximum speed for cars and trucks is 10 mile/h (16 km/h), but in fact due to lack of enforcement trucks are normally driven at speeds around 70 mile/h (113 km/h). Passing two trucks moving side by side is a somewhat difficult operation in a small car because of the 'piston effect' tending to draw the car into the centre lane. However, it becomes highly dangerous in heavy rain when the spray thrown up by the trucks obscures the visability of other road users. The use of extended mudflaps and wheel valances does little to improve the situation because a great deal of water is thrown sideways around the contact area between the truck tyre and the road.

28.2 When the problem first became apparent some 30 years ago, it was felt that increasing the crossfall of the pavement might offer a solution. A full-scale section of pavement was constructed which could be tilted to have slopes in the range 1:400 to 1:24. Under simulated heavy-rainfall conditions the average depth of water in the 'fast lane' remained virtually constant for all slopes within the range referred to above. It was concluded therefore that changing the slope within the practical range of 1:50 to 1:35 would not provide a solution.

28.3 The problem of splash on concrete roads with a well-developed transverse texture is less marked than is the case with flexible pavements with asphalt wearing courses. This has led to a series of full-scale experiments using very open-textured bituminous surfacings.

The use of open-textured wearing-course material

28.4 The pavement research carried out in Britain during the past 50 years has led to the conclusion that bituminous surfacings must be both dense and impervious. It was clear therefore that roads with antisplash surfacings would need to conform to these basic requirements. It was decided therefore to lay experimental open-textured surfacings on top of normal asphalt surfacings. The concept was that the open-textured material would have a large storage capacity for rainwater and allow some sideways drainage towards the low side of the road.

28.5 The first trial section was laid on the M40 motorway in 1967.[1] The grading of the aggregate used is shown in Fig. 28.1. The binder was rubberized bitumen of combined penetration 100 and the thickness was 40 mm laid on a rolled asphalt

546

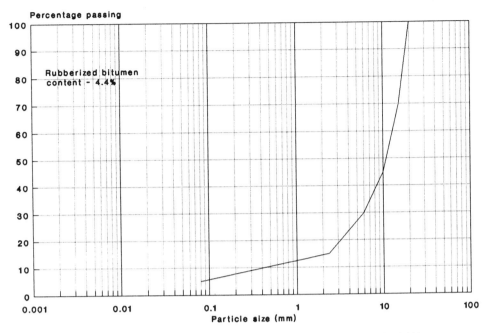

Figure 28.1   Grading and binder content of antisplash surfacing laid on the M40 motorway in 1967

wearing course (unchipped). The air voids in the open-textured material amounted to about 20 per cent. If the voids were interconnected this would permit the storage of about 8 mm of rainwater, neglecting possible drainage.

28.6   The experiment was under observation for several years and showed pronounced antisplash properties, except during abnormal heavy rainstorms.

28.7   A further experiment was constructed in 1970 on the heavily trafficked A45 trunk road in the Midlands of England.[2] The objective was to study the performance of a closely graded aggregate of maximum size 10 mm compared with a similar coarser material as laid at the M40 motorway. The grading of the finer material is shown in Fig. 28.2.

28.8   In addition to the two maximum sizes of aggregate, various binders were used, as indicated in Table 28.1. The thicknesses of material laid were 40 mm for the 19 mm nominal size material and 10 mm for the 10-mm material. Both materials were laid on an existing pavement with a sound impermeable asphalt surfacing. At the low side of the road a shallow drainage channel was left so that sideways drainage of the pervious materials was not impeded.

28.9   Since this experiment was not on a motorway it was possible to gain more frequent access to take samples and carry out tests. Changes in the permeability percentage voids, texture depth, and sideway force coefficient were made and results are shown in Fig. 28.3.

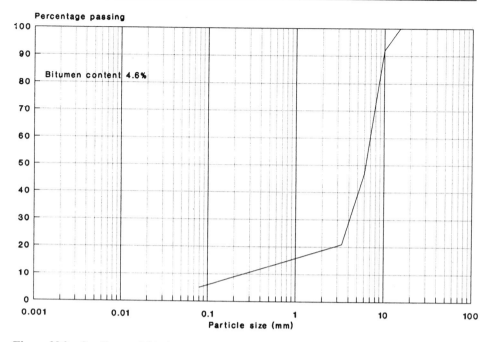

Figure 28.2 Grading and binder content of finer aggregate material laid on the A45 trunk road in 1970

Table 28.1 **Binders used in open-textured antisplash surfacings**

Section No.	Type of binder	Nominal size of gritstone aggregate, mm	Nominal thickness of surfacing, mm
1	100-pen straight-run Venezuelan bitumen	19	40
2	200-pen straight-run Middle East bitumen	19	40
3	100-pen straight-run Middle East bitumen	19	40
4	100-pen rubberized Middle East bitumen	19	40
5	100-pen rubberized Middle East bitumen	10	20
6	100-pen straight-run Middle East bitumen	10	20

28.10 The four following paragraphs giving the conclusions from this experiment are reproduced from Reference 2.

28.11 The permeability values generally fell to between about one half and one fifth of their initial values after twenty-two months of trafficking, while the percentage of air voids in general decreased to about two thirds of their original value. While this means that a 40 mm thick surfacing with originally 25 per cent of voids and capable of accepting 10 mm

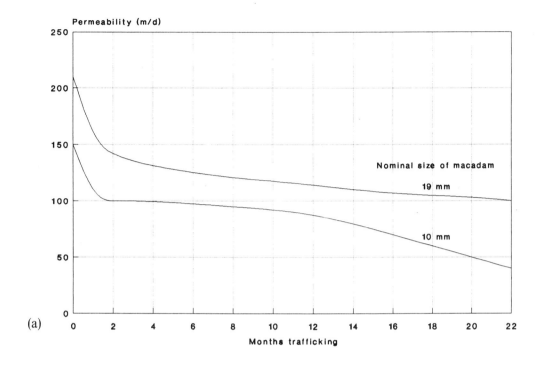

(a)

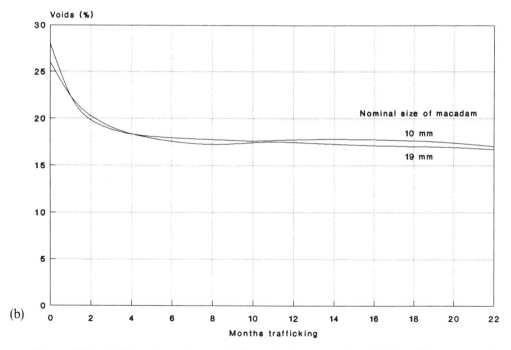

(b)

Figure 28.3 (a) Variation of permeability with duration of trafficking; (b) variation of percentage voids with duration of trafficking

549

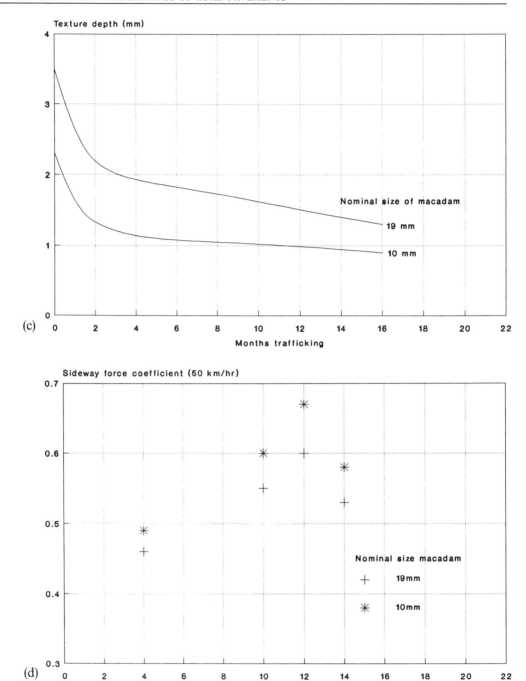

Figure 28.3—*contd*—(c) variation of texture depth with duration of trafficking; (d) variation of SFC at 50 km/h with duration of trafficking

of rainfall will now accept only 6 mm of rain for a void content of 15 per cent, this is adequate under most rainfall conditions to prevent spray. The rate at which rain can permeate through the surfacing has been reduced so that the material now takes between two and five times longer to drain. Unless two very heavy showers occur within a few hours of each other or the rainfall is heavy and prolonged the reduced flow rate will not seriously affect the spray reducing properties of the surfacing. Changes of a decade or more in the permeability are required to seriously affect the flow rate since, in the United Kingdom, there is usually sufficient time between heavy showers for most of the water to drain away.

28.12 Because the pervious surfacing depends upon its voids to provide drainage, its performance will be impaired by loss of these voids through compaction under traffic or filling by detritus. In the experimental sections described herein an attempt has been made to overcome the first of these by using harder binders than normal and by adding rubber to the binder. But the loss in efficiency due to silting up of the pores and oil droppings from vehicles may prove to be a more serious problem than compaction under traffic.

28.13 Generally the permeability in the wheel tracks has, as expected, gradually reduced during the two years. That reductions in the permeability of a similar order have also occurred between the wheel tracks is somewhat surprising and may well be associated with the total waste lubrication system now becoming common on commercial vehicles.

28.14 The 19 mm nominal-size material manufactured using 100-penetration ME bitumen shows the least reduction in voids and permeability and that containing 100 penetration VEN bitumen the greatest reduction. The addition of rubber to the bitumen has not prevented compaction during the early life of the material.

28.15 Recently two further experiments have been constructed on the M1 motorway and on the A38 truck road. Reports on these experiments have not yet been published. Figures 28.4 and 28.5 compare spray from a surfacing of impermeable asphalt with that from an adjacent section with surfacing conforming to Table 28.2.

Figure 28.4 Spray from normal impervious asphalt surfacing

Figure 28.5   Reduced spray from pervious macadam surfacing

Table 28.2   Tentative specifications for open-textured anti-splash surfacings

Aggregate grading—per cent by weight passing	19 mm nominal-size bitumen macadam, %	10 mm nominal-size bitumen macadam, %
28-mm BS sieve	100	
20-mm BS sieve	90–100	
14-mm BS sieve	50–80	100
10-mm BS sieve		90–100
6.3-mm BS sieve	25–35	40–55
3.35-mm BS sieve	10–20	22–28
75-μm 200 BS sieve	3–6	3–5
Binder content, %	4.0–4.4	4.4–4.8

Influence of the antisplash layer on pavement strength

28.16   The provision of an antisplash surfacing 40 or 60 mm thick is clearly a significant addition to the cost of major roads and motorways. In the case of new flexible roads to current design standards, the presence of this additional thickness over the required impermeable asphalt surfacing will remove the need for precoated chippings in the asphalt but will provide some increased strength above that required by the traffic type and intensity. It is reasonable therefore to assume that some reduction could be made in the thickness of asphalt or coated macadam incorporated in the design.

28.17 This matter has been investigated by the TRRL using a structual design procedure.[3] Beams 400 mm long, 100 mm wide, and 50 mm deep were sawn from 450-mm diameter cores taken from an experimental area of antisplash surfacing laid on a rolled-asphalt surfacing. The grading of the material conformed closely to that shown in Fig. 28.1 for the nominal 19 mm maximum size material. The binder used was 100 pen. bitumen and the binder content 3.8 per cent (i.e., a little lower than the values used in the full-scale road experiments).

28.18 The modulus of elasticity of the material was determined at temperatures between 9 and 33 °C at loading frequencies of 0.1 to 80 Hz. The results are shown in Fig. 28.6. The modulus curve for the antisplash material is compared with that for a rolled asphalt wearing-course material. Also shown on the same figure are values for rolled asphalt and dense-coated macadam taken from another TRRL publication.[4] The rolled asphalt values are very similar over the range investigated in reference 3 but the modulus of the pervious macadam is significantly lower than that for dense bitumen macadam. This would be expected.

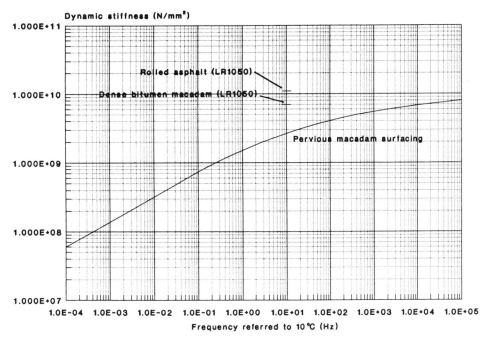

Figure 28.6 Variation of dynamic stiffness with frequency referred to 10 °C

28.19   The result of the structural analysis shows that for a normal design of 80–220 mm of asphalt (wearing course and basecourse/base) on a 150-mm granular sub-base over a soil of CBR 5.5 per cent, the provision of a 40-mm antisplash surfacing on the asphalt wearing course would permit a reduction of 16–20 mm in the bituminous basecourse/base layer. This would probably result in only a small increase of total cost when the antisplash surfacing is used.

References

1. Please, A. B., J. O'Connell, and B. F. Buglass: *A Bituminous Surface-texture Experiment, High Wycombe By-Pass (M40)*, Transport and Road Research Laboratory Report LR307, TRRL, Crowthorne, 1970.
2. Brown, J. R.: *Pervious Bitumen Macadam Surfacings Laid to Reduce Splash and Spray at Stonebridge, Warwickshire*, Transport and Road Research Laboratory Report LR562 TRRL, Crowthorne, 1973.
3. Potter, J. E. and A. R. Halliday: *The Contribution of Pervious Macadam Surfacing to the Structural Performance of Roads*, Transport and Road Research Laboratory Report LR1022, TRRL, Crowthorne, 1981.
4. Goddard, R. T. N.: *Fatigue Resistance of a Bituminous Road Pavement Designed for Very Heavy Traffic*, Transport and Road Research Laboratory Report LR1050, TRRL, Crowthorne, 1982.

PART EIGHT Pavement Maintenance and Rehabilitations

29. Structural maintenance and strengthening of flexible pavements

Introduction

29.1   As is discussed in detail in Chapter 4, the concept of design life applied to pavements entails also a definition of the terminal or 'failure' state towards which the condition of the pavement will deteriorate during the design life. Modern pavements seldom, if ever, become redundant and their ability to carry traffic efficiently must generally be extended beyond the initial design life by structural maintenance. Experience shows that, in the interest of overall economy, structural maintenance should be carried out before the failure condition has been reached. In a pavement which has been adequately designed and constructed, the question of structural maintenance will generally need to be considered early in the last quarter of the initial design life. Surface maintenance may of course be necessary earlier to maintain adequate skid resistance or to improve the riding quality.

29.2   In flexible pavements some early deformation due to traffic compaction of the pavement materials is largely inevitable. The long-term deformation which may follow is associated with shear movements in unbound and some bound materials, which may give rise to and be augmented by cracking in the bound materials. This cracking may not become apparent at the surface for a considerable period of time.

29.3   It has been shown in Chapter 21 that the elastic deflection caused by a loaded wheel moving over a flexible pavement is directly related to the elastic properties of the various layers which constitute the pavement and its foundation. If weakening of the materials by cracking or shearing occurs then it will be expected that the measured deflection will increase. Equally, any factor tending to stiffen any of the materials will be expected to result in a decrease of deflection. This reasoning gives rise to the deflection of a flexible pavement being regarded as an indication of the condition of the pavement.

Measurement of the deflection of flexible pavements

29.4   The simplest and most direct procedure for studying the deflection of flexible pavements under a rolling wheel load is that developed by A. C. Benkelman in the

United States. It uses a long, pivoted beam, known either as the Benkelman Beam or the Deflection Beam to measure the deflection at a point midway between a twin wheel assembly as it passes over the pavement. A long beam is essential to ensure that the points of support are remote from the influence of the loaded wheel at the time of measurement. The design of the beams used in the UK is illustrated in Fig. 29.1 and the dimensions are shown in Fig. 29.2. The aluminium alloy beam is sufficiently slender to pass between the dual rear wheels of a loaded truck. It is 3.66 m in length and is pivoted at a point 2.44 m from the tip, giving a 1:2 length ratio. The pivot is carried on a frame made of aluminium angle supported by three adjustable feet. The frame also carries a dial gauge arranged to measure the movement of the free end of the beam.

29.5   The two-axle truck used for deflection measurements should have a rear-axle load of 6350 kg (14 000 lb) divided equally between the twin-wheel assemblies at each end of the axle. It is of course essential that the load should not shift during operation. The tyre size used should be 7.50×20 or 8.25×20 with a zigzag pattern

Figure 29.1   The Deflection Beam

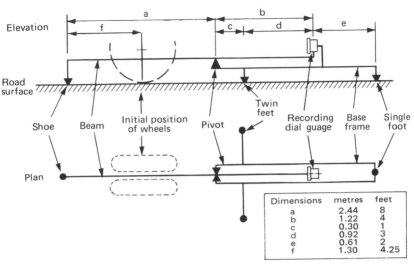

Figure 29.2   Principal dimensions of deflection beam

and an inflation pressure of 590 kN/m². The spacing between the tyre walls should be approximately 45 mm. To assist in alignment, the truck should be fitted with adjustable pointers carried by the chassis on the nearside and offside in line with the wheeltracks and directed towards a point on the road 1.2 m in front of the rear axle. In some countries axle loads other than 6350 kg have been used for deflection studies. In comparing data the axle load used must be taken into account. An approximate comparison can be made using the assumption that deflection is proportional to wheel load.

29.6   Deflection measurements are normally made in the nearside wheel-tracks of the road 0.9–1.2 m from the left-hand verge, but if two beams are available then simultaneous measurements can be made in the nearside and offside wheel-tracks. A transverse line is drawn on the pavement 1.3 m behind the point at which a measurement is required. The truck is positioned parallel with the verge with its front wheels pointing straight ahead and its rear wheels directly over the line. The transverse positioning is such that when the vehicle is driven forward the gap in the rear wheel assembly will pass over the point of measurement. With the truck in this position, the Deflection Beam is placed centrally between the tyre gap with its tip over the point of measurement. The chassis pointer is used to make the final adjustment of alignment. At a signal from the operator the vehicle is driven forward at creep speed to a position where the rear wheels are at least 3 m beyond the test point. The maximum reading of the dial gauge is noted, together with the final reading after the rear axle has reached the point 3 m beyond the test point. The magnitude of the pavement deflection is obtained by adding the maximum reading to the difference between the maximum and final readings. (This sum of deflections is not averaged because of the 2:1 length ratio of the beam arms.) Figure 29.3

Figure 29.3 Deflection Beam—test sequence

illustrates the complete measurement cycle. Two measurements are normally made at each point, particularly if fouling between the test wheels and the beam is suspected. During a deflection survey using this equipment the temperature of the bituminous material is recorded at frequent intervals at a depth of 40 mm below the pavement surface. Further details of the test procedure are given in a TRRL publication.[1]

Pavement performance related to deflection

29.7   If periodic measurements of deflection are made on a road pavement carrying normal traffic, the simplest and in some ways most rational assumption which can be made is that the early-life deflection will increase progressively as the pavement deteriorates, as is shown in Fig. 29.4. The inference is that increasing cumulative traffic will cause deterioration in the form of cracking and shear in the pavement materials which will be reflected in a progressive increase in deflection and at some stage the condition of the pavement will become critical. If no remedial action is taken then this will be followed by failure requiring structural repairs.

29.8   The British procedure for flexible pavement evaluation and for the design of overlays was first outlined in a TRRL publication in 1972.[2] This was followed by two further publications in 1973 and 1978 which defined the method in sufficient detail to enable practising engineers to adopt it as a major factor in their road maintenance programmes.[3,4]

29.9   Figures 29.5 to 29.8 show the relationships between deflection and life for pavements with crushed stone, bituminous, and cemented road bases under asphalt

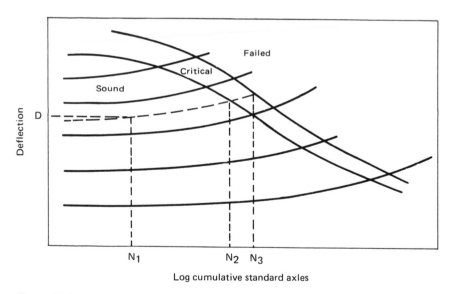

Figure 29.4   Use of deflection-life relationships to estimate future performance

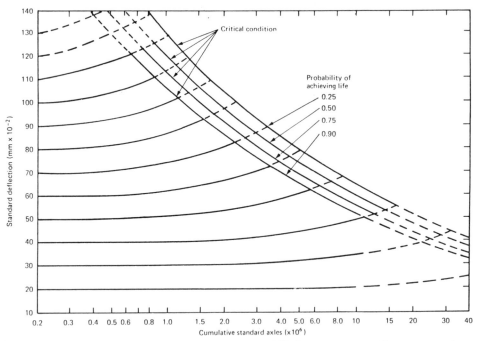

Figure 29.5 Relation between standard deflection and life for pavements with non-cementing granular road bases

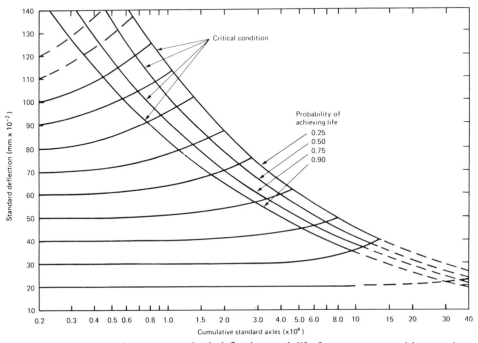

Figure 29.6 Relation between standard deflection and life for pavements with granular roadbases whose aggregates exhibit a natural cementing action

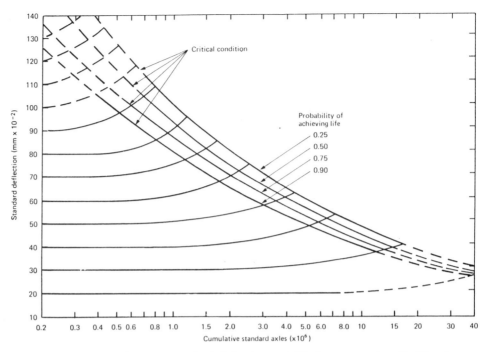

Figure 29.7 Relation between standard deflection and life for pavements with bituminous road bases

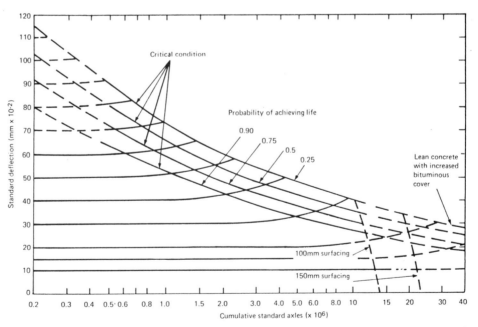

Figure 29.8 Relation between standard deflection and life for pavements with cement-bound road bases

563

surfacings. Because the stiffness of the bituminous components of flexible pavements varies with temperature, it is necessary to convert all deflection measurements to an equivalent deflection at 20 °C. This is termed the 'standard deflection'. The British design procedure as set out in detail in reference 4 provides temperature correction curves for pavements with various thicknesses of bituminous material. A typical curve for 75–195 mm of bituminous material is reproduced as Fig. 29.9.

29.10   The steps in the life evaluation procedure are as follows:

1. Make a deflection measurement and correct the value to 20 °C using the appropriate deflection–temperature relationship.
2. From a knowledge of the traffic already carried calculate the current life in terms

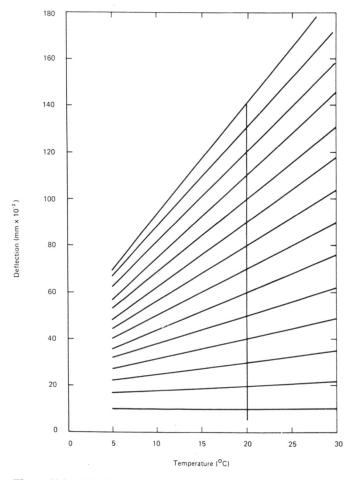

Figure 29.9   Relation between deflection and temperature for pavements with 75–195 mm of bituminous material of which at least 75 mm is dense bituminous material

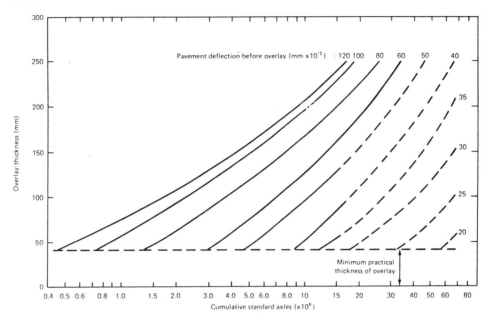

Figure 29.10 Overlay design charts for pavements with bituminous road bases (0.90 probability)

of cumulative standard axles and locate the representative point in the appropriate figure out of Figs 29.5 to 29.8.

3. Follow the appropriate contour on the chosen figure to the life expectancy curve selected (generally 0.75), and read off the total life expectancy from which the life at the time of deflection measurement is deducted.

29.11   Reference 4 also provides a series of charts from which the influence of overlays of various thicknesses on the future life of pavements can be assessed. As an example, Fig. 29.10 refers to a pavement with a bituminous road base. Using the deflection before overlaying the figure shows the future life in standard axles which will result from the application of a selected thickness of overlay. The extension of life resulting from the overlay will then be obtained by subtracting the residual life before overlaying.

Update of the UK procedure for life evaluation and overlay design

29.12   The procedure outlined above was developed almost exclusively from the Alconbury Hill experiment (1957) described in Chapter 18, which was intentionally under-designed with a weak sub-base and a high water table. Problems have arisen from time to time that have prompted a re-examination of the method, particularly directed towards the validity of the contour lines relating deflection with cumulative standard axles shown in Figs 29.5 to 29.8, and the temperature correction process illustrated in Fig. 29.9.

29.13   It is becoming clear that the shape of the deflection contours is much more complex than is envisaged by the current procedure recommended. It depends on the support provided by the sub-base and the subgrade, throughout the life of the pavement. As an example, Fig. 29.11 shows the observed contours for five experimental sections with bituminous bases, two from the Alconbury Hill experiment, two from Conington and one from Nately Scures (see Chapter 18 for details).

29.14   The contours from the Alconbury Hill experiment (Curves 2 and 5) follow the published contours closely, but those for the other experiments do not. All the sections at Conington (where a type 1 sub-base was used) follow the pattern of Curves 1 and 3 on Fig. 29.11, i.e. the deflection declined over a number of years before increasing towards the critical condition. (This also applied to all the other sections at Conington, which had wet-mix bases, and also to a limited number of sections at the Alconbury Bypass and Wheatley Bypass, for which the authors had access to information). Curve 4 shows that at Nately Scures, where the foundation support was intermediate between that at Alconbury Hill and Conington, the deflection increased for several years and then decreased to the time when the commercial traffic was diverted to the newly opened M3 motorway. For some further 15 years after that time the deflection has continued to decline.

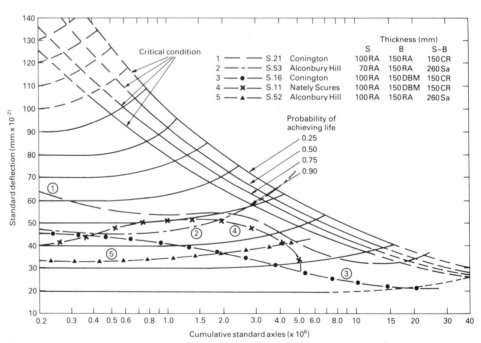

Figure 29.11   Relation between standard deflection and life for pavements with bituminous road bases

29.15   The importance of the down-turn of deflection is apparent. For example from the deflection history indicated by Curve 3 of Figure 29.11, the current procedure would indicate when the road had carried 1 million standard axles that the future life would be about 4 million, whereas the section was still in a satisfactory condition in 1988 after carrying about 30 msa.

29.16   Some decline in deflection with increasing traffic might be expected in the case of pavements with granular bases due to traffic compaction. However, the increase in elastic modulus for such materials would be small over the practical range of density change and could not account for changes of the magnitude shown in Fig. 29.11 for the Conington Lodge sections. Nor is it likely that, in a properly designed and constructed section with a bituminous base, traffic compaction alone would result in so large a change of deflection. The explanation appears to lie in the stiffening of asphalt and other bituminous materials owing to the slow removal of volatile elements in the mixture. Figure 29.12 shows changes in penetration of bitumen with age at six sites in Kenya.[5] Similar results have been reported from Texas.[6] In the case of Fig. 29.12 the first measurements were made on samples from the paver and subsequent measurements were made on recovered samples over a period of 5 years.

29.17   At the Kenya site referred to in Fig. 29.12 deflection measurements were made when the pavements were between 5 and 22 months old. During this period

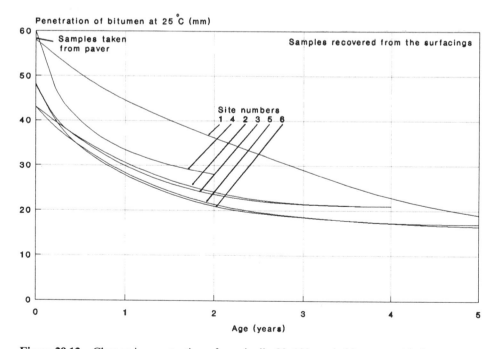

Figure 29.12   Change in penetration of nominally 80–100 grade bitumens with time

the penetration value of the asphalt decreased from about 34 to 24, with a consequent reduction of deflection of 15–20 per cent. An effect of this magnitude would easily account for the reduction of deflection observed at the Conington Lodge site over a period of 10–15 years.

29.18   The mechanism which governs the relationship between deflection and cumulative traffic appears to be (1) strengthening of the pavement due to hardening of the bituminous component and possibly to some compaction of unbound materials under traffic stresses, and (2) weakening of the pavement due to cracking and to a lesser extent shearing of unbound materials. The shape of the deflection–traffic contours will depend on the relative influence of these two factors in relation to a particular pavement. If it is assumed that age strengthening is a major factor in the behaviour of well-designed pavements then conclusions from any form of accelerated testing must be regarded as being of limited value.

29.19   The further investigations now being undertaken will be aimed at developing new deflection–traffic contours applicable to well-designed pavements. How far this will be possible remains to be examined, but it may well be that the forecasting of pavement life will become more complicated.

29.20   Another early conclusion from the examination of deflection data from the later full-scale pavement design experiments is that the temperature–deflection curves referred to in Para. 29.9 and reference 4 relate also to the early life of pavements. Figures 29.13, 29.14 and 29.15 show relations between temperature

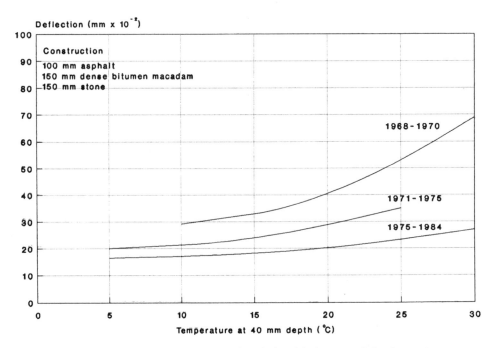

Figure 29.13   Effect of age of pavement on the relationship between deflection and temperature —Coningon section 16

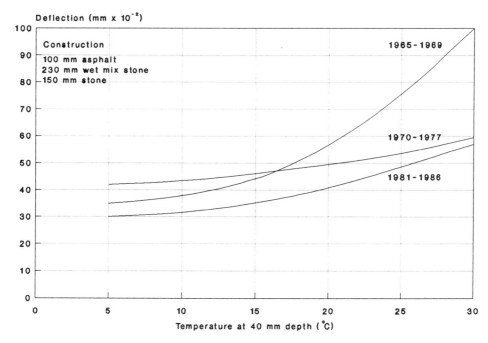

Figure 29.14 Effect of age of pavement on the relationship between deflection and temperature—Conington section 2

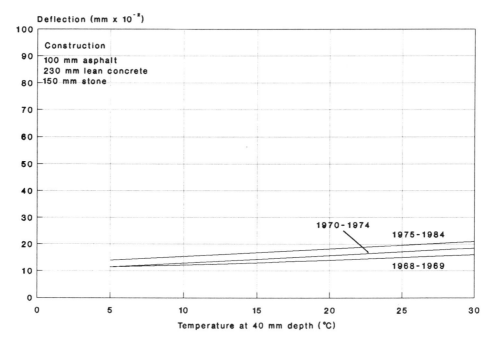

Figure 29.15 Effect of age of pavement on the relationship between deflection and temperature—Conington section 1

569

measured at a depth of 40 mm and deflection for road sections with bituminous, wet-mix, and lean concrete roadbases, respectively. In each case, curves are shown representing the early life, the middle life, and the late life, indicated by the periods shown. Figure 29.13 refers to the same section at the Conington Lodge experiment as is shown in Fig. 29.11. For this section, the deflection at 20 °C falls from 40 to 20×10^{-2} mm over 15 years and the slope of the relationship becomes much flatter. For Figure 29.14, relating to a wet-mix base, the slope again becomes flatter with time. However, as the section approaches failure the late-life curve moves above that for the middle life, as would be expected. Figure 29.15 refers to a section with a lean-concrete base. With such a base, the bituminous surfacing contributes very little to the overall stiffness and although the temperature–deflection curves are arranged in the same order as with the other sections, the decrease of deflection with age probably arises principally from the increase of stiffness of the lean concrete with age. The slope of the temperature–deflection curves is influenced only slightly with time.

29.21   Until a revision of the current UK recommendations for pavement evaluation and overlay design based on deflection measurements has been completed, it is proposed here that the following guidelines should be adopted. Measurements of deflection should be made when the temperature is close to 20 °C, so that little temperature correction is required. Such temperature correction should be based on the late-life curves shown in Figs 29.13–29.15, as appropriate. For pavements with unbound stone bases, a late-life deflection of 50×10^{-2} mm should be regarded as the critical condition, when remedial work should be carried out. For mature pavements with bituminous or lean concrete bases the corresponding figures for late-life deflection appear to be approximately 25×10^{-2} mm and 20×10^{-2} mm respectively.

Procedure for the measurement of deflection

Use of the Deflection Beam

29.22   Figure 29.16 shows a method of presenting Deflection Beam measurements. The total length of the section is about 1 km and measurements were made at 15-m intervals in the nearside wheel track of the left-hand lane. Such a survey could be carried out in a day by an engineer, an assistant, and a competent driver for the truck.

29.23   Assuming that the construction referred to in Fig. 29.16 consisted of an asphalt surfacing on a crushed stone base, the areas with a deflection above 45×10^{-2} mm would be showing cracking and deformation. If the traffic was light (less than 250 commercial vehicles per day) then the economic solution would be to take off the surfacing where the deflection was greater than 45×10^{-2} mm and replace it with 100 mm of rolled asphalt to the existing road level. This could be followed by a surface dressing of hot bitumen and chippings over the whole length.

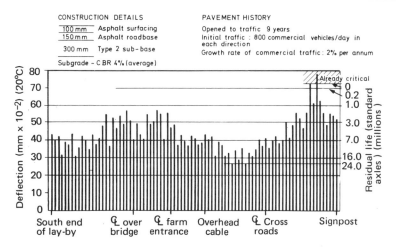

Figure 29.16 Suggested method of presentation for a deflection beam survey

For a higher flow of commercial traffic the surface dressing would be omitted and an overlay of about 50 mm of rolled asphalt applied over the whole length.

Use of the Deflectograph

29.24   Although very considerable lengths of road have been surveyed using the Deflection Beam, the process is slow and is not conducive to close coverage. Various attempts have been made to mechanize the process while retaining the same principle. In these the beam assembly is carried forward by the truck providing the required axle loading, between the points of measurement. A particularly successful machine of this type called the Lacroix Deflectographe was developed in the middle sixties by the Laboratoire Central des Ponts et Chaussees in France. With minor modifications to make it more suitable for the stiffer forms of pavement construction, this machine has been increasingly adopted for routine deflection surveys in Britain. For basic research the use of the Deflection Beam has been continued.

29.25   The Deflectograph (Fig. 29.17) consists of a truck, a deflection beam assembly and an associated recording system. The beam assembly provided with nearside and offside beams rests on the road, suitably aligned between the front and rear axles of the vehicle and deflections are measured as the rear wheel assemblies, each loaded to 3175 kg, approach the tips of the beams, which during this period are at rest in contact with the road surface. As soon as the maximum deflection has been recorded by electrical transducers located near the beam pivots, the beam assembly is pulled forward at approximately twice the speed of the vehicle by an electromagnetic-clutch and winch system, to the initial position ready for the next cycle. An arrangement of guides ensures that the beams are 'aimed' at the centre of the space between the rear twin tyres, even when the vehicle is negotiating bends. The working speed of the Deflectograph is about 2 km/h and the points of measurement are about

Figure 29.17   The Deflectograph

3.8 m apart. Figure 29.18 shows the beam assembly detached from the vehicle, and Fig. 29.19 shows the relevant dimensions in relation to those of the truck.

29.26   Various recording systems are in use. These include photographic and pen recorders supplemented in later machines by a digitized output signal recorded on paper tape suitable for routine computer analysis. Figure 29.20 shows typical output from a photographic recorder. (Some machines have been equipped to record deflection at intervals as the loaded axle approaches the beam tips. From such records the curvature of the pavement surface can be deduced.) A manually controlled 'event marker' enables the location of roadside features to be noted on the record so that the latter can be related accurately to the length of pavement surveyed.

29.27   The initial position for a recording cycle is when the beam first comes to rest in the forward location. There is a short delay corresponding to a few centimetres of vehicle movement before clamping solenoids are energized to connect the transducer armatures to the beams (see Fig. 29.21). This delay allows any

Figure 29.18 Deflectograph: beam assembly

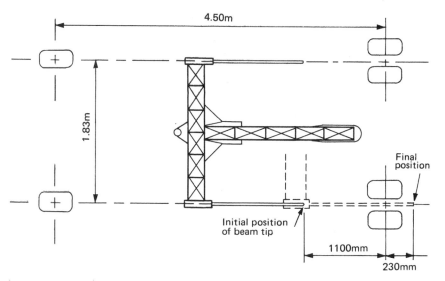

Figure 29.19 Diagrammatic representation of deflectograph

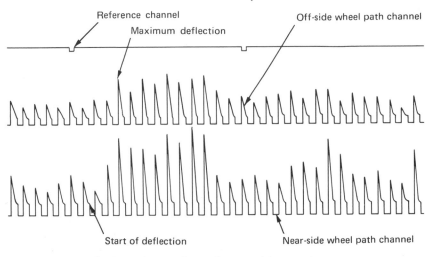

Figure 29.20 Deflectograph: trace from photographic recorder

Figure 29.21 Deflectograph: recording head

vibration of the beams to be damped out. (The main function of the clamping solenoids is to isolate the transducers while the beam assembly is in motion.) The inductance transducers, supplied with alternating current from an oscillator–amplifier unit, are each approximately balanced electrically when in the rest position at the start of a recording cycle. As the rear axle of the truck approaches the beam tips and rotation of the beams takes place, the increasing output from the transducers is, after rectification, fed to the recording galvanometers. The output is linearly related to beam deflection. At the end of the recording cycle, after the maximum deflection has been recorded, the clamping solenoids are de-energized, which allows the transducer armatures to fall back to the rest position. The electromagnetic clutch then engages to draw the beams forward to the starting position for the next cycle. The later version of the Deflectograph records the data on disk for processing using an on-board computer.

29.28   Neither the Deflection Beam nor the Deflectograph measures the absolute deflection of the pavement because the beam supports in both cases are to some extent within the influence of the truck axles during the recording cycle. Since the tyre sizes and the geometries of the beams and the trucks used in the two methods are different the deflections measured on identical pavements are not the same and correlation curves are necessary to relate them. The correlation depends on the specification of the particular Deflectograph being used, and to a lesser extent on the rigidity of the pavement. The correlation curve currently used at TRRL is shown in Fig. 29.22. This is an 'average' curve applicable to pavements with bound and unbound roadbases.

29.29   It is normal practice in Britain to take the mean of three adjacent Deflectograph readings to give an average deflection for approximately 12 m of pavement. This is done primarily to reduce the apparent effect of occasional high-deflection readings arising from 'tipping' of the beam assembly on local high spots, and not from pavement weakness. (There is no implication in this procedure that 12 m of pavement is regarded as a suitable minimum length for strengthening or reconstruction.)

29.30   In using the Deflectograph in conjunction with design curves based on Deflection Beam measurements it is first necessary to convert the Deflectograph measurements to equivalent Deflection Beam values and then to correct to 20 °C values. The computer program designed for use with the Deflectograph carries out these operations.

Other methods for measuring deflection

29.31   Various other methods of measuring deflection are now in use in the USA and Europe. One of these is the Falling Weight Deflectometer (FWD). The load is applied through a steel plate, through a rubber spring system. The effective load can be varied between 7 and 120 kN. Seven seismic deflection transducers covering a radius of 2–3 m are lowered onto the road surface. In this manner the deflection dish, associated with the load and pavement structure, is recorded. Comparisons with

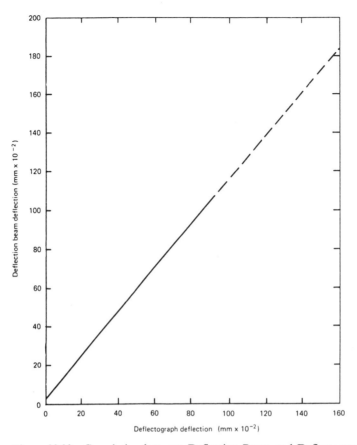

Figure 29.22 Correlation between Deflection Beam and Deflectograph

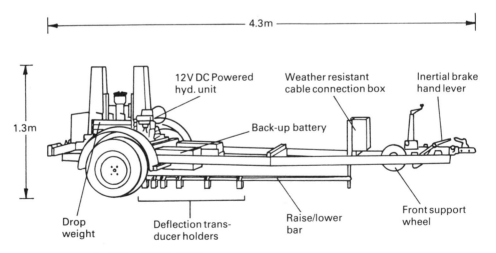

Figure 29.23 The falling Weight Deflectometer

deflections measured by the Deflection Beam and Deflectograph are currently being studied in the UK. The equipment is shown in Fig. 29.23.

Maintenance operations on flexible pavements

29.32   Maintenance operations on flexible pavements fall broadly into three categories, as follows:

1. surface dressing to seal cracks and improve skid resistance;
2. overlaying (generally combined with local repairs) to extend the life of the road and to meet increased traffic demands;
3. reconstruction involving surfacing and base.

Surface dressing

29.33   Approximately 75 per cent of the road mileage in the UK is maintained by regular surface dressing with binder and chippings at about 4-yearly intervals. The main function on secondary roads is to seal the surface and add a small amount of additional strength. Such roads are in fact maintained by this process in the 'critical' condition. This is highly cost-effective since, in contrast to a motorway, for example, capital investment is not being dissipated in a pavement which, throughout its life, is overdesigned for the traffic it is actually carrying. On the more major of secondary roads and on principal roads, trunk roads, and motorways the function of surface dressing is mainly to restore and maintain skid resistance.

29.34   The art of surface dressing is (1) to select the right size of chipping for the hardness of the substratum, (2) to select the chippings of adequate SFC to meet skidding requirements, and (3) to select the appropriate binder and binder content.

29.35   Figure 29.24 summarizes the situation with regard to chipping size.[7] Generally speaking, the size of chipping increases with traffic type and volume and with hardness of the substratum. The diagram also indicates clearly the conditions where surface dressing is not recommended, i.e., where the substratum is very soft and the traffic heavy.

29.36   Table 29.1 presents the data in a more direct form, defining the traffic in numerical terms.

29.37   For flexible pavements, Fig. 29.25 defines the hardness of the substratum in terms of temperature and the penetration measured by a hand-held penetrometer designed at the TRRL.[7] Concrete pavements are of course defined as very hard. Figure 29.25 indicates that the hardness will depend on the season during which the surface dressing is carried out.

29.38   Salt and Szatkowski[8] have suggested polished stone values (PSV) which should be adopted for use in surfacings and surface dressings for roads carrying various intensities of commercial traffic (see Table 29.2). This is to maintain an adequate microtexture. The texture depth of the surface dressing will normally meet requirements to prevent high-speed skidding if the correct size of chippings and the correct binder content are used.

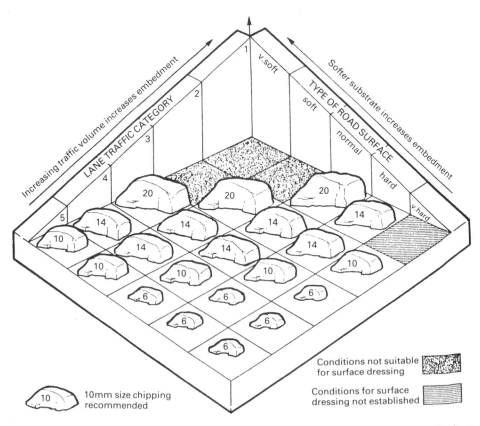

Figure 29.24   Use of different-sized chippings to offset embedment produced by traffic forces in substrates of different hardness

Table 29.1   Recommended nominal size of chippings (mm)

Type of surface	Lane-traffic category Approximate number of commercial vehicles currently carried per day in the lane under consideration				
	(1) over 2 000	(2) 1 000–2 000	(3) 200–1 000	(4) 20–200	(5) Less than 20
Very hard	10	10	6	6	6
Hard	14	14	10	6	6
Normal	20	14	14	10	6
Soft	*	20	14	14	10
Very soft	*	*	20	14	10

*Unsuitable for surface dressing.

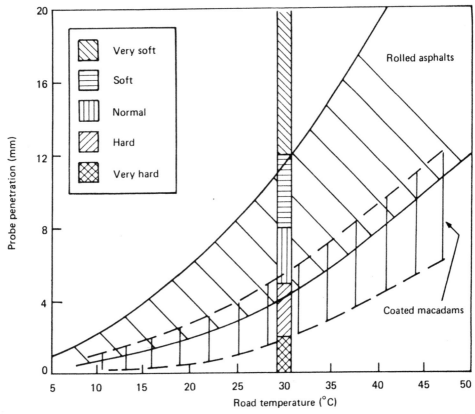

Figure 29.25 Road surface hardness: relationship between depth of probe penetration and road temperature

29.39 Although the vast majority of surface dressing is carried out on roads in lane traffic categories 3, 4, and 5 (less than 1000 commercial vehicles per day per lane), there is a small but vitally important volume of work directed towards retexturing the worn surfaces of heavily trafficked roads. Road Note 39 recommends road tar as the preferred binder for such roads with cut-back bitumen permitted only on a tentative basis.[9] The restriction on the use of cut-back bitumen was imposed because experiments carried out between 1955 and 1965 indicated that there was a risk of dressings using cut-back bitumen binder becoming excessively rich during spells of abnormally hot weather and it was considered that, unlike road tars, they were unlikely to weather away from the surface during periods of cold weather.

29.40 Good results have been obtained using single surface dressings in a full-scale road experiment on the M4 at Tormarton, Avon (carrying traffic in lane traffic category 2), with both cut-back bitumen binder and with road tars from conventional and low-temperature-carbonization sources.[10] The recommendations for target rates of spread of binder are given in Table 29.3.

Table 29.2   PSV of aggregate necessary to achieve the required skidding resistance in bituminous surfacings under different traffic conditions

Required mean summer SFC at 50 km/h	PSV of aggregate necessary Traffic in commercial vehicles per lane per day					
	250 or under	1 000	1 750	2 500	3 250	4 000
0.30	30	35	40	45	50	55
0.35	35	40	45	50	55	60
0.40	40	45	50	55	60	65
0.45	45	50	55	60	65	70
0.50	50	55	60	65	70	75
0.55	55	60	65	70	75	
0.60	60	65	70	75		
0.65	65	70	75			
0.70	70	75				
0.75	75					
AAV	not greater than 12			not greater than 10		

SFC values in these traffic conditions are sometimes achievable with aggregates of extreme hardness and very high resistance to abrasion, such as certain grades of calcined bauxite.

Table 29.3   Targets for the rate of spread of binder

Type of surface	Lane traffic category (Table 1 of RN 39)	Chipping size (mm)	Target rates of spread of binder (l/m^2)	
			Cut-back bitumen	Low-temperature-carbonization tars
Hard	2	14	1.1	1.4
Normal			1.0	1.3

29.41   Measurements of skid resistance and average texture depth were made at this motorway site over the period 1975–8; Table 29.4 shows that all the materials performed in a very similar and generally satisfactory manner.

29.42   For a variety of reasons, bitumen road emulsions now account for a significant proportion of binders used in surface dressing in the UK; it has been estimated that cutback bitumens, bitumen emulsions, and tar–bitumen blends now each provide 30 per cent of the total, the remaining 10 per cent being road tar. In recent years there has been a trend towards the use of higher-bitumen-content emulsions, culminating in the development of 70 per cent bitumen content cationic emulsions (Class K1-70 of BS 434:1973). These materials differ from conventional, cold-applied emulsions in that they are applied by spraying at a temperature of 75–80 °C; they may be applied to damp surfaces. Road experiments have shown that good surface dressings can be achieved using cationic bitumen emulsions (Class

Table 29.4 M4 Tormarton, Avon: average values of resistance to skidding and to texture depth

Section no.	Type of binder	Nominal size of aggregate (mm)	Average values of resistance to skidding										Average texture depth (mm)			
			1975	1976				1977				1978	1975	1976	1977	1978
			SFC50 ×100	SFC50 ×100	BFC50 ×100	BFC80 ×100	BFC130 ×100	SFC50 ×100	BFC50 ×100	BFC80 ×100	BFC130 ×100	SFC50 ×100				
1	Road tar to BS 76:1964	14	58	61	47	42	48	54	45	43	53	57	3.7	3.0	2.4	2.0
2	Grade A46		55	61	46	42	47	54	45	42	53	57	3.9	3.2	2.6	2.1
3	Low-temperature-carbonization road tar		54	61	45	42	44	53	44	42	48	58	3.7	2.9	2.3	1.9
4	Grade A46		54	60	45	42	44	53	43	40	47	58	3.8	3.0	2.3	1.9
5	Cut-back bitumen to BS 3690:1970		54	61	46	41	45	54	44	41	48	57	3.8	3.1	2.3	1.9
6	200 sec at 40°C (STV)		54	60	46	43	46	55	44	41	49	58	3.9	3.2	2.4	1.9

Table 29.5   Rates of spread of cationic bitumen emulsions (Class KI-70)

| Type of surface | Lane traffic category | | | | | |
| | 3 | | 4 | | 5 | |
	Chipping size (mm)	Binder rate (l/m²)	Chipping size (mm)	Binder rate (l/m²)	Chipping size (mm)	Binder rate (l/m²)
Very hard	6	1.2	6	1.3	6	1.4
Hard	10	1.2	6	1.2	6	1.3
Normal	14	1.2	10	1.2	6	1.2
Soft	14	1.1	14	1.2	10	1.2
Very soft	20*	1.1	14	1.1	10	1.1

*At the discretion of the engineer, 20 mm chippings may be used for remedial treatment where traffic speeds are low.

K1-70) on roads carrying traffic in lane traffic category 3. Rates of spread of binder are shown in Table 29.5.

Flexible carriageway repairs

29.43   The approach to carriageway repairs is dictated largely by problems of traffic management. On a single-carriageway two-lane road considerable lengths of lane closure generally cause unacceptable traffic delays, and the normal practice adopted is to repair local areas of deformation and cracking and then to apply a surface dressing in lane widths.

29.44   On dual carriageways the principal damage is likely to be on the slow traffic lanes. If the other lanes are in a satisfactory condition then the economic solution is to repair the slow lanes locally until the other lanes show signs of distress and then to overlay the whole carriageway in lane widths.

29.45   On industrial motorways when carriageways require major repair, carriageway closure accompanied by contraflow on the other carriageway is the most satisfactory procedure. This is often accompanied by inefficient operating procedures on the closed carriageway. To overcome such inefficiency the practice of leasing the carriageway on a period rental to the contractor has been increasingly adopted. This has led to more rapid repairs apparently without any deterioration in standards of workmanship. Traffic on such roads has increased so rapidly in the last few years that there is little difference in the amount of commercial traffic carried by the slow and overtaking lane. While a carriageway is closed it makes sense to overlay all lanes to the same thickness.

Recycling of asphalt wearing courses

29.46   Compared with the USA, there is at present little experience in the UK with the recycling of asphalt surfacings. The stiffer asphalts used in Britain make the process less efficient and less effective. Trial lengths on a number of motorways have shown difficulties in achieving adequate riding quality. The recycled material also appears to have less resistance to wheel-tracking.[11]

References

1. Kennedy, C. K., P. Fevre, and C. Clarke: *Pavement Deflection: Equipment for Measurement in the United Kingdom*, Transport and Road Research Laboratory Report LR834, TRRL, Crowthorne, 1978.
2. Lister, N. W.: *Deflection Criteria for Flexible Pavements*, Transport and Road Research Laboratory Report LR375, TRRL, Crowthorne, 1972.
3. Norman P. J., R. A. Snowdon, and J. C. Jacobs: *Pavement Deflection Measurements and their Application to Structural Maintenance and Overlay Design*, Transport and Road Research Laboratory Report LR571, TRRL, Crowthorne, 1973.
4. Kennedy, C. K. and N. W. Lister: *Prediction of Pavement Performance and the Design of Overlays*, Transport and Road Research Laboratory Report LR833, TRRL, Crowthorne, 1978.
5. Jones, C. R. and H. R. Smith: *Deflection–Temperature Relationships for Bituminous Road Surfacings in Kenya*, Transport and Road Research Laboratory Report LR936, TRRL, Crowthorne, 1980.
6. Traxler, R. N.: Changes in asphalt cements during preparation, laying and service of bituminous pavements, *Proceedings of Association Asphalt Paving Technologists*, **36**, 1967.
7. Wright, N.: *Recent Developments in Surface Dressing in the United Kingdom*, Transport and Road Research Laboratory Report SR486, TRRL, Crowthorne, 1979.
8. Salt, G. F. and W. Szatkowski: *A Guide to Levels of Skid Resistance for Roads*, Transport and Road Research Laboratory Report LR510, TRRL, Crowthorne, 1973.
9. Transport and Road Research Laboratory: *Recommendations for Road Surface Dressing*, Department of the Environment Road Note 39, HMSO, London, 1972.
10. Wright, N.: *Surface Dressing: Proposed Amendments to Road Note No 39*, Transport and Road Research Laboratory Report LR908, TRRL, Crowthorne, 1979.
11. Goodsall, G. D.: *In Situ Recycling of Asphalt Wearing Courses in the UK*, Transport and Road Research Laboratory Report SR675, TRRL, Crowthorne, 1981.

30. The structural maintenance of concrete pavements

Introduction

30.1 Problems involved in the structural maintenance of concrete pavements depend much more on how well the pavements are designed and constructed than is the case with flexible pavements. A well-designed and constructed concrete road will need almost no maintenance during its long life other than occasional joint sealing and restoration of skid resistance in later life. On the other hand, an inadequately designed and poorly constructed concrete road will provide endless and major problems.

Structural maintenance problems on concrete roads

30.2 The importance of structural defects in concrete roads depends on the amount of traffic being carried. There are many thousands of miles of concrete housing estate roads in the UK, many of them 60 or more years old. Cracking has been common, particularly where the joint spacing was too great, but occasional joint and crack sealing is all the maintenance they have required, apart perhaps from a thin bituminous overlay laid largely for cosmetic reasons after 40 years or more.

30.3 Similar cracks on a heavily-trafficked trunk road or motorway are quite a different matter. The problem is less likely to be one of design than of poor construction and supervision. Cracks close to joints are a common fault, owing generally to inaccurate alignment of dowel bars. A great deal of research effort has been devoted to developing standards of joint assembly alignment and rigidity,[1] but all too often this important matter is disregarded. The first result is likely to be corner cracking followed by a transverse crack within a metre of the joint. The only satisfactory method of dealing with this situation is to cut out the joint by transverse sawcuts and to inject a small slab with dowel bars drilled accurately into the existing concrete. This is a specialist procedure and will be very expensive if a number of cracks have to be treated.

30.4 Poor-quality undrained bases are also a common cause of maintenance problems. Water inevitably gets into the base and unless there is provision for drainage, pumping of fines will occur at the joints. This can lead to inadequate slab support followed by transverse cracking. If early signs of pumping occur then the shoulder on the low side of the carriageway should be excavated and a continuous drain installed connecting with the base or sub-base material.

30.5   On heavily trafficked concrete roads the replacement of individual slabs presents particular problems of traffic management due to the long curing period which it is essential to observe. This has led to some authorities using bituminous inserts with a considerable loss of riding quality. When inlay work of this type is contemplated, a thick high-strength, lean-concrete base with an asphalt surfacing let into the pavement is probably the best solution.

30.6   Concrete overlays on existing concrete roads have only been laid on an experimental basis in Britain. Although technically the design of such an overlay is straightforward the concept is hardly practical when applied to heavily trafficked roads where closure of a carriageway for a matter of months is not feasible.

30.7   It is a frequently expressed view that bituminous overlays on existing concrete roads are not satisfactory. This is clearly not the case. Many concrete roads laid in the UK in the twenties and thirties are still carrying traffic very successfully with comparatively thin bituminous overlays. Provided the differential movement at joints under the passage of a 3175-kg wheel load is less than 0.15 mm an asphalt overlay will generally give excellent performance under heavy traffic. The magnitude of differential deflection can be measured using the Deflection Beam described in Chapter 29. If joint movements are greater, reflected cracking through the surfacing will occur and sealing may then be necessary. The reinforcement of bituminous material over cracks has not proved effective in the long term.

30.8   Where very low strength concrete has been laid with resulting widespread cracking, further breaking up of the concrete before overlaying with asphalt has been used. In the United States this is known as the cracking and seating process. The concrete is broken into areas not greater than 1 m square followed by heavy rolling to 'seat' the material. For this purpose a 15-t pneumatic-tyred roller is recommended. The concrete is then overlaid by a two-course asphalt overlay with a fabric interlayer. The process is comparatively new and experience over a period of only about 6 years is available.

Joint sealing

30.9   The sealing of joints in concrete roads is a routine operation which should be carried out at intervals of about 5 years. The life of joint sealants depends largely on the manner and thoroughness of the preliminary cleaning and priming. Specialized plant is needed to carry out the work effectively, and engineers will generally find it more economical to have the work carried out by specialists rather than attempt the work with their own staff.

Skid resistance

30.10   The surface texture of concrete pavements has presented some problems in the last 10 years. Deep grooving intended to extend adequate skid resistance over a design life up to 40 years has proved unpopular from the point of view of the noise generated both inside and outside road vehicles. Surface grooving of existing concrete pavements which have poor skid resistance, although effective, can have noise implications which are difficult to overcome because they affect different vehicles in different ways.

30.11   In recent years there has been a considerable effort devoted to the development of surface-dressing techniques applicable to concrete roads.[2] The conclusions of this work, extracted from reference 2, are as follows:

1. Good results have been obtained in single surface dressings on concrete roads carrying traffic in lane traffic category 1 (over 2000 commercial vehicles a day in one lane in one direction) with three binders, namely rubberized cut-back bitumen, rubberized road tar and tar–bitumen blends. Optimum rates of spread of binder for use with the preferred chipping size of 10 mm are tabulated below:

	Target rate of spread of binder (litre per m^2)
Rubberized cut-back bitumen	1.1
Rubberized road tar	1.4
Tar–bitumen binder	1.3

2. The rate at which aggregates wear under the action of traffic has been shown to be an important factor in the retention of adequate surface texture depth in single surface dressings on concrete roads. It is recommended therefore that aggregates having an aggregate abrasion value (AAV) not exceeding 8 should be specified for use in single surface dressings on concrete roads carrying traffic in lane traffic category 1.

   For roads below this lane traffic category the recommended maximum AAV of 10 specified in Road Note 39[3] for aggregates for use on heavily trafficked high-speed roads is still applicable for surface dressing concrete roads.

3. The application of single surface dressings to ungrooved concrete roads has resulted in improved resistance to skidding compared with the existing concrete surface on all sites at speeds of 50 and 80 km/h where the polished stone value (PSV) of the aggregates used was not less than 60. The improvements amounted to between 0.14 and 0.26 units at 50 km/h and between 0.23 and 0.31 units at 80 km/h. At speeds up to 130 km/h the advantage of surface dressing was maintained, but the effectiveness of the dressings in this respect was found to be dependent upon depth of texture maintained.

4. Previously grooved concrete surfaces which have been subjected to wear under heavy traffic may be effectively retextured by surface dressing. Single dressings have been shown to be suitable for grooved traffic lanes carrying less than 2000 commercial vehicles a day, but double dressings are recommended for more heavily trafficked roads.

5. No evidence was found to suggest that the use of more single-sized aggregate in single surface dressings on concrete roads leads to a better surface texture or to an increase in resistance to skidding over the range of speeds tested (50 to 130 km/h).

6. During the experiments no spalling of joints in the existing concrete roads occurred due to penetration of applied surface dressings. It is concluded that provided the nominal size of the applied chippings does not exceed 10 mm no protection of joints is required.

References

1. Parmenter, B.S.: *The Design and Construction of Joints in Concrete Pavements*, Transport and Road Research Laboratory Report LR512, TRRL, Crowthorne, 1973.

2. Wright, N.: *Surface Dressing on Concrete Roads*, Transport and Road Research Laboratory Report LR736, TRRL, Crowthorne, 1976.

3. Transport and Road Research Laboratory: *Recommendations for Road Surface Dressing*, Department of the Environment Road Note 39, HMSO, London, 1972.

Index